GEOTECHNICAL ENGINEERING FOR COLD REGIONS

Edited by

Orlando B. Andersland

Professor of Civil Engineering
Michigan State University
East Lansing, Michigan

Duwayne M. Anderson

Chief Scientist
Division of Polar Programs
National Science Foundation
Washington, D.C.

McGraw-Hill Book Company

New York   St. Louis   San Francisco   Auckland   Bogotá   Düsseldorf
Johannesburg   London   Madrid   Mexico   Montreal   New Delhi
Panama   Paris   São Paulo   Singapore   Sydney   Tokyo   Toronto

Library of Congress Cataloging in Publication Data

Main entry under title:

Geotechnical engineering for cold regions.

    Includes indexes.
    1. Civil engineering—Cold weather conditions.
2. Cold regions. 3. Frozen ground.
4. Foundations. I. Andersland, Orlando B.
II. Anderson, Duwayne Marlo, date
TA713.G44   624′.151   78-2688
ISBN 0-07-001615-1

GEOTECHNICAL ENGINEERING FOR COLD REGIONS

3 4 5 6 7 8 9 10 K P K P 8 9 8 7 6 5 4 3 2

This book was set in Times Roman. The editor was Rose Ciofalo and
the production supervisor was Robert C. Pedersen.
Kingsport Press, Inc. was printer and binder.

CONTENTS

7 Slope Stability in Cold Regions   363

Edward C. McRoberts

8 Response of Frozen Ground to Dynamic Loading   405

Ted S. Vinson

9 Field Investigations of Frozen Ground   459

B. Ladanyi and G. H. Johnston

10 Ice Pressures and Bearing Capacity   505

L. W. Gold

LIST OF CONTRIBUTORS

ORLANDO B. ANDERSLAND, Professor of Civil Engineering, Michigan State University, East Lansing, Michigan (Chaps. 5 and 6)

DUWAYNE M. ANDERSON, Chief Scientist, Division of Polar Programs, National Science Foundation, Washington, D.C. (Chap. 2)

JOHN L. BURDICK, Head, Department of Civil Engineering, University of Alaska, College, Alaska (Chap. 1)

L. W. GOLD, Assistant Director, Division of Building Research, National Research Council of Canada, Ottawa, Canada (Chap. 10)

R. L. HARLAN, Senior Hydrogeologist, R. M. Hardy & Associates Ltd., Calgary, Alberta, Canada (Chap. 3)

G. H. JOHNSTON, Assistant Head, Geotechnical Section, Division of Building Research, National Research Council of Canada, Ottawa, Canada (Chap. 9)

B. LADANYI, Professor of Civil Engineering. École Polytechnique, Université de Montréal, Montréal, Québec, Canada (Chaps. 4, 5, and 9)

EDWARD C. McROBERTS, Manager, Geotechnical Department, Northern Engineering Services Company Limited, Calgary, Alberta, Canada (Chap. 7)

JOHN F. NIXON, Senior Geotechnical Engineer, R. M. Hardy & Associates Ltd., Calgary, Alberta, Canada (Chaps. 3 and 4)

EDWARD PENNER, Head, Geotechnical Section, Division of Building Research, National Research Council of Canada, Ottawa, Canada (Chap. 2)

ARVIND PHUKAN, Associate Professor of Civil Engineering, University of Alaska, College, Alaska (Chaps. 1 and 6)

ROLAND PUSCH, Professor, Division of Geotechnology, University of Lulea, Lulea, Sweden (Chap. 2)

E. F. RICE, Professor of Civil Engineering, University of Alaska, College, Alaska (Chap. 1)

FRANCIS H. SAYLES, JR., Research Civil Engineer, U.S. Army Cold Regions Research and Engineering Laboratory, Hanover, N.H. (Chap. 5)

TED S. VINSON, Associate Professor of Civil Engineering, Oregon State University, Corvallis, Oregon (Chap. 8)

PREFACE

The development of energy resources and the need for highways, pipelines, and other constructed facilities in the cold regions of the world have created a need for geotechnical information on seasonal and permanently frozen ground. The purpose of this text is to describe the state of the art in a form suitable for instructional use in approaching engineering applications. Since it is intended to follow the usual undergraduate geotechnical engineering courses taken by civil engineering students, it is assumed that the reader is familiar with the physical and mechanical properties of unfrozen soils. A number of numerical examples illustrating typical problems have been included. SI units are used throughout the book; where required, data from other published sources have been converted to the appropriate units. It is our hope that consulting engineers, mining engineers, soil scientists, and geologists will find that much of the book has application to their interests and work in cold regions.

The introductory chapter defines and describes what is meant by cold regions and the most important problems associated with seasonal- and permanently-frozen ground. Various ground features are described, and engineering considerations appropriate to constructed facilities are included. A classification system for frozen soils is described. Physical and thermal properties of soil, water, ice, and frozen soil are presented, also as introductory material, in Chapter 2. Ice formation and frost action are outlined in detail. Particular emphasis on frost-susceptibility criteria for soils has been provided.

The ground thermal regime is discussed in Chapter 3; included are the effects of hydrologic factors and of changes in ground surface cover on soil temperatures. Prediction of temperatures beneath structures and facilities is essential in order to obtain proper foundation design. The problem of melting and settlement is considered in Chapter 4, which includes a discussion of thaw-consolidation theory, residual stress in thawing soils, and layered soil-ice problems. Each is illustrated with practical examples from field studies. The discussion of mechanical properties of frozen ground, Chapter 5, includes the treatment of stress-strain-time relationships, strength for a given service life, and the temperature effect on creep rate and strength. Laboratory measurements of frozen-soil properties on both natural and artificially prepared frozen-soil samples also are described.

Foundations for cold regions, Chapter 6, includes a discussion of design considerations, bearing capacity, shallow and pile foundations, ground anchors, frost-heave forces, pavement structures for cold regions, and excavation in frozen ground. Slope stability in cold regions (Chapter 7) involves first a classification of landslides in permafrost, slopes in thawing permafrost and in frozen soils, and a description of factors contributing to slope instability. The response of frozen ground to dynamic loading depends on its dynamic properties. This is treated in Chapter 8, which includes a discussion of methods for measurement of these dynamic properties and the analysis of the response of frozen ground to dynamic loading.

Chapter 9 is a discussion of field investigations of subsurface conditions in frozen ground, including recommendations on sampling of the materials for examination and testing, ground temperature measurement, field testing of frozen-soil properties, and geophysical methods for delineating permafrost areas and measurement of certain physical properties. The book concludes with Chapter 10, on ice pressures and the bearing capacity of ice covers. The chapter includes a description of typical modes of ice formation, the classification of ice covers, and the forces that may be exerted on engineering structures due to static pressures, change in water level, and dynamic forces from moving ice floes.

The editors express their appreciation to all those who have generously given advice and encouragement in the preparation of this book. They are especially grateful to the contributors for their willingness, cooperation, and assistance in assembling this material and in bringing the book to completion.

Thanks are also due to Phyllis Andersland for preparing the author index and for general editorial assistance, and to Thomas O. and Henrietta P. Burgess for help in proofreading and in preparation of the subject index.

Orlando B. Andersland
Duwayne M. Anderson

COLD REGIONS: DESCRIPTIVE AND GEOTECHNICAL ASPECTS

John L. Burdick, E. F. Rice, and Arvind Phukan

INTRODUCTION

The cold regions of the world, with a few mountain-top exceptions, are centered around the poles. In the Northern Hemisphere the southern limit of the cold regions extends to about the 40th parallel. Exceptions include the northwest coast of both North America and Europe, where ocean currents such as the Japan current and the Gulf Stream moderate the climate of adjacent land areas. Identification of the cold regions requires both climatological and geographical delineation. Climatologists often use the isotherm based upon the average temperature for the warmest month of the year being above 0°C but not above 10°C to identify the southern boundary of the cold regions. The 150- and 300-mm depth of frost penetration or soil freezing has been used by engineers to identify the southern limits of cold regions in the United States. The southern limit of substantial frost penetration is shown in Fig. 1.1. A practical definition of cold regions is one based on the design and operation requirements essential to the maintenance of the industrial and social economy. A city or state geographically located in the midtemperate zone which spends large sums of money to maintain a program of snow removal for operational purposes is located in the cold regions.

Altitude has a marked effect on climate. Vertical temperature gradients up mountain slopes vary from 3°C per 100 m for dry air to 1.6°C per 100 m for saturated air. An average value of 1.8°C (Gerdel, 1969) is commonly used by climatologists when transferring temperature information from low elevations to

1

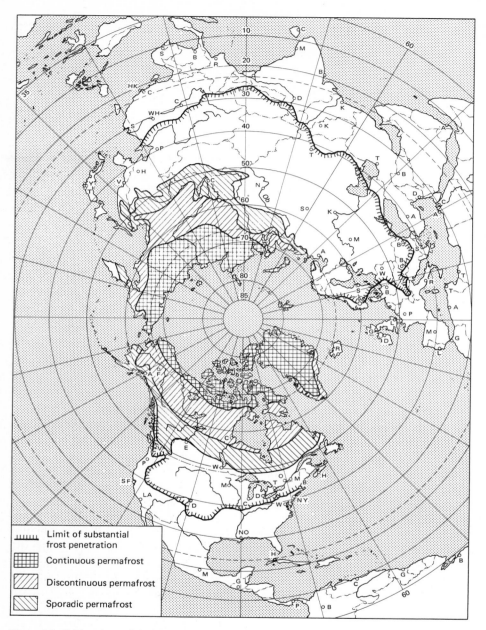

Figure 1.1 Cold regions of the Northern Hemisphere.

higher elevations. The extension of the cold regions into the mountain areas of North America and southeast Eurasia is due to the high elevation in these areas.

Net yearly solar radiation in the polar regions is minimal because of the glancing angle of even the summer sun and further because of atmospheric attenuation: a low sun angle means, that its rays travel an unusually long distance through the atmosphere allowing opportunity for increased diffusion and reflection of the sun's energy back into space. For cold regions in the temperate zone the effect of reduced radiation is primarily a winter phenomenon which decreases in intensity with distance from the poles.

Seasonal and permanently frozen ground are characteristics of cold regions which require special attention from the geotechnical engineer. In areas of seasonal frost, structure loads are taken to depths below the active zone, and use of non-frost-susceptible soils minimizes possible trouble from heave and lateral thrust. In permafrost areas structure loads are often transferred to frozen ground with special care taken to maintain the frozen state. It is essential that the engineer have an understanding of the freezing process, thawing, and permafrost. In permafrost regions, knowledge of polygons, wedges, lakes, and pingos gives an understanding of the ground features which may be encountered. The cold environment may create special problems such as buildup of successive ice layers adjacent to a small stream (*aufeis*), which requires consideration when it occurs near roads or buildings. In all these problems the geotechnical engineer must be able to describe and discuss a frozen soil both with brevity and the assurance that the description will mean the same to another engineer. Subsequent chapters go into detail regarding various areas important to the geotechnical engineer.

1.1 THE ARCTIC

Since the arctic includes a climatic, historical, and cultural area which is relatively distinct from other portions of the cold regions, it is appropriate to provide a broader description of this area which will make the engineering characteristics more understandable. The term *arctic* derives from the Great Bear, Arktos, the constellation also known as the Big Dipper. The *arctic* therefore is related to the part of the world where Arktos, the Great Bear, Ursa Major, never sets—roughly, the world north of latitude 60°N. Astronomically, the arctic encompasses all of the world at latitudes higher than the Arctic Circle, N66°33′, which marks the lowest latitude for which there can be 24 h of sunshine at the summer solstice and 24 h without sun 6 months later. The definition for the arctic serves equally well for the antarctic.

Botanically, the Arctic has been described as the area poleward of the *tree line*. Climatically, there are many definitions, e.g., that part of the Northern Hemisphere whose average temperature is 0°C. Washburn (1951) suggests that "arctic lands will be understood to be those north of the 50 °F July isotherm (or that of which every other month is warmest), provided that the mean temperature for the coldest month is not above 32 °F."

Physically, a convenient definition of the arctic (antarctic) is "that portion of the world underlain by a continuous layer of perennially frozen ground." The subarctic may be similarly defined as being underlain by a broken or discontinuous layer of frozen ground. By this definition, permafrost will be found nearly everywhere in the arctic except under bodies of water too deep to freeze to the bottom. In the subarctic, permafrost is present in many places but does not usually exist under south-facing slopes, streams and lakes, or well-drained ground. The broken layer of permafrost thins and becomes more fragmentary toward its southern boundary, until only isolated patches of permafrost occur. Permafrost underlies about one-fifth of all land surface of the earth, and much of this area is in the Northern Hemisphere. Most of Alaska and at least one-half of the Canadian land area lie within the continuous and discontinuous permafrost zones.

History

Arctic regions were not always so cold. Because of world fluctuation of climate and the drift of continental plates, lands that are now underlain by permafrost were once unfrozen. Extensive coal and petroleum deposits sometimes give testimony that the vegetable types from which they are derived grew in climates ranging from cool to tropical. Coal seams in Antarctica, for example, where no vegetation at all occurs now, imply a lush and long-continued climatic warm period eons ago.

In general, however, the present-day arctic regions have remained cold, with minor fluctuations insufficient to destroy most of the permafrost, since the last interglacial warm period ended maybe 70,000 years ago. This is known to be the case from radiocarbon dating and from the fact that animals of that era are occasionally found, still unrotted near today's permafrost surface, demonstrating that there has been no warm period long enough to thaw the top of the permafrost since the animals were trapped, died, and were frozen in place.

Population

Historically, the peoples of the arctic have been widely dispersed and nomadic, and they depended for subsistence totally upon hunting and fishing. In a region where there could be no intensive agriculture and where no significant exportable commodities were known, few, if any, families were supported other than by their own efforts in living off the land. Dispersion and continual change of living place to exploit each ecological niche at the proper season was the only road to survival, and surpluses were rarely sufficient to allow specialization. Each family contrived its own tools, its own works of art, its own housing, clothing, and transport, and of course its own larder. Some trading was done: soapstone for lamps made its way around the rim of the arctic; sea mammal oil was exchanged for caribou skins, for instance; with the advent of widespread commerce originating in milder lands where actual surpluses could occur, such commodities as tea and metal utensils made their way to the peoples of the arctic. Until the midnineteenth century, the culture of the residents of the North American arctic was Stone Age. The Eskimos and Indians had evolved a lifestyle that was as advanced as seems possible given the absence of metal, the large land and sea areas needed to support each person, and the intermittent periods of privation due to scarcity of game.

This was pretty much the same in the Eurasian arctic, though it is harder there to single out particular groups as "aboriginal" since there was apparently much migration, absorption, and perhaps extinction during prehistory and continuing into the historic period. Nevertheless, many elements of culture are similar to all arctic peoples: types of dwellings, means of subsistence, clothing, and the like. This seems to be true even among populations which immigrated to the arctic from a more complex and organized culture. Teal (1955) commented,

> The excellence of arctic aboriginal cultures' adaptation to environment may be measured by the fact that nowhere else has modern civilization been forced to abandon so many of its own techniques in favor of the aboriginal. In this way, at least, arctic aboriginal culture promises survival for some time.

One difference between the American and several Eurasian aboriginal arctic dwellers was husbandry. Whereas several of the Eurasian people bred and herded reindeer, there was no parallel development in America. There, the only domesticated animal was the universal dog, whose importance was supreme.

In the historic period, within the last two or three centuries, the arctic has been increasingly visited, populated, and exploited by people from the south, who have successively sought the resources of the arctic to supply a growing worldwide demand. Fish, whales, timber, gold, and now oil have drawn people to the north, and often the indigenous peoples have failed to share in the wealth and benefits thus accrued. This is changing now, and the peoples of the north are emerging as citizens of a wider world, at home both with exigencies of the north and the ways of civilization.

1.2 SEASONALLY AND PERENNIALLY FROZEN GROUND

Seasonally Frozen Ground

Where ice in lakes, rivers, and harbors interferes with navigation, where frost heaving affects roadways and the possible snow load on structures must be considered in design, the engineer is dealing with a cold-region environment. Snow and ice control in the United States costs more than 100 million dollars each winter. Regions where frost penetrates the ground to a depth of about 0.3 m or more at least once in 10 years are part of the cold regions of the world. Because the depth of frost penetration is not regularly reported or easy to measure, the annual freezing index is used as a measure of potential frost penetration. The freezing index is the area above the curve of mean daily temperatures and below the 0°C line, i.e., the accumulated negative degree-days during a single freezing season. If the mean freezing index is 50 degree-days or more, the criterion for about 0.3 m of frost penetration is considered to be met. This makes the assessment of the boundary of cold regions independent of the complexities of other factors, such as the variation of thermal diffusivity among differing soils, the variations of freezing temperature among soils, the water contents, the surface cover, and so forth.

The seasonal frost layer may be described as the top layer of the ground in which the temperature fluctuates above and below 0°C during the year. It corresponds to the active layer above perennially frozen ground (permafrost). In the far north the active layer is as shallow as 150 mm. Farther south, near the discontinuous permafrost zone, the active layer or frost penetration can be as much as 3 m thick.

Frost Heave

When damp ground of silty texture freezes, there is a migration of moisture to the freezing surface. Masses of ice begin to form along the freezing front, supplied with water by vapor transfer and by liquid migration. If water is available from a lower layer and if the soil has capillarity, ice layers of considerable thickness (1 to 100 mm are common) may develop, displacing the soil to make room for the ice. This is the familiar *frost heave* that bedevils engineers and others. The accumulation of ice under such circumstances has been known to double the volume of the frozen soil. More commonly, the total amount of heave amounts to anything from 0 to about 150 mm in a season.

Perennially Frozen Ground

Ground of any kind which stays colder than the freezing temperature of water throughout several years qualifies as permafrost. If the ground is dry sand, it is permafrost no less than if it were a conglomerate of soil particles cemented by ice. From an engineering standpoint, frozen soil with no ice in it is nearly as tractable as similar soil in temperate or tropic regions. Much frozen ground tends not only to be cemented by ice but also interbedded with large ice masses, whose melting could bring about subsidence, erosion, and structural distress.

In general, permafrost is associated with the polar regions (Fig. 1.1) and lies as a thick layer (under a thin "active" layer of seasonally melting soil) in the very high latitudes, thinning gradually toward the lower latitudes, until the layer becomes discontinuous, then fragmented, at its southern boundary. On mountain peaks, it is possible to find permafrost near the equator, but permafrost south of the bush country of Alaska, Canada, and Siberia is rare. Even Scandinavia, despite its high latitude (to 72°N), has permafrost only in isolated areas of high altitude. Yet the continuous layer of frozen subsoil extends far southward in continental parts of Canada and Siberia (down to 53°N). Trees can and do grow over frozen soils, but the tree line marks fairly well the southern boundary of the continuous layer of permafrost. It is not far wrong to say that the treeless tundra overlies continuous permafrost and that the forested taiga covers the frayed margins of the permafrost blanket. In the interior of Alaska, in the taiga of the Yukon, Kuskokwim, and Copper River valleys, for instance, the permafrost is marginal. Almost at the melting point, permafrost exists or not in these areas depending on such apparently minor influences as whether the land slopes to the north or to the south, whether the forest cover has remained intact in recent years, or whether the land is swampy. There are sporadic occurrences of permafrost even around Anchorage and on the Kenai Peninsula.

The point is that if the climate is cold enough for long enough, there will be permafrost. One could even create it by keeping the ground surface cold for a long time, and the resulting frozen soil would be indistinguishable from naturally occurring permafrost.

The Whiplash Curve

The annual ground-temperature variation decreases steadily from the ground surface to a depth of from 6 to 15 m or more, as shown in Fig. 1.2. Below this depth the temperature increases steadily under the influence of heat generated deep in the earth, doubtless in major part by nuclear decay. This heat flows upward at a rate dependent on the geothermal gradient. The heat flow is reasonably

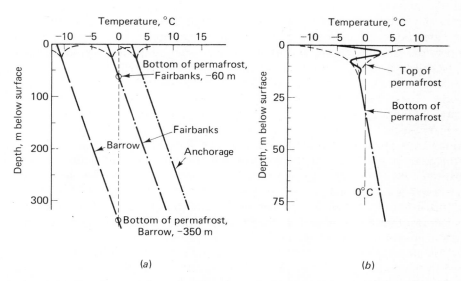

(a)   (b)

Figure 1.2 Near-ground-surface temperature relationships and the geothermal gradient: (a) average ground temperature depends on depth and average surface temperature; (b) variation of ground temperatures by seasons, the *whiplash curve*.

constant all over the world, about the same in polar regions as in temperate. Apart from volcanic areas, the gradient is about 3°C per 100 m. If the soil surface temperature averages, say, 10°C, the earth temperature at a depth of 100 m can be expected to be somewhere around 13°C, and so on. Wherever the average soil temperature is 2 or 3°C or so colder than freezing water, permafrost will be present lower down and of course the colder the average surface temperature the thicker the permafrost layer (Fig. 1.2). This conceptual picture is "true," i.e., represents what really happens, but one should not expect it to represent any single case perfectly. The average geothermal gradient will vary a little with differences in soil material, with long-term changes in climate, and so on. Nevertheless, the picture represents the average case, free of the complexities of surface slope, seasonal temperature variations, and the like.

Real cases (as distinguished from "true" cases) are more complicated. For instance, if the surface temperature were suddenly elevated, the temperature curve would bend sharply toward the right near its top as the surface warmed. Since it takes time and heat to warm up masses of soil, the soil at depth is delayed in "getting the word." This happens every spring. By the time the thaw penetrates a short distance into the frozen ground, it may be autumn again and the surface could be freezing once more. As winter continues, the curve bends sharply to the cold side as the surface temperature goes lower and lower, while a few meters down the soil is still warming up with last summer's heat. Figure 1.2 shows the effect of season on the temperature curves. A moving picture of the curves would show the surface temperature fluctuating wildly between warm late-summer temperatures and cold late-spring temperatures. A few millimeters below, however, the temperature is never quite so hot or so cold as the surface; and greater depths show even smaller fluctuations, until at a depth of 10 to 15 m the fluctuations are too small to measure conveniently. The upper and lower limits of temperature for the soil are asymptotic to the mean temperature gradient, and can be called the *trumpet curves*. The temperature as measured in mid-November is shown for the trumpet curve, and others could have been sketched for other months. These instantaneous temperature curves are called *whiplash curves* because of the way they lash to and fro as the seasons change.

From such a simple plot, one can derive some important insights. For example, it is apparent that for Fairbanks, Alas. the soil is thawed at some time of the year at all levels shallower than about 5 m. The top 5 m therefore constitutes the *active layer*; it is sometimes frozen, sometimes not. Below the active layer is the ground that never gets warmer than 0°C, that is, permafrost. At Fairbanks one can see that the permafrost is also not much colder than 0°C; it is "almost thawed." Any surface changes that would raise the surface temperature a degree or so would in time melt the permafrost.

It is also apparent that, on the average, the active layer must freeze clear down to the permafrost every year. If it should fail to do this for several years running, the permafrost would begin to melt from both the top and the bottom. If the situation continued, the permafrost layer would continue to grow thinner until a new equilibrium condition was reached.

How Permanent Is Permafrost?

What, then, of the supposition that permafrost is a fossil relic of the ice ages? Much of it, maybe most, surely has been frozen since the Pleistocene, but it is not necessary to postulate ice ages to explain permafrost, and to do so hides the truth. Barring a few anomalous cases, permafrost is a product of equilibrium with the present climate.

In places where the permafrost is marginal and near the thawing point, a location on a north-facing slope will be underlain by a deep layer of permafrost whereas permafrost may be entirely absent under a slope that faces south. Swamps tend to be frozen very deep, with only a few inches of thaw during the summers. Well-drained level ground may or may not have permafrost, depending on such subtle things as the vegetal structural cover of its recent past. Mere clearing, in some instances, will so change the surface temperatures that the icy ground will begin to melt. If it is highly ice-filled, many years will be required to reach a new equilibrium.

Referring again to Fig. 1.2, it also can be seen that the thermal situation in Barrow is not at all so precariously balanced as it is in Fairbanks; a little of the surface thaws during the short summer, and that's it. It takes a very great change indeed to cause melting below the top meter of soil. The frozen ground is in little danger of thawing unless someone places a heated slab on it, in which case there can be major structural deformations.

1.3 SURFACE FEATURES OF PERMAFROST REGIONS

The ice-rich permafrost (the kind that is most troublesome) got some of its excess ice by moisture migration to the freezing front when it was originally frozen, but there is another mechanism responsible for truly massive volumes of ice in perennially frozen ground.

Polygons and Wedges

Everyone who has flown over the arctic in summer is impressed by the vast areas of ground that appear to be divided into a more or less regular pattern of rectangles or hexagons. Sometimes the centers are high and the edges low. Always the boundaries prove to overlie masses of ice, wedge-shaped in cross section, with the point of the wedge down. If the ice could be removed without disturbing the surrounding soil, the result would be a network of interconnected wedge-shaped tunnels with their flat tops at the depth of the annual thaw. These tunnels could be as much as 3 m wide at the top and perhaps 10 m deep (Fig. 1.3).

It seems obvious to us now how these polygons were formed with their ice-wedge boundaries. The ground was contracted when frozen hard and cold in the winter, and the cracks became filled with snow and frozen meltwater. The ground reexpanded as it warmed (but did not thaw) during the summer. It could not

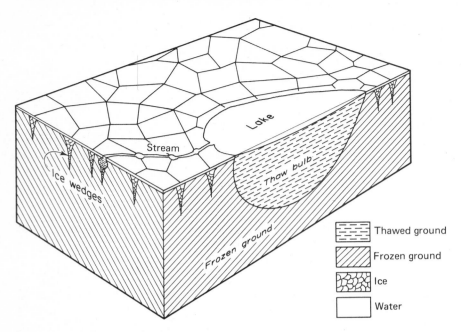

Figure 1.3 Frozen-ground-surface patterns in the Arctic.

expand into its former cracks since they were filled with ice; so it "upset" and expanded (accounting for either raised edges or humped backs of the polygons). As long as the ground never thawed, the ice-filled cracks endured, and the following year, new cracks formed in the same place. The new cracks usually occur right down the center of the ice in the old cracks, and the wedges become wider each year. Ice wedges can grow to startling dimensions. Since the process could go on forever, the dimensions of active wedges form an important clue to their age and possibly also the age of the current cold phase of the climate.

The mechanism of ice-wedge formation was not always so plain. Such acute observers as Nansen (1897) and Stefansson (1924) attempted without success to explain the exposures of massive ice they observed in eroded shorelines. Stefansson, in fact, postulated that sea ice, under pressure of wind and current, pushed its way like a bulldozer under the tundra edge. An ingenious thought, perhaps, but wrong.

There are a few places in the world where ice wedges have grown so wide that their upper parts have coalesced and there is clean ice everywhere under the tundra. Without the explanation just given (originally by Leffingwell, 1919) scientists would still be hard-pressed to explain how all that dirt and vegetation managed to form atop a continuous layer of ice.

The polygons vary in size according to the tensile strength of the ground but generally range from about 8 to 18 m across. Incidentally, the same kinds of polygons occur in temperate zones as well, but where there is no permafrost, the cracks are reclosed each summer. Since they are usually hidden under the snow in winter, temperate-zone polygons are rarely noticed except for their surface manifestation as they cross roadway embankments.

It is not widely realized that the subarctic also has vast areas of ice-wedge polygons under the spruce forests. These show up in a matter of 15 to 20 years after the forest is cleared away, leaving fields filled with humps of rounded polygons, sometimes so high that farm machinery cannot operate until releveling has taken place. Such ice wedges in marginal permafrost often go unsuspected since they are masked by the very deep (about 5-m) active layer and heavy vegetative cover.

Hughes (1970) described the relationship between the occurrence of ground ice and the geology. In glacial till plains, little massive ice is found. Generally, segregated ice is encountered in such formations and is closely associated with the fine-grained soils. Glaciofluvial deposits of sands and gravels typically include pore ice. Ice wedges are also common in these deposits. In glaciolacustrine deposits consisting of silt, clay, and sand deposited in glacial lakes, there is much segregated ice in the form of layers. In alluvial deposits ranging from gravel to silt, the formation of ground ice varies greatly. Typically, alluvial sand and gravel incorporate cement ice only. Ice-wedge formations are common in alluvial silt. Where eolian deposits of silt are thick, thin lenses of segregated ice to regular polygonal network of ice wedges are found.

Lakes and Pingos

Ponds and lakes deeper than a couple of meters do not freeze to the bottom, so that geothermal heat is interrupted in its path to the surface and each such pond comes equipped with an unfrozen *thaw bulb*. The size of such a bulb depends on the rate of heat flow and the climate (the thaw bulb is smaller where the climate is colder). In the arctic, the depth of thaw under medium-sized lakes can approximate the width of the lake.

Larger lakes (over 400 m wide) are likely to have a thaw bulb that completely penetrates the permafrost so that under such a lake there is no ice in the ground and consequently no disastrous settlement due to melting.

Some lakes are newcomers. They may not have been in place long enough to establish their eventual thermal balance, and their bottom may not yet have had time to thaw through. Conversely, when a lake is silted full or freshly drained, its thaw bulb remains, steadily diminishing in volume, to testify that once upon a time there was a lake. If such a thaw bulb is surrounded by impervious frozen material, the freezing water will find its expansion room limited. A slow fountain may result, freezing as it ponderously raises a blister on the earth. Such blisters, ice mounds with a topping of soil, are called *pingos*. There are thousands of them in North America between Prudhoe Bay and Amundsen Gulf, with the most spectacular specimens near Tuktoyaktuk, east of the Mackenzie River delta. In flat areas, pingos (which can be up to 50 m high and 150 m across) provide the only high spots in the landscape and have long been used as sites for geodetic triangulation stations.

Small pingos are also formed in river valleys by an entirely different mechanism. They grow as a result of the pinching of a near-surface aquifer between the top of the permafrost and the advancing freezing front in the active layer.

Permafrost can have ice in several forms: ice between the soil granules, ice built up in the process of frost heave (during initial freezing), ice in wedge form, pingo ice, and possibly ice somehow buried by soil. Seasonally frozen ground can have only the first two of these. It is generally the melting of the ice-rich ground that causes trouble due to subsidence. However, even in a frozen state, there can be troubles with drainage and excavation.

Frozen ground that is unbonded by ice is, of course, very little different from thawed ground, but it is possible to have intermediate stages. Near salt water or in very fine-grained soils considerable water can remain in the liquid state even at very low temperatures, so that ice bonding can range from total to zero, depending on temperature, chemical content of the water, and grain size.

When considering the distribution of permafrost near or under the arctic shoreline, it is sometimes fruitful even to redefine frozen soil to mean *soil bonded by ice.*

1.4 ENGINEERING CONSIDERATIONS

The effects of frozen ground on engineering considerations can be grouped into various categories according to cause or end results. In moderate climates foundations and watermains are protected against the effects of frost by placing them deep enough to avoid frost heave or freezing. The solution for the construction of ice rinks, cold-storage facilities, and liquid-natural-gas storage facilities where continuous subfreezing temperatures may cause deep frost penetration into the soil is usually found by placement of adequate insulation between the cooling system and the subsoil. Pewe (1975) has classified the problems of permafrost as (1) those involving thawing of ice-rich permafrost and subsequent subsidence of the surface under unheated structures such as roads and airfields; (2) those involving subsidence under heated structures; (3) those resulting from frost action, generally intensified by poor drainage caused by permafrost; and (4) those involved only with the temperature of permafrost, causing buried sewer, water, and soil lines to freeze.

For many years permafrost was a geological curiosity, and the early literature on the subject was dominated by reports of geologists who provided a great deal of information in these early studies. Today's engineers dealing with frozen ground owe a debt to these first investigators, who often pursued their studies with little financial support.

When people from the outside began to enter the arctic and subarctic regions to harvest their natural resources or occupy their strategic locations, they were immediately engaged in reproducing the buildings, communication routes and utilities that had become necessities in their civilization. At this time, the properties of frozen ground became an engineering consideration.

Early developers coped with frozen ground as best they could. Their solutions to the problems encountered, while often ingenious, were also often expensive in money and effort, and sometimes the success was very temporary. However, solutions of some sort were found, and many of their accomplishments, especially those in the early mining operations, are impressive even by today's standards. Unfortunately, exchange of information was limited, and many of the mistakes and unsound approaches discovered in one operation were repeated by each succeeding group of engineers or builders. Probably in no other field has so much effort been spent in reinventing the wheel. This problem, while much improved, is still not completely solved. Until quite recently, political considerations have limited exchange of information between some of the major countries working in the arctic. Also, the highly competitive petroleum industry, currently one of the largest sponsors of arctic operations, has historically tended to classify much of the information it discovers as proprietary. It is to be hoped that as more investigators enter the field, the interchange of information will improve.

The approach used here is to divide the engineering problems related to frozen ground into those caused primarily by (1) the freezing process, (2) thawing, and (3) the steady-state frozen condition.

The Freezing Process

While many of the geotechnical engineering problems of cold regions are mainly associated with the arctic and subarctic, the occurrence of most difficulties caused by the freezing of soil depends only upon sufficient degree-days, below 0°C, to freeze approximately the top meter of the soil. This condition, of course, occurs over a large portion of the temperate zone, as shown in Fig. 1.1.

The most troubling aspect of soil freezing is the phenomenon of frost heaving, which has especially plagued highway engineers. Three conditions are required for frost heaving to occur: (1) there must be a cold surface to propagate freezing; (2) there must be a source of water to feed the ice growth; and (3) the physical composition of the soil must promote the migration of the moisture to the freezing front.

When the air temperature drops below freezing, the moisture in the upper soil layer will freeze in place, well distributed through the layer. If the conditions described above exist, the free moisture from below will migrate along the thermal gradient toward the colder surface. When it reaches the frost line, it will freeze, preferentially, to existing ice grains forming small ice lenses. As these lenses grow and expand, the ground surface moves upward. If conditions are uniform, the movement is uniform and for many engineering projects, such as roads and runways, this can be tolerated. However, if the soil profile, drainage pattern, surface cover, or the soil conductivity varies, differential movement will occur, producing undesirable effects. The frost-heave problem is most noticeable in the transportation area, where such linear works as highways, railroad beds, and airport runways designed for high-speed traffic are sensitive to differential displacements. Figure 1.4 shows a large heave in the highway at Potter, Alas. Appearances can be deceptive. Although this heave has the same physical characteristics of a typical frost heave, it was actually caused by a hydrostatic mechanism similar to the one that creates pingos in river valleys. Here, experimental insulation placed under the pavement retarded freezing of the subgrade and when seasonal frost sealed off other paths, seepage from the hillside was concentrated under the pavement.

While frost heave is usually thought of as vertical movement, it can produce displacement in any direction. A vertical face exposed to the freezing temperatures by the retaining wall in Fig. 1.5 creates a horizontal thermal gradient, resulting in the lateral bulge and a forward rotation of this wall. Non-frost-susceptible soils are usually placed behind retaining walls to avoid this problem.

Structures with exposed foundations are also subject to frost heaving. The differential effects are particularly severe where part of the foundation is heated and part is not. Normally footings are placed below the level of frost penetration. Insulation can be used to prevent this frost heave.

Pole jacking is another frost-heave phenomenon. When poles or pilings are installed in frost-susceptible soil, a bond is developed between the pile and frozen earth at the ground surface, transferring uplift forces to the pole. The pole in Fig. 1.6 has been subjected to this action. This pole originally leaned in the opposite direction. The now slack guy wire provided only temporary corrective support, and the timber outriggers are of limited effectiveness.

Another problem produced by the freezing of soil is a result of shrinkage caused by thermal contraction and desiccation. The polygonal cracking of the ground is reflected through surface pavements and creates additional maintenance difficulties. The movement of water through these cracks tends to increase the rate of stripping in asphalt pavements and can result in the formation of an ice lens below the crack which produces an upward lipping of both edges. In some cases localized thawing of the base occurs when deicing solution enters the cracks.

Thawing

For convenience, the engineering considerations pertaining to the thawing of soil can be divided into those relating to seasonal frost, or the active layer, and those relating to permafrost.

In the active layer, when the previously described ice lenses that caused the heaving melt and the resulting water escapes, voids are left in the soil. When loads are applied to pavements, which depend on support from the soil, the pavements sag into the depressions and begin to crack and fail. Even when there is no significant ice segregation, pavement distress may develop. As the 0°C thawing isotherm progresses downward below the plowed roadway surface, the meltwater produced cannot penetrate the frozen soil and often it cannot dissipate laterally

Figure 1.4 Highway heave near Potter, Alas. (*Alaska Department of Highways photograph.*)

15

Figure 1.5 Fill wall, retaining silty gravel, deformed by frost action, Russian River, Alas. (*Alaska Department of Highways photograph.*)

Figure 1.6 Power pole near Fairbanks, Alas.

as snow berms keep the sides of the roadway from thawing quickly. The trapped water induces a high moisture content directly under the pavement, reducing the bearing capacity. Until a drainage path is restored, loads must be restricted to prevent disintegration of the road surface. Chapter 4 discusses a theory which shows how excess pore pressures develop and how they are related to the loss in bearing capacity.

When seasonal ice melts under piles, poles, or spread footings, it is rare for the member to settle back to its original elevation. Instead the surrounding soil may tend to fill (at least partially) the space formerly occupied by the ice; this, combined with skin friction, will restrict downward movement. This cycle of heaving and blocked restoration can be repeated yearly until failure results.

Changing the range of ground surface temperatures on the whiplash curve of Fig. 1.2 will change the elevation of the intersection of the right-hand limit of the temperature fluctuations and the 0°C temperature line, thereby shifting the top limit of the permafrost table. While some variation in the permafrost is caused by changes in the natural weather pattern, more dramatic shifts are caused by modifying the surface cover or introducing sources of artificial heat. The magnitude of the engineering effects caused by lowering the permafrost table depends primarily on the ice content of the soil under consideration. When ice is well distributed and its volume is less than the pore volume of the soil, the consolidation and resultant settlement are negligible. As the ice content increases, so does the potential for settlement. Buildings which introduce a concentrated heat source, like the house shown in Fig. 1.7, are particularly vulnerable to settlement. Methods for estimating the settlement are given in Chap. 4.

Thermal equilibrium can be changed by changing the existing ground cover. Unless the new construction provides a heat balance that matches that of the original surface, the permafrost level will change. In high-arctic roadway embankments, gravel 1 to 2 m thick will approximate the natural cover. In the subarctic, where the permafrost temperature approaches 0°C, the height of fill required to maintain equilibrium becomes prohibitive. Roadway settlements similar to the one shown in Fig. 1.8 can be expected when normal fills are placed over ice-rich permafrost. Vigorous maintenance can keep a gravel surface serviceable while a new thermal equilibrium is reached.

The thawing of large ice wedges similar to the one in Fig. 1.9, which was exposed during construction of the pipeline haul road to the Prudhoe Bay, Alas., oilfield, can produce impressive depressions called *thermokarst pits*. The large thermokarst depression in Fig. 1.10, which filled with water creating a rustic pond, was selected by a developer as the focal point of a residential subdivision. It will be interesting to observe the performance of houses built in this neighborhood.

In addition to settlement, the general stability of soil can be lowered by thawing. Not only is the binding force of the ice removed, but the released moisture may act both as a "lubricant" and under some conditions as a transport agent in promoting soil flow. Slope stability should be investigated whenever an engineering project changes the thermal regime of a permafrost region. Chapter 7

Figure 1.7 House built over permafrost, College, Alas.

Figure 1.8 Settlement of a new road crossing over ice-rich ground, Fairbanks, Alas.

20

Figure 1.9 Ice wedge exposed during construction of the pipeline haul road near Hess Creek, Alas.

Figure 1.10 Large thermokarsk depression that has filled with water near Fairbanks, Alas.

will discuss this problem in depth. Thawing permafrost can have effects on drainage patterns which must be considered. Water which cannot penetrate the frozen ground will follow porous paths thawed in the permafrost. Buried pipes transporting warm liquids can create new drainage channels below ground, and vehicle traffic can thaw out surface channels. That these changes can direct water to new locations must be recognized. In addition to allowing the passage of water, thawing also permits the movement of the soil particles, and the combination of these two conditions may produce serious erosion with its resultant problems.

Steady-State Permafrost

Permafrost that does not thaw also influences the engineering consideration of projects in cold regions. Permafrost, by definition, is soil that maintains a maximum temperature below the freezing point of water. Therefore, placing anything that holds or transports water in contact with permafrost invites freezing of the enclosed water. Wells drilled to tap aquifers below the permafrost are subject to freezing where the pipe passes through the frozen soil unless flow rates are continuously high or heat is supplied to create a thaw tube around the pipe. As previously mentioned, heating the tube to solve one problem can create a new one. Utility lines placed in or on permafrost face the same hazards as

Figure 1.11 Steam truck thawing sewer lines in Fairbanks, Alas. (*Hilton Pumping & Thawing photograph.*)

pipes. If the flow of water or sewage cannot keep it thawed, three possibilities exist: (1) the operating temperature can be increased by adding heat to the system, (2) the lines can be protected from the environment by placing them in utilidors, or (3) continuous maintenance can be provided, e.g., the thawing being conducted on the buried lines in Fig. 1.11.

The impermeability of frozen ground must always be considered. Disposal of the liquid effluent from sewage-collection systems into impervious ground is not possible, complicating the environmental problems in permafrost regions. Impermeable barriers created by permafrost also increase the seasonal thaw problems by hindering the removal of surface water and causing saturated soil conditions and reduced stability.

The cementing action of frozen soil moisture is an important consideration when permafrost must be excavated. The effort required depends on the soil type and moisture content. Dry permafrost presents no special problems, while high-moisture-content gravel may require preblasting before excavating equipment can remove it. Early methods of excavation relied on prethawing the material, a time- and energy-consuming process.

The increased size and power of modern excavation equipment have permitted improvements in the ability to move frozen ground, but much research remains to be done on methods and equipment to improve the efficiency of this difficult operation. Excavation of frozen ground is discussed in Sec. 6.9.

Aufeis

In shallow or slow-flowing streams, ice may form not only on the surface but also on the bottom of the channel. A stream in a permafrost region that generates only a small thaw bulb during the summer is particularly susceptible to this phenomenon. The bottom icing constricts or even stops the flow in the channel, forcing the water over the banks or out through porous formations that may border the stream. As this water overflows the stream bed or emerges some distance from the original channel, it freezes in sheets, building up successive layers over the adjacent ground. By the end of winter even small streams can build sheets of ice up to 4 m thick covering many square kilometers. When this occurs next to roads, traffic can be blocked until the ice is ripped away by bulldozers. Figure 1.12 illustrates the use of polyethelene-covered snow fences to retard the spread of the aufeis. When buildings are affected by this condition, evacuation is a common response. The seriousness of this phenomenon has not always been considered in site selection.

Useful Aspects of Frozen Ground

Permafrost is not necessarily troublesome; sometimes it is a valuable asset. The most obvious beneficial aspect of frozen ground is its stability and strength. In much of the arctic, it is impractical to traverse the ground surface unless it is frozen. Not only does freezing provide necessary bearing capacity, but it also

Figure 1.12 Surface icing along highways near Paxson, Alas.

protects the land from off-road operations. As for road travel, the gravel road on which you fought dust, mud, washboarding, or potholes (individually and sometimes all at the same time) in the summer can become a high-quality road in winter thanks to the bond strength of frozen moisture.

Permafrost can provide excellent bearing capacity for supporting structural loads. Sometimes, when permafrost does not exist at the project location, it is advantageous to create your own by the use of "heat tubes." Permafrost can also be used to provide an anchorage for piling otherwise subject to seasonal frost jacking. Some precautions must, of course, be taken when using permafrost. Keeping the frozen ground frozen is the most obvious consideration. This can be accomplished by carrying the loads deep enough to ensure that the load-bearing strata will not be melted during summer or by supplying artificial refrigeration.

Another consideration in placing loads on frozen ground is the creep characteristics of ice and frozen soil. As ice will flow under sustained load, ice-rich soils must be investigated to determine whether creep rates are critical. This subject is discussed in Chaps. 5 and 6.

The impervious nature of frozen ground has also been used to advantage. The freezing of soil to construct cofferdams and to reduce infiltration into excavations has proved economical even in temperate zones. In cold regions this method has the advantage of having nature provide a cold sink.

Table 1.1 Unified Soil Classification System (adapted from U.S. Army Corps of Engineers, 1953)

Major division			Group symbol	Typical name
Coarse-grained soils, more than half of material larger than no. 200 sieve size	Gravels, more than half of coarse fraction larger than no. 4 sieve size	Clean gravels (little or no fines)	GW	Well-graded, gravel-sand mixtures, little or no fines
			GP	Poorly graded gravels or gravel-sand mixtures, little or no fines
		Gravels with fines (appreciable amount of fines)	GM	Silty gravels, gravel-sand-silt mixtures
			GC	Clayey gravels, gravel-sand-clay mixtures
	Sands, more than half of coarse fraction smaller than no. 4 sieve size	Clean sands (little or no fines)	SW	Well-graded sands, gravelly sands, little or no fines
			SP	Poorly-graded sands or gravelly sands, little or no fines
		Sands with fines (appreciable amount of fines)	SM	Silty sands, sand-silt mixtures
			SC	Clayey sands, sand-clay mixtures
Fine-grained soils, more than half of material smaller than no. 200 sieve size	Silts and clays, liquid limit < 50		ML	Inorganic silts and very fine sands, rock flour, silty or clayey fine sands or clayey silts with slight plasticity
			CL	Inorganic clays of low to medium plasticity, gravelly clays, sandy clays, silty clays, lean clays
			OL	Organic silts and organic silty clays of low plasticity
	Silts and clays, liquid limit > 50		MH	Inorganic silts, micaceous or diatomaceous fine sandy or silty soils, elastic silts
			CH	Inorganic clays of high plasticity, fat clays
			OH	Organic clays of medium to high plasticity, organic silts
Highly organic soils			Pt	Peat and other highly organic soils

Field identification procedure	Laboratory classification procedure (see Fig. 1.13)		
Wide range in grain sizes and substantial amounts of intermediate particle sizes	Determine percentages of gravel and sand from grain-size curve; depending on percentage of fines (fraction smaller than no. 200 sieve size) coarse-grained soils are classified as follows: Less than 5% = GW, GP, SW, SP More than 12% = GM, GC, SM, SC 5–12% = borderline cases requiring use of dual symbols	$C_u = D_{60}/D_{10} > 4$ $C_c = 1 < D_{30}^2/D_{10}\,D_{60} < 3$	
Predominantly one size or a range of sizes with some intermediate sizes missing		Not meeting all gradation requirements for GW	
Nonplastic fines or fines with low plasticity (for identification procedures see ML)		Atterberg limits below A line or PI < 4	Above A line with $4 < PI < 7$ are borderline cases requiring use of dual symbols
Plastic fines (for identification procedures see CL)		Atterberg limits above A line with PI > 7	
Wide range in grain size and substantial amounts of all intermediate particle sizes		$C_u = D_{60}/D_{10} > 6$ $C_c = 1 < D_{30}^2/D_{10}\,D_{60} < 3$	
Predominantly one size or a range of sizes with some intermediate sizes missing		Not meeting all gradation requirements for SW	
Nonplastic fines or fines with low plasticity (for indentification procedures see ML)		Atterberg limits below A line or PI < 4	Above A line with $4 < PI < 7$ are borderline cases requiring use of dual symbols
Plastic fines (for indentification procedures see CL)		Atterberg limits above A line with PI > 7	

Identification procedures on fraction smaller than no. 40 sieve size

Dry strength (crushing characteristics)	Dilatancy (reaction to shaking)	Toughness (consistency near PL)
None to slight	Quick to slow	None
Medium to high	None to very slow	Medium
Slight to medium	Slow	Slight
Slight to medium	Slow to none	Slight to medium
High to very high	None	None
Medium to high	None to very slow	Slight to medium

Readily identified by color, odor, spongy feel, and frequently by fibrous texture

(see notes on p. 28)

1. Boundary classifications: soils possessing characteristics of two groups are designated by combinations of group symbols. For example, GW-GC, well-graded gravel-sand mixture with clay binder.
2. All sieve sizes on this chart are United States standard.

Field identification procedures for fine-grained soils or fractions

---

These procedures are to be performed on the minus no. 40 sieve-size particles, approximately 0.4 mm. For field classification purposes, screening is not intended; simply remove by hand the coarse particles that interfere with the tests.

Dilatancy (reaction to shaking)

After removing particles larger than no. 40 sieve size, prepare a pat of moist soil with a volume of about 160 mm³. If necessary, add enough water to make the soil soft but not sticky.

Place the pat in the open palm of one hand and shake horizontally, striking vigorously against the other hand several times. A positive reaction consists of the appearance of water on the surface of the pat, which changes to a livery consistency and becomes glossy. When the sample is squeezed between the fingers, the water and gloss disappear from the surface and the pat stiffens; finally it cracks or crumbles. The rapidity of appearance of water during shaking and of its disappearance during squeezing assists in identifying the character of the fines in a soil.

Very fine clean sands give the quickest and most distinct reaction whereas a plastic clay has no reaction. Inorganic silts, such as a typical rock flour, show a moderately quick reaction.

Dry strength (crushing characteristics)

After removing particles larger than no. 40 sieve size, mold a pat of soil to the consistency of putty, adding water if necessary. Allow the pat to dry completely by oven, sun, or air drying and then test its strength by breaking and crumbling between the fingers. This strength is a measure of the character and quantity of the colloidal fraction contained in the soil. The dry strength increases with increasing plasticity.

High dry strength is characteristic for clays of the CH group. A typical inorganic silt possesses only very slight dry strength. Silty fine sands and silts have about the same slight dry strength but can be distinguished by the feel when powdering the dried specimen. Fine sand feels gritty whereas a typical silt has the smooth feel of flour.

Toughness (consistency near plastic limit)

After particles larger than the no. 40 sieve size are removed, a specimen of soil about 160 mm³ in size is molded to the consistency of putty. If too dry, water must be added, and if sticky, the specimen should be spread out in a thin layer and allowed to lose some moisture by evaporation. Then the specimen is rolled out by hand on a smooth surface or between the palms into a thread about 3 mm in diameter. The thread is then folded and rerolled repeatedly. During this manipulation the moisture content is gradually reduced and the specimen stiffens, finally loses its plasticity, and crumbles when the plastic limit is reached.

After the thread crumbles, the pieces should be lumped together and a slight kneading action continued until the lump crumbles.

The tougher the thread near the plastic limit and the stiffer the lump when it finally crumbles, the more potent the colloidal clay fraction in the soil. Weakness of the thread at the plastic limit and quick loss of coherence of the lump below the plastic limit indicate either inorganic clay of low plasticity or materials such as kaolin-type clays and organic clays which occur below the A line.

Highly organic clays have a very weak and spongy feel at the plastic limit.

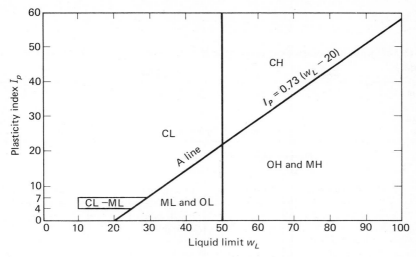

Figure 1.13 Plasticity chart for laboratory classification of fine grained soils.

Cores for earth dams can be made impermeable by freezing. Where suitable impervious material is scarce, this can provide an economical solution. Here again, keeping the core frozen is critical.

Another proposed use of frozen ground is for the containment of liquids or gases that can be stored at temperatures below 0°C. As improvements are made in tunneling methods for permafrost, this may become an important method of storing petroleum products from the arctic fields.

Finding ways of adapting to frozen ground and utilizing its properties is one of the most challenging fields in arctic engineering.

1.5 FROZEN-SOIL CLASSIFICATION

A classification system for frozen soils is needed so that the geotechnical engineer can describe and discuss a frozen soil both with brevity and the assurance that his description will mean the same to another engineer. The term *frozen* includes all earth materials below 0°C regardless of the water-ice content and phase condition. The descriptive classification presented here assumes that the reader has knowledge of unfrozen soils. The physical and thermal properties of soil, water, ice, and frozen soil are discussed in Chap. 2. Field investigations of frozen ground, including sampling, borehole logs, and field testing of frozen soil properties, are covered in Chap. 9. A genetic classification of ice is given in Chap. 10 with reference to ice covers.

The Unified Soil Classification System (U.S. Army Corps of Engineers, 1953) is the most generally accepted system for unfrozen soils at present and needs only

Table 1.2 Description and classification of frozen soils (adapted from Linnell and Kaplar, 1966)

I: Description of soil phase (independent of frozen state)	Classify soil phase by the unified soil classification system					
	Major group		**Subgroup**			
	Description	Designation	Description		Designation	
II: Description of frozen soil	Segregated ice not visible by eye	N	Poorly bonded or friable		Nf	
			Well bonded	No excess ice	Nb	n
				Excess ice		e
	Segregated ice visible by eye (ice 25 mm or less thick)	V	Individual ice crystals or inclusions		Vx	
			Ice coatings on particles		Vc	
			Random or irregularly oriented ice formations		Vr	
			Stratified or distinctly oriented ice formations		Vs	
III: Description of substantial ice strata	Ice greater than 25 mm thick	ICE	Ice with soil inclusions		ICE + soil type	
			Ice without soil inclusions		ICE	

Classify soil phase by the unified soil classification system

Field identification	Pertinent properties of frozen materials which can be measured by physical tests to supplement field identification	Thaw characteristics

Identify by visual examination; to determine presence of excess ice, use procedure under note (3) and hand magnifying lens as necessary; for soils not fully saturated estimate degree of ice saturation (medium, low); note presence of crystals or of ice coatings around larger particles	In-place temperature
	Density and void ratio
	  a. In frozen state
	  b. After thawing in place
	Water content (total H_2O, including ice)
	  a. Average
	  b. Distribution
		Usually thaw-stable

For ice phase, record the following as applicable
 	
Location   Size
Orientation Shape
Thickness   Pattern of
Length   arrangement
Spacing
Hardness ⎫
Structure ⎬ per part III below
Color   ⎭
 	
Estimate volume of visible segregated ice present as percent of total sample volume
	Strength
	  a. Compressive
	  b. Tensile
	  c. Shear
	  d. Adfreeze
	Elastic properties
	Plastic properties
	Thermal properties
	Ice crystal structure (using optical instruments)
	  a. Orientation of axes
	  b. Crystal size
	  c. Crystal shape
	  d. Pattern of
	      arrangement
		Usually thaw-unstable

Designate material as ice and use descriptive terms as follows, usually one item from each group, as applicable: Hardness: hard, soft (of mass, not of individual crystals) Structure: clear, cloudy, porous, candled, granular, stratified Color: colorless, gray, blue Admixtures: contains few thin silt inclusions	Same as part II above, as applicable, with special emphasis on ice crystal structure	

(see notes on p. 32)

Definitions

Ice coatings on particles are discernible layers of ice found on or below the larger soil particles in a frozen soil mass. They are sometimes associated with hoarfrost crystals, which have grown into voids produced by the freezing action.

Ice crystal is a very small individual ice particle visible in the face of a soil mass. Crystals may be present alone or in combination with other ice formations.

Clear ice is transparent and contains only a moderate number of air bubbles.

Cloudy ice is translucent but essentially sound and nonpervious.

Porous ice contains numerous voids, usually interconnected and resulting (1) from melting at air bubbles or along crystal interfaces from presence of salt or other materials in the water or (2) from the freezing of saturated snow. Though porous, the mass retains its structural unity.

Candled ice is ice which has rotted or otherwise formed into long columnar crystals, very loosely bonded together.

Granular ice is composed of coarse, more or less equidimensional, ice crystals weakly bonded together.

Ice lenses are lenticular ice formations in soil occurring essentially parallel to each other, generally normal to the direction of heat loss and commonly in repeated layers.

Ice segregation is the growth of ice as distinct lenses, layers, veins, and masses in soils, commonly but not always oriented normal to direction of heat loss.

Well bonded signifies that the soil particles are strongly held together by the ice and that the frozen soil possesses relatively high resistance to chipping or breaking.

Poorly bonded signifies that the soil particles are weakly held together by the ice and that the frozen soil consequently has poor resistance to chipping or breaking.

Friable denotes a condition in which material is easily broken up under light to moderate pressure.

Thaw-stable frozen soils do not, on thawing, show loss of strength below normal long-time thawed values or produce detrimental settlement.

Thaw-unstable frozen soils show, on thawing, significant loss of strength below normal long-time thawed values and/or significant settlement, as a direct result of the melting of the excess ice in the soil.

Notes

1. When rock is encountered, standard rock-classification terminology should be used.
2. Frozen soils in the N group may, on close examination, indicate presence of ice within the voids of the material by crystalline reflections or by a sheen on fractured or trimmed surfaces. However, the impression to the unaided eye is that none of the frozen water occupies space in excess of the original voids in the soil. The opposite is true of frozen soils in the V group.
3. When visual methods may be inadequate, a simple field test to aid evaluation of volume of excess ice can be made by placing some frozen soil in a small jar, allowing it to melt and observing the quantity of supernatant water as a percent of total volume.
4. Where special forms of ice, such as hoarfrost, can be distinguished, more explicit description should be given.
5. The observer should be careful to avoid being misled by surface scratches or frost coating on the ice.
6. The letter symbols shown are to be affixed to the Unified Soil Classification letter designations or may be used in conjunction with graphic symbols, in exploration logs or geologic profiles. For example, a lean clay with essentially horizontal ice lenses:

The descriptive name of the frozen soil type and a complete description of the frozen material are the fundamental elements of this classification scheme. Additional descriptive data should be added where necessary. The letter symbols are secondary and are intended only for convenience in preparing graphical presentations. Since it is frequently impractical to describe ice formations in frozen soils by words alone, sketches and photographs should be used where appropriate to supplement descriptions.

to be extended for frozen soils. The extension of the unified classification system (Table 1.1) should be independent of the geologic history or mode of origin for the material. Samples that are representative and which show the natural structure of the frozen soil are needed for the classification. The frozen soil is described and classified in three steps (Linell and Kaplar, 1966): (1) the soil phase is identified independent of the frozen state using the Unified Soil Classification System given in Table 1.1, (2) soil characteristics resulting from freezing of the material (Table 1.2) are added to the description, and (3) ice found in the frozen materials is described (Table 1.2).

The identification of the soil phase (step 1), using Table 1.1, involves placement into one of three major divisions: coarse-grained soils, fine-grained soils, or highly organic soils. The coarse-grained soils are subdivided into gravels (symbol G) or sand (symbol S) based on whether one-half the particles by weight are larger or smaller than 4.76 mm, respectively. Further subdivision of the gravels and sands includes well-graded clean materials (symbol W), fairly clean gap-graded materials (symbol P), coarse materials containing silt (symbol M), and coarse materials containing clay (symbol C). The fine-grained soils with more than one-half of the material smaller than 0.074 mm include the inorganic silty and very fine sandy soils (symbol M), inorganic clays (symbol C), and organic silts and clays (symbol O). These silts and clays are further subdivided as to their compressibility: low (symbol L) and high compressibility (symbol H) based on a liquid limit below or above 50, respectively. Highly organic soils (symbol Pt) usually have a fibrous texture and feel spongy and can usually be identified by their brown or black color and characteristic odor.

Frozen-soil characteristics are added (step 2) based on two major groups (Table 1.2): soils in which segregated ice is not visible to the unaided eye (group symbol N) and soils in which segregated ice is visible (group symbol V). The presence of ice within the soil voids for group N is commonly revealed by crystalline reflections or by a sheen on fractured or trimmed surfaces. Subgroups include poorly bonded (symbol Nf) and well bonded (symbol Nb). Segregated ice visible in group V includes a thickness of up to 25 mm. Subgroups for Group V with visible ice include Vx for individual ice inclusions, Ve for ice coating on particles, Vr for random or irregularly oriented ice inclusions, and Vs for stratified or clearly oriented ice inclusions.

When substantial ice is present in inclusions thicker than 25 mm, the material is designated ice as part of step 3 (Table 1.2). Subgroups include ice plus soil type or only ice when no soil inclusions are present. Some organic soils found in cold regions may be described by special terms, e.g., *muskeg*, for additional clarification. When more than one subgroup characteristic is present in the same material, multiple subgroup designations may be used, as Vs, r shown in Fig. 1.14*b*. When exact evaluation of the presence of ice is required, procedures outlined in Chap. 4 using consolidation apparatus may be used. Typical boring logs using the frozen-soil classification system are shown in Fig. 9.3 and Table 9.1.

A field description of frozen soil often will include specific terrain features

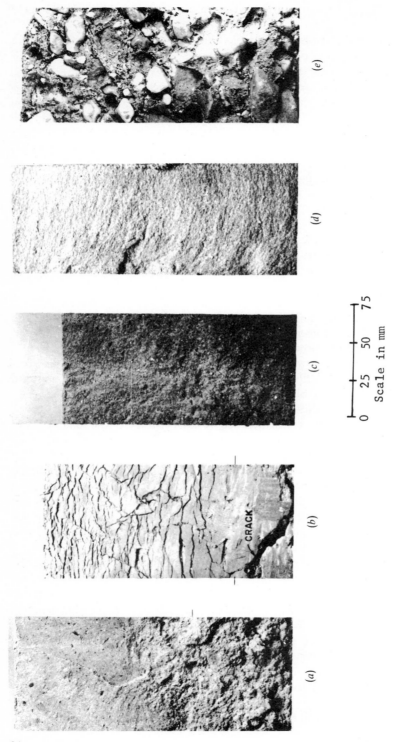

(e)

(d)

(c)

Scale in mm

0   25   50   75

(b)

CRACK

(a)

34

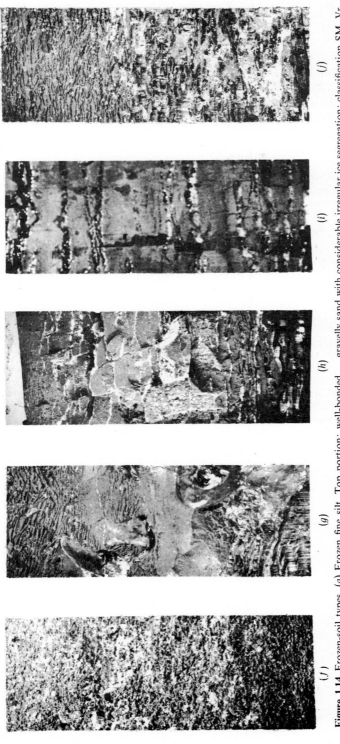

Figure 1.14 Frozen-soil types. (a) Frozen fine silt. Top portion: well-bonded, saturated; classification ML, Nb.n. Bottom portion: friable; classification ML, Nf. (b) Frozen lean clay. Ice lenses in top portion formed from moisture drawn from below; classification CL, Vs.r. Bottom portion: medium-bonded and somewhat friable; classification CL, Nf. (c) Frozen, well-graded silty sand. Well-bonded; classification SM, Nb.n. (d) Frozen fine sand. Well-bonded, high degree of saturation; classification SM, Nb,e. (e) Frozen, clayey sandy gravel with ice saturation; classification SM. Nb,e. (f) Frozen, clayey, gravelly sand with considerable irregular ice segregation; classification SM, Vr. (g) Upper portion: frozen clayey silt with occasional stones; classification ML-CL, Vr. Lower portion: ice, irregular, up to 2 in. thick, and containing some silt inclusions. (h) Frozen lean clay with stratified ice lenses; classification CL-OL, Vs. (i) Frozen lean clay with stratified ice lenses; classification CL, Vs. (j) Upper portion: frozen silty clay, with stratified ice lenses; classification CL, Vs. Lower portions: ice with numerous clay inclusions. (Total ice volume approximately 87 percent). (*After Linell and Kaplar, 1966.*)

35

which influence the existence of permafrost. Surface characteristics (Pihlainen and Johnston, 1963) include vegetation cover, snow cover, relief, and drainage. The major combinations of vegetation may be described using the system outlined by MacFarlane (1958). The snow type, snow-cover depth, and variability over a site throughout the winter season are of interest to the engineer.

REFERENCES

Gerdel, R. W., 1969. Characteristics of the Cold Regions, *U.S. Army Cold Reg. Res. Eng. Lab.*, *Monogr.* I-A. Hanover, N.H.

Hughes, O. L., 1970. Recent Advances in Permafrost Engineering, unpublished lecture notes, Calgary, Alta.

Leffingwell, Ernest de K. 1919. The Canning River Region, Northern Alaska, *U.S. Geol. Surv. Prof. Pap.* 109.

Linell, K. A., and C. W. Kaplar. 1966. Description and Classification of Frozen Soils, *U.S. Army Cold Reg. Res. Eng. Lab. Tech. Rep.* 150. Hanover, N.H.

MacFarlane, I. C., 1958. Guide to a Field Description of Muskeg, *Natl. Res. Counc. Can. Ass. Comm. Soil Snow Mech. Tech. Mem.* 44.

Nansen, Fridtjof. 1897. "Farthest North: The Voyage and Exploration of the Fram, 1893–96," vol. 1, Constable, London.

Pewe, Troy L. 1975. Permafrost: Challenge of the Arctic, in "1976 Yearbook of Science and the Future," Encyclopedia Britannica, *Ariz. State Univ. Repr. Ser.* 194.

Pihlainen, J. A., and G. H. Johnston. 1963. Guide to a Field Description of Permafrost, *Natl. Res. Counc. Can. Ass. Comm. Soil Snow Mech. Tech. Mem.* 79.

Stefansson, Vilhjalmur. 1924. "My Life with the Eskimos," Macmillan, New York.

Teal, John J., Jr. 1955. Aboriginal Populations, in George T. Kimble and Dorothy Good (eds.), "Geography of the Northlands," Wiley, New York (*Am. Geogr. Soc. Spec. Publ.* 32, p. 140).

U.S. Army Corps of Engineers. 1953. The Unified Soil Classification System, *Waterw. Exp. Stn. Tech. Mem.* 3-357, Vicksburg, Miss., March.

Washburn, A. L. 1951. Geography and Arctic Lands, in Thomas G. Taylor, "Geography in the Twentieth Century," pp. 269–271, Philosophical Library, New York.

PHYSICAL AND THERMAL PROPERTIES OF FROZEN GROUND

Duwayne M. Anderson, Roland Pusch, and Edward Penner

INTRODUCTION

The general characteristics of frozen ground and the principal differences between seasonally frozen ground and permafrost were described in Chap. 1. Now the basic physical properties and behavior of frozen ground will be examined. Attention will be paid to the properties and processes of most importance in geotechnical engineering. Sufficient detail is given to provide the physical basis for the material presented in subsequent chapters and to enable one to apply these principles to the analysis and solution of most geotechnical problems.

The discussions, of necessity, are brief; the space available precludes the exhaustive development of each topic presented. Consequently, much reliance is placed on the availability of introductory and basic texts in soil mechanics, soil physics, soil chemistry, and clay mineralogy. Nevertheless, it should be possible to derive from the discussions, however brief, an insight into the peculiarities of behavior and some of the most important and unusual properties of soils subjected to freezing and thawing and soils frozen for long periods.

The discussion is organized so that it begins with a consideration of the three major constituents and ends with a consideration of the frozen complex. The examples at the end of the chapter illustrate and emphasize several of the more important topics. They also test the memory and dexterity of the reader in dealing with utilitarian computations, derivations, and illustrations. Others can easily be devised as needed.

At several points attention is directed toward puzzling problems requiring additional theoretical research before geotechnical engineering design and practice can be considered to be firmly based when frozen ground is involved.

2.1 SOIL

Soils of the earth have formed as a result of the comminution and decomposition of the rocks and minerals that form the earth's regolith together with the decay and admixing of the remains of plant and animal life. But the term soils applied to terrestrial soils (as distinct from planetary soils in general) comprises more than the complex of this physical mixture. It includes also a recognition of the continuation of the processes of soil formation and development. Many of these processes are those associated with soil microorganisms and plant and animal communities. Biological processes are responsible for the production of humus, the dark-colored colloidal organic matter that is characteristic of soils of high agricultural fertility.

Soil Constituents

The soil system is complex. It is made up of a large number of constituents existing in all three phases of matter: gases and liquids as well as solids. The solid phase consists of mineral and organic matter. The liquid phase, often referred to as the *soil solution*, ranges in composition from nearly pure water on the one hand to more or less concentrated brines of various compositions on the other. Most often it is a dilute solution consisting of a mixture of ionic and molecular inorganic and organic solutes. The liquid phase generally fills the pore space partially; the remaining volume of the intergranular space is occupied by the soil air. The relative proportions of these two phases is expressed as the degree of water saturation. This commonly ranges from virtually complete saturation to near zero, as soils alternately are wetted or dried. The range of physical and chemical relationships found between the soil constituents as they exist in the gaseous, liquid, and solid phases is very large, and, in general, these relationships are in a more or less constant state of fluctuation and change.

Mineralogy The mineral matter consists partly of crystalline minerals of primary or secondary origin in various states of comminution or aggradation and partly of noncrystalline, amorphous mineral matter such as colloidal gels and precipitates of hydrated aluminum, iron, and other oxides. The variation in the composition of soils throughout the world, considering the extremely large number of rock types and mineral assemblages from which soils are derived, can be imagined to be practically infinite. Similarly, the range and proportions of particle sizes are extremely large. Because experience has established that particle size, in general, is a more important soil characteristic than the chemical consequences of mineralogical composition, the differentiation of soils according to the relative proportions of the various particle-size classes (textural classes) facilitates comparison, analysis, and prediction of soil behavior. This matter is discussed further in a later section.

The minerals identifiable in the silt and sand size fractions generally are quartz, the feldspars and other aluminosilicates, the ferromagnesiums, and other accessory minerals. As mentioned earlier, these minerals are seldom found in the clay fraction. Coarser fractions contain rock fragments. To a large extent soils reflect the mineralogical composition of their parent rock materials, but because the properties of soils depend so much on the amount and composition of the clay fraction, and because the clay fraction consists practically in its entirety of secondary minerals formed during weathering of the parent rock, factors such as climate and other environmental determinants often predominate.

The crystalline clay minerals are divided into four major groups: the kaolin group, the hydrous-mica group, the smectite† group, and the palygorskite, or fribrous-clay-minerals, group. Two additional groups are recognized, however, the chlorites and the interstratified clays. For the most part, all these are platy aluminosilicate minerals composed of alternating layers of silicon and oxygen in tetrahedral coordination and aluminum and oxygen in octahedral coordination. Layered in 2:1 or 1:1 sequences, they form elementary crystalline sheets. Several elementary sheets then stack to form quasicrystalline packets termed *tactoids*. Geometrical and electrostatic defects in the sheets arising from the occasional incorporation of aluminum for silicon in the tetrahedral layer and iron or magnesium for aluminum in the octahedral layer are common. This isomorphous substitution of a slightly larger or smaller metallic ion with a lesser positive electrostatic charge for silicon and aluminum leads to a net negative overall charge in the clay lattice. This charge is balanced by adsorbed cations, usually sodium, potassium, calcium, etc. Taking the common smectite montmorillonite as an example, the naturally occurring particle is an alumino-silicate sheet about 0.1 nm thick and up to 100 or 1000 times larger in lateral extent. Faces of the sheets consist of oxygen atoms in a planar hexagonal array. Tactoids normally contain 2 to 15 elementary sheets, depending principally upon the type of exchangeable cation(s) present to satisfy the net negative lattice charge. The principal effect of variations in tactoid size is to bring about changes in the ratio of internal to external mineral surface area for the stacked lamellae. They are free to swell and shrink when wetted or dried by imbibition or removal of interlammellar water. The other clay minerals differ somewhat in structural detail and in their physical and chemical behavior but in general have similar characteristics. A summary of some of the characteristics of the clays belonging to the first three groups mentioned above is given in Table 2.1. More detailed information is available in several texts devoted to clay mineralogy, e.g., Grimshaw (1971), Grim (1953), and subsequent authors.

---

† Commonly known as montmorillonites.

Table 2.1 Major characteristics of four common clay minerals

Mineral	Lattice stacking unit†	Total surface area, m^2/g	Internal surface area, %	Cation exchange capacity meq/g	Area per unit electrostatic charge, $cm^2 \times 10^6$	Free swelling in water,‡ mL/g	Range of interlamellar expansion, $cm \times 10^8$
Kaolinite	1:1	25–50	0	0.02–0.10	180–200	0–0.3	0
Vermiculite	2:1	700–800	80–90	1.2–2.0	60–100	0.5–15.0	6–200
Illite	2:1	100–200	0	0.15–0.40	80–110	0.1–1.2	0
Montmorillonit	2:1	700–800	10–90	0.8–1.2	110–150	0.5–20.0	6–240

† Ratio of silica tetrahedral layers to alumina octahedral layers.
‡ Depending upon exchangeable cation.

The organic fraction As freshly exposed rocks undergo comminution and weathering and the resultant new soil material is deposited in locations where plants and animals flourish, soil microorganisms usually precede them and also flourish. This results in the addition of organic matter to the soil in the form of plant and animal residues in various stages of decomposition, together with the hosts of soil microorganisms that are involved in these processes. Ultimately there is an increasing accumulation of humus, the dark-colored, complex mixture of undegradable or very slowly degradable organic residues. In time humus usually comes to dominate the soil organic-matter fraction although it seldom exceeds 5 to 10 percent by weight of the inorganic mineral matter.

Humus can be dispersed in water to particles of colloidal dimensions and smaller. It has acidic properties and exhibits the property of ion exchange of the same general type as the clay fraction. It has, in general, a favorable effect on the physical properties of soils, enhancing aggregate stability, and its presence tends to counteract the unfavorable effects of the presence of high exchangeable sodium levels, for example.

In sediments, too, microorganisms, mainly bacteria and fungi laid down with soil particles, form an organic complex. Exposed to a new milieu when locked in the sediment, most of the organisms perish, but certain enzymes appear not to be deactivated and persist a long time. The degradation process in this case also leads to the production of most, if not all, of the characteristic substances that make up humus, including microbial cells in various stages of decomposition.

The substances making up humus range from fairly low- to high-molecular-weight compounds, including polymeric substances. The most important are the humic acids. The composition of the major components of the humic acids varies somewhat from soil to soil:

C, %	H, %	N, %	O, %	C/N	C/H	O/H
56–62	3–4.5	3.5–4.5	32–39	14–19	10–22	8–10.5

These humic acids typically contain several functional groups: carboxyl (COOH), phenol and alcohol (OH), methoxyl (OCH_3), carbonyl (C—O), and quinone (C=O). In general, structures consist of aromatic (hydrophobic) and aliphatic (hydrophilic) rings and side chains. This leads to the possibility of a number of types of interactions with the clay fraction. Humic acids, for instance, are adsorbed on particle surfaces through hydrophilic groups. Depending on the pore-water chemistry, this may lead to the production of a protective envelope that inhibits particle dispersion. Quick clays may be created in this way. The cementation of particles may be affected when a group of polyvalent cations in the exchange complex forms irreversible complexes with the humic acid.

In many soils, such as postglacial clays and muds, a rich plant community has resulted in the accumulation of large amounts of undecomposed cellulose. When partially decomposed plant fragments form part of the microstructure, as in peat, fibrous networks with properties similar to that of rubber and randomly oriented crystalline polymers are formed. Mutual interaction between the clay minerals and these cellulose networks, similar to that mentioned above, may occur. Bonding may take place through hydrophilic and other functional groups. In addition, hydrogen bonding between the hydroxyl groups of the cellulose molecules and clay mineral lattices may contribute.

The production of gas during degradation of organic materials may be considerable. In many soils hydrogen sulfide is produced. This in turn reacts with free or mineral iron to form iron sulfide, sometimes in such large quantities that the sediment is colored a dense black. This is the case in many coastal areas.

A proper determination of organic matter in any detail is difficult and time-consuming. Generally, only an integrated determination is made. The content of matter is then expressed as mass of organic substance in percent by weight of the dry soil mass. The normal procedure in soil mechanics is to determine the ignition loss with a correction for the escape of constituent mineral hydroxyls and the thermal decomposition of carbonates. Wet-combustion techniques can be recommended as being the most simple accurate method available for determination of the total carbon content, which is multiplied by a factor, usually 1.72, to yield the quantity of combined organic substance. This procedure gives a value of the organic content sufficiently reliable for all engineering purposes.

Colloids and gels Since colloids are materials in a state of fine subdivision, the colloidal state is one in which surface and interfacial effects predominate. The colloidal complex in soils is made up of the clay fraction and components of the organic-matter fraction. Because of the enormous surface area per unit of mass, the capacity for adsorption is very large. A useful description of the electric forces associated with the surfaces of colloidal particles is provided by the theory of the diffuse electric double layer. When applied to the lamellar clay minerals, the relationships between electrical potential, ionic concentration, and distance from the particle surfaces are as shown in Fig. 2.1. As illustrated in these diagrams, because of the net negative charge of the individual clay particles, exchangeable cations are drawn to them. Conversely, anions tend to be repelled.

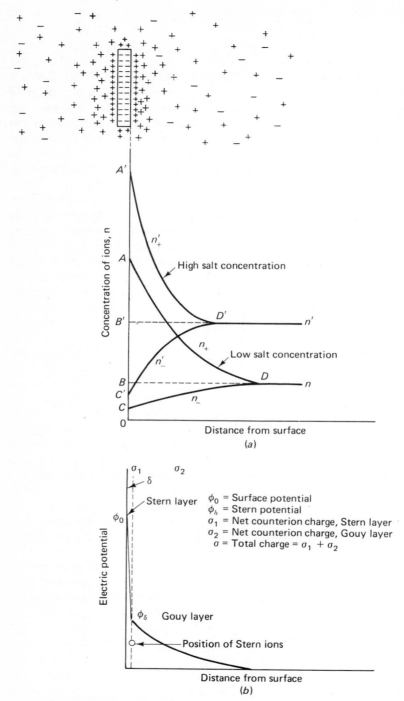

Figure 2.1 Diffuse electric-double-layer relationships. (*Adapted by permission from van Olphen "Clay Colloid Chemistry," Interscience Publishers, New York, 1963.*)

These relationships, in general, satisfactorily explain such colloidal phenomena as the movement of particles in an electric field, the swelling of clays, etc.

Soil colloids are very much more complex than is generally recognized. Although the qualitative relationships shown in Fig. 2.1 are useful generalizations, they are not completely successful in quantitative terms for the full range of clay-water interaction. For example, the presence of adsorbed gases and other surface-moderating substances and the fact that clay-water systems are seldom in equilibrium have yet to be dealt with adequately.

The surfaces of mineral grains probably never represent a boundary between perfect crystal lattices and pore water. Freshly ground quartz, for instance, undergoes rapid aging, which leads to the formation of a hydrated gellike material separated from the regular crystal lattice by a transition zone of uncertain thickness characterized by distortions in the crystal lattice. Similar effects have been observed with freshly ground feldspars. The same process can be assumed to have affected all mineral grains in developing soils and sediments. Where groundwater percolation has caused leaching or introduction of humic agents, the minerals may be severely attacked. These products form the basic constituents of gels and gellike substances. Silica gel, hydrated iron hydroxides, and iron sulfides are the most common inorganic gel substances. Decomposed organic substances also form gels commonly found in soils.

Texture

The term *soil texture* refers to the particle-size distribution of constituent particles, the shape of the particles, the orientation of the particles in space and with respect to each other, and the forces tending to bind the particles together. In low-temperature soil mechanics the size distribution and the arrangement of particles are of major interest, and only these textural factors are considered here. The arrangement of particles and the general patterns of particle networks including discontinuities are of particular interest.

Particle-size distribution Residual and transported soils, deposited in lake, river, or sea or formed by wind or frost, present an infinite variety of particle-size gradings. For practical purposes, especially with respect to frost action, it is convenient to classify all soils into three main classes: coarse-grained soils (noncohesive), fine-grained soils (cohesive), and organic soils (cohesive). The Unified Soil Classification System shown in Table 1.1 follows this scheme.

In virtually all classification schemes in common use it is recognized that soil particles are anisometric, i.e., not truly spherical. Consequently, they are separated according to their equivalent spherical diameters. Thus for larger-sized particles the diameter refers to a circular opening through which they can be passed. For the smaller particles the equivalent diameter refers to the diameter of a sphere of equivalent density that will have the same settling velocity in a viscous fluid. The differences between the various classification schemes in common use reflect the fact that the subdivisions are largely arbitrary. Nevertheless, the size

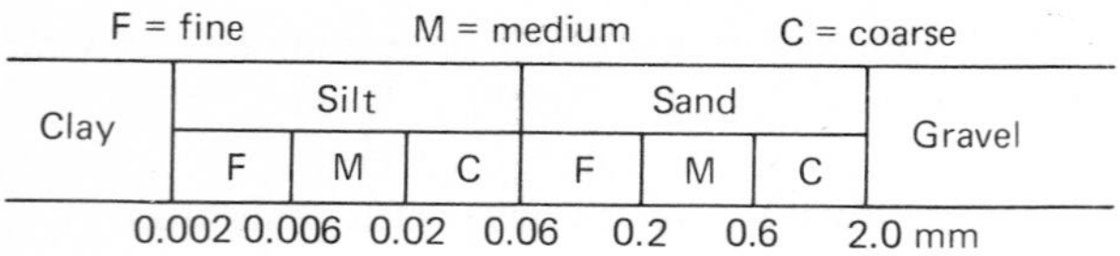

F = fine   M = medium   C = coarse

Clay	Silt			Sand			Gravel
	F	M	C	F	M	C	

0.002 0.006 0.02   0.06   0.2   0.6   2.0 mm

Figure 2.2 Particle-size classification.

limits separating the classes do correspond roughly to discernable changes in physical and chemical properties. For example, the class of particles smaller than a few micrometers in equivalent diameter (clays) contains few if any primary minerals; secondary minerals, mostly the lamellar lattice clay minerals, predominate. Because of the extremely rapid rise in specific surface area with diminishing equivalent spherical diameter, the clay fraction of soils comprises the surface-active portion of the soil mass. Several classification systems are in use. The system originally suggested by the Massachusetts Institute of Technology and later adopted by the British Standards Institution is shown for purposes of illustration in Fig. 2.2. It does not specify limits above 2 mm; this is of no practical importance as concerns frost susceptibility or the properties of frozen soil.

The mechanical analysis required to accomplish classification is carried out in two stages: (1) the separation of the coarser fractions by sieving on a series of standard sieves and (2) the determination of the proportions of the finer particles by a sedimentation process, generally known as *wet analysis*. The methods employed for these separations are well known (Lambe, 1951) and are described in detail in many elementary soil-mechanics textbooks. The results are plotted as grading curves (Fig. 2.3). The abscissas represent particle size to a logarithmic scale and the ordinates the percentage by weight finer than the corresponding particle size. The general trend of the curve indicates the type of grading. A well-graded mixture contains an assortment of particles covering a wide range of sizes, a typical example being till. In poorly graded soils the grains are more uniform in size.

There is generally a large variation in particle size within the clay fraction also. This variation, which is best investigated by the electron microscope, is of great importance with respect to the formation of clay microstructure and indirectly for ice nucleation and the growth of ice crystals in clay matrices. Figure 2.4 illustrates a typical grading of clay particles. Two grading criteria are of importance in classifying soils with respect to frost susceptibility: the effective size, which is the maximum particle size of the smallest 10 percent of the sample, and the uniformity coefficient, which is the ratio of the maximum size of the smallest 60 percent to the effective size.

Microstructure Microstructure is best observed and classified by optical and electron microscopy. Microstructural studies of clays and clayey soils are of importance in associating the geological processes involved in the soil formation and the engineering properties it exhibits. Recent investigations have shown that single-particle behavior in fine-grained soils is extremely rare; clay plates are nearly

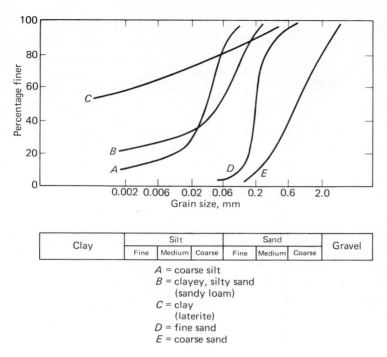

A = coarse silt
B = clayey, silty sand
    (sandy loam)
C = clay
    (laterite)
D = fine sand
E = coarse sand

Figure 2.3 Grading curves.

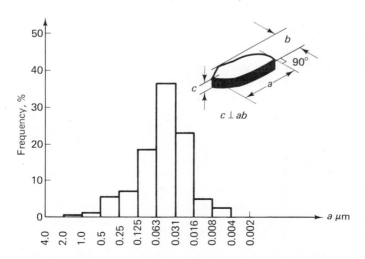

Figure 2.4 Example of histogram of particle size in the clay fraction.

always aggregated in some way. Recognition of this fact is most important. There is a resemblance between clays and granular soils in this respect. The most important factors influencing the final structure of fine-grained sediments are the electrochemical environment at sedimentation and the overburden stress.

The preferential coupling of small particles leading to big units and their tendency to be connected to larger particles in the course of sedimentation implies a heterogeneous, aggregated microstructural network. Two basic principles which have to do with the influence of electrolytes govern the final particle arrangement. The first takes into account the influence of the concentration and kind of cations in the pore water on the interparticle distance. This can be described qualitatively by the theory of the diffuse electric double layer. An increased concentration of cations reduces the zeta potential and the range of the double layer, thus reducing the repulsive force between the particles. This explanation of the influence of electrolyte concentration on clay-particle flocculation is currently favored. The applicability of this theory, however, is strongly dependent on particle size and concentration of electrolytes. The other principle takes the structural order of the interparticle water molecules into consideration. Cations in the soil solution are attracted to the negatively charged clay particles. When they diffuse into the intercrystalline space, depending on the size and charge of the ions, they may interact with the water lattice in such a way as partially to offset the repulsion between adjacent particles, thereby facilitating a closer juxtaposition. Both lead to the expectation that clays deposited in seawater should contain relatively large, dense aggregates whereas freshwater clays should consist of less dense aggregates characterized by a more uniform distribution of particles (dispersion). These differences in structure have been verified by a large number of microstructural investigations and lead to quite different geotechnical properties.

In marine as well as in freshwater clays the majority of the observed particle contacts are of the edge-to-edge type, but edge-to-face and face-to-face modes also are frequent. Since considerable particle movement must take place during consolidation, the latter modes of association probably do not reflect the primary coupling of adjacent particles during sedimentation. The most characteristic microstructural pattern of clay deposited in salinic waters is of the type shown in Fig. 2.5.

Micrographs of ultrathin sections offer a possibility of applying statistical methods to describe the patterns (Pusch, 1968, 1970). The total pore area P in percent of the total area T of the micrograph and the pore size a_p are convenient parameters. The pore size is defined as the longest intercept. When these parameters are used, the microstructural patterns of fine-grained soils can be described mathematically. For homogeneous soils it has been shown that the parameters are representative of soil volumes of several cubic centimeters even when the sections analyzed are very small. For pore size, the median value has been found to be in the range of 0.11 to 0.24 μm for marine as well as for freshwater illitic clays. However, marine clays also contain a number of very large pores which give the major contribution to the P/T value. Figure 2.6

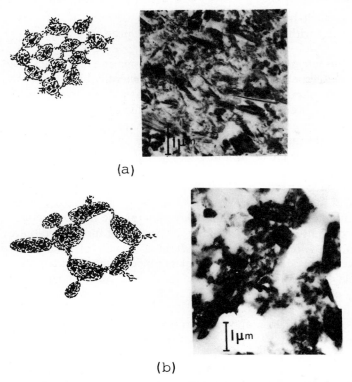

(a)

(b)

Figure 2.5 Clay microstructure as observed in a transmission electron microscope using ultrathin acrylate-treated specimens. Left pictures show schematic, generalized patterns: (*a*) fresh-water illitic clay; (*b*) marine illitic clay. Dark parts represent mineral substance.

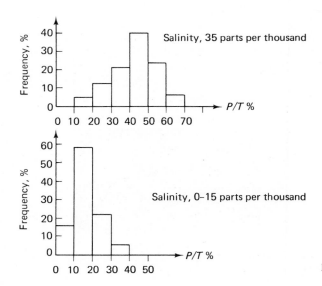

Figure 2.6 *P/T* vs. salinity.

illustrates that P/T is much higher for soft marine and brackish-water clays than for freshwater clays with similar preconsolidation pressures and water contents.

Preferred orientation is generally not obvious in soft marine and brackish-water clays. In freshwater clays a preferred orientation is generally observed only for particles coarser than about 0.5 μm. For marine clays it has been found that a consolidation pressure of 120 kPa is not sufficient to produce a preferred orientation. Local groups of parallel particles (domains) are fairly frequent in marine clays but rather rare in brackish-water and freshwater clays. In heavily compacted clays, such as moraine clays, high pressure and shear stresses produce a breakdown of the majority of the weak particle links between more rigid aggregates or larger particles. The links are then changed into domains, as shown in Fig. 2.7.

Where montmorillonite is the predominant clay mineral, the microstructural pattern is different. A content of more than about 20 percent of montmorillonite with sodium as saturating ion appears to result in a system of interwoven laminae of face-to-face associated particles with a less obvious degree of aggregation than in illitic clays. Calcium montmorillonite, on the other hand, often consists of irregularly oriented particles collected in dense aggregates and interlinking groups as in illitic clays.

Examination of electron micrographs of ultrathin sections usually shows organic matter existing in the form of fluffy bodies or distinct objects associated with clay-particle aggregates or enclosed in them (Pusch, 1973). The occurrence of observable organic substance ranges from widely spaced local bodies in organic-poor clays to almost continuous systems of organic matter in organic-rich clays. In the case of humic substances in undisturbed clay it may be assumed that they are confined to the pore regions where the humus-producing microorganisms existed since the diffusion of such large molecules into the surroundings is effectively hindered. In clays where the degradation of plant tissues is not complete, organic networks are present. Gas-filled voids are fairly common in organic clays, the gas arising from microbial activity. When climatic, topographical, and environmental conditions favor it, organic-rich deposits of the peaty type are formed. For present purposes it is sufficient to distinguish

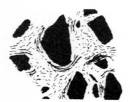 

I μm

Figure 2.7 Domain formation in heavily compressed clay; (*a*) schematic pattern; (*b*) electron micrograph of heavily compressed illitic clay.

 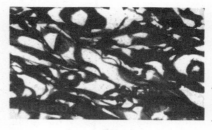

Figure 2.8 (*a*) Fringed micelle structure of an unoriented polymer and (*b*) micrograph of humified peat.

between peats with low, medium, and high degree of humification. From a structural point of view the three classes—amorphous granular, fine fibrous, and coarse fibrous—are useful in classification.

Where the organic substance consists of humus, only the general patterns in Fig. 2.5 may still be observed when the organic content is in the range of 2 to 6 percent by weight of dry soil. In this situation the humus substance is generally most visible in the form of local bodies in the pore space. Where numerous plant fragments or fibers form part of the microstructural network, a system with structural properties similar to those of rubber and unoriented crystalline polymers results (Fig. 2.8).

Microstructural constitution is of extreme importance in governing ice nucleation and ice-crystal growth when fine-grained soils are frozen. This is discussed further when structural changes due to freezing (ice lensing, etc.) and thawing are treated.

Macrostructure Since transportation and sedimentation are functions of water velocity and concentration of suspended material, some degree of stratification is a characteristic property of all sedimented soils. Large variations in soil composition and grain-size distribution in soil profiles even within local areas are common. Natural soils therefore are seldom homogeneous or isotropic. A number of structural features important in determining the mechanical and physical properties of soils can be observed by the unaided eye. In coarse-grained sedimentary soils, variation in grain size in concordant or discordant layers is the principal characteristic macrostructural feature. The most obvious features of fine-grained soils are dry crusts, slump structures, cracks and fissures, root channels, organic structures, boulders, and concretions.

As concerns frost susceptibility, the most important macrostructural features are those affecting groundwater access and mobility. Thus, the presence of continuous coarse-grained layers or laminae in dense clays, such as in varved clays (Fig. 2.9), is of major importance. A high frequency of open cracks and fissures or root channels is also important since they increase the average permeability of the soil and conduct water readily to the freezing zone in the soil profile.

Figure 2.9 Split core of finely varved clay-silt from northern Sweden. The core diameter is 50 mm.

Physical Properties

In a discussion of the physical properties of soils important in geotechnical considerations, the following basic definitions are required (Fig. 2.10). Mass m is the material content of the soil. It is sometimes measured inertially but generally is determined by weighing. The term weight is therefore often used interchangeably with mass, which is the proper word. In geotechnical discussions the distinction usually is not required. Bulk volume V is defined as the total volume of a soil sample including open as well as closed voids. The compact volume (previously called specific volume) V_s is defined as the volume of a soil sample with both open and closed voids excluded. The bulk density ρ is defined as the ratio of a sample's mass to its bulk (total) volume:

$$\rho = \frac{m}{V} \tag{2.1}$$

The dry density ρ_d is defined as the ratio of the mass of a sample's solid substance to its bulk volume:

$$\rho_d = \frac{m_s}{V} \tag{2.2}$$

The compact density ρ_s (previously called specific gravity) is defined as the ratio of the mass of a sample's solid substance to its compact volume:

$$\rho_s = \frac{m_s}{V_s} \tag{2.3}$$

The expression grain or particle density, which is the ratio of the mass of a sample's solid substance to the volume of this substance (including voids in the

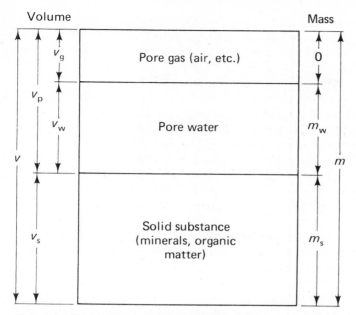

Figure 2.10 Schematic constitution of a soil element.

particles), is also used. The compact density and grain density generally are almost identical. In coarser fractions, especially where sandstone or carbonate grains are represented, the difference can be substantial. The void ratio e is defined as the ratio of a sample's pore volume to its compact volume:

$$e = \frac{V_p}{V_s} \tag{2.4}$$

The porosity n is defined as the ratio of a sample's pore volume to its bulk volume (generally given in percent):

$$n = \frac{V_p}{V} \tag{2.5}$$

The water content w (also moisture content) is defined as the ratio of a sample's pore-water mass to the mass of its solid substance (generally given in percent):

$$w = \frac{m_w}{m_s} \tag{2.6}$$

This quantity is also known as the moisture ratio. The degree of saturation S_r is the ratio of a sample's pore-water volume to its pore volume:

$$S_r = \frac{V_w}{V_p} \tag{2.7}$$

In frozen soils, additional definitions are required, e.g., the ratio of the masses of frozen and unfrozen water and the ice-to-soil ratio. At present, no generally accepted definitions or symbols are available. They are defined when needed in subsequent sections.

Density, void ratio, and porosity The bulk density and void ratio are characteristic soil parameters used in many geotechnical calculations. The compact density is used for evaluation of the grain size during wet analysis and for evaluation of the void ratio and the degree of water saturation. The last three properties are of special importance in considering the frost susceptibility of soils.

The determination of bulk density for clay, silt, and organic soils is a laboratory measurement using samples taken usually by means of piston samplers. The determination simply involves the measurement of the bulk volume V and the total mass m. When dealing with shallow layers of gravel, sand, or coarse silt, the bulk density is best determined in the field by applying replacement (water or sand volumeters) or nuclear-radiation techniques. The methods are described in standard soil-mechanics textbooks and need no elaboration here. Field determination of the bulk density using replacement techniques involves an average error of ± 2 to 3 percent. The corresponding error is much less in laboratory determinations using tube samples, but considerable error is caused if the sampling operation has caused separation of the soil in the tube. This is a fairly common occurrence in soft clay and stratified coarse- and fine-grained soils. Table 2.2 illustrates the range in bulk density of various water-saturated soils.

The compact density is determined by means of pycnometers. In principle the method involves measuring mass m_s and the volume V_s of the solid substance. The volume measurement is based on the determination of the amount of water which is equivalent to the volume of the solid substance. The detailed procedure is described in standard texts. The compact density is expressed in terms of the dry soil mass obtained by simple weighing:

$$\rho_s = \frac{\rho_w(m_d - m_b)}{m_a - m_b - m_c - m_d} \tag{2.8}$$

Table 2.2 Characteristic bulk/density values of water/saturated soils

Soil	ρ, kg/m^3
Peat	1000
Mud	1000–1300
Clay, silt	1400–2000
Sand, gravel	1700–2300
Till	2000–2400

where m_a = mass of pycnometer filled with distilled water

m_b = mass of empty, dry, and clean pycnometer

m_c = mass of pycnometer filled with soil (approximately one-third of volume) and water

m_d = mass of the dry pycnometer with soil dried at 105°C

ρ_w = density of distilled water

The influence of temperature should be allowed for.

Reliable determinations require that dissolved air be completely removed from the water in the pycnometer and that the dry soil be prevented from absorbing hygroscopic water from the air. Table 2.3 illustrates the range of compact densities of common solid soil constituents.

For coarse-grained soils, such as gravel, the void ratio can be determined experimentally by measuring the amount of water required to fill the pore space of a known volume of the dry soil material. For more fine-grained soils the void ratio must be calculated from experimentally determined values of bulk volume, compact density, and mass of the solid substance:

$$e = \frac{V}{m_s} \rho_s - 1 \tag{2.9}$$

The porosity can be computed as follows:

$$n = 1 - \frac{m_s}{V \rho_s} \tag{2.10}$$

It is important that the same quantity of soil be used for determining the total volume and mass of solid substance. This mass is determined by weighing the sample after drying at 105°C, as described in the next section. It should be noted that a small error in ρ_s produces a considerably larger error in e and n. Table 2.4 illustrates the range of void ratios and porosities of typical soils.

Table 2.3 Characteristic compact/density values

Mineral	ρ_s, kg/m^3
Amphibole	2800–3400
Biotite	2700–3100
Muscovite	2800–3000
Calcite	2700
Quartz	2650
Feldspar	2500–2900
Pyrite	5000–5100
Pyroxene	3100–3600
Illite	2600–2700
Kaolinite	2600–2700
Montmorillonite	2400–2600
Chlorite	2600–3000
Organic substance	1400–1700

Table 2.4 Characteristic void-ratio and porosity values

Soil	e	n, %
Peat	>5	>85
Mud	3–6	75–85
Clay, soft	1–3	50–75
Stiff	0.3–0.8	25–45
Silt	0.3–1.4	25–60
Sand, poorly graded	0.5–0.9	35–45
Well graded	0.15–0.4	15–30
Till	0.1–0.3	10–25

The soil water content An unfrozen soil element containing water of various kinds is illustrated in Fig. 2.11. In sediments deposited in water the natural water content is affected by the grain-size distribution, organic content, mineral composition, and stress history. Above the groundwater table (phreatic surface) evaporation produces desiccation to a greater or lesser degree. Pore water exists

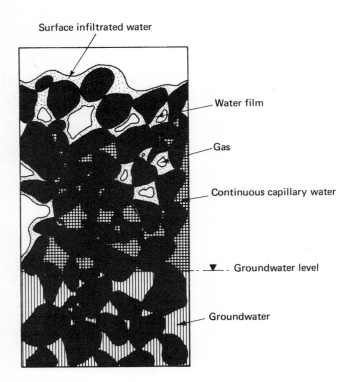

Figure 2.11 Water in soil.

in a variety of physical states. Generally, a distinction is made between free and bound water. Free water may be ponded surface water, infiltrating free water, or free groundwater. Bound water, on the other hand, may be chemically bound water, adsorbed water, or water experiencing capillary forces. These distinctions are of importance in ice nucleation and growth, as shown later in this section.

The amounts of free pore water and bound water in unfrozen soil can be determined by thermogravimetry. For ordinary geotechnical purposes the water content is simply determined by weighing the sample before and after drying. The dominant water loss occurs when temperature is increased from room temperature to about 100°C. Water-content determinations are therefore performed at a slightly higher temperature; in practice 105°C is used. Free water and most of the bound water are thus included. The most strongly bound adsorbed water and chemically condensed forms require distinctly higher temperatures for their evolution.

The accuracy of water contents determined gravimetrically depends on drying time. For 20-g samples of inorganic or weakly organic soils 12 h is sufficient; for larger inorganic samples (300 g) and all organic soil samples 24 h is required. For very large samples, such as tube samples, at least 48 h drying time is necessary. Table 2.5 illustrates the ranges in water content of typical water-saturated soils.

The degree of water saturation S_r indicates to what extent the pore volume is filled with water. From the definition, the following relationship can be deduced:

$$S_r = \frac{m_w}{(V - m_s/\rho_s)\rho_w} \tag{2.11}$$

Since large samples are usually involved, care must be taken to ensure that the drying time in the determination of m_s is sufficient. The accuracy of the value of S_r is largely dependent on the compact density. If, for instance, the water content is 100 percent, for $\rho_w = 1000$ kg/m^3, $\rho = 1460$ kg/m^3, and $\rho_s = 2700$ kg/m^3, we have $S_r = 1.00$. If, on the other hand, $\rho_s = 3100$ kg/m^3, $S_r = 0.95$. Thus, a careful determination of ρ_s is necessary to obtain a reliable value of S_r.

Table 2.5 Characteristic water-content values of water-saturated soils

Soil	w, %
Peat	> 500
Mud	150–300
Clay, soft (inorganic)	40–100
Stiff	10–40
Silt	10–50
Sand, gravel	10–35
Till	5–10

For frozen soils the problems involved in the determination of the water content are similar. To obtain reliable values of the total water content (ice and water) somewhat longer drying times may be required than for unfrozen soil. For the determination of the ratio of frozen and unfrozen water no simple standard technique is available. Dilatometry, adiabatic calorimetry, x-ray diffraction, heat-capacity measurement, nuclear magnetic resonance, differential thermal analysis, and isothermal calorimetry have all been used. These techniques, which yield similar but somewhat different values, require special laboratory resources. A discussion of this problem has been given by Anderson and Tice (1973).

Deformation The relationship between soil stress and strain is central to soil mechanics. The presentation and application of the basic theory of settlement, including immediate (elastic) and compressive deformation (consolidation), and of the theory of creep deformation is readily available in many recent textbooks. Consequently no elaboration is needed here. However, it is appropriate to comment on certain aspects of the physical basis of the theories in order to provide a background for material presented in subsequent chapters. For present purposes the discussion will be limited to fine-grained soils.

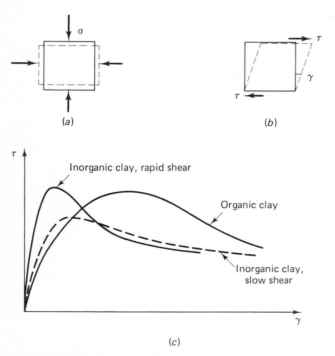

(c)

Figure 2.12 Basic shear stress-strain relationship: (a) pure shear (bi- or triaxial condition); (b) simple shear (shear-box condition); (c) stress-strain diagram.

Shear deformation under undrained conditions is represented by the basic relationships shown in Fig. 2.12. It involves deformation of the various bonding complexes that exist in soils. The particle bonds can be considered as flow units which lead to time-dependent shear strain (creep). In dense, inorganic clays and in cemented soils, the stress-strain properties of most bonds are similar, and the stress distribution is fairly uniform. Such clays show small and complementary slow creep deformations for shear stresses below a marked yield value, which is fairly close to the ultimate shear stress. Similarly, in soft inorganic clays and silty clays the creep is quite small at low and moderate shear stresses. On the other hand, soils in which bond complexes consisting wholly or partly of organic substances or gels (as in sulfidic clays) exhibit high creep rates and large creep deformation, especially when fibrous organic members predominate, as in peats. This is illustrated in Fig. 2.13, in which test results of the relationship between time and axial strain for soils of varying organic contents under uniaxial compression are shown. At low and moderate shear stresses, i.e., where structural breakdown is unimportant or where the number of flow units stays fairly constant, the general mechanism involved in creep is that of successive slipping of individual flow units, e.g., segments of organic polymers, over one another into new temporary or permanent equilibrium positions. Generally, the strain rate is roughly proportional to $\log t$ or $\exp t$, where t is time (Fig. 2.14). Creep rate and strain are functions of stress. Assuming that the strain mechanism can be described by rate-process theory, if the number of flow units is constant, the creep rate will be of the form

$$\frac{d\gamma}{dt} = K \sinh \alpha \, \tau \tag{2.12}$$

where γ = shear strain
$\quad\;\, \tau$ = shear stress
$\quad K, \alpha$ = constants

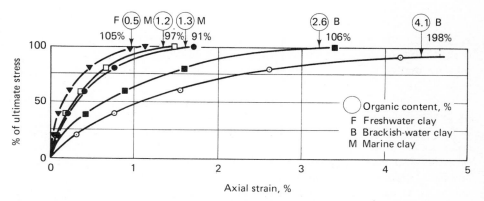

Figure 2.13 Axial strain for uniaxial unconfined loading of clays with different amounts of organic matter. Values below circles are percentage water content.

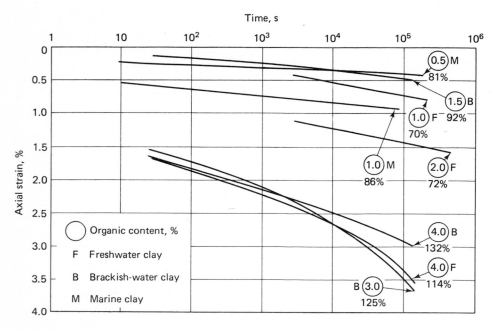

Figure 2.14 Axial strain vs. time at uniaxial unconfined loading of clays with different amounts of organic matter. Constant load corresponding to one-third of the load at bulk failure. Values below circles are percentage water content.

For a given temperature, K increases exponentially. When the number of flow units decreases, α increases. In soils with collapsible microstructural networks, such as soft clays, the number of flow units decreases with increasing stress. Thus, shear strain under constant-deviator stress conditions is a nonlinear function of stress. In general, organic soils show larger strain than inorganic soils. This behavior is illustrated in Fig. 2.14.

Consolidation is illustrated by the basic relationships shown in Fig. 2.15. In general, time-dependent processes which also depend on the microstructural constitution are involved. When the preconsolidation pressure of clays low in organic matter is exceeded, local failure of the weakest parts of the particle network takes place by compression of larger pores. In this primary stage, resistance against compression is due to water-flow resistance and to the strength of the intact continuous parts of the network together with the strength remaining in the local failure zones. The deformation of the particle network is caused by creep in the intact bond regions throughout the sample and the movement of particles over each other in the local failure zones. Taking the detailed micro-structural patterns into consideration, it is obvious that if the compression is small, successive establishment of new contacts in the broken-down regions can occur. The primary stage of creep can therefore be regarded as dominated by a process involving a successively increasing number of flow units. This produces the well known S shape in the consolidation curve of strain vs. log time.

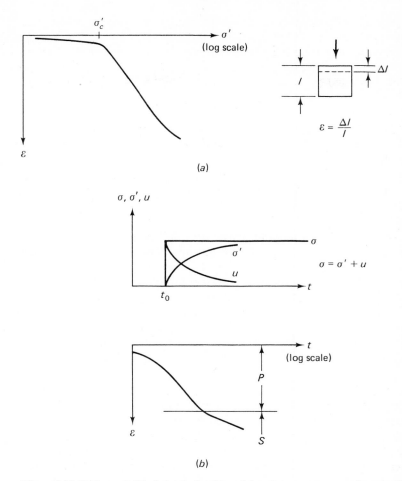

Figure 2.15 Basic consolidation relationships: (*a*) oedometer stress-strain curve for normally consolidated clay (σ' = preconsolidation pressure); (*b*) oedometer time-strain curve for pressures exceeding the preconsolidation pressure (P = primary consolidation, S = secondary consolidation).

In the subsequent secondary stage, where pore excess pressure has dissipated, the main process tends to be that of creep at low or moderate shear stresses with a fairly constant number of flow domains. It is therefore logical that, as commonly observed, the compression tends to be proportional to log time.

Although the pore-size distribution may be similar in organic-poor clays and in clays rich in organic matter, the processes involved in compression are somewhat different. This is no doubt due to the fact that organic substances and organic bond complexes may deform considerably without failure. Local structural breakdown is thus not so pronounced. Consequently the passage between the primary and secondary stages of consolidation is not so obvious in organic clays. In this case compression is governed by a creep process in which the number of flow units remains fairly constant or the number of activated flow units is not markedly discontinuous, as in the case of inorganic clays. Consequently the consolidation curve may be nearly straight in a diagram of strain vs. log time. This is indeed the case. Similar behavior is to be expected for inorganic as well as organic silts or sands.

Shear strength The various methods for testing soils in the field and laboratory with reference to the drainage conditions (undrained, consolidated-undrained, drained, and undrained with pore-pressure measurement) are well known and fully described in a number of textbooks and laboratory guides. For present purposes it is sufficient only to single out the shear failure of fine-grained soils for additional comment. The general relationships shown in Fig. 2.16 will be helpful in the discussion.

It is well known that in inorganic clays with sufficiently high stresses a local breakdown of the bonded clay-particle groups bridging between denser aggregates or larger particles (domains, Fig. 2.17) is initiated. If the water content is moderate or high, the resulting reorientation of particles increases the interparticle distance on the average, with a concomitant influx of water from pore space into the affected domains. Within these domains, slipping of particles takes place easily; thus the contribution of these regions to the bulk strength is small. Failure is fully developed when a sufficient number of slip domains becomes involved. This creep failure occurs when the development of the domains reaches or exceeds a critical level.

In organic soils the flexibility of the organic components leads to a more progressive failure. Where undecomposed or only partially decomposed cellulose tissues are abundant, there are interconnected networks of soil particles and organic fibers that may be more or less continuous throughout the soil mass. In general, failure of such a system occurs partly by cross-link breakage and partly by the cleavage of molecular bonds which can be reestablished in the course of strain. In such systems flow may go on almost indefinitely, with less tendency to show creep failure than in inorganic soils. Where there are integrated clay particle and organic networks, the strength of the more flexible organic system is apparent even at small strains, but this component of soil strength becomes most effective when local failure in the clay-particle network begins. It then governs the deformation and strength properties of the soil at large strains. It follows from this that the rate of stress increase or rate of strain during shear testing greatly influences these stress-strain relationships. This is of fundamental importance. The average shear stress is low in large, dense aggregates while it must be very high in the weak particle links which connect larger aggregates. This fundamental idea is the essence of the modern concept of clay shear strength. Cohesion is equivalent to the integrated strength of the links while internal friction is due to viscous effects and dilatency. Cohesion forms the major part of the shear strength at small deformations while internal friction produces the main shear resistance at larger deformations.

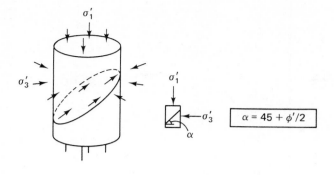

$$\alpha = 45 + \phi'/2$$

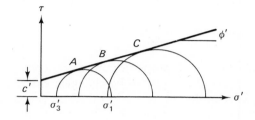

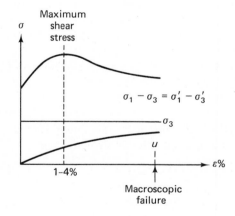

$$\sigma_1 - \sigma_3 = \sigma_1' - \sigma_3'$$

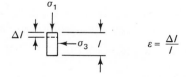

$$\varepsilon = \frac{\Delta l}{l}$$

Figure 2.16 Basic shear-strength relationships with special reference to consolidated, undrained triaxial tests.

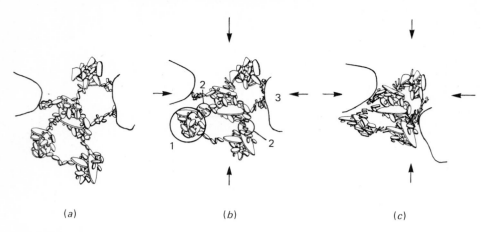

(a)   (b)   (c)

Figure 2.17 Domain formation due to internal shear under triaxial conditions.

Thermal properties Two fundamental soil properties must be considered in discussing the response of soils to heat fluxes caused by changing environmental temperatures. They are the capacity of the soil to absorb thermal energy on the one hand and to transmit it on the other. The former is the specific heat. It can be expressed either on a gravimetric or a volumetric basis, the latter being expressed either as the thermal conductivity or as the thermal diffusivity of the soil. Thermal diffusivity has come to be preferred because of observational and mathematical convenience. Extensive treatment of this subject is available in textbooks. Only the briefest summary of commonly needed quantities is given here.

The specific heat of a substance is defined as energy required to raise its temperature 1 K. The specific heat of water, at atmospheric pressure is by definition 4.186 kJ/kg K. The dry mineral and organic matter in soils under similar conditions have specific heats of about 0.84 and 1.88 kJ/kg K, respectively. The specific heat of soil at any water content is adequately approximated by a simple summation of the specific heats of the constituents, e.g.,

$$C_s = 0.84 \times 10^3 X_m + 1.88 \times 10^3 X_o + 4.186 \times 10^3 X_w \qquad \text{J/kg K} \qquad (2.13)$$

where X_m = weight fraction mineral matter
X_o = weight fraction organic matter
X_w = weight fraction water

The contribution of the soil air is small enough to be neglected. An often used formula (DeVries, 1952) for the specific heat of soils on a volumetric basis is

$$C_s = 1.9 \times 10^3 V_m + 2.5 \times 10^3 V_o + 4.186 \times 10^3 V_w \qquad \text{J/kg K} \qquad (2.14)$$

where V_m = volume fraction mineral matter
V_o = volume fraction organic matter
V_w = volume fraction water

Specific heats vary sensibly with temperature, but the effect is negligibly small in this instance. The interfacial interaction between the mineral and organic constituents and soil water is complex, leading to a variety of phenomena of importance. It has been found that this leads to a small but significant effect on the specific heats of the constituents. This effect, for all practical purposes, is also negligibly small.

Chemical Properties

From the point of view of freezing and thawing, the most important chemical properties of soils can be discussed under three headings: pore-water composition, ion-exchange capacity, and surface chemistry.

Pore-water composition Considering the wide variety of soils that exist and the wide range of environmental conditions from place to place, it is not surprising that the composition of the soil pore water is highly variable. The concentrations of dissolved substances also vary widely as soils are wetted with waters of varying quality or desiccated to various degrees. From the point of view of this volume, the most interesting effect of solutes in the soil pore water is to depress the freezing point of the soil solution. Equations and formulas based on the laws of chemical thermodynamics are presented in all basic texts on physical chemistry and are capable of predicting freezing-point depressions in terms of concentrations and activity coefficients of the dissolved species. The information generally needed is incomplete in all but carefully controlled laboratory experiments. For this reason, when freezing points of the soil solution must be known, they usually are determined experimentally.

The most abundant common cations present in soil pore water are sodium, calcium, magnesium, and potassium, present as chlorides, sulfates, carbonates and bicarbonates, and occasionally as nitrates. Minor constituents are aluminum, iron, boron, etc. The principal soil properties affected by the type of solute present in the pore water are its state of aggregation and its tendency to shrink and swell. The former greatly affects the permeability and hydraulic conductivity of the soil. Both affect the thermal and soil-water suction relationships during freezing and thawing and thus the frost susceptibility of soils.

Ion-exchange capacity Attention was drawn to ion-exchange phenomena in soils in an earlier section. The actual situation is considerably more complicated than can be effectively dealt with here. Adequate discussions are readily available in nearly all texts on soil chemistry and the physical chemistry of clays. In brief, lattice substitution and other defects lead, in general, to a net negative charge at the surfaces of soil particles. This leads to an attraction of positively charged counterions and the formation of the diffuse electric double layer, shown schematically in Fig. 2.1. Repulsion of anions leads to a reduction in concentration below that in the bulk pore water. This effect is known as *negative adsorption.*

When soils contain large clay fractions, the effects associated with existence of the diffuse electric double layer can be quite large and often may be of practical significance. The results are swelling by the imbibition of water, migration and movement of colloidal-sized particles, i.e., the exchangeable counterions, movement of water in an electric field (electroosmosis), and the development of an electric field when the soil solution is forced to move through the soil matrix (streaming potential). Effects of the electric double layer are sensible up to several tens of ionic diameters, and particles closer than this have interpenetrating ion swarms and experience a net repulsion due partly to their mutually repulsive net negative charges. More important is an osmotic repulsive force due to the tendency of the pore water to enter and dilute the excess ionic concentration compared with the bulk soil solution. Freezing and thawing obviously disturb the balance that exists in the unfrozen state. Some of the resulting effects of this disturbance will be considered shortly.

As may be inferred from the foregoing, most of the cations counterbalancing the negatively charged soil particles can be exchanged for cations of another species simply by flushing away with a solution of the replacement ion. The cations swept out can be identified and their concentration measured. For simple ions, the quantity easily exchanged per unit weight of soil is relatively constant and is called the *cation-exchange capacity*. It is expressed in milliequivalents per 100 g soil on a dry-weight basis. It ranges for most common, predominately mineral soils from 2 or 3 to 60 or 70 meq per 100 g soil and is usually determined at pH 7 since it varies noticeably with pH. In predominantly organic soils the range is much higher, 150 to 300 meq per 100 g soil. As mentioned above, the exchangeable-cation capacity is related to the specific surface area of the mineral matter. Therefore for the three main types of clay it diminishes rapidly in the order smectites > illites > kaolinite.

In terms of ease of replacement of one cation by another a qualitative understanding can be reached from a consideration of simple electrostatic relationships. The attraction between the sites of negative charge on the mineral surfaces and a counterion must vary with the product of the magnitude of their charge and inversely with their separation. Thus small or highly charged cations will be held more tenaciously than large singly charged cations. Experimental work confirms this. The ease of replacement often found is in the order $Li > Na > K > Mg > Ca > Ba > Al$. The small lithium ion might be expected to be held more tightly than sodium or potassium were it not for the hydration shell that increases its effective radius and apparently prevents its close approach and the formation of a strong bond to the soil surface.

Surface chemistry Two aspects of surface chemistry are of significance in geotechnical engineering. One is simply the extent of the surface area present per unit per weight of solid. Although there are variations from mineral to mineral that make each surface singular and unique in its chemical reactivity and other properties, the variation in specific surface area from soil to soil generally is of more importance. An appreciation of this is easily obtained by constructing a table of specific surface area for particles ranging from sand to colloidal size. For spherical particles the relationship is derived from the definition

$$\text{Specific surface} = \frac{\text{particle surface area}}{\text{particle weight}} = \frac{3}{\rho r} \qquad (2.15)$$

Similar expressions can be derived for particles of any regular configuration. The actual measurement of specific surface areas can be accomplished by direct microscopic observations or by liquid- or gas-phase adsorption measurements. There is nearly always a significant uncertainty in the results, but except for relatively coarse soils very useful qualitative comparisons are possible. A useful empirical rule of thumb for determining the water-ice phase composition of frozen ground from a knowledge of its specific surface area will be given shortly.

The second aspect concerns the various types of chemical reactions that may occur. The variety of these is large, and this is an active field of research. In addition to the formation of chemisorption bonds, addition reactions, polymerization reactions, and catalytic recombinations are common. Interactions between the mineral surfaces, their closest held cations, and nearby water molecules lead to increased proton motion and mobility at the surface which in effect increases its "acidity." Thus protonation reactions are particularly easy to accomplish. Free radicals also are very likely to exist in this environment of intense interplay of chemical forces. Fuller coverage is beyond the scope of this chapter. A discussion adequate for geotechnical purposes together with an introduction to the literature has been given by Anderson and Morgenstern (1973).

Soil-Water Relationships

It is well known from conventional soil mechanics that the relationships between soil and water are of great importance to the physical and mechanical properties of soils. Frost susceptibility, ice formation, and frost heave depend largely on the state of the pore water and the freedom of water migration in the soil. The most important of these relationships will be discussed here under the headings capillarity, the soil-water potential, consistency limits, and hydraulic permeability.

Capillarity Above the water table in soils the water is maintained in place, against the force of gravity, by capillary attraction, i.e., by surface tension developed within the voids. Capillary water can exist in three states:

1. Capillary saturation, where the voids are completely filled with water
2. Partial saturation, where air is present but the water in the voids forms a continuous phase
3. Contact moisture, where air predominates and the water is discontinuous

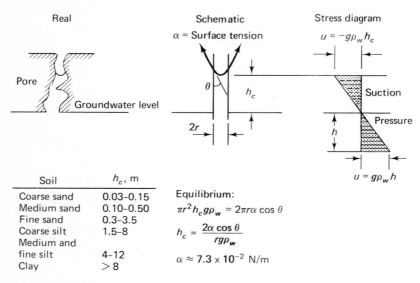

Soil	h_c, m
Coarse sand	0.03–0.15
Medium sand	0.10–0.50
Fine sand	0.3–3.5
Coarse silt	1.5–8
Medium and	
fine silt	4–12
Clay	>8

Equilibrium:

$$\pi r^2 h_c g \rho_w = 2\pi r \alpha \cos \theta$$

$$h_c = \frac{2\alpha \cos \theta}{r g \rho_w}$$

$$\alpha \approx 7.3 \times 10^{-2} \ \text{N/m}$$

Figure 2.18 Explanation of capillary rise in soils.

Capillary rise h_c in soils is analogous in many respects to the corresponding phenomenon in cylindrical capillaries (Fig. 2.18). An approximate relationship between h_c and grain size is

$$h_c = \frac{C}{e D_{10}} \tag{2.16}$$

where C is a constant depending upon grain shape and surface character. It varies from 0.1 to 0.5.

The soil-water potential Because of capillary forces and the intimate relationships that obtain between the soil water and the surfaces of the mineral grains, the spontaneous movement and redistribution of water within a soil mass can best be described in terms of the potential energy of the soil water. The total potential energy is defined as the work required to transfer a unit mass (or a unit volume) of water from a standard reference state (a reservoir of pure water at atmospheric pressure and at an arbitrary but explicitly stated elevation) to the location and situation of interest. The total potential is expressed by the mathematical means of partial derivatives as the summation of its component potentials. By definition water tends to move spontaneously from a high to a lower potential. Thus the total potential ψ held within a soil matrix is

$$\psi = \psi_m + \psi_g + \psi_p + \psi_\pi = \psi_\Omega \tag{2.17}$$

where ψ_m = matric potential
ψ_g = gravitational potential
ψ_p = pressure potential
ψ_π = osmotic potential
ψ_Ω = overburden potential

The matric potential arises because of the forces of capillarity and other interfacial interactions associated with the soil grains. Above the water table it is negative; below the water table it is zero. It is measured by using water columns of various lengths that are in communication with the soil matrix via a ceramic plate or by measuring the gas pressure above the soil-water menisci required to force them down and empty the soil pore space.

The gravity potential is simply the work required to move a unit weight (or volume) of water from a reference elevation to the point in question in the earth's gravitational field. If the water must be lifted, the gravity potential is positive; if the water is to be lowered, the gravity potential is negative. In practice, the gravity potential is simply calculated from spatial relationships, water density, and the gravitational constant.

The pressure potential, sometimes called the submergence potential, arises from the weight of any water that may be above the point in question or a gas pressure acting on the soil-water menisci or both. It can be measured by a piezometer or equivalent device.

The osmotic potential arises from the presence of solutes in the pore water and the exchangeable ion complex. It is of significance when membrane or membranelike situations exist at interfaces. It is difficult to measure directly; usually it can be known only approximately.

The overburden potential arises whenever soil is settling or otherwise is free to move and exert a force on the pore water. Since it is difficult in many cases to separate it from the pressure potential, it is often included in it.

Of the component potentials separated and defined above, the matric potential is the one that is characteristic of the soil itself. The relationship between the soil-water content and the matric potential depends upon a number of factors such as its state of compaction, previous cycles of wetting and drying, etc. For a given soil, the relationship retains certain relatively constant features. Consequently, it is referred to as the *soil-moisture characteristic*. This is illustrated in Fig. 2.19.

A more complete discussion of this important topic is precluded here. An appreciation of how the concept of the soil-water potential has developed and an understanding of its general usefulness can be gained from Day et al. (1967), Miller and Klute (1967), Holmes et al. (1967), Rose (1966), and Bauer et al. (1972). The principal application here will be made in discussing the water-ice phase composition of frozen ground.

Consistency limits A well-known effect that depends on the amount and state of water in fine-grained soils is described by the consistency (Atterberg) limits. A suspension of fine particles in water behaves like a liquid, but as the soil is slowly

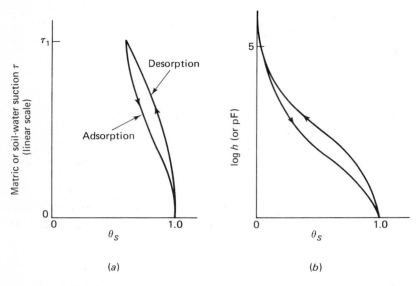

Figure 2.19 Soil-moisture characteristics showing hysteresis (the arrows indicate direction of change of water content): (a) both τ and saturation ratio θ_S plotted linearly; (b) τ expressed as $\log h$ as a function of θ_S.

dried out, a point is reached where the system begins to gel and exhibits a small shear resistance and plastic behavior. The water content corresponding to this transition is the *liquid limit* w_L. As further moisture is drawn from the soil, resistance to larger shear stresses becomes possible. Eventually a water content is reached at which the soil simply fractures with no plastic deformation and thus acts as a brittle solid. The water content defining the limit of plastic behavior and the initiation of brittle failure is the *plastic limit* w_P. If the drying process is prolonged beyond the plastic limit, the soil will continue to decrease in volume until another critical water content, the shrinkage limit w_S, is reached. Methods of determining the limits w_L, w_P, and w_S are described in elementary texts on soil mechanics.

The stages mentioned are shown diagrammatically in Fig. 2.20. Normal values of the consistency limits for different soil types are given in Fig. 2.21. As the predominant particle size decreases, both the liquid and the plastic limits increase, the former at the greater rate. Mechanical analysis does not indicate the varying properties of soils within the clay range, but for such soils the consistency limits, especially expressed in terms of the *plasticity index* $w_L - w_P$, are very useful as an additional means of soil identification.

Hydraulic permeability For practical purposes Darcy's law usually is assumed to be applicable, namely,

$$v = ki \qquad (2.18)$$

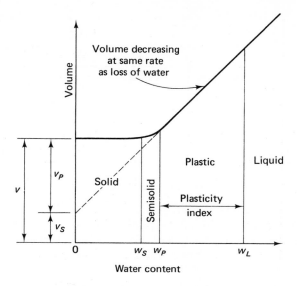

Figure 2.20 Consistency limits.

where v = discharge velocity
k = coefficient of permeability
i = hydraulic gradient

The coefficient of permeability k has the dimensions of a velocity and should be expressed in meters per second. It is a function of the void ratio, the shape and

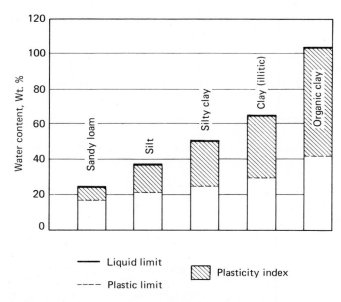

Figure 2.21 Common w_P and w_L ranges for fine-grained soils.

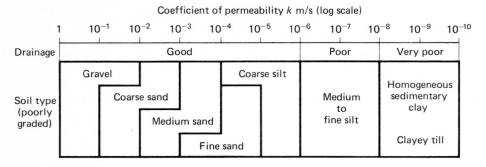

Figure 2.22 Typical values of hydraulic conductivity for representative soil types.

size of the voids, and the density and viscosity of the pore fluid. For granular materials the permeability generally varies inversely with the specific surface area of the particles, while for saturated clays it varies considerably with the water content. Figure 2.22 shows the average values of k for various soils.

The laboratory and field techniques for determining the permeability are described in elementary textbooks and require no elaboration here. The results of some recent research will be discussed briefly since they bear on one aspect of the physical processes involved in water migration in soils. It appears that very fine-grained clays do not obey Darcy's law at small hydraulic gradients. In Swedish postglacial (Ska-Edeby) clay having a clay content of the order of 70 to 80 percent there is such a deviation; no threshold gradient value was found (Fig. 2.23). Research has shown that when water flow persists in a constant direction, there is a migration of some of the minute particles blocking the smaller voids, which in turn reduces the permeability. This illustrates the importance of the microstructural configuration in limiting the permeability. Pusch (1970) obtained the relationship shown in Fig. 2.24, which shows that the microstructural parameter P/T largely controls the water flow. The Ska-Edeby

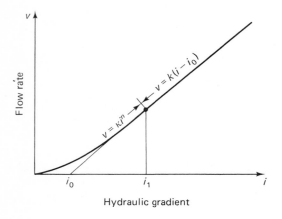

Figure 2.23 Relationship between flow rate and hydraulic gradient for a fat Swedish clay subjected to small hydraulic gradients. (Hansbo, 1960.)

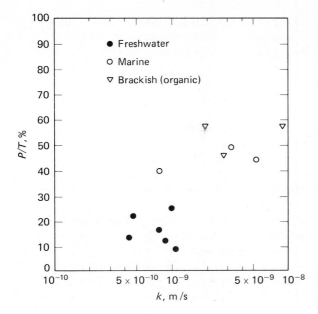

Figure 2.24 A plot of the microstructure parameter P/T vs. hydraulic conductivity.

clay is a freshwater-deposited clay characterized by small, fairly open particle aggregates separated by small pores, while the other two clays are marine or brackish and have large, dense particle aggregates separated by fairly large pores. This investigation indicated that, in general, marine clays are more permeable than freshwater clays when the water content is of the same order.

2.2 WATER

Water is ubiquitous, and because of the large quantities with which the earth is endowed, together with its remarkable physical and chemical properties, it exerts a large influence whenever it is found in significant quantities. Pure water does not occur naturally. It is such a powerful, universal solvent that it quickly dissolves gases from the atmosphere and both inorganic and organic substances with which it comes in contact. In addition, it frequently contains suspended inorganic and organic colloids, silt-sized material, and floating debris. Thus, the purification and the preservation of the pure substance of water is exceedingly difficult.

A single water molecule has a diameter of about 300 pm. In the liquid phase the molecules are in constant motion and dissociate and recombine rapidly, so that the species H_2O, OH^-, and H_3O^+ all can be distinguished. Since there are three common isotopes of hydrogen and three of oxygen, the number of separately identifiable subspecies is very large. These facts undoubtedly are significant in accounting for many important properties of the water substance.

Water is the most studied of the known chemical substances; since a number of exhaustive compilations and discussions are readily available, it will be necessary here to mention only those properties which normally must be taken into account in geotechnical engineering.

Structure

Notwithstanding the enormous expenditure of time and effort, the structure of liquid water is not sufficiently well known to have a generally recognized description. Many geometrical and conceptual models have been proposed, and each has its strengths and weaknesses. Here again the literature is extensive; Eisenberg and Kauzmann (1969), for example, have presented a comprehensive discussion.

A useful concept is that of a broken-down ice lattice. The water molecule itself is configured so that tetrahedral coordination is preferred. The nuclei of the free H_2O molecule form an isosceles triangle with a $H—O—H$ angle of $104.52°$. The actual dimensions of the molecule vary somewhat depending upon its quantum state, but it is common to take the bond lengths to be 9.9 nm and the angle to be $105°$. If a charge of -7 esu is regarded as being located on the bisector of the bond angle 0.24 nm from the oxygen nucleus, it gives a dipole moment of 1.87 D (1.87×10^{-18} esu $\cdot$ cm); this is very close to the best measurements of 1.84 D. This gives rise to a relatively high dielectric constant, about 80 at room temperature. It varies from 88 at $0°C$ to 55.3 at $100°C$. In addition to being important in conferring the property of a powerful solvent, this leads to other electrical properties useful in geotechnical surveys, remote sensing surveys, electroosmosis, etc.

The liquid, more dense than the solid, has a density maximum at $4°C$ but freezes at $0°C$. From the molecular geometry, the strength of the hydrogen bond, and the latent heat of fusion, 334 kJ/kg, it has been inferred that only 15 percent of the hydrogen bonds are broken when ice melts and that the liquid must consist of molecular clusters or discrete time domains in which the ice structure is found in the liquid. This view has to a large degree been substantiated by x-ray-defraction, spectroscopic, and other physical measurements.

Physiochemical Properties

The density of water varies with temperature, according to the extensive tabulations available, but for practical computations may be taken as 10^3 kg/m^3. The viscosity is about 1.8 mPa $\cdot$ s at $0°C$ and diminishes with increasing temperature to about 280 Pa $\cdot$ s at $100°C$. The surface tension against air at 1 atm is 75.6 and 58.9 mN/m at 0 and $100°C$, respectively. Extensive tabulations of these and other properties as they vary with temperature and pressure are readily available in standard reference works. Attention has already been called to the surface acidity of soil minerals. In pure water the product of the H_3O^+ and OH^- concentrations is 1×10^{-14}; about 1 in 5.5×10^8 molecules are ionized. This is a very small number. Near mineral surfaces in a zone of intense electrical interaction, the number is larger by several orders of magnitude. This may be important in certain geotechnical applications where surface reactions may be important, e.g., grouting.

2.3 ICE

Structure

Ice is defined as any of the solid states of pure water. Water also exists in solid forms that are not usually referred to as ice. There are a number of clathrate compounds involving water as a solid, e.g., natural gas hydrate. Normally water tends to crystallize as ice I. It belongs to the hexagonal system and finds expression in the myriad forms and shapes of snow and ice crystals and frost figures. Other forms of ice known to exist at higher pressure are ice II, III, and IV to VIII. Phase diagrams showing their temperature-pressure stability fields are widely available. A cubic and amorphous ice have been described as forming by vapor condensation at very low temperatures (-120 to $-140°C$). There seems little doubt that these two forms can occur, but to date neither has been found in naturally occurring frozen soil or rock; the only pure solid phase so far unambiguously reported is hexagonal ice I.

Two structural features are common to all the ice polymorphs:

1. The water molecule is intact in each with bond angles and lengths not greatly different from those of the free molecule, H_2O.
2. Each water molecule is hydrogen-bonded to four other molecules in an approximately tetrahedral coordination.

In the high-pressure forms some additional non-hydrogen-bonded molecules are found, and the crystal lattices tend to interpenetrate. At low temperatures, the hydrogen atoms tend to become localized.

Physical Properties

Extensive tabulations of thermodynamic, electrical, and other physical properties of ice are readily available. In general it is found that all vary significantly with temperature and pressure. Empirical formulas from which a desired property can be computed are generally included. A complete discussion is given by Eisenberg and Kauzmann (1969) and by Hobbs (1974), for example, and useful practical tabulations are given in practically all handbooks of physical data.

A number of properties of interest in the physics and chemistry of frozen ground are insufficiently known. Interfacial phenomena are of great importance in frost heaving and the development and sustenance of heaving pressures. Considerably more information on the surface energies of ice is needed. Data on the specific free energy (the work required to create a unit area) of the various interfaces present would advance and facilitate the development of a quantitative theory for the frost-heaving pressures. Energies for the vapor-liquid interface σ_{vl}, the vapor-solid interface σ_{vs}, the liquid-solid interface σ_{ls}, the grain-boundary interface σ_{gb}, and the unfrozen adsorbed water-ice interface $\sigma_{w_u s}$ are needed. Hobbs (1974) gives for σ_{vl} the value of 75.7 mJ/m² at 0°C. Values for σ_{ls} range from 7.7 to 14.5 mJ/m² at −40°C. The variation of σ_{ls} with temperature is given as 0.1 to 0.35 mJ/m² K. At 0°C, σ_{ls} is given as 33 ± 3 mJ/m²; σ_{vs} is given as 109 ± 3 mJ/m², and σ_{gb} is given as 65 ± 3 mJ/m². No values have yet been determined for $\sigma_{w_u s}$. Data on the partial specific volumes and partial specific enthalpies of the unfrozen water-ice phase change also are needed. Additional data are also needed on the thermal conductivity of ice at low temperatures. At present, sufficient data for computations and for testing the theory of heat conduction rigorously are not available.

2.4 FROZEN SOIL

When soils are frozen, their complexity is increased by the appearance of the new solid phase, by the formation of new interfaces, and by the appearance here and there of air bubbles and brine pockets. Although they become much more resistant to deformation as ice forms in the voids, the increase in strength cannot be described in simple terms.

Thermodynamic formalism in frozen soils follows that for the same unfrozen materials. Temperature T (θ when expressed in degrees below freezing), volume V, and the external pressure P are the three principal variables. The vapor phase usually is neglected, and the water is separated into two categories, the remaining unfrozen water w_u and the ice w_i. The total water content w is

$$w = w_u + w_i \tag{2.19}$$

Mineralogical and chemical heterogeneity usually is avoided by simply specifying each soil as unique. Thus, each of the compositional variables including those associated with the cation-exchange complex is fixed by specifying the soil name. The concentration of solutes in the pore water must be specified separately when it is not negligible. Geometrical aspects relate primarily to the extent and nature of the interfaces present. In certain cases these must be specified. Recently it has been shown that as a first approximation the specific area S' can be used to represent the combined effects of soil texture and matrix geometry of the frozen soils. This approximation is valid below about −5°C but fails at temperatures approaching 0°C. Near 0°C the extent and the specific free energies of each of the interfaces must be known in detail to define the water-ice phase composition and other surface-dependent properties. Thus, within the framework of equilibrium thermodynamics, the static physical and mechanical states of frozen soils can be expressed in terms of the specific energies of the interfaces, the specific surface area in some instances, and the concentration of solute present.

Of the various types of force fields that might exist, only electric fields are of sufficient importance to warrant attention. Gravitational and magnetic fields are usually negligible, although there are instances in which the former may be important.

Standard reference states usually are taken as the "dry" solid at 1 atm and some convenient temperature, the gas phases normally are neglected, and for water the choice is either ice I or the pure supercooled liquid at 1 atm and the temperature in question (Anderson and Morgenstern, 1973).

Ice Formation and Occurrence

Ice nucleation The theory of ice nucleation has been compiled and set forth by Hobbs (1974). The freezing of soil water would seem to fall under the treatment of heterogeneous nucleation, the case where freezing is induced by the presence of particulates. Anderson (1967) has contended that the freezing of soil water may be a special case of homogeneous nucleation. For practical purposes it makes little difference. It is sufficient to note that as the temperature drops below 0°C, a point is reached at which nucleation occurs and ice crystals begin to enlarge within the pore space. They seem not to be attached in any way to the mineral grains. The temperature at which this occurs in degrees below 0°C is called the *freezing-point depression*, θ_f.

A general freezing-point-depression equation has been derived from basic thermodynamical arguments by Low et al. (1968). Direct measurement of the freezing-point depression is complicated by the phenomenon of supercooling. In agreement with the homogeneous-nucleation theory (Hobbs, 1974), the temperature of spontaneous nucleation is nearly always lower than the temperature at which the unfrozen soil water is in equilibrium with ice. Two to eight degrees supercooling is not uncommon. This is an interesting topic for additional research, as considerably more basic information remains to be obtained on this phenomenon.

Occurrence Once nucleation occurs, ice crystals grow until they interfere with each other. They then may intermingle, but eventually grain boundaries form and begin readjusting toward the configuration of minimum surface energy. Depending upon whether many freeze-thaw cycles are involved, the ready availability of soil moisture, the rate of freezing, etc., the type of ice formed varies widely. When the ice does not fill all the soil pores, frozen ground is said to be unsaturated. When the pore space is filled, it is said to be saturated, and when there is still more ice present, the ground is said to be supersaturated with ice. When the ice approaches 100 percent, it is referred to as *massive ice*. The terms *ice gneiss* and *disseminated* or *interstitial ice* are used to distinguish lensed or well-foliated ground ice from ice lacking a clearly defined structure. The possible variation is infinite, and no adequate classification has been generally agreed upon. The development and adoption of standard descriptive and genetic classification schemes are needed. A genetic classification of ground ice has been constructed by Mackay (1972), and Linnell and Kaplar (1963) have developed a descriptive classification of frozen soil suitable for engineering purposes (Chap. 1). Nevertheless, in most geotechnical projects ad hoc schemes still are being employed.

Unfrozen water It is now generally understood that an unfrozen water phase separates ice from the mineral grains in frozen soil. Evidence bearing on this point can be summarized briefly as follows. The imposition of an electric field causes the movement of both solutes and water (electroosmosis). In conditions of high ice content the particles themselves can be induced to move slowly through the ice matrix. Ionic diffusion is observed in frozen soils; the path seems to be the unfrozen interface separating the particle surfaces from the neighboring ice grains. The magnitude of the diffusion coefficients is consistent with this view $(10^{-11}$ m^2/s). Nuclear-magnetic-resonance data and observations on the change of color during freeze-thaw cycles, etc., also provide evidence sustaining this view. The quantity of water making up this interface and the variations associated with changing temperature are of fundamental interest and importance in geotechnical engineering.

An insight into this problem can be gained by considering the freezing-point-depression–water-content relationship. At the freezing-point depression θ_f of the soil-water solution at any given water content that water content may be regarded as equivalent to the unfrozen water content w_u at that temperature, since either a slight lowering of the temperature or a slight increase in the water content would create a condition in which a small quantity of ice could coexist with the unfrozen water. Let us look at it from a slightly different point of view. For a soil with ice and unfrozen water contents w_i and w_u, at a temperature θ_i, any removal of water from the soil by evaporation or sublimation must be accomplished at the expense of w_i. Therefore the total water content w diminishes as $w_i \rightarrow 0$. At this point

$$w = w_u \tag{2.20}$$

and
$$\theta_i = \theta_f \tag{2.21}$$

It will be recognized that this argument is an oversimplification since a number of factors, such as hysteresis in the soil-water-potential–water-content curve (the soil-moisture characteristic), for example, makes the functional relationship between the unfrozen-water-temperature curve multivalued. Nevertheless, it is a useful rule of thumb.

Measurements of unfrozen water contents in soils of varying water contents and physical properties have been made by dilatometry, adiabatic calorimetry, x-ray diffraction, heat capacity, nuclear magnetic resonance, differential thermal analysis, and several indirect techniques (Anderson and Morgenstern, 1973). Although each involves its own set of assumptions and approximations, the results obtained on the same or similar soils by each method are remarkably consistent.

In recent years a large number of phase-composition data has become available. Williams (1964b) has given the complete curve for Leda clay, Winnipeg clay, and Niagara silt down to $-5°C$. Koopmans and Miller (1966) have reported the data for several size fractions of New Hampshire silt. Data for a suite of representative soils and soil materials are given down to about $-5°C$ in Fig. 2.25.

During the course of this work it was recognized that the phase-composition data of most frozen soils are conveniently represented by a simple power curve, $w_u = \alpha \theta^\beta$, where the coefficients α and β are characteristic of each soil. For soils with very high clay contents a more complex expression involving segments of two different curves is required. This probably represents contributions from two distinct interfacial domains of the unfrozen water in the clay fraction, each with its own freeze-thaw phase equilibria (Anderson and Tice, 1971).

Examination of the published data and the coefficients α and β reveals the relationship

$$\ln w_u = a + b \ln S + cS^d \ln \theta \tag{2.22}$$

where S is the specific surface area in square meters per gram. The values of the coefficients obtained from experimental data for 11 representative soils are $a = 0.2618$, $b = 0.5519$, $c = -1.449$, and $d = -0.264$ (Anderson et al., 1973). The ability to calculate phase-composition data to a first approximation from a knowledge of the specific surface is indeed welcome. This equation has been used to obtain the variation of w_u with temperature and from that the exchange of heat with the surrounding permafrost in designing the vertical support members for the trans-Alaska pipeline.

Dillon and Andersland (1966) earlier had recognized the importance of knowing the interrelationships between phase composition and such soil properties as specific surface, soil consistency, clay mineral type, etc. The availability of complete phase-composition data for representative soils has permitted simplification of the approach they suggested. Meanwhile it also has been found possible to calculate phase-composition curves from liquid-limit data. The data required are $N = 25$ and $N = 100$ (where N is the number of blows required to close the standard groove) and the relationship given earlier, $w_u = \alpha \theta^\beta$. The empirical relationships found were

$$w_{u, \theta = 1} = 0.346 w_{N = 25} \tag{2.23}$$

$$w_{u, \theta = 2} = 0.338 w_{N = 100} - 3.72 \tag{2.24}$$

each with a correlation coefficient of 0.98. In these equations $w_{N = 25}$ and $w_{N = 100}$ refer to the water contents at which the standard groove is closed with 25 and 100 blows, respectively; $\theta = 1$ and $\theta = 2$ refer to temperatures of -1 and $-2°C$, respectively. With the two resulting values of w_u, the coefficients α and β can be evaluated and the complete phase-composition curve computed. The agreement between measured and calculated values for the several soils is shown in Fig. 2.26.

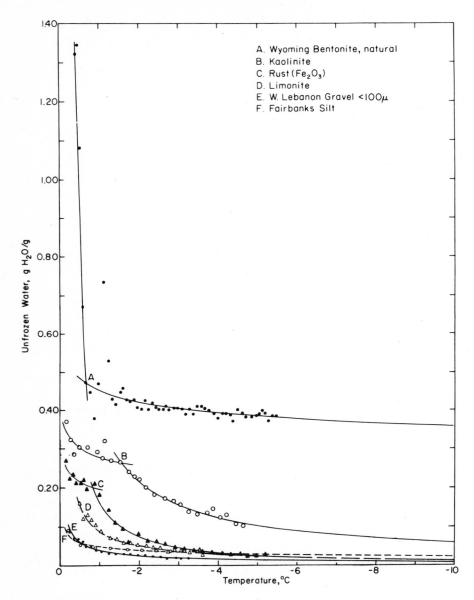

Figure 2.25 Phase-composition curves for six representative soils and soil constituents. (*After Anderson and Morgenstern, 1973.*)

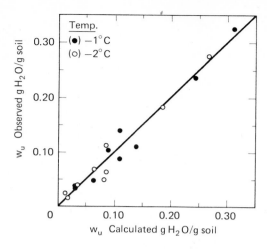

Figure 2.26 Plot of the amount of unfrozen water at -1 and $-2°C$ (from phase-composition data) vs. the amount of unfrozen water at -1 and $-2°C$ calculated from Eqs. (2.23) and (2.24).

Clay mineral type, the nature of the cation complex, previous freeze-thaw history, etc., are of secondary importance, of the order of that shown in Fig. 2.25, in which the effect of the two interfacial domains spoken of earlier is illustrated. This is not to say that these effects are negligible. In most practical situations the improvement in accuracy obtained by taking them into account will not be worth the time and effort required to obtain the data accurately enough to refine the estimates. In certain cases, however, the best accuracy obtainable is required. Direct measurement is necessary then.

One effect, often neglected, deserves special mention. It has been widely assumed, based on early work by Tsytovich (1945, 1958), that w_u can be regarded as independent of the ice content of frozen ground. Not all investigators have accepted this assertion, however, and modern workers, while often employing it, have always regarded the assumption as tentative. Investigations to date have been insufficient to establish the validity or the limitations of this assumption. Recent work by Tice et al. (1978) using the nuclear-magnetic-resonance technique indicates that there is a noticeable increase in w_u with increasing water content. The results for three representative soils at two different water contents are shown in Fig. 2.27.

The effect of solutes in the soil solution must also be taken into account. The treatment of this problem follows conventional thermodynamic arguments involving ionic strength; it has been set forth recently by Banin and Anderson (1974).

The accurate determination of phase-composition data for potentially trouble-some soils (fine-grained or organic soils, for the most part) is becoming widely recognized as essential in a variety of geotechnical engineering activities. It is quite apparent that in situ determinations on undisturbed soils would be desirable in some instances. More often than not the tests can be done adequately on disturbed samples. A rapid method that can be employed on site or in the field clearly is needed. The pulsed-nuclear-magnetic-resonance method of Tice et al. (1978) is the most promising of the several methods used so far.

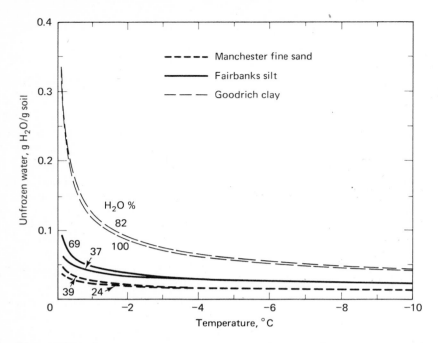

Figure 2.27 Unfrozen water contents vs. temperature for three soils.

Phase Compositions Curve

Frost Action

At least four major contributions in the last 50 years have led to a more complete understanding of frost-action processes in soils. In 1925, a conference on frost action in soils was sponsored by the Swedish Institute for Roads, probably the earliest on this subject. This was followed by Beskow's treatise in 1935. The 1952 review of frost-action literature by Johnson, covering the period from 1765 to 1951, brought all the relevant information together from different disciplines for the first time. Finally, there was the 1974 publication Roadway Design in Seasonal Frost Areas, a joint effort of the Transportation Research Board, Washington, and the U.S. Army Corps of Engineers, Cold Regions Research and Engineering Laboratory (National Cooperative Highway Research Program, 1974).

As a result, the three conditions involving water, temperature, and soil that must exist simultaneously for frost heaving to occur in soils are well known, namely, a soil-moisture supply, sufficiently cold temperatures to cause soil freezing, and a frost-susceptible soil. The simultaneous occurrence and interaction process that results is referred to as the *mechanism of frost heaving*. The problem of frost-action damage is widespread; it occurs in all temperate zones wherever there is seasonal soil freezing as well as in the active layer of more northerly, permafrost regions.

Two very destructive effects are associated with frost action in soils, the expansion and lifting of the soil (frost heaving) in winter and the loss of soil-bearing strength by thaw weakening in the spring. Soils that display one or both of these manifestations are referred to as *frost-susceptible*. Which of these processes is the more serious depends on the type of engineering structure involved and the severity of the resulting damage. A small amount of uniform or even some differential heaving can be tolerated in secondary roads and streets. During the thawing period, however, the loss of soil strength often culminates in rutting of the surface and in some cases in more serious damage. This rarely occurs in first-class highways since highways, streets, and airport runways, etc., are designed to have a year-round capability. High standards of smoothness and safety require very close control of all aspects of frost action in order to accommodate high-speed vehicular traffic and the high takeoff and landing speeds of modern aircraft. The problem is more common in secondary roads built to lower standards.

For unheated buildings, e.g., warehouses, carports and garages, ice rinks and cold-storage facilities, and other structures, e.g., transmission towers and switching stations, deformation of the structure by heaving rather than thaw softening is the principal frost problem. Normally such structures do not heave uniformly, nor do they return to the orginal elevation after the thawing period; hence uplifts tend to be cumulative and may become progressively serious with time.

Frost heaving Frost heaving is appropriately discussed under four headings: frost-heaving processes, phenomena associated with ice lensing, ice-segregation efficiency ratio, and the ice-lensing mechanism.

Frost-heaving processes The heaving of frost-susceptible soil can be attributed to two processes. Freezing of in situ pore water during frost penetration contributes to the total heave by the 9 percent volume change unless pore-water expulsion occurs, e.g., in coarse sands (McRoberts and Morgenstern, 1975). The amount of heave by ice lensing depends on the frost-susceptibility characteristics, principally the hydraulic permeability of the soil. Although the process may be destructive, particularly in many building materials, a larger portion of heaving in frost-susceptible soils is from the formation of ice lenses at the freezing plane.

There are important differences in the structure of frost-susceptible soils after freezing. Examples of the extremes are shown in Fig. 2.28. The conchoidally shaped occluded soil particles and the undulating freezing front in clay soils are in sharp contrast to the uniformly spaced alternate layers of soil and ice in silts. The low permeability of clays causes the actively growing ice lens to induce local shrinkage as the freezing front advances.

The heave attributable to the expansion of pore water and that attributed to ice lensing are shown in Fig. 2.29. The in situ water expansion calculated was adjusted for the unfrozen water content from experimentally determined water-content–temperature relationships below freezing. The upper curves show the total heave, consisting of the expansion of the in situ water during frost penetration

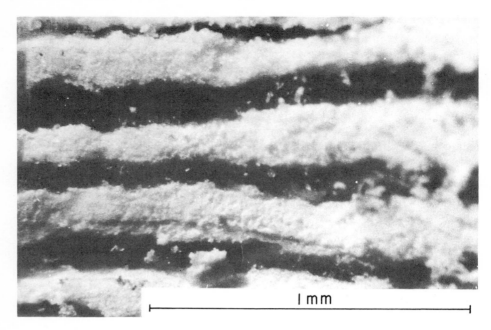

(a)   SILTY SOIL

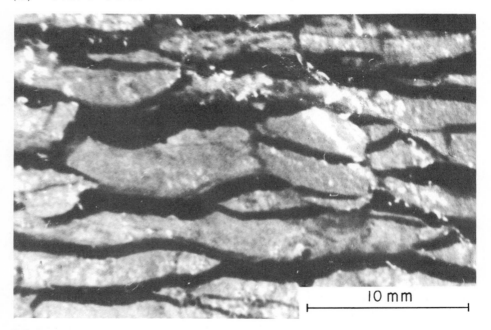

(b)   CLAY SOIL

Figure 2.28 Ice-lens morphology for (a) silty soil and (b) clay soil.

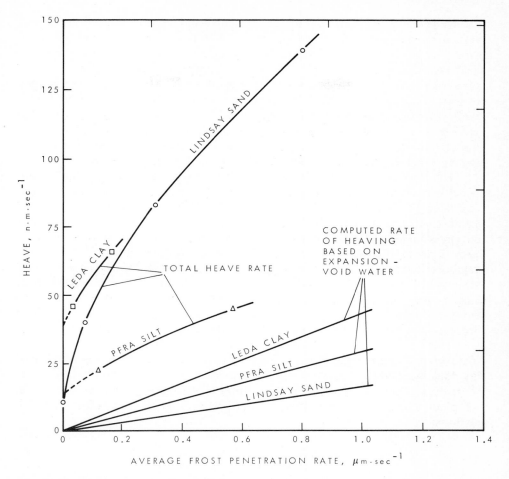

Figure 2.29 Heave rate as a function of frost penetration rate.

as well as additional water moved into the freezing zone by the ice-lensing phenomenon. The lower curves give the heave assigned to the in-place expansion of in situ water. The in situ expansion for these soils varied directly as the initial water content, i.e., Leda clay > PFRA silt > Lindsay sand, whereas the heave by ice lensing was a function of their frost susceptibility, i.e., Leda clay > Lindsay sand > PFRA silt.

Phenomena associated with ice lensing Heaving can be attributed mainly to the growth of ice lenses in highly frost-susceptible soils. Beskow (1935) in his treatise on frost action claimed that this was shown by Johansson (1914) in the early 1900s, at a time when the popular belief was that frost heaving resulted solely from the expansion associated with the water-ice phase change during freezing.

Ice lenses usually form parallel to the isothermal freezing plane although any vertical cracks present in the soil will also fill with ice. Heaving is always in the direction of heat flow and normal to the horizontal ground surface under natural field conditions. Work must be done to lift the overburden and any surface surcharges and to provide space for the growing ice lenses. The necessary supply of water is normally obtained from the surrounding soil or the groundwater table, so that further work is required to induce and maintain the suction gradient that sustains water flow to the freezing front (Penner, 1958). The energy required for these two processes proceeding simultaneously is made available at the ice-water interface of the actively growing ice lens (Everett, 1961).

The horizontal dimensions of an ice lens depend on soil type and homogeneity, uniformity of water supply, and temperature gradient. The lens thickness and lens spacing depend on heat-flow rate and are also contingent on the balance between moisture and heat flow (Penner, 1960). When the potential water supply is equal to or exceeds the existing heat-removal rate, the lens will continue growth at one site indefinitely. When the heat-removal rate at the freezing plane temporarily exceeds the moisture supply, the temperature at the ice-water interface decreases, the freezing plane advances, and a new location for lens development may be established when a more favorable water supply is encountered. These events, repeated, are referred to as *rhythmic ice lensing*, a common feature of frost-susceptible soil. They are described in detail by Martin (1959).

Ice-segregation efficiency ratio The ice-segregation efficiency ratio was introduced by Arakawa (1966) as a useful soil frost-susceptibility index. The efficiency ratio E in Eq. (2.25) is the proportion of the total heat resulting from the latent heat of phase change that is removed from the soil in ice segregation. In this expression

$$E = \frac{\sigma L}{k_1 \, \delta T_1/\delta x - k_2 \, \delta T_2/\delta x} \tag{2.25}$$

where σ = ice segregation rate, kg/m^2 per unit time
$\quad L$ = latent heat of fusion, J/kg
$\quad k_1$ = thermal conductivity of frozen layer, W/m K
$\quad k_2$ = thermal conductivity of unfrozen layer, W/m K
$\delta T_1/\delta x$ = thermal gradient in frozen layer, K/m
$\delta T_2/\delta x$ = thermal gradient in unfrozen layer, K/m

In unidirectionally frozen laboratory samples the measured water inflow to the sample gives the value for σL. The denominator on the right side of the equation is the net heat removed from the sample, i.e., heat out minus heat in. The range of values for E lies between 0 and 1. Perfect ice segregation occurs when E equals one; when $0 < E < 1$, imperfect ice segregation results; no ice segregation occurs when E equals zero. Figure 2.30 illustrates the reduction of the efficiency ratio E under laboratory conditions as the rate of frost penetration is increased.

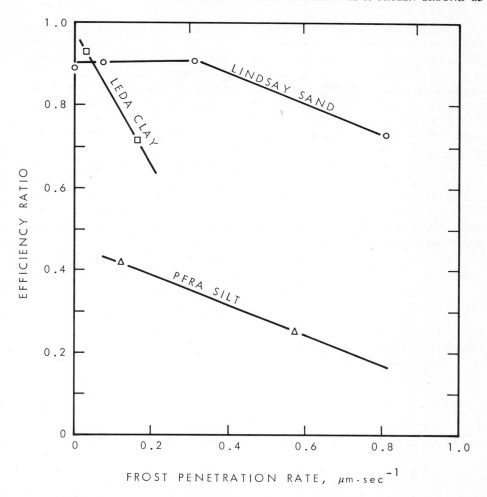

Figure 2.30 The ice-segregation efficiency ratio as a function of frost-penetration rate.

Ice-lensing mechanism The Kelvin equation has been applied to give the temperature T at which ice will propagate through a pore restriction of radius r_i:

$$T_m - T = \Delta T = \frac{2 T_m \sigma_{iw}}{Q_f \rho_i r_i} \tag{2.26}$$

where r_i = curvature radius of ice-water interface and also pore radius, μm
  ρ_i = density of ice, kg/m^3
  Q_f = latent heat of fusion, J/kg
  T_m = temperature of melting ice at zero curvature, K
  T = temperature of the ice-water curvature of radius r_i, K
  σ_{iw} = ice-water interfacial energy, J/m^2

Following the thermodynamic considerations on the freezing of water in unconsolidated porous materials [Edlefson and Anderson (1943), Winterkorn (1955), Jumikis (1956), Penner (1957), and Gold (1957)], Everett (1961) developed an acceptable self-consistent theory of ice-lens growth in porous media under idealized conditions. Expansion of the theory to include complex pore geometries has also been accomplished to the extent that meaningful tests are possible (Everett and Haynes, 1965). This was done by Penner (1966) on ice lenses grown under rigidly controlled conditions on a close-packed array of uniformly sized glass spheres, as shown schematically in Fig. 2.31a and b.

Although it does not enter directly into the thermodynamic considerations, the absorbed unfrozen water phase on the sphere surfaces is a very necessary feature. The flow of water to the region where heaving occurs, i.e., between the bottom of the ice lens and the top of the spheres, is via this adsorbed liquid like phase. If the sphere surfaces are rendered hydrophobic so that this surface film is diminished, ice lensing does not occur.

The drop in pressure across the ice-water interface in the pore at C (Fig. 2.31) is given by

$$p^i - p^w = \frac{2\sigma_{iw}}{r_i} \tag{2.27}$$

where r_i = radius of curvature of ice-water interface, μm
$\quad\quad p^i$ = pressure on ice, N/m^2
$\quad\quad \sigma_{iw}$ = interfacial energy term for ice-water interface, J/m^2

The pressure difference across the ice-solid interface is given by

$$p^i - p^s = -\frac{2\sigma_{is}}{r} \tag{2.28}$$

where the radius of curvature of the sphere is given by r and p^s in the solid sphere. Pressure in the solid at A is obtained by combining Eq. (2.27) and (2.28):

$$p_A^s = p^w + \frac{2\sigma_{iw}}{r_i} + \frac{2\sigma_{is}}{r} \tag{2.29}$$

The pressure at B in the solid is

$$p_B^w = p^w + \frac{2\sigma_{ws}}{r} \tag{2.30}$$

What is required is the difference in the pressure that the bead experiences between positions A and B. It is obtained by bringing A and B in the vicinity of C. Then it follows that

$$\Delta p = p_A^s - p_B^s = \frac{2\sigma_{iw}}{r_i} + \frac{2}{r}(\sigma_{is} - \sigma_{ws}) \tag{2.31}$$

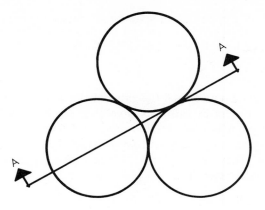

(a)   SPHERES IN CLOSE-PACK ARRAY

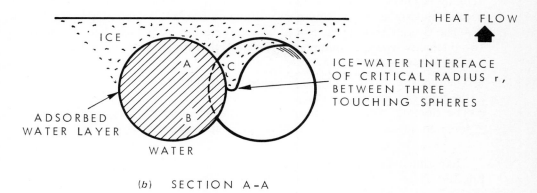

(b)   SECTION A-A

Figure 2.31 Schematic drawing of ice-water interface before propagating through pore restriction between touching sphere: (a) spheres in close-packed array, (b) section A-A.

When we define

$$B' = \frac{r}{r_i} \frac{1}{\cos \theta}$$

and introducing it into Eq. (2.31) as well as the Young-Depre equation, we get

$$\sigma_{is} - \sigma_{ws} = \sigma_{is} \cos \theta \qquad (2.32)$$

and Eq. (2.31) becomes

$$\Delta p = \frac{2\sigma_{iw} \cos \theta \, (1 + B')}{r} \qquad (2.33)$$

Geometrically the radius of the smallest sphere that passes through the pore in Fig. 2.31a is given by

$$\frac{r}{r_i} \approx 6.41 \tag{2.34}$$

Everett and Haynes (1965) determined the ratio of the sphere radius to the critical pore radius by a series of experiments involving capillary rise between close-packed cylindrical rods, maximum bubble pressure between three spheres in mutual contact, and drainage of a liquid from a pyramid of steel balls in a close-packed arrangement. These experiments gave an average critical radius thought to apply to the present case, i.e.,

$$\frac{r}{r_i} \approx 5.60 \tag{2.35}$$

Their reason for questioning the value given in Eq. (2.34) was that the interface between three touching spheres is not a surface of revolution. What is actually needed is the critical radius of curvature at which a nonwetting phase completely displaces a wetting phase through a triangular window (Fig. 2.31).

The Everett-Haynes concept of heaving pressure recognizes the existence of two distinctly separate components [Eq. (2.31)] of the pressure parameter:

1. The increase in pressure on the ice that is required for ice to pass through the pore restriction.
2. The floating effect, a concept demonstrated earlier by Corté (1962). The force on a bead on an advancing ice-water interface is given by $2\pi r \sigma_{iw}$.

Experimental results supporting the Everett-Haynes theory are shown in Fig. 2.32. The curves give the pressure–particle-size relationship using two different values for the interfacial energy term, 0.03 and 0.04 J/m^2. The heaving-pressure experiments were repeated 12 times using spherical glass beads 12 μm in diameter and twice with beads of 19.4 μm diameter. Subsequently heave-pressure measurements were carried out with angular fragments from potter's flint and natural soil (Penner, 1967, 1968). The experiments were carried out the same way as with the spherical glass beads. The measured ice-lens heaving pressure for the smallest size in each fraction yields a relationship (Fig. 2.33) not unlike the theoretical one (Everett and Haynes, 1965). Thus it appears that grain (or aggregate) size is a valid basis for defining and classifying frost susceptibility. Grain size and grain-size distribution are in fact commonly used for identifying frost susceptibility, although the search for more sophisticated methods continues. It should be recognized that there is no sharp dividing line—by any standard—between a frost-susceptible and non-frost-susceptible soil. In addition, the characterization of a soil by its degree of frost susceptibility is meaningful only if all the environmental factors, such as moisture availability and all the other aspects of the freezing condition, are taken into account.

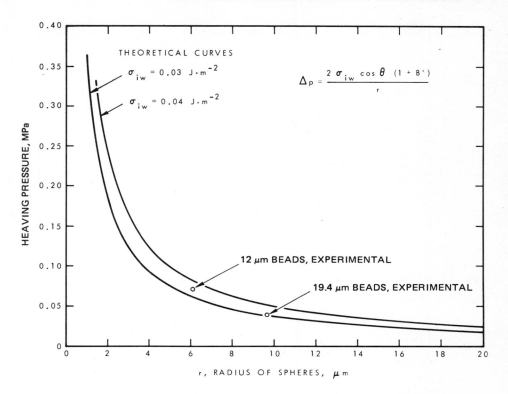

Figure 2.32 Everett-Haynes equation, relationship of measured and theoretical heaving pressure to sphere radius.

Effects of thawing As mentioned above, the two most destructive manifestations associated with the frost action are frost heaving and the loss of bearing strength by thaw weakening. Thaw weakening usually is not important in the stability of building foundations, transmission towers, etc. Where the load is dynamic, on the other hand, as with moving vehicles, thaw weakening is of paramount importance. This is especially evident in the improper design of streets, highways, airport runways, etc. Since loss of bearing strength in pavements during and after the thawing period may not always be preceded by excessive or even noticeable heaving, design considerations not directly associated with the control of frost heave in the winter are involved.

Thaw weakening preceded by ice segregation Nordal (1973) illustrated the relationship between excessive heaving and the subsequent loss of strength by thaw weakening. Measurements of heave, depth of the freezing front, and pavement deflection are shown during the period of strength loss and recovery (Fig. 2.34).

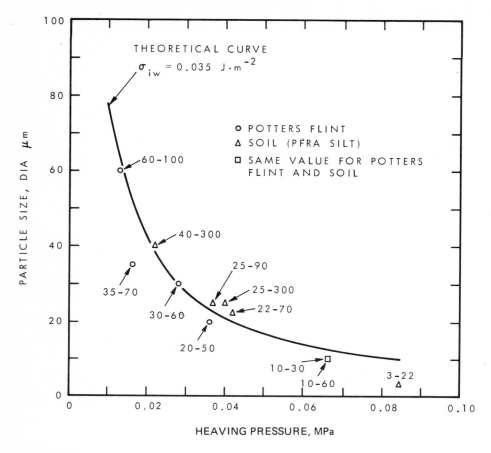

Figure 2.33 Relation between experimental heaving pressures and smallest particle in fraction.

Thawing is usually more rapid downward from the top than upward from the freezing plane, particularly if the road has a black asphaltic concrete surface. This leads to the entrapment of water from the melting ice lenses—above the impervious frozen layer at depth. Thaw penetration is frequently greater in the center of the road, thus impeding lateral drainage.

Numerous references could be cited drawing attention to the detrimental effect of successive freeze-thaw cycles. It is noteworthy that Crawford and Boyd (1956) were unable to establish this for the Ottawa (Canada) area. Heavy precipitation before the thawing (Dolch, 1952) appears to increase the severity of frost damage in the spring thaw. Rengmark (1963) has drawn attention to the detrimental effect of high traffic density and load during the thawing period.

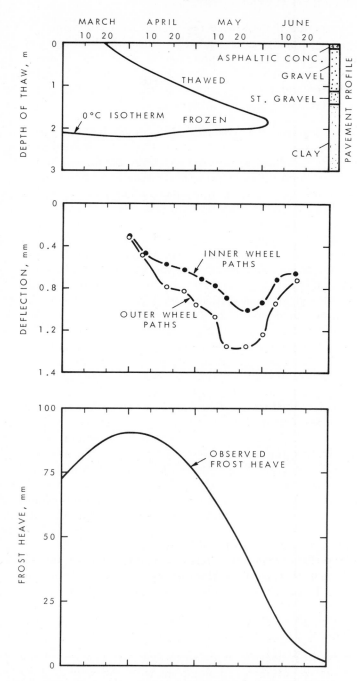

Figure 2.34 Relation between frost heave, deflection, and 0°C isotherm at the Vormsund test road, Norway.

Broms and Yao (1964) suggested that thawing segregated ice accompanied by loading leads to excessive pore pressures and greatly reduces the load-carrying capacity of pavements. This is the basis for spring load restrictions in many countries. Now, however, modern road systems for vehicular traffic and airport runways usually are built to standards high enough to maintain a year-round capability; seasonal restrictions are no longer acceptable.

Thaw weakening without ice segregation in fine-grained subgrades Ice segregation during freezing is not always a necessary precursor for the thaw weakening of pavements. This subtle type of thaw weakening has been confirmed in the laboratory (Bergen and Fredlund, 1973). The exact mechanism, however, is imperfectly understood. Chamberlain (1973), in a paper on computer modeling for the prediction of closed-system freeze-thaw strength loss, referred to investigations by Cook (1963) and Titov (1965); they observed nodule or nugget structures which appeared to have higher surface moisture contents and loss of cohesion although no visible ice heaving had occurred. Mikhailov and Bredyuk (1966) attributed the reduced cohesion in clay to the conversion of bound water into free water. Chamberlain (1973) concluded that closed-system freeze-thaw will induce a strength reduction in clay soils with or without visible ice segregation and that compressive strength and static and repetitive moduli are also affected. It is noted that the rate of strength reduction decreases as the number of freeze-thaw cycles is increased. This suggests that ice segregation on the microscopic scale is also involved (Anderson and Morgenstern, 1973).

Hamilton (1966) first noted the curious phenomenon of shrinkage when unsaturated soils were subjected to freezing in the field. This has also been observed (Penner et al., 1974) in the freezing of laboratory samples in preparation for thermal-conductivity measurements. The reduction in thermal conductivity is evidence that the adsorbed surface water on the soil particles is withdrawn by crystallization inside the air-filled pores. When thawing takes place, the adsorbed films thicken, causing swelling. This shrinkage and swelling phenomenon induced by the freeze-thaw process is a remolding process which might well contribute to thaw weakening in unsaturated subgrades when no ice lensing occurs. Additional research on the thaw-softening process without the supply of water from melting ice lenses clearly is needed.

Frost-susceptibility criteria Frost-susceptibility criteria for soils may be divided into two broad groups according to the nature of the resulting frost-action damage.

Group I. Frost heaving and thaw weakening
Group II. Thaw weakening only

Uniform or differential frost heaving is an invariable characteristic of the first group. Group I applies to pavements in situations where thaw weakening is preceded by heaving. Load-bearing capacity usually deteriorates rapidly on thawing frost-susceptible soils unless traffic movement is curtailed or halted.

Frost-susceptibility criteria in group I apply to foundations of various engineering structures even though thaw weakening is of little or no consequence.

In some areas of seasonal frost, heaving may be negligible yet pavements still exhibit the characteristic loss of subgrade support on thawing; their evaluation is dealt with in group II. The characteristic pattern of subgrade support is marked by a sharp increase over their autumn strength during freezing, an abrupt decrease in strength during the spring thaw, and a gradual recovery of stability in the summer, reaching characteristic values again in the autumn. In group II it is the thaw-weakening aspect of the frost-action problem that is of prime importance in design considerations.

The main frost-susceptibility criteria belonging to group I are listed below with a partial citing of relevant literature. Features these criteria have in common are that heaving characteristics are evaluated in, and strength tests are all dependent on, laboratory determinations.

Group I

(a) Frost-heave rate, Kaplar (1971, 1974), Linell and Kaplar (1959), Jacobs (1965)
(b) Particle size and particle-size distribution, Casagrande (1931, 1938), Riis (1948), Beskow (1935), U.S. Corps of Engineers (1953)
(c) Air intrusion, Beskow (1935), Williams (1972)
(d) Maximum ice-lens pressure, Hoekstra et al. (1965), Wissa and Martin (1973)
(e) Pore-size distribution, Townsend and Csathy (1962)
(f) Permeability, Wissa et al. (1972)

Group II criteria are subdivided according to whether they are based on a laboratory or field evaluation. It should be noted that not all have been fully evaluated nor do they have the full status of a frost-action criterion. The areas studied show promise, and herein lies their importance since thaw weakening has not been investigated and developed to the same extent as the heave phenomenon. Again, the references listed are not intended to be exhaustive but give easy entry into the literature.

Group IIA Laboratory evaluation

The thaw-weakening evaluation methods studied in the laboratory are as follows:

(a) California bearing ratio, Jessberger and Carbee (1970)
(b) Excess pore pressure, Broms and Yao (1964)
(c) Resilient strain and resilient modulus, Culley (1971)
(d) Unconfined compressive strength (modeling study), Chamberlain (1973)

Group IIB Field evaluation

Thaw-weakening evaluations based on field studies are:

(a) Combined basis of field California bearing ratio and plate-bearing and traffic tests to establish four soil groups, F1 to F4, as well as the Unified Soil Classification System, Linell (1953)
(b) Plate bearing, Sayman (1955)
(c) Benkelman beam, Preus and Tomes (1959)
(d) Field California bearing ratio, Turner (1957)

The frost-susceptibility-criteria classification system does not identify all the factors that were used when the criteria originally were put forward by the various investigators; e.g., in some grain-size criteria, Atterberg limits are also included; in others it is the uniformity coefficient that was added. The various criteria are referenced in such a way that this level of detail is easily obtained.

The frost-susceptibility classification schemes have been presented in such detail partly to draw attention to their limitations when applied to thaw-weakening damage in the absence of frost heaving and to emphasize the current trend in soil engineering away from laboratory testing to in situ field testing. It is generally recognized now that it is important to conduct field tests in evaluating frost susceptibility as a backup to a laboratory evaluation, at least. Placing the emphasis almost entirely on the properties of the soil, as in group I, has led to disappointing results because the conditions of water and freezing in nature are so important and so variable; e.g., good soils have been excluded by them and sometimes frost-susceptible soils have been used. A stronger emphasis on the environmentally controlled factors brings into focus the importance of the availability of water and nature of the freezing conditions. The criteria listed above cannot be discussed in detail; in summary it can be said that in areas of seasonal frost in the continental North America the criteria developed by the U.S. Army Corps of Engineers, group IIB(a), has found wide acceptance. It has as its basis the F1 to F4 design classification groups based on field California bearing ratio and plate-bearing tests during the thaw-weakening period. It is interconnected with the United States classification and laboratory frost-heave rate tests. This has been a central characteristic of the conventional engineering design approach described again recently by Lobacz et al. (1973).

Thermal Properties

The apparent specific heat capacity As with unfrozen soil, the heat capacity of frozen soil can be expressed as the sum of the heat capacities of the main constituents. There is one important difference. In frozen soils the liquid-solid phase change is gradual and continual, and the term *specific heat capacity* is therefore not strictly appropriate, *apparent specific heat capacity* being preferable (Williams, 1964a). Neglecting the gas phase, we may regard frozen soil as consisting of two components and three phases: the soil matrix, ice, and the unfrozen water. Therefore, the apparent specific heat can be expressed as the sum of an appropriate term for each of these plus a term to account for the latent heat of phase change that is continually being given off or absorbed:

$$C_a = C_s + C_i(w - w_u) + C_u w_u + \frac{1}{\Delta T} \int_{T_1}^{T_2} L \frac{\partial w_u}{\partial T} dT \qquad (2.36)$$

where C_a = apparent specific heat capacity of frozen soil
C_s = specific heat capacity of dry soil matrix
C_i = specific heat capacity of ice
C_u = specific heat capacity of unfrozen water
w = total water content
w_u = unfrozen water content
T = temperature
L = latent heat of liquid-solid phase change

Strictly speaking, all these are partial specific quantities, a term familiar to those well versed in chemical thermodynamics; for practical purposes this distinction is seldom required.

The use of Eq. (2.36) was demonstrated recently by Anderson et al. (1973) in calculating cumulative heats required to raise the temperature of six representative frozen soils (Table 2.6) from -10 to $+10°C$ at water contents ranging from 0.25 to 1.0 g H_2O per gram of soil. Their results are shown in Fig. 2.35. These soils envelop the full range of naturally occurring surface properties for mineral soils. Therefore, the curves illustrated here may be regarded as defining the envelope of possible values of cumulative heats for this situation. Similar calculations for other situations are easily accomplished.

Table 2.6 Specific surface area, experimental values of α and β, and freezing-point-depression values for six representative soils (after Anderson et al., 1973)

Soil	Specific surface area, m²/g	Experimental value[†] α	β	w_w, g H_2O/g soil 0.25	0.50	1.00
				Freezing-point depression θ, °C		
Manchester very fine sand	0.016[‡]	0.0346	-0.048	1.00×10^{-18}	1.00×10^{-25}	1.00×10^{-31}
Fairbanks silt	40[§]	0.0481	-0.326	6.37×10^{-3}	7.60×10^{-4}	9.07×10^{-5}
Kaolinite	84[§]	0.2380	-0.360	8.72×10^{-1}	1.27×10^{-1}	1.85×10^{-2}
Suffield silty clay	140[§]	0.1392	-0.315	1.56×10^{-1}	7.3×10^{-1}	1.91×10^{-3}
Hawaiian clay	382[§]	0.3242	-0.243	2.91	1.68×10^{-1}	9.7×10^{-3}
Umiat bentonite	800[§]	0.6755	-0.343	18.2	2.41	3.19×10^{-1}

† Values for α and β obtained by least-squares regression of the data for each individual soil
‡ Geometrical specific surface estimated from a grain-size distribution curve.
§ Surface area determined by the ethylene glycol–retention method.

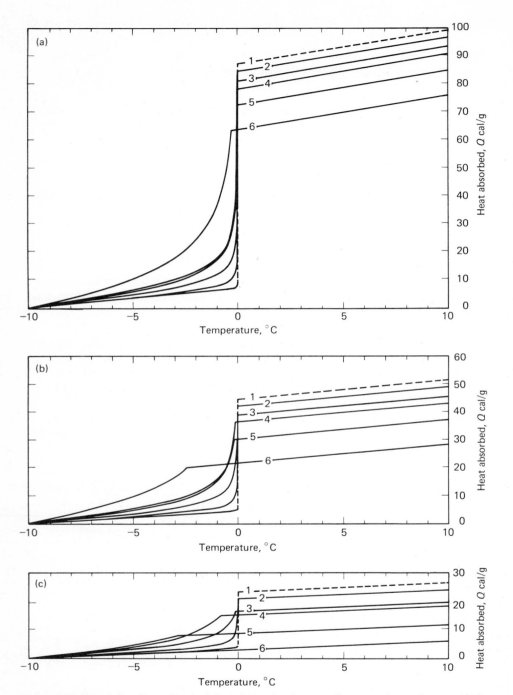

Figure 2.35 Cumulative heat absorbed in raising the frozen soil-water mixture from $-10°C$ through the melting point (calories per gram of soil): (*a*) 1.0, (*b*) 0.5, and (*c*) 0.25 g H_2O per gram of soil. The original units (calories) have been retained. 1 = Manchester very fine sand; 2 = Fairbanks silt; 3 = kaolinite; 4 = Suffield silty clay; 5 = Hawaiian clay; 6 = Umiat bentonite.

Thermal conduction Two defined parameters, the thermal conductivity k and the thermal diffusivity D, are used to describe the conductive transfer of heat in frozen ground. Other transfer mechanisms usually can be neglected. These two parameters are related through the relation $D = k/\rho C_a$, where ρ is the density of the frozen medium and C_a is its apparent specific heat capacity. The treatment of heat transfer in frozen ground has been thoroughly conventional for the most part, and standard textbooks have furnished the basic equations.

When the equations are formulated in terms of the diffusivity, the gravimetric apparent specific heat is required. When the equations are formulated in terms of the thermal conductivity, the volumetric specific heat capacity is required. The latter can be formulated easily in a manner similar to that illustrated in the preceding section. The latent heat of phase change involved can be accommodated by a variable $D(T)$ or a variable apparent specific heat capacity. Because of the lack of data and an appropriate function to represent them, the conventional approach, until recently, was to neglect the unfrozen water and the associated phase change altogether. Ho et al. (1970), Nakano and Brown (1972), and others have shown how the nonlinear relationship between the water-ice phase composition curve can be incorporated explicitly.

Example 2.1 Calculate the freezing-point depression θ_f for Umiat bentonite with a water content of 1 g H_2O per gram of soil. In the equation $w_u = \alpha\theta^\beta$ $\alpha = 0.6755$ and $\beta = -0.343$ (Anderson et al., 1973).

SOLUTION Rearrange the equation for w_u and solve for θ_f:

$$\theta = \left(\frac{w_u}{\alpha}\right)^{1/\beta} = \left(\frac{1.00}{0.6755}\right)^{1/-0.343} = 0.3186°C$$

The freezing-point depression $\theta_f \approx 0.32°C$.

Example 2.2 For the Umiat bentonite calculate the heat required (per unit mass of mineral solids) to increase the temperature from $-10°C$ to (a) $-2°C$, (b) the freezing-point depression θ_f (Example 2.1), and (c) $10°C$. Assume that $C_s = 0.687$ J/g °C, $C_i = 2.1$ J/g °C, $C_u = 4.2$ J/g °C, and $L = 333.7$ J/g. Note that Eq. (2.36) can be written

$$C_a = C_s + C_i w + \left[(C_u - C_i) - \frac{L\beta}{\theta}\right]\alpha\theta^\beta$$

where $\beta < 0$ and $\theta \geq \theta_f > 0$. The heat required can be expressed as

$$Q_{1-2} = \int_{\theta_1}^{\theta_2} C_a\,d\theta$$

$$= (C_s + C_i w)(\theta_1 - \theta_2) + \frac{(C_u - C_i)\alpha}{1 + \beta}(\theta_1^{1+\beta} - \theta_2^{1+\beta}) + \alpha L(\theta_2^\beta - \theta_1^\beta)$$

where θ_1 and $\theta_2 \geq \theta_f$.

SOLUTION Heat for 1 g from $-10°C$ to θ_2:

$$Q = [0.687 + 2.1(1.0)](10 - \theta_2) + \frac{(4.2 - 2.1)(0.6755)}{1 - 0.343}(10^{1-0.343} - \theta_2^{1-0.343})$$

$$+ 0.6755(333.7)(\theta_2^{-0.343} - 10^{-0.343})$$

$$Q = -64.654 - 2.787\theta_2 - 2.1591\theta_2^{0.657} + 225.4143\theta_2^{-0.343}$$

T_2, °C		θ_2, °C		Q, J/g
$T_f = $	$\begin{cases} -2 \\ -0.319 \\ 10 \end{cases}$	$\theta_f = $	$\begin{cases} +2 \\ +0.319 \\ -10 \end{cases}$	104.0 266.9 317.3

At $T = +10°C$, $Q = (C_s + C_w w) \Delta T + (Q \text{ at } \theta_f)$.

$$Q = [0.687 + 4.2(1.0)](10 + 0.319) + 266.91 = 317.3 \text{ J/g}$$

Example 2.3 Repeat Example 2.2 using the simplifying assumption that all the water is frozen below 0°C and melts at 0°C. Prepare a plot of increase in temperature (vertical scale) from -10 to $+10°C$ as a function of the heat added to the soil. Compare this curve with data from Example 2.2.

SOLUTION Assume that all pore water is frozen and melts at 0°C. Below 0°C

$$Q = (C_s + C_i w)(\theta_1 - \theta_2) = [0.687 + 2.1(1.0)](10 - \theta_2)$$
$$Q = 2.787(10 - \theta_2) = 2.787(10 + T_2)$$

Above 0°C

$$Q = (C_s + C_i w)(\theta_1) + Lw + (C_s + C_w w)(-\theta_2)$$
$$Q = 27.87 + 333.7 + [0.687 + 4.2(1.0)]T_2 = 361.57 + 4.887T_2$$

T_2, °C	Q, J/g
-2	22.23
-0.319	26.92
-0	27.80
$+0$	361.57
$+10$	410.44

A comparison of the two curves (unfrozen-water model and simplified model) is shown in Fig. 2.36.

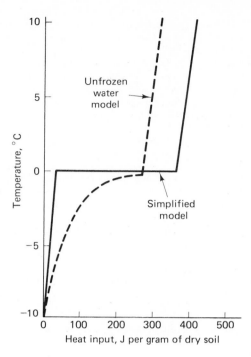

Figure 2.36 Solution to Example 2.3.

Example 2.4 Frozen Umiat bentonite at a construction site has a temperature close to $-10°C$. It is planned to raise the temperature of a soil volume 30 by 30 by 3 m deep to $+10°C$. How many kilowatthours of electric energy will be required? Assume that the soil dry density equals 800 kg/m³ and neglect all energy losses ($1 J = 2.778 \times 10^{-7}$ kWh).

SOLUTION From Example 2.2 obtain $Q = 317.3$ J/g. Compute the total $Q_{tot} = Q(\text{vol}) \rho_d$.

$$Q_{tot} = (317.3 \text{ J/g})(30)(30)(3 \text{ m}^3)(8 \times 10^5 \text{ g/m}^3)(2.778 \times 10^{-7} \text{ kWh/J})$$

$$= 190{,}380 \text{ kWh} = \text{required electric energy}$$

REFERENCES

Anderson, D. M. 1967. Ice Nucleation and the Substrate-Ice Interface, *Nature*, **216**: 563–566.
———— and N. R. Morgenstern. 1973. Physics, Chemistry, and Mechanics of Frozen Ground, *North Am. Contrib. 2d. Int. Conf. Permafrost, Yakutsk, U.S.S.R.*, National Academy of Sciences, Washington, pp. 257–288.
———— and A. R. Tice. 1973. The Unfrozen Interfacial Phase in Frozen Soil Water Systems, *Ecol. Stud.*, **4**: 107–125.
———— and ————. 1971. Low-Temperature Phases of Interfacial Water in Clay-Water Systems, *Soil Sci. Soc. Am. Proc.*, **35**(1): 47–54.

————, ————, and H. L. McKim. 1973. The Unfrozen Water and the Apparent Specific Heat Capacity of Frozen Soils, *North Am. Contrib. 2d Int. Conf. Permafrost, Yakutsk, U.S.S.R.,* National Academy of Sciences, Washington, pp. 289–295.

Arakawa, K. 1966. Theoretical Studies of Ice Segregation in Soil. *J. Glaciol.,* **6**(44): 255–260.

Banin, A., and D. M. Anderson. 1974. Effects of Salt Concentration Changes during Freezing on the Unfrozen Water Content of Porous Materials, *Water Resour. Res.,* **10**(1): 124–128.

Bauer, L. D., W. H. Gardner, and W. R. Gardner. 1972. "Soil Physics," 4th ed., Wiley, New York.

Bergen, A. T., and D. G. Fredlund. 1973. Characterization of Freeze-Thaw Effects on Subgrade Soils, *Proc. Symp. Frost Action Roads, Oslo,* pp. 169–172.

Beskow, G. 1935. Soil Freezing and Frost Heaving with Special Application to Roads and Railways, *Sver. Geol. Unders.,* ser. C, vol. 375, trans. J. O. Osterberg, Technical Institute, Northwestern Univ., Evanston, Ill., 1947.

Broms, B. B., and L. Y. C. Yao. 1964. Shear Strength of a Soil after Freezing and Thawing, *J. Soil Mech. Found. Div. Am. Soc. Civ. Eng.,* **90**(SM4): 1–26.

Casagrande, A. 1931. Discussion on "A New Theory of Frost Heaving," by A. C. Benkelman and F. R. Olmstead, *Highw. Res. Board Proc.,* **11**(1): 168–172.

————. 1938. Effects of Frost in Soils, *Perm. Int. Ass. Road Congr.* 1st and 2nd Sec., *8th Congr.* The Hague, 6th Quest., p. 10.

Chamberlain, E. J. 1973. A Model for Predicting the Influence of Closed System Freeze-Thaw on the Strength of Thawed soil, *Proc. Symp. Frost Action Roads, Oslo,* 94–97.

Cook, R. D. 1963. Some Effects of Closed-System Freeze-Thaw Cycles on a Compacted Highly Plastic Clay, M. S. thesis, Department of Civil Engineering, University of Alberta.

Corté, A. E. 1962. Vertical Migration of Particles in Front of a Moving Freezing Plane, *J. Geophys. Res.,* **67**: 1085–1090.

Crawford, C. B., and D. W. Boyd. 1956. Climate in Relation to Frost Action, *Highw. Res. Board Bull.* 111, NAS-NRC, Washington, pp. 63–75.

Culley, R. W. 1971. Effect of Freeze-Thaw Cycling on Stress-Strain Characteristics and Volume Change of a Till Subjected to Repetitive Loading, *Can. Geotech. J.,* **8**(3): 359–371.

Day, P. R., G. H. Bolt, and D. M. Anderson. 1967. The Nature of Soil Water, in R. M. Hagan, H. R. Haise, and T. W. Edminster (eds.), "Irrigation of Agricultural Lands," American Society of Agronomy, Madison, Wis.

DeVries, D. A. 1952. The Thermal Conductivity of Granular Materials. *Bull. Inst. Int. Froid Annexe,* 1952, p. 115.

Dillon, H. B., and O. B. Andersland. 1966. Predicting Unfrozen Water Contents in Frozen Soils, *Can. Geotech. J.,* **3**(2): 53–60.

Dolch, W. L. 1952. A Survey of Winter Weather: Indiana 1935–51, preliminary report, Purdue University, Lafayette, Ind.

Edlefson, N. E., and A. B. B. Anderson. 1943. Thermodynamics of Soil Moisture, *Hilgardia,* **15**: 31–268.

Eisenberg, D., and W. Kauzmann. 1969. "The Structure and Properties of Water," Oxford University Press, London.

Everett, D. H. 1961. The Thermodynamics of Frost Action in Porous Solids, *Trans. Faraday Soc.* **57**: 1541–1551.

———— and J. M. Haynes. 1965. Capillary Properties of Some Model Pore Systems with Reference to Frost Damage, RILEM Bull., n. s., **27**: 31–38.

Gold, L. W. 1957. A Possible Force Mechanism Associated with the Freezing of Water and Porous Materials, *Highw. Res. Board Bull.* 168, NAS-NRC, Washington, pp. 65–72.

Grim, R. E. 1953. "Clay Mineralogy," McGraw-Hill, New York.

Grimshaw, R. W. 1971. The Chemistry and Physics of Clays," 4th ed., Wiley-Interscience, New York.

Hamilton, A. B. 1966. Freezing Shrinkage in Compacted Clays, *Can. Geotech. J.,* **3**: 1–17.

Hansbo, S. 1960. Consolidation of Clay, with Special Reference to Influence of Vertical Sand Drains, *Swed. Geot. Inst. Proc.* 18.

Ho, D. M., M. E. Harr, and G. A. Leonards. 1970. Transient Temperature Distribution in Insulated Pavements: Predictions vs. Observations, *Can. Geotech. J.,* **7**: 275–284.

Hobbs, P. V. 1974. "The Physics of Ice," Clarendon Press, Oxford.

Hoekstra, P., E. Chamberlain, and A. Frate. 1965. Frost Heaving Pressures, *Highw. Res. Board Rec.* 101, NAS-NRC, Washington, pp. 28–38.

Holmes, J. W., S. A. Taylor, and S. J. Richards. 1967. Measurement of Soil Water, in R. M. Hagan, H. R. Haise, and T. W. Edminster (eds.), in "Irrigation of Agricultural Lands," American Society of Agronomy, Madison, Wis.

Jacobs, J. C. 1965. The Road Research Laboratory Frost Heave Test. *G.B. Dep. Sci. Ind. Res. Lab. Note* LN/765/JCJ.

Jessberger, H. L., and D. L. Carbee. 1970. Influence of Frost Action on the Bearing Capacity of Soils, *Highw. Res. Board Rec.* 304, NAS-NRC, Washington, pp. 14–26.

Johansson, S. 1914. Die Festigkeit der Bodenarten bei verschiedenem Wassergehalt, *Sver. Geol. Unders.*, ser. C, no. 256 (Aisbok 7, 1913).

Johnson, A. W. 1952. Frost Action in Roads and Airfields: A Review of the Literature, *Highw. Res. Board Spec. Rep.* 1, NAS-NRC, Washington.

Jumikis, A. R. 1956. The Soil Freezing Experiment, *Highw. Res. Board Bull.* 135, NAS-NRC, Washington, pp. 150–165.

Kaplar, C. W. 1971. Experiments to Simplify Frost Susceptibility Testing of Soils. *U.S. Army Corps Eng. Cold Reg. Res. Eng. Lab. Tech. Rep.* 223, Hanover, N.H.

————. 1974. Freezing Test for Evaluating Relative Frost Susceptibility of Various Soils, *U.S. Army Corps Eng. Cold Reg. Res. Eng. Lab. Tech. Rep.* 250, Hanover, N.H.

Koopmans, R. W. R., and R. D. Miller. 1966. Soil Freezing and Soil Water Characteristic Curves, *Soil Sci. Soc. Am. Proc.*, **30:** 680–685.

Lambe, T. W. 1951. "Soil Testing for Engineers," Wiley, New York.

Linell, K. A. 1953. Frost Design Criteria for Pavements in Soil Temperature and Ground Freezing, *Highw. Res. Board Bull.* 71, NAS-NRC, Washington, pp. 18–32.

———— and C. W. Kaplar. 1959. The Factor of Soil and Material Type in Frost Action, *Highw. Res. Board Bull.* 225, NAS-NRC, Washington, pp. 81–126.

———— and ————. 1963. Description and Classification of Frozen Soils, *Proc. 1st Int. Conf. Permafrost, Lafayette, Ind., NAS-NRC Publ.* 1287, pp. 481–486.

Lobacz, E. F., G. D. Gilman, and F. B. Hennion. 1973. Corps of Engineers' Design of Highway Pavements in Areas of Seasonal Frost, *Proc. Symp. Frost Action Roads, Oslo*, pp. 142–152.

Low, P. F., D. M. Anderson, and P. Hoekstra. 1968. Some Thermodynamic Relationships for Soils at or Below the Freezing Point; 1, Freezing Point Depression and Heat Capacity, *Water Resour. Res.*, **4:** 379–394 (also *U.S. Army Cold Reg. Res. Eng. Res. Rep.* 222, pt. 1, Hanover, N. H).

Mackay, J. R. 1972. The world of underground ice, *Ann. Ass. Am. Geogr.*, **62:** 1–22.

Martin, R. T. 1959. Rhythmic Ice Banding in Soil. *Highw. Res. Board Bull.* 218, NAS-NRC, Washington, pp. 11–23.

McRoberts, E. C., and N. R. Morgenstern. 1975. Pore Water Expulsion during Freezing, *Can. Geotechn. J.* **12**(1): 130–141.

Mikhailov, G. D., and G. P. Bredyuk. 1966. Shear Strength of Clayey Ground during Thawing. Materially VIII vsesoyuznogo mezhduvedom stennogo soveschaniya po Geokriologii (Merzlotovedeniya), *Akad. Nauk SSSR, Sibirskogoe otd. merzlotoved.* n. 5, pp. 51–60; draft *trans., U.S. Army Cold. Reg. Res. Eng. Trans.* 265, Hanover, N. H., 1971.

Miller, E. E., and A. Klute. 1967. The Dynamics of Soil Water, in R. M. Hagan, H. R. Haise, and T. W. Edminster (eds.), "Irrigation of Agricultural Lands," American Society of Agronomy, Madison, Wis.

Nakano, Y., and J. Brown. 1972. Mathematical Modeling and Validation of the Thermal Regimes in Tundra Soils, Barrow, Alaska, *Arct. Alp. Res.*, **4:** 19–38.

National Cooperative Highway Research Program, 1974. Roadway Design in Seasonal Frost Areas, *Natl. Coop. Highw. Res. Prog. Synth.* 26, Transportation Research Board, NAS-NRC, Washington.

Nordal, R. S. 1973. Frost Heave and Bearing Capacity during Spring Thaw at the Vormsund Test Road, *Proc. Symp. Frost Action Roads, Oslo*, pp. 159–163.

Penner, E. 1957. Soil Moisture Tension and Ice Segregation, *Highw. Res. Board Bull.* 168, NAS-NRC, Washington, pp. 50–64.

————. 1958. Pressures Developed: A Porous System as a Result of Ice Segregation, *Highw. Res. Board Spec. Rep.* 40, NAS-NRC, Washington, pp. 191–199.

————. 1960. The Importance of Freezing Rate in Frost Action in Soils, *Proc. ASTM*, **60:** 1151–1165.

————. 1966. Pressures Developed during Unidirectional Freezing of Water-saturated Porous Materials, *Proc. Int. Conf. Low Temp. Sci. Sapporo, Japan,* **1**(2): 1401-1412.

————. 1967. Heaving Pressures in Soil during Unidirectional Freezing. *Can. Geotech. J.,* **4**(4): 398–408.

————. 1968. Particle Size as a Basis for Predicting Frost Action in Soil, *Soil Found.,* **8**(4): 21–29.

————, G. H. Johnston, and L. E. Goodrich. 1974. Thermal Conductivity Laboratory Studies of Some Mackenzie Highway Soils, *Can. Geotech. J.,* **12**(3): 271–289.

Preus, C. K., and L. A. Tomes. 1959. Frost Action and Load Carrying Capacity Evaluation by Deflection Profiles, *Highw. Res. Board Bull.* 218, NAS-NRC, Washington, pp. 1–10.

Pusch, R. 1968. "A Technique for Investigation of Clay Microstructure," Rapp fr Byggforskningen, Stockholm.

————. 1970. Clay Microstructure, *Natl. Swed. Build. Res. Doc.* D8,

————. 1973. Influence of Organic Matter on the Geotechnical Properties of Clays, *Natl. Swed. Build. Res. Doc.* D11.

Rengmark, F. 1963. Highway Pavement Design in Frost Areas in Sweden, *Highw. Res. Board Bull.* 33, NAS-NRC, Washington, pp. 139–157.

Riis, J. 1948. Frost Damage to Roads in Denmark, *Proc. 2d Int. Conf. Soil Mech. Found. Eng., Rotterdam,* **2:** 287.

Rose, C. W. 1966. "Agricultural Physics," Pergamon, New York.

Sayman, W. C. 1955. Plate-bearing Study of Loss of Pavement Supporting Capacity Due to Frost, *Highw. Res. Board Bull.* 111, NAS-NRC, Washington, pp. 99–106.

Tice, A. R., C. M. Burrous, and D. M. Anderson. 1978. Determination of Unfrozen Water in Frozen Soil by Pulsed Nuclear Magnetic Resonance Proc. 3d Int. Conf. Permafrost, National Research Council of Canada, Ottawa, 1: 150–155.

Titov, V. P. 1965. Strength of Thawing Ground, Kom. po. zem. pol, Bor'ba s puchinami na zheleznykh; avtomobil'nykh doragakh pp. 178–183, draft trans. *U.S. Army Cold Reg. Res. Eng. Lab. Trans.* 156, Hanover, N. H., 1970.

Townsend, D. L., and T. I. Csathy. 1962. Pore Size and Field Frost Performance of Soils, *Highw. Res. Board Bull.* 331, NAS-NRC. Washington, pp. 67–80.

Tsytovich, N. A. 1945. On the Theory of the Equilibrium State of Water in Frozen Soils, Izv. AN SSSR, ser. Geogr., **9:** 5–6.

————. 1958. Bases and Foundations on Frozen Soil, *Highw. Res. Board Spec. Rep.* 58.

Turner, K. A. 1957. Loss and Recovery of Bearing Capacity of 30 New Jersey Soil Materials as Determined by Field CBR Tests 1954–5, *Highw. Res. Board Bull.* 168, NAS-NRC, Washington, pp. 9–49.

U.S. Corps of Engineers. 1953. The Unified Soil Classification System, Appendix B, Characteristics of Soil Groups Pertaining to Roads and Airfields, *U.S. Dep. Army, Waterw. Exp. Stn., Vicksburg, Miss., Tech. Mem.* 3–357, p. 3.

van Olphen, H. 1963. "Clay Colloid Chemistry," Interscience, New York.

Williams, P. J. 1964a. Specific Heat and Apparent Specific Heat of Frozen Soils, *Geotechnique,* **14**(2): 133–142.

————. 1964b. Unfrozen Water Content of Frozen Soils and Soil Moisture Suction, *Geotechnique,* **14**(3): 231–246.

————. 1972. Use of the Ice-Water Surface Tension Concept in Engineering Practice, *Highw. Res. Rec.* 393, NAS-NRC, Washington, pp. 19–29.

Winterkorn, H. F. 1955. Discussion of Suction Force on Soil upon Freezing, *Proc. Am. Soc. Civ. Eng.,* **81;** 6–9, sep. no. 656.

Wissa, A. E., and R. T. Martin. 1973. Frost Susceptibility of Massachusetts Soils: Evaluation of Rapid Frost-Susceptibility Tests, *M.I.T. Soils Publ.* 320.

————, ————, and D. Koutsoftas. 1972. Equipment for Measuring the Water Permeability as a Function of Degree of Saturation for Frost Susceptible soils, *M.I.T. Soils Publ.* 316.

THREE

GROUND THERMAL REGIME

R. L. Harlan and John F. Nixon

INTRODUCTION

The temperature at the surface of the earth is the upper condition affecting the ground thermal regime. The surface temperature, which varies spatially across the earth's surface and temporally from day to day, is largely governed by energy sources external to the solid earth, namely air temperatures and general weather conditions.

In permafrost, the temperature tends to vary seasonally with depth below the ground surface to a depth of 15 to 30 m. Below this depth, the temperature increases gradually under the geothermal heat flux. Seasonal variations in the temperature at the ground surface produce a temperature wave which propagates downward in the order of 15 m with a time lag increasing with depth below the ground surface. The depth below which the seasonal variation becomes small is referred to as the *level of zero annual amplitude* (Fig. 3.1). Below this depth, the influence of the annual air temperature cycle is not felt, and ground temperatures change only in response to long-term changes extending over many hundreds or thousands of years.

Each temperature change at the ground surface imposes a response which travels downward to a depth beneath the ground surface dependent on the time scale involved and on the thermal properties of the ground. In earth materials, heat may be transferred by conduction, radiation, and mass-transfer processes, i.e., convection. Of these heat-transfer mechanisms, radiative heat transfer is important only at temperatures greater than about 1000°C. Radiative heating and cooling, however, are of primary importance at the earth's surface. The relative importance of heat transfer by conduction and by convection as they

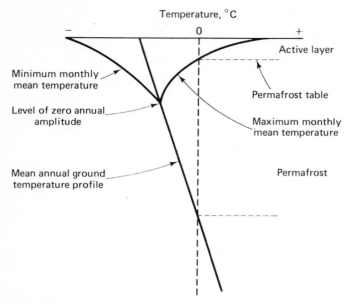

Figure 3.1 Idealized ground-temperature profile in permafrost terrain.

affect the ground thermal regime are discussed later in this chapter. When conduction is the predominant mechanism for heat transfer in cold regions, there are situations where heat transport associated with groundwater and surface-water bodies may have a significant or dominant effect on the ground thermal regime in general and on soil freezing and thawing in particular.

The presence or absence of permafrost in a given area depends solely on the persistence of ground temperatures below 0°C for 2 or more years. The temperature below which permafrost is said to exist is defined relative to the freezing point of pure water at standard atmospheric pressure. By definition, a soil is described as permafrost if it exists at a temperature below 0°C, irrespective of whether it is frozen or unfrozen. A soil, for example, may be partially frozen (containing various proportions of ice and water), unfrozen, or completely frozen.

In that the engineering properties of soil materials change dramatically on freezing or thawing, the ability to predict the depths of freeze and thaw with time as a result of imposed ground-surface-temperature conditions is an essential element of cold-region engineering. As an example, an increase in the ground surface temperature by a sufficient amount will result in an increase in the depth of seasonal thaw in an area underlain by permafrost. If ice-rich materials are thawed, catastrophic effects as a consequence of differential settlement or loss of strength may result. Such temperature changes occur naturally due to climatic change, forest fires, etc., resulting in the development of thermokarst lakes and landslides on slopes.

A decrease in the ground surface temperature may result in an opposite effect, namely an increase in the depth of freezing. A natural volume expansion as water contained in the soil pores freezes and an increase in potential for frost heaving are related to an increase in the depth of freezing.

From a geotechnical engineering viewpoint the depth to which freezing and thawing may occur in soils is important to the design of pavements, structures, and utilities in areas of seasonal frost as well as in permafrost. In this chapter, the fundamentals of heat transfer in soils are reviewed, some of the factors affecting the ground thermal regime are discussed, and methods are presented for predicting the depth of freeze and thaw in areas of seasonal freezing and in permafrost terrain.

3.1 FUNDAMENTALS OF HEAT TRANSFER

The transfer of thermal energy or heat in earth materials can occur by conduction, convection, and radiation. Of these only conduction and convection are of importance in most engineering applications. The relative importance of conduction and convection in heat-transfer problems depends on a number of factors, including the nature of the medium and its physical and thermal properties, the temperature of the medium and whether it is frozen or unfrozen, its porosity and permeability, and water content.

If the water present in a material is totally frozen, conduction will be the predominant mechanism for heat transfer and little opportunity will exist for mass transfer and associated convective heat transfer. If the material is unfrozen, however, an opportunity for convective heat transfer in association with mass transfer will exist.

Heat transfer due to both conduction and convection can also occur in partially frozen earth materials at temperatures close to 0°C, where both liquid water and ice coexist. In this case the heat-transfer process is complicated by an additional process. In a material where both ice and water coexist, water may migrate to the freezing front or zone under a potential gradient set up by the thermal or temperature gradient. This water migration to the cold side will continue as long as the potential gradient exceeds some critical value (the activation energy) provided that water is available. As a result, the material at or close to the freezing front may contain more ice than indicated by the total porosity of the soil at its original unfrozen state.

In the following sections, the mechanisms for heat transfer in earth materials are discussed, along with the basic thermal properties of soils and other construction materials used in engineering applications in cold regions.

Heat Conduction

The principal mechanism for heat transport in soils in most engineering applications involving freezing and thawing is conduction. Conduction is the transmission of heat by the passage of energy from particle to particle or through the soil pore fluids. Conduction, as such, is independent of mass-transfer processes.

Because conduction is the principal mode of heat transfer in soils, most analytical techniques developed for the prediction of rates and depths of freezing and thawing have been based on heat-conduction theory. Techniques have been developed whereby the effects of convection can also be accommodated in the application of the analytical techniques developed from conduction theory to problems also involving mass transfer. For example, where the direction of groundwater or soil-water flow is the same as the thermal gradient, an effective thermal conductivity can be used to augment conductive heat flow. The use of an effective or augmented thermal conductivity, however, requires knowledge of the direction and rate of mass transport.

The steady rate of heat transfer in a material by conduction is given by

$$Q_c = -k \frac{\Delta\theta}{\Delta x} A \tag{3.1}$$

where Q_c = heat flow per unit time, W†
k = thermal conductivity, W/m K
θ = temperature, K
x = distance, m
A = area, m^2

As shown by Eq. (3.1), heat transfer due to conduction is directly dependent on the thermal conductivity k of the medium and the thermal or temperature gradient, that is, $\Delta\theta/\Delta x$.

The direction of heat flow due to conduction is always in the direction of the lower temperature, i.e., from the warm to the cold side. The time rate of change of the heat content depends on the temperature differential in the direction of heat flow and on the thermal properties of the soil, as discussed in Sec. 3.4.

Convective Heat Transfer in Soil

Convection is defined as the transmission of heat by mass movement of the heated particles. In porous earth materials convection occurs both by the movement of water or other fluids contained in the soil pores and by the movement of air and other gases through the interconnected pore spaces.

The transport of water in unsaturated soil systems under the influence of a thermal gradient has been studied by Habib and Soeiro (1953) using radioactive tracers and by Gurr et al. (1952) using salt tracers. The results of these studies show that although some water circulation to the warm side by liquid diffusion does occur, the dominant transport mechanism under a thermal gradient at temperatures above 0°C is vapor diffusion to the cold side. Both studies further

† W = 1 J/S.

show that vapor transfer is important quantitatively only in situations where there is a net gain or loss of water from the system due to condensation or evaporation. In most field situations in which the thermal gradient normally lies in the range of 0.01 to 0.1°C/m, thermally affected water transport at temperatures above 0°C is small and may be neglected without appreciable error.

As thermally induced water transport in soils is generally smaller than that under hydraulic or suction gradients, the rate and direction of water movement is generally independent of the temperature field.

The steady-state heat flux per unit time due to convection, i.e., movement of the pore fluid, is given by

$$Q_{conv} = c_0 \rho_0 V_0 \frac{\Delta \theta}{\Delta x} A \qquad (3.2)$$

where Q_{conv} = convective heat flow per unit time, W/m
V_0 = fluid flow velocity in x direction, m/s
c_0 = specific heat of fluid, J/kg K
ρ_0 = density of fluid, kg/m^3

and θ, A, and x are as previously defined.

Heat transfer associated with groundwater flow The occurrence of groundwater in permafrost regions is not basically different from its occurrence in general except for several important modifications: (1) in frozen ground much of the water is rendered immobile on a short-term basis in the form of ice; (2) the characteristically low temperatures in permafrost regions reduce the rate of groundwater circulation by increasing the viscosity of water, commonly by a factor of 1.2 to 1.8 over that in more temperate regions; and (3) frozen ground provides an effective barrier to groundwater flow and significantly alters the nature of the groundwater flow patterns. In turn, the groundwater flow patterns may alter the occurrence and distribution of permafrost.

Van Orstrand (1934), among others, indicated that the transfer of heat by migrating water could cause significant variations in the thermal gradient within the earth depending on (1) the velocity and distribution of water movements, and (2) the thermal properties of the rock-soil-fluid complex. According to Lovering and Goode (1963), groundwater aquifers act as a heat sink, interrupting the flow of geothermal heat to the earth's surface and causing a slight cooling of the ground surface. Estimates suggest that as much as 15 percent of the geothermal heat flux can be redistributed in this way (Cartwright, 1971).

In permafrost regions, groundwater can significantly alter the ground thermal regime, as in nonpermafrost areas, through the redistribution of geothermal heat, which in turn can locally favor or prevent the formation and persistence of permafrost.

Stallman (1963) derived a general mathematical expression describing the simultaneous flow of heat and water in porous media and suggested that temperature measurements might provide an indirect measurement of ground-

Table 3.1 Augmentation of heat flow by ground-water movement in the direction of the thermal gradient between surfaces separated by 2.44 and 4.88 m with a temperature differential of 80°C (adapted from Lachenbruch, 1970)

Groundwater flow velocity		Convection + conduction	
		Conduction	
m/year	m/day	2.44 m	4.88 m
0.30	0.0008	1.05	1.1
1.52	0.0042	1.3	1.6
3.05	0.0084	1.6	3.2
6.10	0.0167	2.3	4.6
15.2	0.0418	5.0	10
30.4	0.0835	10	20
305.0	0.835	100	200
3050.0	8.35	1000	2000

water flow. Bredehoeft and Papadopulos (1965) provided a solution to Stallman's general equation for the one-dimensional steady-state case and a set of type curves that can be matched with an observed temperature profile in a drill hole to compute the rate of vertical groundwater flow.

Under isotropic and steady-state conditions with no groundwater flow, the thermal gradient increases linearly with depth. With the occurrence of ground-water flow the thermal profile with depth becomes convex upward or downward, depending on the direction of water movement. The resultant curvature of the thermal profile increases with increasing velocity of groundwater flow.

Table 3.1 illustrates the relative importance of convection and conduction where the groundwater flow is in the same direction as the thermal gradient, i.e., from the warm to the cold side. As convective heat transport amplifies the amount of heat transferred by conduction, this represents the worse case. The comparisons presented in Table 3.1 were derived assuming a temperature difference of 80°C over distances of 2.44 and 4.88 m.

Referring to Table 3.1, for a hydraulic gradient of 1 percent and for saturated hydraulic conductivities less than about 1 μm/s, the flow velocities would be less than 10 nm/s. As a result, the convective-heat-transfer component would be less than 5 and 10 percent of the total heat transfer if the temperature difference occurred over distances of 2.44 and 4.88 m, respectively. This example suggests that for the thermal conditions specified, the convective-heat-transfer component for soils finer than a fine sand subject to a 1 percent hydraulic gradient would be small compared with heat transfer by conduction.

Convective heat transfer during thaw settlement Whereas coarse-grained materials such as sand and gravel are normally stable when thawed, fine-grained silts and clays, which frequently contain excess ice, can be highly unstable. If thawing occurs slowly, the water generated on thawing (if not confined) will migrate from the thaw front at about the same rate at which it is produced. In this case, excess pore pressures will not be sustained, and settlement will proceed concurrently with thawing and at or close to the same rate.

If thawing occurs at a faster rate, however, excess pore pressures due to the self weight of the soil or a combination of self weight and an applied load can be generated. The upward redistribution of water during thaw settlement will tend to reduce the magnitude of the thermal gradient and also the temperature at the ground surface. Upward convective heat transfer during thaw settlement will tend to reduce the rate of thawing and the rate at which free water is generated. The effect of upward vertical water migration on the temperature profile during thaw settlement is illustrated by Fig. 3.2. The vertical flow velocities are shown in Table 3.2 for values of a calculation parameter β and the depth of thaw. The coefficient β is defined in the table.

Figure 3.3 shows the effect of a constant upward flow velocity on the thermal profile for three depths of thaw. As shown, the effect of convection on the thermal gradient becomes more pronounced with increase in thaw depth.

From a parametric study of the factors affecting thaw settlement, Nixon (1975) concluded that the effect of convective heat transfer in the thawed zone during thaw problems may be ignored in any practical analysis without incurring errors greater than 2 or 3 percent in the estimation of thaw rates. Similarly Charlwood and Svec (1972) concluded on the basis of a computer simulation study that convective heat transfer within the thaw bulb in typical hot-oil-pipeline situations is small compared with heat transfer by conduction and that it is reasonable to ignore convection in most practical thaw-depth calculations.

In summary, if the effect of upward water migration during thaw settlement is ignored, any resulting errors incurred would result in a slightly conservative

Table 3.2 Vertical fluid-flow velocities in meters per second as a function of β and depth of thaw L

$k = 0.84$ W/m K

	β				
L, m	0.5	1.0	2.0	5.0	10.0
0.01	1×10^{-5}	2×10^{-5}	4×10^{-5}	1×10^{-5}	2×10^{-5}
0.1	1×10^{-6}	2×10^{-6}	4×10^{-6}	1×10^{-6}	2×10^{-6}
1.0	1×10^{-7}	2×10^{-7}	4×10^{-7}	1×10^{-7}	2×10^{-7}
10	1×10^{-8}	2×10^{-8}	4×10^{-8}	1×10^{-8}	2×10^{-8}
100	1×10^{-9}	2×10^{-9}	4×10^{-9}	1×10^{-9}	2×10^{-9}

† $\beta = \dfrac{c_0 \rho_0}{k} V z L$

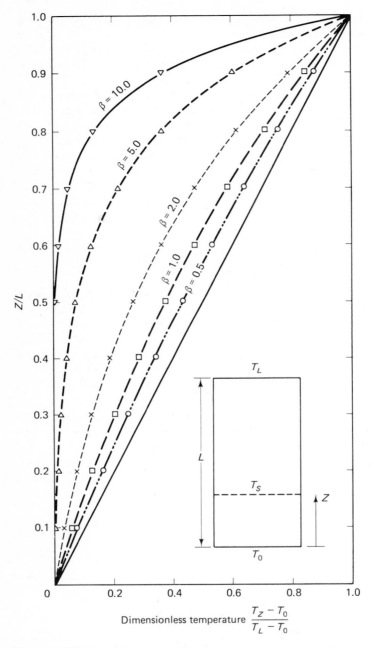

Figure 3.2 Effect of vertical water migration on the temperature profile during thaw settlement.

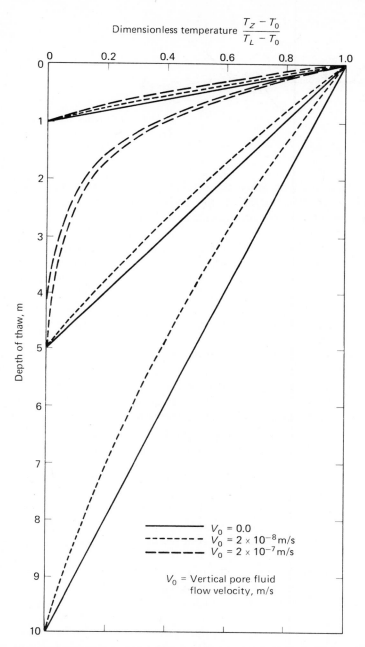

Figure 3.3 Effect of vertical water migration on the temperature profile during thaw settlement as related to depth of thaw.

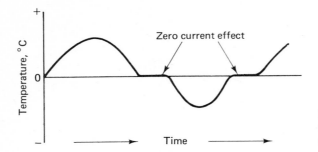

Figure 3.4 Ground temperature regime illustrating the zero curtain effect due to latent heat.

estimate of rates of thaw. Further, since the rate of upward seepage generally decreases as the depth of thaw increases, the consequences of ignoring the convective-heat-transport component also decrease with time.

Thermal effects of infiltration to thawed soils In only a few instances has the temperature of infiltrating water been reported to have a decided effect on the ground-temperature regime. For those few cases where an effect was reported, the observed changes in ground temperatures during or immediately following an infiltration event have been attributed to (1) increased evaporation from the soil surface, and/or (2) changes in the thermal conductivity and diffusivity of the soil due to an increase in water content.

With respect to the second point, infiltration and the resultant increase in water content results in an increase in the heat capacity of the soil; wet soils tend to warm up slower in the spring than drier soils. The latent heat also has a major effect on maintaining soil temperatures at or close to 0°C during cold periods and also causes a significant time lag in the spring relative to the warming up of the soil. In relation to the freezing and thawing of soils, this time lag has been referred to as the *zero curtain effect* and is illustrated in Fig. 3.4.

Effect of moisture migration to a freezing front In a freezing soil, the occurrence of water migration to the freezing front and the resultant occurrence of frost heave have a direct and pronounced effect on the ground thermal regime, particularly in relation to the rate of penetration of the freezing front. The occurrence of water migration to the freezing front increases the quantity of heat liberated on freezing, which must be removed in order for the freezing front to advance. It follows that the more intensive the migration of water to the freezing front, the more heat must be removed from the freezing plane.

Figure 3.5 illustrates the relative significance of heat transfer by conduction and by convection compared with the additional latent heat associated with the flux of water to a freezing front. The heat-flux rates as illustrated were calculated on the basis of a unit temperature gradient of 1°C/cm parallel to the direction of mass transfer. As shown, the rate of heat flux due to conduction alone is independent of mass transport. At the lower end of the range of mass fluxes shown, the convective-heat-transfer component is small compared with heat

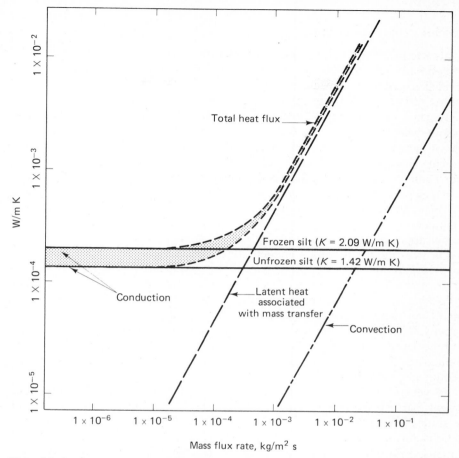

Figure 3.5 Comparison of the heat-transfer components due to conduction, convection, and latent heat associated with mass flux under a thermal gradient of 1°C/cm parallel to the direction of fluid flow.

transfer by conduction. At mass flux rates greater than about 5.0×10^{-4} kg/m^2 s, the latent heat component is small compared with heat transfer by conduction. At mass-flux rates greater than about 5.0×10^{-4} kg/m^2 s, however, the latent-heat component associated with mass transport becomes dominant. Whereas it may be reasonable to neglect convection per se, the additional latent-heat term must be considered in cases where the permeability of the soil and water availability are sufficient to sustain mass flow.

Under some situations the effect of ice-lensing and frost-heave phenomena can significantly delay the downward advancement of freezing, thereby affecting the trafficability of soils in winter. This has presented construction difficulties in relation to deep excavations in fine-grained soils where it was planned to allow natural freezing to occur and then excavate the frozen materials using heavy construction equipment.

Thermal Properties of Soils

In this section, the fundamental thermal properties of soils are defined. In addition, sufficient information on the thermal properties of different soils is provided to enable the reader to apply the various analytical methods for calculation of freezing and thawing to realistic sets of conditions.

Thermal conductivity k, which characterizes the ability of a material to transmit heat by conduction, is defined as the quantity of heat flow that will occur in unit time through a unit area of a substance under a unit temperature gradient. The thermal conductivity of a substance is independent of whether any fluids contained within the interstitial pores are in motion.

At temperatures above 0°C, the thermal conductivity of soils tends to increase with temperature. The temperature dependency of thermal conductivity for soils at temperatures above 0°C, however, is not pronounced and can be ignored without appreciable error in most engineering applications.

On freezing, the thermal conductivity of soil is highly dependent on water content and on the ice-water phase relationship. Whereas there is little change in the thermal conductivity on freezing of air-dry soils, the conductivity decreases on freezing at low water contents and increases at high. At a constant water content, an increase in the dry density results in an increase in thermal conductivity. The rate of increase is about the same at all water contents. For a constant density, an increase in water content results in an increase in thermal conductivity. This latter relationship applies to both frozen and unfrozen soils up to complete saturation.

In general, the thermal conductivity of soil depends on its density, water content, particle shape, temperature, solid, liquid, and vapor constituents, and the state of the pore water. Kersten (1949) has determined the thermal conductivity for a wide range of both frozen and unfrozen soils at differing water contents. From Kersten's basic work, the average thermal conductivities for frozen and unfrozen sandy soils, silt and clay soils, and for peat have been determined and are given as a function of water content and dry bulk density in Figs. 3.6 to 3.11.

The thermal conductivity and volumetric heat capacity for a number of common materials of particular relevance to cold-region engineering are given in Table 3.3.

The heat capacity c is defined as the quantity of heat required to raise the temperature of a given material by 1°C. When expressed on a per unit weight basis, this quantity of heat is referred to as the *specific heat capacity*, and when expressed on a unit volume basis, the quantity is known as the *volumetric heat capacity*.

For unfrozen soils, the heat capacity can be closely approximated by the sum of the products of the heat capacities for each soil constituent, i.e., soil particles, water, and air, and their respective weight fractions. When a change of phase is involved, however, the term specific heat capacity is no longer strictly applicable. In this case, as noted in Chap. 2, the alternate term apparent specific

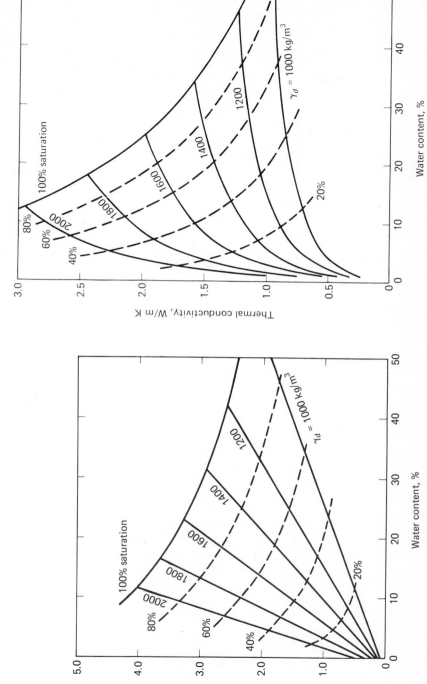

Figure 3.7 Average thermal conductivity for sandy soils as a function of water content and dry density, unfrozen.

Figure 3.6 Average thermal conductivity for sandy soils as a function of water content and dry density, frozen.

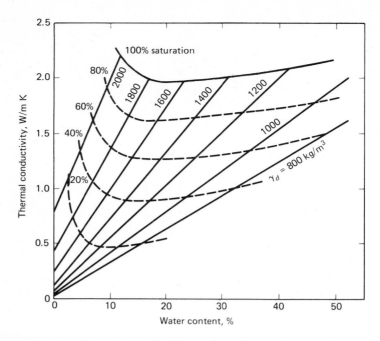

Figure 3.8 Average thermal conductivity for silt and clay soils as a function of water content and dry density, frozen.

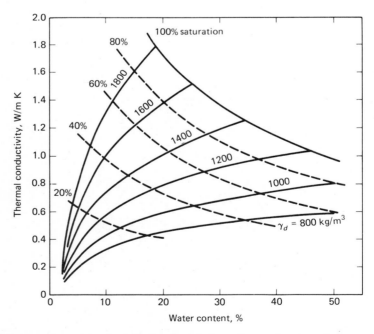

Figure 3.9 Average thermal conductivity for silt and clay soils as a function of water content and dry density, unfrozen.

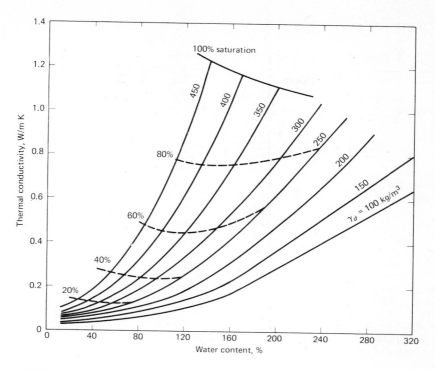

Figure 3.10 Average thermal conductivity for peat as a function of water content and dry density, frozen.

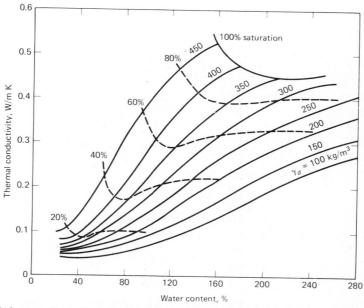

Figure 3.11 Average thermal conductivity for peat as a function of water content and dry bulk density, unfrozen.

Table 3.3 Thermal properties of common materials

Description	Thermal conductivity W/m K	Volumetric heat capacity MJ/m³ K
Water	0.602	4.18
Ice	2.22	1.93
Air	0.024	0.00126
Snow, fresh	0.105	0.209
drifted and compacted	0.335	0.419–0.628
Granite	2.51–2.93	2.30–2.68
Limestone	1.674–2.93	2.39–4.18
Dolomite	5.02	2.51
Sandstone	2.51	2.51
Shale	1.46	1.84
Asphalt paving	1.51	2.05
Glass	0.879	1.76
Concrete with sand and gravel or stone aggregate	0.920	2.18
Steel	46.0	3.89
Wood (softwood)	0.126–0.230	0.502–0.544
Synthetic insulations e.g., polystyrene	0.029–0.063	0.0586
Sawdust	0.084	†

† Calculated from heat capacity of wood reduced by the ratio of the density of sawdust to the density of wood.

heat capacity is used; it is given by the sum of the products of the heat capacity of each soil constituent and its respective weight fraction plus an additional term incorporating the latent heat involved in the ice-water phase transformation. This relationship (Hoekstra, 1969) for the apparent specific heat capacity is given by

$$c = c_s x_s + c_i x_i + c_u x_u + c_a x_a + \frac{1}{\Delta\theta} \int_{\theta}^{\theta+\Delta\theta} L \frac{\partial w_u}{\partial \theta} d\theta \qquad (3.3)$$

where c_s, c_i, c_u, c_a = heat capacity of soil, ice, unfrozen water, and air phases, respectively

x_s, x_i, x_u, x_a = corresponding weight fractions

L = latent heat of fusion of ice

θ = temperature

w_u = unfrozen water content by dry weight

As water in soil exists at an energy state less than that of pure water in bulk, its latent heat is less than that of bulk water at atmospheric pressure. Anderson et al. (1973) found that the dependence of latent heat on the unfrozen water content is significant only for temperatures below about $-20°C$ and can be neglected for most engineering applications.

Anderson et al. (1973) calculated the apparent specific heat capacities as a function of temperature for six soils at each of three water contents using a functional relationship identical to that given in Eq. (3.3). The curves depicting the cumulative heat absorbed in bringing each of the six soils from $-10°C$ through the melting point were computed and presented in graphical form. These curves were presented in Fig. 2.35 (see also Table 2.6).

Referring to Fig. 2.35, as the soil becomes coarser, a greater proportion of the latent heat associated with the ice-water transformation is absorbed at temperatures closer to $0°C$, the normal freezing point of water. Further, in sands and gravels practically all the water contained in the interstitial pores freezes or melts at temperatures very close to $0°C$.

The volumetric heat capacity c of a soil is (as previously defined) the quantity of heat required to change the temperature of a unit volume by $1°C$. For dry soils, the volumetric heat capacity is given by

$$c = c_1 \gamma_d \tag{3.4}$$

where c = volumetric heat capacity
c_1 = specific heat capacity
γ_d = dry unit weight of soil

The specific heat capacity of soil grains usually lies between 0.17 and 0.2; an average value of 0.18 is adopted below.

The volumetric heat capacity for moist unfrozen soils is given by

$$c_u = \frac{\gamma_d}{\gamma_w} \left(0.18 + 1.0 \frac{w}{100}\right) c_w \tag{3.5}$$

where c_w is the volumetric heat capacity of water, and for moist frozen soils by

$$c_f = \frac{\gamma_d}{\gamma_w} \left(0.18 + 0.5 \frac{w}{100}\right) c_w \tag{3.6}$$

where w is the water content of the soil expressed in percent of dry weight. An average value for the volumetric heat capacity for partially frozen soils is given by

$$c_{av} = \frac{\gamma_d}{\gamma_w} \left(0.18 + 0.75 \frac{w}{100}\right) c_w \tag{3.7}$$

The thermal diffusivity α is defined as the rise in temperature per unit volume produced by a given quantity of heat and is proportional to the thermal conductivity k and inversely proportional to the volumetric heat capacity c:

$$\alpha = \frac{k}{c} \tag{3.8}$$

The thermal diffusivity provides, in effect, an index of the rate at which a material will undergo a temperature change in response to external temperature changes.

For some problems, the diffusivity of frozen or unfrozen soils may be considered as constant, although significant variation with temperature may occur close to the melting point.

The thermal resistance R is defined as the reciprocal of the time rate of heat flow through a unit area of a layer of given thickness per unit temperature difference, i.e.,

$$\text{Thermal resistance} = \frac{\text{temperature difference}}{\text{heat flow}} \tag{3.9}$$

3.2 TEMPERATURE CONDITIONS AT THE GROUND SURFACE

Permafrost is defined on the basis of the persistence of ground temperature below 0°C for 2 or more years. Technically, a soil is described as in permafrost whether it is frozen, partially frozen, or unfrozen. By definition, the presence of ice is not essential for permafrost. As already pointed out, however, with the occurrence of freezing or thawing, the mechanical properties of soil change significantly, as do the thermal properties. The thermal conductivity of ice is approximately 4 times that of water. Further, because the thermal diffusivity of ice is of the order of 8 times that of water, transient temperature disturbances are propagated more quickly in frozen than unfrozen soil.

The ground thermal regime reflects the temperature pattern existing within a body in relation to seasonal variations at the boundaries. The prediction of changes in the ground thermal regime in response to changes in conditions at the boundaries must be based on a knowledge of the physical and thermal properties of the soil profile, the existing or prevailing thermal regime, and the nature and duration of the boundary conditions causing a change in the thermal regime.

In this section, the factors affecting the temperature conditions at the ground surface are discussed. The concept of indexes to define surface boundary conditions for use in thermal calculations is also discussed.

The difference between the mean annual air and ground-surface temperature and variations in this difference spatially are caused by climatic factors other than air temperature in combination with surface and subsurface terrain factors. This complex energy-exchange regime at the ground surface, which is influenced by this combination of factors, is such that the mean annual ground temperature is several degrees warmer than the mean annual air temperature (Brown, 1963b). In this perspective, the mean ground surface temperature in permafrost terrain can vary at any given depth within a region of only a few square kilometers due to variations in surface cover, ground type, moisture conditions, geological structure, or geothermal gradient.

Energy Balance at the Ground Surface

In its simplest form, the annual heat exchange at the earth's surface is given by

$$R + LE + P + B = 0 \tag{3.10}$$

where R = annual radiation balance (net radiation)
LE = heat evolved in evaporation, including evapotranspiration, minus condensation
P = heat involved in conduction-convection (turbulent heat exchange)
B = thermal heat flux at ground surface

The contribution of each of these components to heat-transfer mechanisms operating between the soil surface and the atmosphere is modified by properties of vegetation as well as other factors at the ground surface (Brown, 1963a).

Of the factors affecting the heat exchange at the earth's surface, radiation is the most important. The radiation balance consists of two radiation streams of different spectral ranges. According to Geiger (1965), there is a short-wavelength part during the daytime as long as the sun shines. Radiation reaching the surface of the earth consists of that part of the direct solar radiation which is not reflected by clouds, absorbed by the atmosphere, or scattered diffusely and also that part of the nondirectional sky radiation which represents diffusely scattered radiation reaching the ground and providing daylight within the visible spectrum.

Part of the radiation reaching the ground surface is reflected back into the earth's atmosphere. The amount of incoming radiation that is reflected depends on the nature of the ground surface. The ratio of reflected to the incident radiation is referred to as the *reflection factor* or *albedo*.

Whereas the incoming long-wave radiation is of little or no significance in the radiation balance of the earth, it is of importance in the radiation balance of the ground surface. The earth's atmosphere contains water vapor, carbon dioxide, and ozone, all of which absorb radiation and themselves radiate. This long-wave atmospheric radiation is termed *counterradiation* since it counteracts the terrestrial radiation loss from the surface of the earth (Geiger, 1965).

Because of the complexity of the radiation balance at the ground surface, the difficulty of measurement of the individual components, and the paucity of continuing observations in most permafrost areas in Alaska and Canada, the occurrence of permafrost has been related to air temperatures rather than to the energy balance at the ground surface. In this perspective, climate is basic to permafrost formation and is a most important factor influencing its existence. Of all the climatic factors, air temperature is most readily measured and most directly related to ground-heat loss and gain, i.e., to the energy balance of the ground surface (Brown, 1963b). Observations in Canada and other countries indicate a broad relationship between mean annual air and ground temperatures in permafrost regions. Brown (1963b) has pointed out that the mean annual ground temperature differs from the mean annual air temperature by several degrees and this difference is not constant. For this reason precise prediction of the distribution of permafrost cannot be based solely on air temperature.

Relationship between Mean Air and Mean Ground Surface Temperatures

The relationship between the mean annual air temperature and the mean ground surface temperature is highly complex and to a large degree inadequately defined. It is known, for example, that local spatial variations in the surface temperature exist over short distances due to differences in vegetation, microclimate, snow cover, slope orientation, and surface and subsurface drainage. These local variations in the surface temperature give rise to lateral heat flow, which further tends to mask the spatial variability. The mean annual ground surface temperature varies on different terrain types in response to differences in soil-moisture conditions, albedo, etc. Peatlands, for example, tend to be several degrees cooler than adjacent areas where mineral soil is exposed at the ground surface. Differences in the duration and depth of snow cover and received solar radiation between north- and south-facing slopes will similarly cause local spatial variation in the mean ground surface temperature. These local variations are particularly important near the margins of the areas of permafrost occurrence, i.e., areas where the mean ground surface temperature is close to 0°C, giving rise to areas of discontinuous permafrost.

The difference between mean annual air and ground temperatures is explained in part by the fact that the ground surface is heated by solar radiation during the day to a much higher temperature than the air above it. This excess heat more than balances the cooling of the ground surface by radiation during the night.

If the mean annual surface temperature were constant for an extended period of time, the temperature would increase with depth below the maximum depth of the annual wave at a rate dependent only on the heat flux from the earth's interior and the thermal conductivity of the ground. This relatively simple picture is complicated by the effects of changes in the ground surface temperature in the past. The rate of increase of temperatures with depth within the ground profile, i.e., the geothermal gradient, retains a memory of past changes to greater or lesser amounts due to the relatively low thermal conductivity of earth materials and the thermal inertia of the system.

In areas where the mean surface temperature is below 0°C, the increase in temperatures with depth will result in the temperature's rising to 0°C at a depth which defines the thickness of the permafrost. This base of the permafrost, if several hundred meters below the ground surface, may be in equilibrium with the mean annual ground surface temperature of several thousand years ago (Judge, 1973*b*). In this perspective, if the existing climatic conditions prevail long enough, the permafrost will degrade or aggrade in response to the existing conditions. These changes occur gradually over a period of many hundreds of years. It should be realized that small changes in the annual range of surface temperatures and the mean annual temperature from year to year may result in layers of ground which are at temperatures above 0°C below the active layer. Such conditions are not stable in the long run.

Effect of vegetative cover Vegetation exerts both an indirect influence on the mean ground surface temperature and on permafrost by modifying climatic and other terrain features, which themselves influence the distribution of permafrost, and a direct influence by its role in the heat-transfer mechanisms between the ground and the atmosphere (Brown, 1963*a*). The influence of vegetation on microclimate, drainage and soil-water conditions, snow accumulation, and the influence of one vegetation type on another are important considerations in assessing the ground thermal regime. These features are so closely interrelated that it is difficult to assess their individual contributions.

Vegetation directly influences the occurrence of permafrost by its thermal characteristics, which determine the quantity of heat that enters and leaves the surface of the underlying ground. In this respect, the components of the energy balance at the ground surface and contribution of each are modified by the surface vegetative cover. For example, vegetation decreases air-current velocities within the strata and thereby impedes heat radiation from the soil to the air. Wind velocities are lower in areas of tall, dense tree growth, resulting in less heat loss than in areas of sparse tree growth. For this reason, in the southern fringe of the permafrost region, permafrost is more commonly associated with areas of sparse or no tree growth because of the possibility of slightly lower air temperatures in these areas due to higher wind velocities.

Effect of disturbance The effects of disturbance of the surface organic layer and the removal of the vegetative cover in permafrost terrain, whether it is related to natural causes such as fire or to human disturbance, are similar and depend on the nature and degree of the disturbance. The effects of surface disturbance on the depth of the active layer and permafrost degradation have been studied by Bliss and Wein (1971), Brown et al. (1969), Heginbottom (1971, 1973), Linell (1973), and Mackay (1970), among others.

The removal of the tree cover, e.g., on a road, utility, or pipeline right-of-way, generally results in a deepening of the active layer after clearing. The magnitude of the effect of the disturbance on thaw depth will depend on the degree and nature of the disturbance and on the prevailing climatic conditions. In the more northerly latitudes permafrost regression is generally small.

For example, in the Mackenzie Delta–Tuktoyaktuk Peninsula areas, observations on cut lines dating back to 1965 through black spruce and tall willow shrubs indicate that the thickness of the active layer has increased 16 to 27 cm over control plots located in black spruce and 12 to 18 cm over control plots located in the willows (Bliss and Wein, 1971). Heginbottom (1971) reported that following a forest fire in the Inuvik, N.W.T., area in 1968, the maximum depth of the active layer increased about 9 cm more in the first year in areas that were intensively burned over than in unburned areas. Heginbottom has further reported that the median depth of thaw during the first summer following the fire was of the order of 22 cm greater in areas that were disturbed by a bulldozer cutting firelines than in adjacent undisturbed areas. In August 1970, 2 years after the fire, the difference in the depth of active layer was 86 cm between the disturbed and undisturbed areas.

At the Inuvik Experimental Farm in the Mackenzie Delta area, the removal of the native spruce-birch vegetation and cultivation increased the depth of thaw from 36 to 147 cm during the first two summers following clearing and cultivation. The depth of thaw stabilized after 6 years at about 183 cm (Mackay, 1970; Nowosai, 1963).

In contrast to the more northerly latitudes within the continuous permafrost zone, in the discontinuous permafrost zone the removal of the tree and brush cover can lead to significant degradation of the permafrost within a few years. The more rapid rates of permafrost degradation, however, are usually associated with low-ice-content materials. Test drilling along the Canol Road, which is located in the central Mackenzie Valley near the settlement of Norman Wells, N.W.T., for example, has shown the permafrost immediately beneath the road to have degraded to a considerable depth or entirely since the early 1950s (Heginbottom and Kurfurst, 1973; Isaacs, 1973). The original thickness of the permafrost was of the order of 60 m.

A long-term study of the effects of climatic and near-surface conditions on ground temperatures was initiated in 1946 near Fairbanks, Alas., by the U.S. Army Corps of Engineers. As part of this study, three 61-m-square test sections were established. One of these sections, the natural tree-covered section, has remained free from permafrost degradation over a 26-year observation period. In both the cleared and stripped sections permafrost degradation is still continuing after 26 years though at a distinctly slower rate in the area that was only cleared. After 26 years the depth of thaw beneath the undisturbed section has remained stable at about 0.8 m. Beneath the cleared section the depth of thaw is 4.4 m and still increasing, whereas beneath the stripped section the depth of thaw is 6.7 m and still increasing.

On the basis of these results, Linell (1973) concluded that under climatic and environmental conditions similar to those in Fairbanks, the maintenance or reestablishment of a random mixed type of low vegetative cover cannot be counted on to stop or prevent permafrost degradation in an area subject to surface disturbance.

Effect of snow cover Thanks to its low thermal conductivity, snow acts as an insulating layer and inhibits both frost penetration during the winter and thaw in the spring. Snow cover also reduces the amount of solar radiation received at the ground surface, thus affecting the differences between the mean annual air and ground surface temperatures. In forested areas, the snow cover tends to remain on the ground longer than in open areas, thereby retarding the thaw of the underlying soil.

Where strong winds prevail, more snow tends to accumulate under a low vegetative cover than in open areas. In isolated open areas in tall vegetation, e.g., a cut line through a heavily treed area, snow can drift and inhibit freezeback in winter. The fact that snow tends to accumulate in certain areas also results in increased soil-moisture levels in summer, contributing to lower summer ground temperatures (Brown, 1963a). In general, the difference between the mean annual air and mean annual ground surface temperatures is greatest in areas where snowfall and accumulation are greatest.

In freeze-thaw computations, the effect of the snow cover can be treated as a layer in the solution of multilayered problems with the thickness of the snow cover being estimated on a seasonal basis from historical observations of snowfall. It can also be approximated by the use of a heat-transfer coefficient h_s, where

$$h_s = \frac{k_s}{H_s} \tag{3.11}$$

and k_s and H_s are the average snow conductivity and thickness, respectively, through the winter season. The surface boundary condition then becomes

$$Q = h_s(T_a - T_s) \tag{3.12}$$

where Q is the ground heat flux and T_a and T_s are the ambient and soil surface temperatures, respectively.

Influence of terrain and other climatic factors Terrain has a pronounced influence on microclimatic conditions, which in turn influence the ground-surface-temperature regime. For example, downslope drainage of cold air at night from an elevated area into a depression is a microclimatic feature directly associated with relief which may have a significant effect. Even microrelief features such as peat plateaus may produce sufficient differences in elevation to cause downslope air drainage at night (Brown, 1963a). Another terrain factor of significance is related to aspect. North-facing slopes, for instance, receive less direct solar radiation than south-facing slopes. Drainage, a factor that can be related to different terrains, also has a significant influence on the ground thermal regime. For example, ground that permits the greatest degree of water penetration usually thaws to the greatest depth.

Influence of surface water bodies Measurements relating to the effect of a lake on the thermal regime of the Mackenzie River delta have been made by Brewer (1958) and Johnston and Brown (1964), among others. Their observations show that the presence of a lake or other surface water body in a permafrost environment causes the formation and maintenance of a deep thaw zone under the water body. They further note that the thawing effect of the lake is confined to the ground lying under the lake, as evidenced by the presence of permafrost at the shoreline. Ground temperatures measured inland from the shore of the lake show that the thermal influence of the lake extends for some distance beyond its perimeter.

Along the Alaskan arctic coastal plain, permafrost temperatures below shallow lakes are 0 to 3°C higher than those under the surrounding tundra, depending on the size and depth of the lake. Lakes 2 to 3 m deep do not freeze to the bottom, and consequently an unfrozen zone, or *talik*, exists beneath the lake. The depth of the unfrozen basin beneath a lake varies according to the size of the lake, depth, and long-term average annual temperature of the water (Brewer, 1958). Since shallow bodies of water, for example, 0.6 to 1 m deep, generally freeze to the bottom in winter, permafrost will normally exist directly beneath them.

Brown et al. (1964) presented a comparison of observed and calculated ground temperatures and the distribution of permafrost under a lake. Although there were some uncertainties in the definition of ground surface and water-temperature boundary conditions, they obtained results which were in reasonable agreement with observed conditions.

Lachenbruch (1957) studied the effect of the ocean on the temperature and distribution of permafrost. On the basis of theoretical considerations, Lachenbruch concluded that along the arctic coast of the North American mainland, a few hundred meters offshore, permafrost is not expected to occur at depths below the sea bottom greater than 60 to 90 m unless the shoreline has undergone large transgressions in the last few thousand years. He further concluded that if the shoreline has been stationary or regressing, permafrost depths are not expected to exceed 30 m at points more than 300 to 600 m offshore.

MacCarthy (1953) observed that on the Alaskan arctic coast the depth of permafrost increases inland from the coastline, from 200 m at a distance of 122 m inland to 319 m at a distance of 12.9 km. At a distance of 119 m offshore, the depth of permafrost estimated from temperature observations was approximately 122 m.

Freezing and Thawing Indexes

The depth of freezing and thawing depends in part on the magnitude and duration of the temperature differential below or above freezing (0°C), respectively, at the ground surface. The magnitude of the temperature differential is normally expressed as the number of degrees the air or ground surface temperature is above (positive) or below (negative) 0°C, and the duration is expressed in days. The freezing or thawing index is therefore given by the summation of the degree-days for a freezing or thawing season (U.S. Department of the Army, 1966).

For a given day, the degree-days are directly equivalent to the mean daily

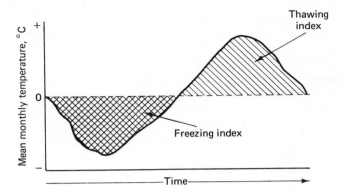

Figure 3.12 Ground-surface-temperature regime showing freezing and thawing indexes.

temperature expressed in degrees Celsius. In most situations the mean daily temperature is approximated by the mean of the maximum daily and minimum daily temperatures. Where an average daily temperature based on observed hourly temperatures would provide a more accurate value, such precision is usually not required for freeze-thaw computations.

For most applications the freezing and/or thawing indexes can be calculated by determining the area between the average monthly temperature curve and the 0°C line and time taken over the appropriate season. The area can be determined by planimeter or by a simple approximation. The concept of freezing and thawing indexes is illustrated by Fig. 3.12. The freezing index is represented by the area of the temperature-time curve as defined by that period when temperatures are below the 0°C line. In simple terms, the freezing index is the yearly sum of the differences between 0°C and the daily mean temperature of the days with means below 0°C (Brown, 1960). The thawing index, on the other hand, is represented by the area defined by that region lying above the 0°C line and that portion of the temperature-time curve where temperatures are above 0°C. The thawing index is therefore the yearly sum of the differences between 0°C and the daily mean temperature of the days with means above 0°C.

Since air-temperature data are routinely collected at most meteorological stations and surface temperatures are not, a correlation between these two is required to define the thermal boundary condition at the ground surface. We have already noted that a simple relationship between air and ground surface temperatures universally applicable under different climatic and surface conditions does not exist. The relationship between the two, however, is influenced by latitude, cloud cover, time of year, time of day, atmospheric conditions, wind speed, surface characteristics, and subsurface thermal properties.

The ratio of the surface index to the corresponding air-temperature index has been designated for analysis purposes as the *n factor*. To directly determine the *n* factor for a specific location would require the concurrent measurement of the air and surface temperatures throughout a number of complete freezing and thawing seasons. As these types of measurements are rarely available, several general relationships have been developed for both freezing and thawing situations.

In general for freezing conditions (U.S. Department of the Army, 1966):

1. The n factor increases with increase in latitude.
2. Snow-covered surfaces reflect a larger portion of incoming solar radiation with resultant higher surface freezing indexes.
3. The effect of turf and/or organic surface cover on the heat-flow processes at the air-ground interface is variable. Similarly the influence of wind, rainfall, evaporation, etc., is variable and difficult to evaluate.

On the basis of their observations and studies, the U.S. Department of the Army (1966) has suggested the following n factors for use under freezing conditions in the absence of specific measurements at the site of interest.

Surface type	Freezing ✻ n factor
Snow	1.0
Pavement free of snow cover	0.9
Sand and gravel	0.9
Turf	0.5

← For thawing

For thawing conditions, an n factor of 1.0 is suggested for turf surfaces and an n factor of 1.5 to 2.0 for sand and gravel surfaces.

Design freezing and thawing indexes For design purposes, the design freezing (or thawing) index is defined as the average air-freezing (or thawing) index for the three coldest winters (or warmest summers) in the latest 30 years of record. In situations where 30 years of record are not available, the air-freezing (or thawing) index for the coldest winter (or warmest summer) in the latest 10-year period may be used (U.S. Department of the Army, 1966).

Surface-temperature variations Both air and ground surface temperatures exhibit daily and annual variations due to climatic factors, as we have seen. In order to facilitate the mathematical solution of heat-transfer problems, the surface temperature is generally assumed to vary in a manner that can be approximated by a simple mathematical expression. Two of the commonly assumed temperature fluctuations correspond to (1) a step change in surface temperature and (2) a sinusoidal change in surface temperature. The value of a step or constant change in surface temperature can be calculated by dividing the thaw (freezing) index

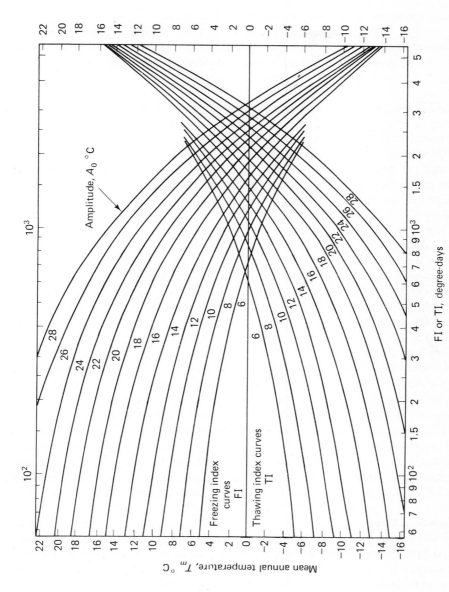

Figure 3.13 Indexes and equivalent sinusoidal temperature; $T_m = [(-FI + TI)/365]°C$

129

by the length of the thawing (freezing) season. The latter, namely a sinusoidal variation in surface temperature over an annual cycle, provides a good approximation of actual conditions for most situations.

The relationship between sinusoidal amplitude, freezing index, thawing index, and average annual temperature is shown in Fig. 3.13. The graph provides a convenient method for determining the mean and amplitude of a sinusoidal temperature variation when the freezing and thawing indexes are given.

3.3 GEOTHERMAL GRADIENT AND HEAT FLUX

The geothermal gradient is defined as the change in temperature of the earth with depth and is usually expressed either in degrees per unit depth or in units of depth per degree. The geothermal heat flux, which is effectively the product of the geothermal gradient and the corresponding thermal conductivity of the earth materials at depth, provides the basal boundary condition to practically all thermal calculations related to the ground-temperature regime.

The "normal" geothermal heat flux is of the order of 0.046 W/m^2, which is associated with a "normal" geothermal gradient of about 15°C/km. The geothermal gradient varies spatially in response to the thermal properties of the rock strata at depth and to external influences. Published terrestrial heat-flow values, corrected for the effects of the Pleistocene ice sheets, range between 0.025 and 0.054 with a mean of 0.042 ± 0.008 W/m^2 for the Canadian shield. Values for the Great Plains and the cordillera of western Canada vary from 0.067 to 0.084 W/m^2. Values from maritime Canada range between 0.042 and 0.071 W/m^2 (Judge, 1973a).

On the basis of analytical studies Lachenbruch (1957) found that the effect of the ocean on the geothermal gradients could be very great near the shorelines in cold regions and suggested that the effects should be taken into account in studies of the outward flow of heat from the earth in such places.

The presence of groundwater flow within an area provides an effective mechanism for the redistribution of geothermal heat. In this context, groundwater acts as a heat sink; e.g., in areas of downward groundwater flow or recharge the geothermal heat flux to the ground surface tends to be reduced by its redistribution of groundwater flow. In groundwater discharge areas, the opposite is true, i.e., the normal geothermal heat flux is augmented by the heat carried by the upward groundwater flow.

With regard to the definition of the basal boundary conditions in thermal calculations, several comments are appropriate here. The use of a specified temperature boundary condition in problems not involving a relatively short period of real time can lead to erroneous results if caution is not observed because the temperatures are forcing functions and force the temperatures to satisfy the solution. The use of a flux boundary condition on the basal boundary of the computational domain tends to preserve the cause-effect relationship between heat flux and temperatures.

3.4 THERMAL ANALYSIS

Having established the dominant mode of heat transfer in the soil and estimated values for the thermal properties of the soil, we turn our attention to obtaining a solution to the thermal problem of interest. The previous two subsections described the upper (ground surface) thermal boundary condition and the lower thermal condition (geothermal gradient) necessary to solve a heat-transfer problem within the region of interest. Initial temperatures are also required if a transient (time-dependent) problem is being formulated.

For most engineering applications, conduction is the dominant mode of heat transfer, and the governing equation of heat transfer assuming no phase change is

$$\frac{\partial \theta}{\partial t} = \kappa \frac{\partial^2 \theta}{\partial z^2} \qquad (3.13)$$

where θ = temperature
  z = depth
  t = time
  κ = thermal diffusivity = k/c

where k and c are the thermal conductivity and volumetric heat capacity, respectively.

Equation (3.13) is applicable to heat-flow problems in one dimension, z. When two dimensions x and z are involved, the governing equation becomes

$$\frac{\partial \theta}{\partial t} = \kappa \left(\frac{\partial^2 \theta}{\partial z^2} + \frac{\partial^2 \theta}{\partial x^2} \right) \qquad (3.14)$$

If, for example, a frozen and thawed layer are in contact, two equations of the type (3.13) would be required to describe the system, one each for the frozen and the thawed layer.

Steady-State Conditions

If the boundary conditions remain unchanged for a long time, the temperature distribution within a body of soil will tend toward some steady, unchanging value. The governing equation can be obtained from Eq. (3.13) or (3.14) by setting the rate of change of temperature with time equal to zero; that is, $\partial \theta / \partial t = 0$. For a one-dimensional steady-state problem Eq. (3.13) becomes

$$\frac{\partial^2 \theta}{\partial z^2} = 0 \qquad (3.15)$$

Equation (3.15) can be integrated directly to give the linear temperature profile

$$\theta = Az + B \qquad (3.16)$$

where A and B are constants obtained from the two boundary conditions at the upper and lower boundaries. In two dimensions, the governing equation is obtained by setting the left-hand side of Eq. (3.14) to zero, obtaining the well-known Laplace equation

$$\frac{\partial^2\theta}{\partial z^2} + \frac{\partial^2\theta}{\partial x^2} = 0 \tag{3.17}$$

The same equation describes steady-state fluid flow in porous media. A variety of mathematical and graphical methods of solving this equation have been developed depending on the boundary conditions. For example, it is common practice in geotechnical engineering to draw a flow net to obtain a solution for hydraulic flow in soils.

The solutions to some problems can be written down to obtain the steady temperature beneath heated or cooled areas on the ground surface. The temperature distribution near the junction between an infinitely wide heated area and a colder area is similar to that presented by Brown (1963) and is

$$T - T_g = \frac{T_s - T_g}{\pi} \tan^{-1} \frac{z}{x} \tag{3.18}$$

where T = desired temperature
T_g = mean ground surface temperature outside heated or cooled area
T_s = temperature of heated or cooled area

This solution is shown graphically in Fig. 3.14a. The effect of a geothermal gradient G in degrees Celsius per meter is obtained by superposition, and the solution is

$$T - T_g = \frac{T_s - T_g}{\pi} \tan^{-1} \frac{z}{x} + Gz \qquad \text{for } x > 0 \tag{3.19}$$

which is shown in Fig. 3.14b.

For a long, linear strip on the ground surface, of width $2a$, the temperature field can be written

$$T - T_g = \frac{T_s - T_g}{\pi} \left[\tan^{-1}\left(\frac{z}{x-a}\right) - \tan^{-1}\left(\frac{z}{x+a}\right) \right] + Gz \qquad \text{for } x > 0 \quad (3.20)$$

$$\text{and} \quad T = T_s + \frac{T_s - T_g}{\pi} \left[\tan^{-1}\left(\frac{z}{x-a}\right) - \tan^{-1}\left(\frac{z}{x+a}\right) \right] + Gz$$

$$\text{for } 0 < x < a \quad (3.21)$$

A typical example of this solution is given in Fig. 3.14c.

These solutions are extremely useful in estimating the temperature regime beneath roads, rivers, and heated or cooled structures on frozen or unfrozen ground. If the position of a thaw boundary is the primary concern, the above solutions can be rearranged to give the equation of the thaw boundary.

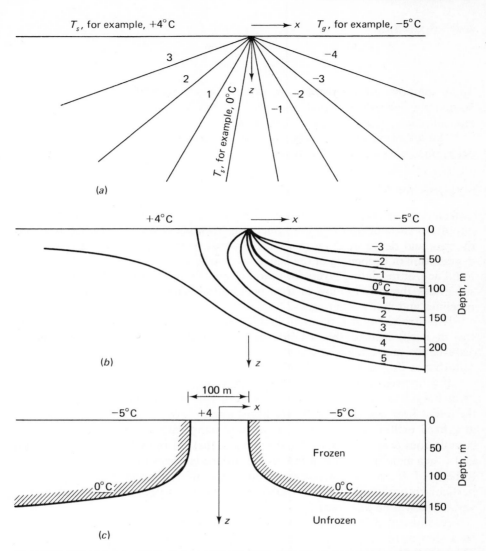

Figure 3.14 Temperature distributions for heated or cooled areas: (*a*) temperature distribution near an infinitely wide heated area, $G = 0$; (*b*) temperature distribution as above with $G = 1°C$ per 30 m; (*c*) permafrost profile, $G = 1°C$ per 30 m, $a = 50$ m.

For example, the depth of thaw beneath the centerline of a heated strip area with zero geothermal gradient can be obtained by rearranging Eq. (3.21) with $x = 0$ and $T = T_f$, giving

$$\frac{z}{a} = \tan\left[\frac{\pi}{2}\frac{T_s - T_f}{T_s - T_g}\right] \tag{3.22}$$

In no case can the depth z exceed the maximum possible depth of permafrost, which is given by

$$z_{max} = \frac{T_f - T_g}{G} \tag{3.23}$$

These solutions are often useful in predicting the maximum extent of thaw in permafrost beneath a heated area (or conversely, maximum frost penetration into unfrozen ground beneath a chilled area).

The following section deals with the rate at which melting or freezing may occur once a disturbance has taken place.

Solutions for Melting or Freezing in Soils

Calculations of the rate of freezing or thawing constitute one of the most important parts of cold-region engineering. Such solutions are required to define the rate and depth of thaw in the permafrost active layer, rates of permafrost degradation or deepening of the active layer following disturbance, depth of thaw in fill and/or insulating layers for road and pad design, depth of frost in highway subgrades, the rates of thaw or frost penetration beneath warm or chilled buried pipelines and many other areas.

It is stressed that a thermal solution for thawing or freezing is seldom an end in itself; instead the solution is an indicator of the extent of thermal disturbance and an aid to solving geotechnical problems resulting from the disturbance (for example, see Chap. 4).

If a homogeneous mass of frozen soil is subjected to a temperature above its melting point at the surface, a thaw front will advance into the soil. Whether the latent heat associated with the transformation of ice into water is liberated at a fixed melting point or over a range of temperatures, certain mathematical complexities arise. Assuming for the present that all the latent heat is liberated at 0°C in a melting soil, the nature of the surface-temperature application remains to be fixed. If a sudden step increase in temperature is applied at the surface, a particularly useful solution is available. Some time-dependent surface-temperature variations will be discussed later.

As illustrated in Fig. 3.15, a uniform homogeneous frozen soil is subjected to a step increase in temperature from T_g in the ground to T_s at the surface. The properties of the frozen and thawed regions are assumed to be homogeneous and independent of temperature. The solution for the advance of the thaw front and the associated temperature fields was derived by Neumann about 1860 and is given by Carslaw and Jaeger (1947). The movement of the interface between the thawed and frozen zones is given by

$$X = \alpha t^{1/2} \tag{3.24}$$

where X is the depth of thaw and α is a constant which is determined as a root of the transcendental equation

$$\frac{e^{-\alpha^2/4\kappa_u}}{\text{erf}\,[\alpha/2(\kappa_u)^{1/2}]} - \frac{T_g k_f}{T_s k_u}\left(\frac{\kappa_u}{\kappa_f}\right)^{1/2} \frac{e^{-\alpha^2/4\kappa_f}}{\text{erfc}\,[\alpha/2(\kappa_f)^{1/2}]} = \frac{L\pi^{1/2}\alpha}{2(\kappa_u)^{1/2}c_u T_s} \tag{3.25}$$

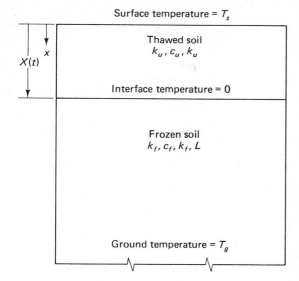

Figure 3.15 The Neumann problem. (*After Nixon and McRoberts, 1973.*)

where erf [ ] = error function

erfc [ ] = $1 - $ erf [ ]

κ_u, κ_f = diffusivities of unfrozen and frozen soil, m²/s

k_u, k_f = thermal conductivities of unfrozen and frozen soil, W/m K

c_u, c_f = volumetric heat capacities of unfrozen and frozen soil, J/m³ K

L = volumetric latent heat of soil, J/m³

T_g = (uniform) initial ground temperature, °C below freezing

T_s = applied constant surface temperature, °C

As the diffusivity of a zone is simply the conductivity divided by the volumetric heat capacity for that zone, α is defined as a function of seven variables:

$$\alpha = f(k_u, k_f, c_u, c_f, T_g, T_s, L)$$

The relative importance of these seven factors will be examined later.

As shown by Nixon and McRoberts (1973), Eq. (3.25) can be rewritten so that only three dimensionless variables remain:

$$\frac{\alpha}{2(\kappa_u)^{1/2}} = f\left\{ \text{Ste}, \left[-\frac{T_g}{T_s} \frac{k_f}{k_u} \left(\frac{\kappa_u}{\kappa_f} \right)^{1/2} \right], \left(\frac{\kappa_u}{\kappa_f} \right)^{1/2} \right\} \qquad (3.26)$$

Ste is the Stefan number, defined as the ratio of sensible heat to latent heat by

$$\text{Ste} = \frac{c_u T_s}{L} \qquad (3.27)$$

The results are almost totally independent of the ratio $(\kappa_u/\kappa_f)^{1/2}$. The results for the normalized thaw rate $\alpha/2(\kappa_u)^{1/2}$ are presented in Fig. 3.16 as a function

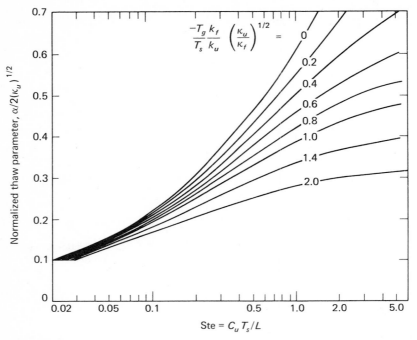

Figure 3.16 Graphical solution of the Neumann equation. (*After Nixon and McRoberts, 1973.*)

of the two significant variables

$$\text{Ste} \qquad \text{and} \qquad -\frac{T_g}{T_s}\frac{k_f}{k_u}\left(\frac{\kappa_u}{\kappa_f}\right)^{1/2}$$

This chart represents a complete and accurate solution to the Neumann problem with no assumptions other than those inherent in the original formulation. The range of the parameter

$$-\frac{T_g}{T_s}\frac{k_f}{k_u}\left(\frac{\kappa_u}{\kappa_f}\right)^{1/2}$$

shown in Fig. 3.16 is extreme. It usually lies between 0.0 and 0.4.

When the ground temperature is close to the melting point, the thaw parameter α may be approximated to high accuracy by

$$\frac{\alpha}{2(\kappa_u)^{1/2}} = \frac{(\text{Ste})^{1/2}}{2}\left(1 - \frac{\text{Ste}}{8}\right) \tag{3.28}$$

If a linear temperature distribution is assumed in the thawed zone and the temperature profile in the frozen zone is ignored, we obtain (Stefan, 1890):

$$X = \left(\frac{2k_u T_s}{L} t\right)^{1/2} = \alpha t^{1/2} \tag{3.29}$$

The solution to the Neumann equation is presented in chart form in Fig. 3.16, and the α value can be extracted from it with a high degree of accuracy. If the ground temperatures are close to the melting point, the simple solutions given by Eq. (3.28) or (3.29) can be used to predict α, the relationship between depth of thaw and the square root of time.

It may often be necessary to investigate the velocity of a thaw front caused by surface-temperature variations other than the step increase in temperature. Finite-difference methods, discussed later, may be employed quite easily to solve the heat-conduction equation for arbitrary surface-temperature variations, but an approximate method can be used as follows. From Eq. (3.29) note that the product of T_s and t is part of the square root. For this problem the product of T_s and t represents the surface thawing index in degree-days. For any problem having variable surface temperatures, Eq. (3.29) can be rewritten

$$X = \left(\frac{2k_u I_{th}}{L}\right)^{1/2} \tag{3.30}$$

where I_{th} is the surface thaw index.

All the above solutions apply equally to freezing problems, provided the thermal properties for frozen and thawed soils are interchanged. The simplifications introduced by various authors suggest that some thermal properties may influence the thaw rate more than others. For instance, the Stefan solution in Eq. (3.29) depends only on k_u, L, and T_s. Parametric studies conducted by Nixon and McRoberts (1973) have indicated that k_u, L, and T_s are the most important variables in solutions for thaw depth.

As the latent heat and thermal conductivity both depend on the water content of a soil, it is a dominant parameter in thermal calculations. As has been shown, the thermal conductivity and volumetric specific heats of both thawed and frozen saturated soils can be expressed as functions of the water content. At temperatures below 0°C, some water exists in the liquid state. The volume of unfrozen water is the unfrozen water content w_u and for convenience is expressed as a fraction of the total water content w.

The volumetric latent heat of the soil L has a dominant role in thermal calculations and represents on a volume basis the amount of heat that must be supplied to a soil below 0°C to change ice into water. Problems arise in defining the value of L to be used. First, at the temperature T_g applicable in a problem, the unfrozen water content must be known. Second, the effect of a gradual change of state of ice to water over the range T_g to 0°C must be considered.

The first approach that can be taken is to calculate the amount of ice per unit volume once the appropriate $W_u = w_u/w$ is known; i.e.,

$$L = \gamma_d w(1 - W_u)L' \tag{3.31}$$

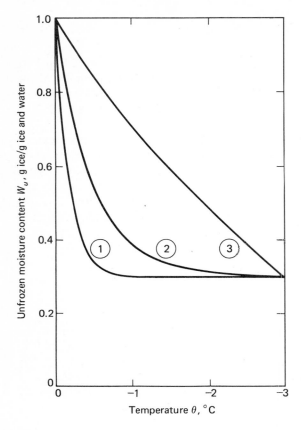

Figure 3.17 Unfrozen-moisture-content curves used in numerical analysis. (*After Nixon and McRoberts, 1973.*)

where L is the latent heat of water ($=333 \times 10^3$ J/kg) and γ_d is the dry density of soil. The rate of thaw can then be calculated from the Neumann formulation by using the total water content w to define k_u, c_u, and c_f and taking k_f equal to a constant value. This approach has the effect of lumping the total latent heat at 0°C. Implicit is that all the ice initially present in a unit volume of soil at T_g melts at 0°C rather than over the range T_g to 0°C.

The effect of different unfrozen moisture-content–temperature relationships, given in Fig. 3.17, on the movement of the 0°C isotherm has been studied by Nixon and McRoberts (1973). The equations of heat conduction were solved using a finite-difference technique discussed later in this section.

The movement of the 0°C isotherm was plotted against the square root of time in Fig. 3.18 for the three relationships of Fig. 3.17. Other parameters for the example chosen are included in Fig. 3.18. A linear relationship between the depth to the 0°C isotherm and square root of time was always obtained, and so an α value could always be extracted from the results. Figure 3.19 also compares the calculated α values with a Neumann solution where the latent heat L is calculated by Eq. (3.31) and lumped at 0°C. A Neumann solution based on

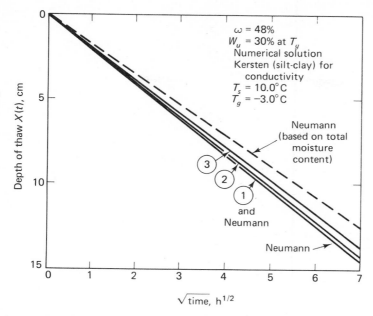

Figure 3.18 Effect of unfrozen-moisture-content curve on depth of thaw penetration. (*After Nixon and McRoberts, 1973.*)

the assumption that $W_u = 0$ at T_g is also included and shown by the dotted line in Fig. 3.19.

It may be thought that the Neumann approach in dealing with the unfrozen moisture content relationship will underestimate the rate of thaw. This is true only if it is erroneously assumed that $W_u = 0$. It can be seen that the rate of thaw obtained by the Neumann analysis actually overestimates by an insignificant amount the α value calculated when the melting range is accounted for.

Although there is little deviation in the rate of movement of the 0°C isotherm, the temperature distributions in the frozen zone are affected by the temperature-dependent relationship. Temperature distributions for problems solved in Fig. 3.18 are presented in Fig. 3.19. It can be concluded then that the solution obtained by lumping L as defined by Eq. (3.31) is a satisfactory solution to rate-of-thaw problems. Ignoring temperature-dependent latent heat effects introduces insignificant errors and furthermore is a conservative assumption for thaw depth in soils.

Practical Extensions to the Stefan and Neumann Solutions

In order to apply the approach developed to field problems involving the thawing of frozen soils under a prescribed surface-temperature variation, some other difficulties may have to be resolved which could cause deviations from the solutions already obtained. Some are considered below.

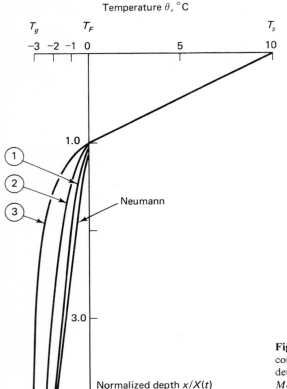

Figure 3.19 Effect of unfrozen-moisture-content curve on temperature distribution; details as in Fig. 3.18. (*After Nixon and McRoberts, 1973.*)

Presence of a surficial layer of different thermal properties Consider the case of a surficial layer of height H and thermal conductivity k_1 overlying an infinite depth of soil with properties k_2 and L_2 (Fig. 3.20). If we ignore the temperature distribution in the frozen soil, the time to thaw the overlying layer completely due to the application of a step increase in surface temperature is

$$t_0 = \frac{H^2 L_1}{2k_1 T_s} \tag{3.32}$$

since

$$\alpha = \left(\frac{2k_1 T_s}{L_1}\right)^{1/2}$$

from the Stefan solution for layer 1.

When the depth of thaw X becomes greater than H, two layers of different thermal properties coexist in the thawed zone. Assuming, for consistency with the Stefan solution, that the temperature distribution in each layer is linear, we can derive a simple solution for the rate of thaw in the underlying layer. The heat balance relationships are as follows:

at $x = H$:
$$k_1 \frac{\partial \theta_1}{\partial x} = k_2 \frac{\partial \theta_2}{\partial x} \tag{3.33}$$

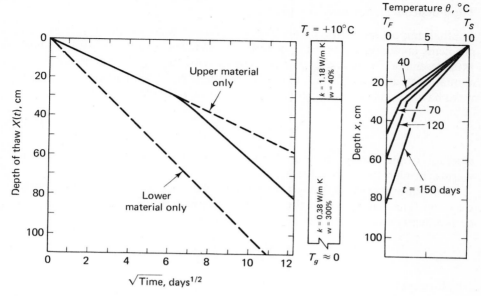

Figure 3.20 Thawing in a two-layer system. (*After Nixon and McRoberts, 1973.*)

and at $x = X(t)$:
$$-k_s \frac{\partial \theta_2}{\partial x} = L_2 \frac{dx}{dt} \tag{3.34}$$

where $\partial \theta_1 / \partial x$ and $\partial \theta_2 / \partial x$ are the temperature gradients in layers 1 and 2, respectively. This leads eventually to the depth of thaw

$$X = \left[\left(\frac{k_2}{k_1} H \right)^2 + \frac{2k_2 T_s(t - t_0)}{L_2} \right]^{1/2} - \left(\frac{k_2}{k_1} - 1 \right) H \tag{3.35}$$

and the interface temperature between the two layers $T_1(t)$ is

$$T_1 = \frac{T_s}{1 - [H/(H - X)]k_2/k_1} \tag{3.36}$$

The melting temperature is always taken to be zero.

A sample solution is included in Fig. 3.20 for the case of a peat layer overlying a fine-grained soil of 40 percent moisture content. The thaw rate through the lower material only is shown as a dotted line. At longer periods the thaw rate becomes parallel to the thaw rate for the two-layer system. The results of the simplified solution were checked rigorously by a finite-difference solution, and the results were found to be in good agreement. Linear temperature profiles were maintained in each layer throughout the thawing process. The analysis can also be applied to calculating rates of thaw in the underlying soil when the surficial layer is dry or without latent heat, as might be the case with materials such as gravel or synthetic insulation.

Time-dependent Surface Temperature

Another important series of problems becomes apparent when solving field problems involving the thawing of soils in which the surface temperature bears little resemblance to a constant or step increase in surface temperature. The annual fluctuations in surface temperature can often be approximated by a sine wave having a mean temperature of T_g, and an amplitude of A_0, that is,

$$T_s = T_g + A_0 \sin \frac{2\pi t}{365} \tag{3.37}$$

where t is time in days, measured from the time when the surface temperature warms through its mean value T_g.

The thaw index is defined as the number of degrees above freezing integrated over the time during which the surface is above freezing. The time when the surface temperature increases above zero is given by

$$t_0 = \frac{365}{2\pi} \sin^{-1} \frac{T_f - T_g}{A_0} \tag{3.38}$$

which is approximately equal to

$$t_0 = \frac{365(T_f - T_g)}{2\pi A_0} \tag{3.39}$$

The thaw index up to any time t during the thaw season is defined as

$$I_{th} = \int_{t_0}^{t} (T_s - T_f)\, dt$$

$$= \int_{t_0}^{t} \left(T_g - T_f + A_0 \sin\frac{2\pi t}{365} \right) dt \tag{3.40}$$

On integration this yields

$$I_{th} = (T_g - T_f)(t - t_0) - \frac{365 A_0}{2\pi} \left(\cos\frac{2\pi t}{365} - \cos\frac{2\pi t_0}{365} \right) \qquad \text{for } t > t_0 \tag{3.41}$$

Equation (3.41) together with Eq. (3.39) can be substituted in the simple Stefan equation (3.30) to obtain a solution for the depth of thaw resulting from a surface-temperature sine wave. A sample calculation using this technique is plotted in Fig. 3.21. The surface sine wave has a mean of $-4°C$ and an amplitude of $18°C$. This is typical of an undisturbed tundra site within the continuous permafrost zone. A single homogeneous soil layer of 40 percent moisture content and an unfrozen water content of 5 percent by dry weight is assumed. The thermal properties calculated from Kersten's (1949) data are also shown.

It is interesting to compare the thaw depth-time curve resulting from the surface sine wave with that calculated using an equivalent constant surface temperature. The equivalent constant surface temperature may be defined as the

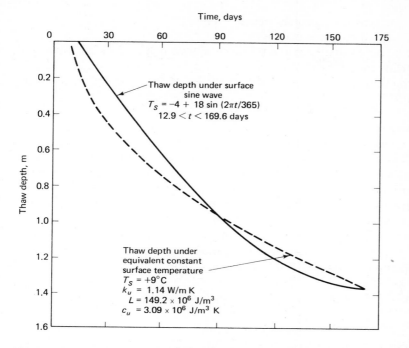

Figure 3.21 Solution for thaw depth under sinusoidal and equivalent constant surface temperatures. A more accurate solution would be obtained by multiplying both the above solutions by $1 - Ste/8$.

final thaw index divided by the length of the thaw season. The last day of the thaw season t_f can be calculated from

$$t_f = \frac{365}{2} - t_0$$

The length of the thaw season is

$$t_f - t_0 = \frac{365}{2} - 2t_0$$

If we use the above value of t_f to calculate the final thaw index, the equivalent surface temperature can be calculated. The results of a simple calculation using the same thermal properties as above and the calculated equivalent constant surface temperature ($T_s = 9.0°C$) are shown also in Fig. 3.21. Clearly, the final thaw depth in each case will be the same since the thaw indexes have the same value. The rates of thaw during the thaw season are significantly different, however, and appear to be somewhat faster in the latter part of the thaw season. This may become important when considering thaw consolidation or shallow-slope stability.

It should be noted that both the solutions shown in Fig. 3.21 are based on the simple Stefan equations (3.29) and (3.30) and the accuracy of both may be improved by multiplying by the correction factor $1 - \text{Ste}/8$, which for the problem considered is 0.977.

Surface-temperature sine wave with no phase change in the soil Although a solution for thawing resulting from a sine variation in surface temperature is available as long as the surface temperature remains above 0°C, it is not simple to predict the thermal behavior analytically during the remainder of the temperature cycle. In situations where the surface material subjected to freezing and thawing cycles has a low moisture content and is not involved in significant ice-water phase change, a very useful solution becomes available. This solution is applied to dry fill overlying permanently frozen ground. The procedure provides an estimate of the fill thickness required for permafrost protection.

The temperature variation T with depth and time is given by

$$\frac{T - T_g}{A_0} = \exp\left[-x\left(\frac{\pi}{365\kappa}\right)^{1/2}\right] \sin\left[\frac{2\pi t}{365} - x\left(\frac{\pi}{365\kappa}\right)^{1/2}\right] \qquad (3.42)$$

where κ is the thermal diffusivity in square meters or square centimeters per day.

If it is desired to limit the maximum value of T at some depth, $x = X$, to 0°C, the term involving the sine function is set equal to 1 (its maximum possible value) and T is set equal to zero. Hence, we obtain

$$\frac{-T_g}{A_0} = \exp\left[-x\left(\frac{\pi}{365\kappa}\right)^{1/2}\right]$$

or

$$X = -\left(\frac{365\kappa}{\pi}\right)^{1/2} \ln\frac{-T_g}{A_0} \qquad (3.43)$$

This relationship provides an estimate of the thickness of dry fill required to offer complete permafrost protection, and is shown in Sec. 3.5 for comparison purposes with later problems where insulation is involved. Equation (3.43) predicts large fill thicknesses in warmer permafrost areas, where the ratio T_g/A_0 is small.

In conclusion, for problems involving the thaw of a frozen soil, the dominant variables are the ground surface temperature, the thermal properties of the thawed soil, and the total quantity of water that changes state in a unit volume of soil. The thermal properties of the frozen zone play a secondary role in the computation of thaw rates.

In soils, thaw occurs over a range of temperatures, and the depth to the 0°C isotherm is proportional to the square root of time for the boundary conditions of the Neumann problem. Moreover, there are no significant differences in the rates of thaw α calculated by assuming that all ice involved in the change of state melts at 0°C or by accounting for the melting range of ice in soil. In fact the melting range retards the propagation of a 0°C isotherm rather than accelerating it. If the rate of thaw is the primary concern, a precise determination of the unfrozen-water-content–temperature curve is considered unnecessary in a thawing problem provided that the correct quantity of water changing state is used in the analysis. If the temperature distribution in the freezing zone is important, the actual shape of the unfrozen-water-content–temperature curve must be accounted for.

Melting or Freezing around Pipes

An important class of problems that occurs commonly in cold regions involves freezing or thawing around buried utility lines and pipelines. The simplest approximate solution for thaw (or freezing) around a buried pipe is based on the assumption of a steady-state temperature distribution within the thawed (inner) annulus and ignores the temperature distribution outside the circular thaw zone. This solution is modified from that given by Carslaw and Jaeger (1947), and the radius of the circular thaw bulb is given by

$$2\bar{R}^2 \ln \bar{R} - \bar{R}^2 + 1 = \frac{4k_u(T_s - T_f)t}{r_0^2 L} \tag{3.44}$$

where $\bar{R} = R/r_0$ is the dimensionless thaw radius and r_0 is the pipe radius. The left-hand side of Eq. (3.44) is shown plotted as a function of $\bar{R}$ in Fig. 3.22. Once the right-hand side of Eq. (3.44) is evaluated, Fig. 3.22 can be used to obtain the radius of the thaw bulb for any time t. This solution assumes that the ground surface has no effect on the progression of the thaw (or frost) bulb and is equivalent to assuming that the pipe is buried infinitely deep. This involves some error when the pipe is located close to the ground surface but is a useful approximation for thaw depth below the pipe centerline.

Based on work by Pekeris and Slichter (1939), a better approximation for the thaw radius to account for a nonsteady temperature distribution in the thawed (inner) zone is given by

$$R_1 = R_0(1 - 0.12 \text{ Ste})^{1/2} \tag{3.45}$$

where R_0 is the initial approximation of the thaw radius from Fig. 3.22 and R_1 is a solution of improved accuracy.

If insulation of thickness d and conductivity k_I surrounds the pipe, the dimensionless thaw radius $\bar{R}$ can be derived:

$$2\bar{R}^2 \ln \bar{R} - \bar{R} + 1 + \frac{4\pi k_u}{C_I}\bar{R}^2 = \frac{4k_u(T_s - T_f)t}{r_0^2 L} \tag{3.46}$$

where

$$C_I = \frac{2\pi k_I}{\ln [r_0/(r_0 - d)]}$$

and r_0 is the outer radius of the insulated pipe.

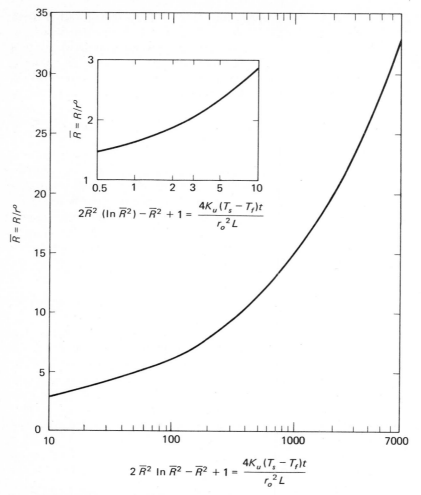

Figure 3.22 Solution for radial thawing around a long cylinder of radius r_0. To obtain a more accurate solution multiply the calculated radius R by $(1 - 0.12 \, \text{Ste})^{1/2}$.

For small values of $\bar{R}$ (less than a few pipe diameters) the actual thaw radius is approximated by

$$R = \left\{ \frac{2 k_I \, T_s t / L}{\ln \left[r_0 / (r_0 - d) \right]} + r_0^2 \right\}^{1/2} \tag{3.47}$$

Solutions (3.46) and (3.47) should each be modified by the correction given by Eq. (3.45).

The above solutions ignore the presence of the ground surface in thaw-depth calculations. The simple solutions presented here tend to overestimate thaw depth and therefore, are conservative. Clearly, if the problem warrants improved accuracy, two-dimensional numerical methods can be programmed for a digital computer. More complex approximate analytical solutions that account for the presence of the ground surface have been derived by Thornton (1976) and Hwang (1977).

The problem of preventing freeze-up in water or sewer lines buried in unfrozen soil is best treated using the same method as that used for providing frost protection for frost-susceptible subgrades using fill and/or insulation. These are considered in the next section. Once a thickness of insulation and/or fill is estimated to prevent the frost line from passing through the insulation, the insulation is usually continued for one to two pipe diameters on both sides.

Numerical Methods

Temperature and spatially dependent thermal properties, varying surface conditions, and complex geometrical shapes introduce difficulties that are not readily solvable using approximate hand-calculation methods. In such cases, numerical methods must be employed to obtain a solution. It is beyond the scope of this chapter to provide details of numerical schemes that have been successfully used for problems involving heat transfer with change of state. Such techniques are generally classed as finite-difference or finite-element methods. The reader is referred to Lachenbruch (1970), Hwang et al. (1972), Gold et al. (1972), Jahns et al. (1973), and Goodrich (1974) for descriptions and details of such numerical schemes and solution methods.

The region under consideration is subdivided into a number of elements, or grid points. The heat flow through each element at a given time is approximated by a linear equation. The set of linear equations is then solved simultaneously. The solution is then advanced to the next time step. The resulting accuracy can be of a high order, provided restrictions on element size, time step, and numerical accuracy are observed. The conditions at the boundary of the selected region can be specified temperatures, heat flux, or combinations of both.

To provide an insight into methods of numerical analysis for geothermal problems, a relatively simple finite-difference technique is considered below. It is based on a technique published by Ho et al. (1970) and is valid for one-dimensional heat transfer with phase change and variable thermal properties. The method handles the phase change in an efficient manner but suffers from the disadvantage that the size of the time increment must be restricted.

The thermal equilibrium for a layer j can be written

$$\Delta Q_j = Q_{j+1, j} - Q_{j, j-1} + Q_{wj} \tag{3.48}$$

where ΔQ_j = change of heat at layer j
$Q_{j+1, j}$ = heat entering layer j from the layer $j + 1$
$Q_{j, j-1}$ = heat leaving layer j for the layer $j - 1$
Q_{wj} = heat generated or absorbed in layer j

The change of temperature $\Delta\theta$ due to the change of heat is related by

$$\Delta Q = c_0(\Delta x\,\Delta y\,\Delta z)\,\Delta\theta \tag{3.49a}$$

where c_0 is the volumetric heat of the mass. The heat generated or absorbed is directly proportional to the amount of ice formed or thawed:

$$Q_w = -L\gamma_d w\,\Delta W_u(\Delta x\,\Delta y\,\Delta z) \tag{3.49b}$$

where $\quad L =$ latent heat of fusion of water 333 kJ/kg

$\quad\quad \gamma_d, w =$ dry unit weight and water content of the soil

$\quad\quad \Delta W_u =$ fraction of total moisture content that changes phase during interval

The heat entering and leaving the jth layer is given by

$$Q_{j+1,\,j} = \frac{2(\theta_{j+1} - \theta_j)\,\Delta x\,\Delta y\,\Delta t}{\Delta z_{j+1}/k_{j+1} + \Delta z_j/k_j} \tag{3.49c}$$

and

$$Q_{j,\,j-1} = \frac{2(\theta_j - \theta_{j-1})\,\Delta x\,\Delta y\,\Delta t}{\Delta z_j/k_j + \Delta z_{j-1}/k_{j-1}} \tag{3.49d}$$

where k_j is the thermal conductivity of layer j, etc. Substituting Eqs. (3.49) into (3.48) and rearranging gives the finite difference equation for one-dimensional heat conduction as

$$\theta_{j,\,k+1} = \frac{2(\theta_{j+1,\,k} - \theta_{j,\,k})\,\Delta t}{c_{0,\,j}(\Delta z_{j+1}/k_{j+1} + \Delta z_j/k_j)\,\Delta z_j} - \frac{2(\theta_{j,\,k} - \theta_{j-1,\,k})\,\Delta t}{c_{0,\,j}(\Delta z_j/k_j + \Delta z_{j-1}/k_{j-1})\,\Delta z_j}$$

$$+\,\theta_{j,\,k} - \frac{L\gamma_d w\,\Delta W_u}{c_{0,\,j}} \tag{3.50}$$

where the subscripts j and k here denote position and time, respectively. Letting

$$A = \frac{2\Delta t}{c_{0,\,j}(\Delta z_{j+1}/k_{j+1} + \Delta z_j/k_j)\,\Delta z_j} \tag{3.51a}$$

and

$$B = \frac{2\Delta t}{c_{0,\,j}(\Delta z_j/k_j + \Delta z_{j-1}/k_{j-1})\,\Delta z_j} \tag{3.51b}$$

be the moduli of the finite-difference equation, we can write Eq. (3.50) as

$$\theta_{j,\,k+1} = A\theta_{j+1,\,k} - (A + B - 1)\theta_{j,\,k} + B\theta_{j-1,\,k} - L\gamma_d w\,\Delta W_u/c_{0,\,j} \tag{3.52}$$

For a stable solution the inequality

$$A + B \le 1 \tag{3.53}$$

must be satisfied.

The requirement of stability relates the choice of the time increment to the physical properties of the layer. The time increment Δt for a stable solution can be obtained by substituting Eq. (3.51) into Eq. (3.50) and rearranging:

$$\Delta t \le \frac{c_{0,j} \Delta z_j}{2} \frac{\left(\dfrac{\Delta z_{j+1}}{k_{j+1}} + \dfrac{\Delta z_j}{k_j}\right)\left(\dfrac{\Delta z_j}{k_j} + \dfrac{\Delta z_{j-1}}{k_{j-1}}\right)}{\left(\dfrac{\Delta z_{j+1}}{k_{j+1}} + \dfrac{\Delta z_j}{k_j}\right) + \left(\dfrac{\Delta z_j}{k_j} + \dfrac{\Delta z_{j-1}}{k_{j-1}}\right)} \tag{3.54}$$

Since the percent of total moisture frozen can be expressed as a function of temperature, during a small time interval the amount of soil moisture changing phase can be related to the temperatures at the beginning and at the end of that interval. This indicates that the derived finite-difference equation is essentially an implicit equation and hence Newton's iterative method can be used to obtain the required solutions. This is done by noting that W_u is a function of temperature θ and that

$$\Delta W_u = W_u(\theta_{j,k+1}) - W_u(\theta_{j,k}) \tag{3.55}$$

Now $\theta_{j,k+1}$ and $W_u(\theta_{j,k+1})$ are both functions of $\theta_{j,k+1}$, the unknown temperature at the next time step. Provided an unfrozen-moisture-content function $W_u(\theta)$ is adopted, Eq. (3.52) can be written

$$F(\theta_{j,k+1}) = 0 \tag{3.56}$$

and hence the Newton iteration scheme can be applied to give rapid convergence. Once the complete array of temperatures at the next time step $\theta_{j,k+1}$ $(j = 1, m)$ is known, the solution can be output if required and then used to step forward the next time interval.

At the top of the region, it is often desired to specify a temperature. This is done by calculating a special value for the constant B at the topmost layer, i.e., for $j = 1$

$$B = \frac{2k_1 \Delta t}{c_{0,j} \Delta z_1^2} \tag{3.57}$$

and set $\theta_{j-1,k} = \theta_{0,k} = T_s$.

At the lower boundary, it is often required to specify a geothermal gradient in degrees Celsius per meter, and this is done using the equation

$$\theta_{m+1,k} = \theta_{m-1,k} + 2G\,\Delta z_m \qquad \text{for } j = m \tag{3.58}$$

This specifies a value $\theta_{m+1,k}$ for a fictional element $m + 1$ outside the region and allows the geothermal base condition to be satisfied.

This finite-difference method has been used successfully on many problems and is relatively easy to program. It was used for investigating the effects of the shape of the unfrozen-moisture-content relationship on thaw depth, as shown in Fig. 3.18.

3.5 APPLICATIONS OF GEOTHERMAL ANALYSIS AND SAMPLE PROBLEMS

In this section, some of the methods of analysis outlined previously are applied to engineering problems in cold regions.

Thawing or Freezing beneath Heated or Chilled Structures

If a heated structure of finite width is founded on permafrost, a thaw line will progress into the foundation soils. Section 3.4 demonstrated how the final equilibrium thaw depth is established beneath a heated area on permafrost and how the thaw depth X can be obtained at any time for a one-dimensional situation. The rate of thawing beneath such a structure and the time required to thaw (or freeze) a certain depth is required for design. The steady-state solutions given earlier provide an estimate of the maximum possible thaw penetration, and the one-dimensional solutions estimate the thaw depth under an infinitely wide area. The actual thaw-depth calculation under a structure of finite width should account for two-dimensional heat-flow effects.

An approximate solution to this problem has been discussed by Tsytovich (1975) and is presented in Fig. 3.23. These charts provide a method of relating the thaw depth beneath a building to the thaw depth calculated for the corresponding one-dimensional problem, which assumes no horizontal heat flow. The calculation of a two-dimensional thaw bowl beneath a structure finds application in:

1. Investigation of foundations of heated structures on permafrost that have disregarded the presence of permafrost and have since experienced difficulties
2. Estimating the magnitude and time required for preconstruction thawing
3. Calculating the rate and depth of thaw beneath structures where thaw and the accompanying settlements are considered tolerable

The application of this solution can be seen in a case history reported by Tsytovich (1975). In a period of 8 years following the construction of a single-story building in Vorkuta, U.S.S.R., thawing had proceeded to 13 m below the center of the floor slab, as shown on Fig. 3.24, with consequent settlements of 20 cm or more. Thawing extended below the massive and costly footings installed 3.5 m below the slab, causing serious cracking and deformations in the structure.

Assuming that the moisture content of the foundation soil was 25 percent by dry weight and that the structure floor was maintained at a temperature of 20°C, the following thermal parameters can be calculated or obtained from Kersten's data discussed earlier:

$$w = 0.25 \qquad \gamma_d = 1600 \text{ kg/m}^3 \qquad W_u = 5\%$$
$$k_u = 1.51 \text{ W/m K}$$
$$L = 106 \text{ MJ/m}^3$$
$$T_s = 20°C$$

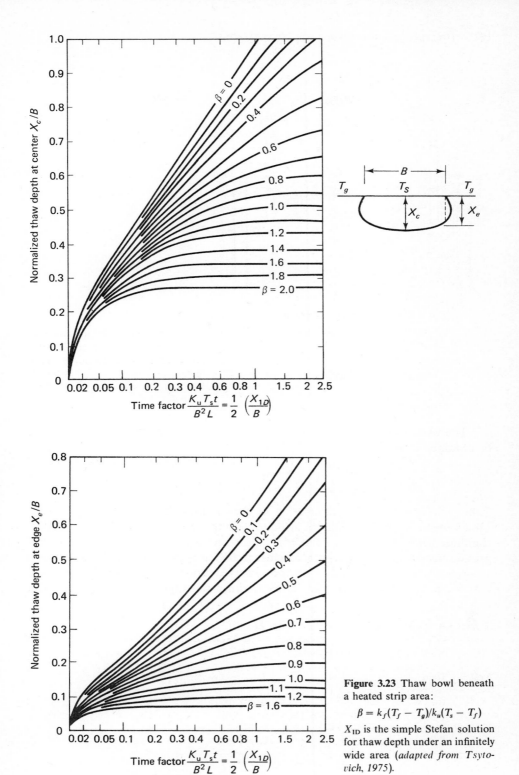

Figure 3.23 Thaw bowl beneath a heated strip area:

$$\beta = k_f(T_f - T_g)/k_u(T_s - T_f)$$

X_{1D} is the simple Stefan solution for thaw depth under an infinitely wide area (*adapted from Tsytovich, 1975*).

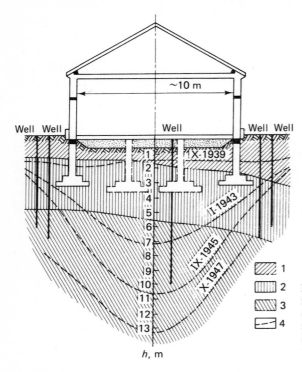

Figure 3.24 Deep thawing of permafrost under a building in Vorkuta: (1) cover loam; (2) loams of upper moraine; (3) loams of lower moraine; (4) upper permafrost boundary. (*After Tsytovich, 1975.*)

The value for the thaw parameter α, for a simple one-dimensional case can be obtained from Eq. (3.59)

$$\alpha = \left(\frac{2k_u T_s}{L}\right)^{1/2} = 7.5 \times 10^{-4} \text{ m/s}^{1/2} = 4.23 \text{ m/year}^{1/2} \qquad (3.59)$$

Table 3.4 summarizes the calculation of the modified thaw depths required to obtain the thaw bowl beneath the structure, using the charts in Fig. 3.23 to obtain the thaw depth at the center and edge of a structure of width $B = 10$ m. As the ground temperatures at Vorkuta are close to 0°C, it may be assumed that $\beta = 0.1$.

Comparing these results with the observed thaw depths (Fig. 3.24) shows that the prediction is reasonable at early times but underpredicts thaw depths

Table 3.4 Calculation of modified thaw depths

Year	Time, years	One-dimensional thaw depth, m [Eq. (3.59)]	I	Thaw depth, m In center X_c	At edge X_e
1939	0	0	0	0	0
1943	4	8.46	0.358	6.6	3.8
1945	6	10.36	0.537	7.6	4.7
1947	8	11.96	0.715	8.4	5.3

at later times. This may be due in part to thaw accentuated by groundwater conditions or by settlement of the structure itself. Reasons for the discrepancy are not entirely clear. The example demonstrates the method of calculating a thaw bowl using hand-calculation methods, and the case history indicates that a thaw bowl like this will develop under a heated building placed directly on frozen ground where no special precautions to preserve the frozen soil have been taken.

Thermal Design of Road and Airstrip Pads

As before, this subsection will refer to thaw-related effects in initially frozen ground, but the same relations developed are valid for frost effects in unfrozen ground provided the thermal properties are interchanged.

For many engineering applications, allowing deep thaw penetration during summer (or frost penetration in winter) into subgrade soils beneath road or airstrip pads may prove intolerable because of the excessive settlement or heaving that may occur. The resulting damage and subsequent maintenance may prove considerably more costly than providing some measure of thermal protection for the subgrade. This is often done in one of three ways:

1. An increased thickness of granular fill is used to limit thaw penetration and dissipate stresses resulting from wheel loads in the thawing subgrade.
2. A layer of organic insulation such as wood chips, brush, or sawdust is introduced within the fill pad.
3. A layer of synthetic insulation, e.g., rigid polystyrene board, is installed at some elevation within the granular pad.

Increasing granular fill may prove very expensive in many cases and often does not prevent thaw penetration into the native soils. Organic or natural insulating layers suffer from the disadvantage that they are likely to become waterlogged in time, with consequent deterioration in thermal properties. Synthetic insulations such as polystyrene are water-resistant and relatively inexpensive. These materials have been used successfully on many projects in both temperate and arctic latitudes.

The design of roads involving insulation must satisfy several criteria, including structural protection of the insulation, the prevention of excessive settlements or shear failure within any thawed subgrade layer, the suitability of the granular fill material for base and surface courses, and the overall thermal design. Our attention is confined to the last of these criteria, concerning the geothermal aspects. The configuration of interest involves at least three materials of different thermal properties, i.e., granular fill, insulation, and the underlying permafrost. Numerical solutions like those discussed in Sec. 3.4 provide the most accurate means of assessing the thaw penetration through pad configurations having different thermal properties. A surface-temperature wave for the fill pad can be established using the methods outlined in Sec. 3.2, and once the initial ground temperatures and the geothermal gradient (base condition) are measured or estimated, a solution can be obtained. In the absence of a numerical model, how-

Table 3.5 Thermal properties for Lachenbruch analysis for permafrost protection

Material	Thermal conductivity, W/m K	Heat capacity, MJ/m³ K	Thermal diffusivity, $\mu m^2/s$
Dry gravel	2.26	1.99	1.13
Polystyrene insulation	0.042	0.058	0.71
Frozen silt subgrade	1.67	2.67	0.62

ever, an estimate can be made of the thickness of fill and/or insulation using the analytical method of Lachenbruch (1959) for profiles having two or three layers. The analytical relationships are too lengthy to reproduce here, but they have the same form as Eq. (3.43), derived earlier for the depth of fill required for permafrost protection, assuming the granular fill and underlying frozen ground have the same thermal properties.

A specific solution for the three-layer permafrost-protection problem has been calculated for the set of thermal properties shown in Table 3.5, which are typical for a relatively dry granular fill, polystyrene insulation, and fine-grained frozen soil. Specific solutions have been calculated for the equivalent frost-protection problem, for the same fill and insulation properties, but with the properties of an unfrozen fine-grained subgrade soil with 20 percent moisture content. The results are quite similar to those for the thaw-protection problem, and the same solution can be used to provide estimates for the required fill and insulation thicknesses for both problems.

The specific solution to the permafrost-protection problem for the thermal properties in Table 3.5 is shown plotted in Fig. 3.25 as a plot of the temperature ratio T_g/A_0 against the required fill thickness for different thicknesses of insulation. The temperature ratio is shown schematically in Fig. 3.25 and is defined as the mean pad surface temperature (in degrees Celsius above or below freezing) divided by the amplitude of the pad-surface sine wave. For a given location, this temperature ratio can be calculated from previous pad-surface temperature measurements or estimated using the methods outlined in Sec. 3.2. By drawing a horizontal line in Fig. 3.25, the required thicknesses of insulation and gravel can be selected. A further graph can then be prepared to illustrate the required thickness of each material for a particular location (or T_g/A_0 value).

The resulting pad configuration is particularly sensitive to the value for the temperature ratio selected. For very cold regions, the ratio T_g/A_0 is large, and only minimal thicknesses of gravel and/or insulation are required. For warmer areas corresponding to the discontinuous permafrost zone, the required thickness of each material may be excessive, indicating that it is not feasible to prevent any

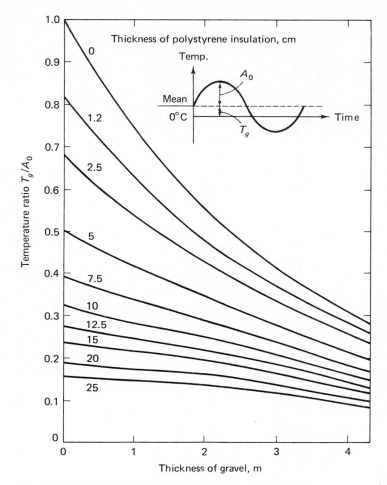

Figure 3.25 Lachenbruch analysis for thaw or frost protection.

thaw penetration into the underlying frozen ground. Indeed, some studies show that it may not be possible to prevent continual deepening of the permafrost table within parts of the discontinuous permafrost zone where ground temperatures are close to the melting point. Certainly the use of insulation in such areas will greatly reduce the rate of permafrost degradation but may not prevent it entirely.

Finally, the specific solution presented above should be checked on all major projects using numerical techniques, which model the phase change in the fill more correctly, together with the thermal response of the permafrost immediately below the pad.

Utilities

The protection of buried water and sewer lines against frost action in temperate regions can be treated as outlined above. Insulation can be placed around the utility in a number of ways. One method suggested involves designing the depth of cover and insulation thickness as outlined above and placing the insulation along the sides of the trench excavation and over the top of the pipe to form an inverted U configuration. Sand bedding is normally placed between the pipe and insulation. Heated utilities in permafrost are usually heavily insulated if buried, and allowance is made for the limited thaw and settlement that will occur. More usually, however, they are located in above-ground utilidors, which are insulated box structures supported on piles or wooden shims.

Pipelines

Heated pipelines in permafrost can thaw significant depths of permafrost beneath the pipe. The resulting thaw settlement and slope instability can threaten the integrity of the pipe if the foundation conditions are thaw-unstable. Lachenbruch (1970) provided some numerical solutions to this important problem. It is of interest to demonstrate the use of simple solutions to the problem of a heated pipeline which operates continuously for several years. The radial-thawing solution reviewed in Sec. 3.4 can be used to estimate the growth of a thaw bulb beneath a pipe. The same thermal properties used by Gold et al. (1972) for a silt soil and a warm ground temperature $(T_g = -8.3°C)$ for a pipeline problem are adopted here:

$$k_u = 1.61 \text{ W/m K} \qquad k_f = 2.13 \text{ W/m K}$$

$$c_u = 3.02 \text{ MJ/m}^3 \text{ K} \qquad L = 147.5 \text{ MJ/m}^3$$

$$a = \text{pipe radius} = 0.61 \text{ m} \qquad \text{Ste} = \frac{C_u T_s}{L} = 1.23$$

$$T_s = \text{pipe temperature} = 60°C$$

The simplified solution given in Fig. 3.22 and corrected by Eq. (3.45) would be expected to overpredict the thaw depth, as it ignores the cooling effects of the ground surface. The parameter $4k_u T_s t/a^2 L$ is given by

$$\frac{4(1.61)(60t)(31.5 \times 10^6)}{0.61(0.61)(147.5 \times 10^6)} = 221.6t$$

where t is in years. The correction factor $(1 - 0.12 \text{ Ste})^{1/2}$ is equal to 0.923.

Table 3.6 summarizes the calculation for thaw depth beneath the pipe axis and compares the results with those calculated numerically by Gold et al. (1972). In fact, the analytical solution given here has underpredicted the thaw-depth–time relationship to some degree, although in other cases it may overpredict the thaw depth by a similar amount.

Table 3.6 Calculation of thaw depth beneath the pipe axis

Radial thawing solution				Numerical solution, results for R, m (Gold et al. 1972)
Time, years	$221.6t$	$\bar{R}$	Thaw depth beneath pipe axis $0.923R$, m	
1	221.6	8.2	4.62	6.10
5	1108	15.8	8.89	9.76
10	2216	21.0	11.82	12.20

The solution presented in Fig. 3.22 is capable of providing a reasonable first approximation of thawing around a cylindrical heat source. Numerical methods should be considered where accuracy is critical to the project under consideration.

Foundations Involving Ventilated Pads

If structures like garages, warehouses, or heated storage tanks are subjected to heavy floor loadings, it may be economical to place them directly on a fill pad. No reasonable thickness of fill or insulation will totally prevent thaw penetration beneath a heated structure on grade unless some method of removing heat from the foundation is employed. This might be done using a combination of insulation and refrigerating lines placed in the pad beneath the insulation. A more common method, however, is to circulate cold air during the winter season through a series of ventilating ducts installed in the fill pad. During the summer season air circulation is discontinued, and the thickness of fill and insulation is designed to prevent the thaw line from penetrating completely to the original ground surface before the ventilating ducts become operative again at the end of the summer. Two design criteria are of primary importance. In the summer, the thickness of fill and insulation must be sufficient to prevent thawing of the underlying permafrost, and in the winter the ventilation capacity must be sufficient to remove heat from the heated structure and also to freezeback and chill the underlying pad.

Assuming that the insulation is placed directly beneath the heated structure, as shown in Fig. 3.26, Eq. (3.35) can be used to predict the thaw penetration into the gravel. The time to thaw the insulation t_0 is negligible and should be taken as zero. The time t during which thawing in the gravel is actively taking place should be equated to the period over which the ducts are inoperative. Normally, ventilation will cease when ambient air temperatures are above about $-4°C$, and this period is usually in the range of 140 to 160 days for many areas. The depth of thaw in the fill pad layer should be multiplied by the correction factor $(1 - \text{Ste}/8)$ as outlined by Eq. (3.28).

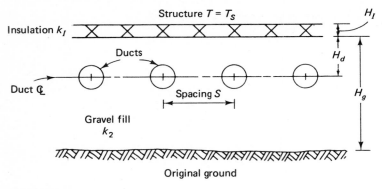

Figure 3.26 Ventilated pad foundation.

The ventilating requirements are estimated by adding the heat gained by the ducts from the structure and from the underlying pad. Assuming that the ambient temperatures T_a follow a sinusoidal law, we can write

$$T_a = T_{av} + A_0 \sin \frac{2\pi t}{365} \tag{3.60}$$

A steady (linear) temperature distribution between the structure $(T = T_s)$ and the ducts $(T = T_a)$ may be assumed. The heat gain from the structure q_s is the product of the thermal conductivity of the insulation and the temperature gradient through the insulation, i.e.,

$$q_s = \frac{k_I}{H_I + k_I H_d/k_2} (T_s - T_a) \tag{3.61}$$

where k_I and H_I are the conductivity and thickness of the insulation, respectively, and the term $k_I H_d/k_2$ accounts for the small thickness of gravel fill between the insulation and the duct centerline. The heat gain from the structure can be calculated by combining Eqs. (3.60) and 3.61). The heat gain from the pad can be estimated by calculating the heat flux removed from a pad subjected to a sinusoidal change in surface temperature. This heat gain Q_p is given by

$$q_p = k_s \frac{\partial T}{\partial x} \quad \text{at } x = 0 \tag{3.62}$$

The equation for the temperature distribution in a uniform material subjected to a sinusoidal surface-temperature variation has been given by Eq. (3.42). Differentiating this expression to obtain the surface temperature gradient and substituting in Eq. (3.62), we obtain

$$q_p = -k_2 A_0 \left(\frac{\pi}{365\kappa} \right)^{1/2} \left(\sin \frac{2\pi t}{365} + \cos \frac{2\pi t}{365} \right) \tag{3.63}$$

The total heat flux F is given by

$$F = q_p + q_s \tag{3.64}$$

It can be shown that the total heat flux reaches a peak at a time t is given by

$$t_{max} = \frac{365}{2\pi} \tan^{-1} \left[\frac{k_I}{k_2(\pi/365\kappa)^{1/2}H_I} + 1 \right] + 182.5 \tag{3.65}$$

where H_I can be increased by $k_I H_a/k_2$ to account for the gravel above the ducts. If this time is substituted in Eqs. (3.61) and (3.63), the peak heat gain to the ducts F_{max} can be calculated.

It remains only to determine the air ventilation rate to remove this heat flux from the foundation without causing an excessive rise in temperature through the ducts. It is usually desirable to limit the temperature rise through the ducts to 2 or 3°C, as greater temperature increases might cause warming near the outlet end of the ducts. Each duct must remove heat over an area equal to SL, where S is the duct spacing and L the length. The maximum heat flux must be balanced by

$$F_{max} SL = Qc_a \Delta T \tag{3.66}$$

where Q = air flow rate per duct, m³/s
$\quad c_a$ = volumetric heat capacity of air = 1329 J/m³ K
$\quad \Delta T$ = desired temperature rise, °C

Rearranging Eq. (3.66) gives

$$\frac{Q}{SL} = \frac{F_{max}}{c_a \Delta T} \tag{3.67}$$

where Q/SL is the ventilation rate per unit area of the base of the structure.

The flow rates normally calculated by the above procedure usually cannot be attained by natural ventilation methods, i.e., wind-induced or chimney effects, and are most reliably provided by electric fans, thermostatically controlled to operate when the temperature falls below a certain level. The following example illustrates the use of this procedure in estimating pad and ventilation requirements.

Example 3.1 A garage heated continuously to 20°C is to be founded on an area of sensitive permafrost. The air temperatures during a warm year have a mean of -6°C and an amplitude of 22°C. A 100-mm layer of insulation will be placed directly beneath the floor slab. Ventilation ducts 450 mm in diameter and spaced 1.8 m apart will be located 0.6 m beneath the insulation. The following thermal properties are typical for rigid insulation and gravel fill:

$$k_I = 0.042 \text{ W/m K} \qquad k_2 = 2.0 \text{ W/m K}$$

$$\kappa = \frac{k_2}{c_\mu} = \frac{2.0}{2.26 \times 10^6} = 0.89 \times 10^{-6} \text{ m}^2/\text{s} = 0.076 \text{ m}^2/\text{day}$$

The moisture content and dry density of the gravel are 7 percent by dry weight and 2000 kg/m³, respectively. The remaining thermal properties of the gravel are therefore

$$L = L_w w \gamma_d = 46.4 \text{ MJ/m}^3$$

$$c_u = \frac{\gamma_d}{\gamma_w} (0.18 + w)(4.18 \times 10^6) = 2.09 \text{ MJ/m}^3 \text{ K}$$

$$\text{Ste} = c_u T_s/L = 0.90 \qquad 1 - \frac{\text{Ste}}{8} = 0.88$$

The length of time the ambient air is above $-4°C$ is about 165 days. From Eq. (3.35) the parameter $k_2 H/k_I$ is

$$\frac{2.0}{0.042} \times 0.1 = 4.8 \text{ m}$$

and the thaw depth into the gravel after 165 days is

$$X - H = \left[4.80^2 + \frac{2(2.0)(20)(165)(86,400)}{46.4 \times 10^6} \right]^{1/2} - 4.80 = 2.10 \text{ m}$$

This value can be corrected using the factor $1 - \text{Ste}/8$, giving

$$X - H = 2.10(0.88) = 1.85 \text{ m}$$

Therefore, a 1.85-m pad is required in addition to 10 cm of insulation to prevent thawing of the underlying frozen ground. The equivalent insulation thickness is

$$H_I + \frac{k_I H_d}{k_2} = 10 + 1.25 = 11.25 \text{ cm} = 0.1125 \text{ m}$$

According to Eq. (3.65), the peak heat flux to the ducts will be obtained by $t_{max} = 240.5$ days. The ambient temperature T_a at this time is $T_a = -24.5°C$. Substituting this value in Eq. (3.61) gives the heat gain from the structure:

$$q_s = \frac{0.042[20 - (-24.5)]}{0.1125} = 16.61 \text{ J/m}^2 \text{ s}$$

The heat gain from the pad, from Eq. (3.63), is

$$q_p = -14.78 (-0.841 - 0.542) = 20.43 \text{ J/m}^2 \text{ s}$$

The maximum heat flux is

$$F_{max} = 16.61 + 20.43 = 37.04 \text{ J/m}^2 \text{ s}$$

The required ventilation capacity (assuming an allowable ΔT of 3°C) is obtained from Eq. (3.67) and is

$$\frac{Q}{SL} = \frac{37.04}{1329(3)} = 0.00929 \text{ m}^3/\text{s m}^2$$

The total ventilation capacity for a 60 by 30-m structure is

$$Q = 0.00929(60)(30) = 16.7 \text{ m}^3/\text{s}$$

This could be supplied by six vertical stacks, each equipped with an electric fan rated at 3 m^3/s.

REFERENCES

Anderson, D. M., A. R. Tice, and H. L. McKim. 1973. The Unfrozen Water and the Apparent Specific Heat Capacity of Frozen Soils, *North Am. Contrib. 2d Int. Conf. Permafrost, Yakutsk, U.S.S.R*; National Academy of Sciences, Washington, pp. 289–295.

Bliss, W. C., and R. W. Wein. 1971. Changes to the Active Layer caused by Surface Disturbance, *Proc. Sem. Permafrost Active Layer, Natl. Res. Counc. Can. Tech. Mem.* 103, pp. 37–46.

Bredehoeft, J. D., and I. S. Papadopulos. 1965. Rates of Vertical Groundwater Movement Estimated from the Earth's Thermal Profile, *Water Resour. Res.*, **1**: 325–328.

Brewer, Max C. 1958. The Thermal Regime of an Arctic Lake, *Trans. Am. Geophys. Union*, **39**: 278–284.

Brown, J., W. Rickard, and D. Vietor. 1969. The Effect of Disturbance on Permafrost Terrain, *U.S. Army Cold Reg. Res. Eng. Lab. Spec. Rep.* 138, Hanover, N.H.

Brown, R. J. E. 1960. The Distribution of Permafrost and Its Relation to Air Temperature in Canada and the U.S.S.R., *Arctic*, **13**(3): 163–177.

———. 1963a. Influence of Vegetation on Permafrost, *Proc. 1st Int. Permafrost Conf., Lafayette, Ind., NAS-NRC Publ.* 1287, pp. 20–25.

———. 1963b. Relation between Mean Annual Air and Ground Temperatures in the Permafrost Regions of Canada, *Proc. 1st Int. Permafrost Conf., Lafayette, Ind., NAS-NRC Publ.* 1287, pp. 241–247.

Brown, W. G. 1963. Graphical Determination of Temperatures under Heated or Cooled Areas on the Ground Surface, *Natl. Res. Counc. Can. Tech. Pap.* 163.

Brown, W. G., G. H. Johnston, and R. J. E. Brown. 1964. Comparison of Observed and Calculated Ground Temperatures with Permafrost Distribution under a Northern Lake, *Can. Geotech. J.* **1**(3): 147–154.

Carslaw, H. S., and J. C. Jaeger. 1947. "Conduction of Heat in Solids," Clarendon Press, Oxford.

Cartwright, Keros. 1971. Redistribution of Geothermal Heat by a Shallow Aquifer, *Geol. Soc. Am. Bull.*, **82**: 3197–3200.

Charlwood, R. G., and O. Svec, 1972. Northern Pipelines: An Application for Numerical Analysis, pt. II, *Proc. Symp. Appl. Solid Mech., Univ. Waterloo, Waterloo, Ont.*, pp. 65–80.

Geiger, Rudolf. 1965. "The Climate near the Ground," trans. by Scripta Technica Inc., Harvard University Press, Cambridge, Mass.

Gold, L. W., G. H. Johnston, W. A. Slusarchuk, and L. E. Goodrich. 1972. Thermal Effects in Permafrost, *Proc. Can. North. Pipeline Res. Conf., Ottawa, Natl. Res. Counc. Can. Tech. Mem.* 104.

Goodrich, L. E. 1974. A One-dimensional numerical model for Geothermal Problems, *Natl. Res. Counc. Can. Div. Build. Res. Tech. Pap.* 421.

Gurr, C. G., T. J. Marshall, and J. T. Hutton. 1952. Water Movement in Soil Due to a Temperature Gradient, *Soil Sci.*, **24**: 335–344.

Habib, P., and F. Soeiro. 1953. Migration d'eau dans les sols provoquées par une différence de température, *Proc. 3d Int. Conf. Soil Mech. Found. Eng.*, **3**: Zurich 155–156.

Heginbottom, J. A. 1971. Some Effects of a Forest Fire on the Permafrost Active Layer at Inuvik, N.W.T., *Proc. Sem. Permafrost Active Layer, Natl. Res. Counc. Can. Tech. Mem.* 103, pp. 31–36.
———. 1973. Some Effects of Surface Disturbance on the Permafrost Active Layer at Inuvik, N.W.T., [*Gov. Can.*] *Environ. Soc. Comm., North. Pipelines Rep.* 73–16.
———. and P. L. Kurfurst. 1973. Terrain Sensitivity and Mapping, Mackenzie Valley Transportation Corridor, *Geol. Surv. Can. Rep. Act. Pap.* 73–1, pt. A, pp. 226–229.
Ho, D. M., M. E. Harr, and G. A. Leonards. 1970. Transient Temperature Distribution in Insulated Pavements: Predictions and Observations, *Can. Geotech. J.*, **7**: 275–284.
Hoekstra, P. 1969. The Physics and Chemistry of Frozen Soils, *Highw. Res. Board Spec. Rep.* 103, pp. 78–90.
Hwang, C. T., 1977. On Quasi-static Solutions for Buried Pipes in Permafrost, *Proc. Can. Geotech. J.*, **14**(2): 180–192.
———, D. W. Murray, and E. W. Brooker. 1972. A Thermal Analysis for Structures on Permafrost, *Can. Geotech. J.*, **9**: 33–46.
Isaacs, R. M. 1973. Engineering Geology, Mackenzie Valley Transportation Corridor, *Geol. Surv. Can. Rep. Act. Pap.* 73–1, pt. A, pp. 230–231.
Jahns, H. O., T. W. Miller, L. D. Power, W. P. Rickey, T. P. Taylor, and J. A. Wheeler. 1973. Permafrost Protection for Pipelines, *North Am. Contrib. Proc. 2d Int. Permafrost Conf., Yakutsk, U.S.S.R.*, National Academy of Sciences, Washington, pp. 673–684.
Johnston, G. H., and R. J. E. Brown. 1964. Some Observations on Permafrost Distribution at a Lake in the Mackenzie Delta, N.W.T., Canada, *Arctic*, **17**(3): 162–175.
Judge, A. S. 1973*a*. The Prediction of Permafrost Thickness, *Can. Geotech. J.*, **10**(1): 1–11.
———. 1973*b*. The Thermal Regime of the Mackenzie Valley: Observations of the Natural State, [*Gov. Can.*] *Environ. Soc. Comm. North. Pipelines, Task Force North. Oil Dev. Rep.* 73–38.
Kersten, M. S., 1949. Laboratory Research for the Determination of the Thermal Properties of Soils, *Univ. Minn. Eng. Exp. Stn., Final Rep.*
Lachenbruch, A. H., 1957. Thermal Effects of the Ocean on Permafrost, *Geol. Soc. Am. Bull.*, **68**: 1515–1530.
———. 1959. Periodic Heat Flow in a Stratified Medium with Application in Permafrost Problems, *U.S. Geol. Surv. Bull.* 1052, p. 51.
———. 1970. Some Estimates of the Thermal Effects of a Heated Pipeline in Permafrost, *U.S. Geol. Surv. Circ.* 632.
Linell, K. A. 1973. Long-Term Effects of Vegetative Cover on Permafrost Stability in an Area of Discontinuous Permafrost. *North Am. Contrib. 2d Int. Conf. Permafrost, Yakutsk, U.S.S.R.*, National Academy of Science, Washington, pp. 688–693.
Lovering, T. S., and H. D. Goode. 1963. Measuring Geothermal Gradients in Drill Holes Less than 60 Feet Deep, East Tintic District, Utah, *U.S. Geol. Surv. Bull.* 1172.
MacCarthy, G. R. 1953. Recent Changes in the Shoreline near Point Barrow, Alaska, *Arctic*, **6**: 44–51.
Mackay, J. R. 1970. Disturbances to the Tundra and Forest Tundra Environment of the Western Arctic, *Can. Geotech. J.*, **7**(4): 420–432.
Nixon, J. F. 1975. The Role of Convective Heat Transfer in the Thawing of Frozen Soils, *Can. Geotech. J.*, **12**: 425–429.
———, and E. C. McRoberts. 1973. A Study of Some Factors Affecting the Thawing of Frozen Soils, *Can. Geotech. J.*, **10**: 439–452.
Nowosai, T. S. 1963. Growing Vegetables on Permafrost, *North*, **10**: 42–45.
Pekeris, C. L., and L. B. Slichter. 1939. Problem of Ice Formation, *J. Appl. Phys.*, **10**: 135–137.
Stallman, R. W. 1963. Notes on the Use of Temperature Data for Computing Groundwater Velocity, R. Bentall (compiler), Methods of Collecting and Interpreting Ground-water Data, *U.S. Geol. Surv. Water Supply Pap.* 1544H, pp. 36–46.
Stefan. J. 1890. Über die Theorie der Eisbildung, insbesondere über die Eisbildung im Polarmeere, vol. XCVIII, no. IIa: *Sitzungsberichte der Mathematisch-Naturwissenschaftlichen Classe der Kaiserlichen Akademie der Wissenschaften*, Wien, pp. 965–983.
Thornton, D. E. 1976. Steady-State and Quasi-static Thermal Results for Bare and Insulated Pipes in Permafrost, *Can. Geotech. J.*, **13**: 161–120.

Tsytovich, N. A. 1975. in G. K. Swinzow (ed.), "The Mechanics of Frozen Ground," McGraw-Hill, New York.

Van Orstrand, C. E. 1934. Temperature Gradients, "Problems of Petroleum Geology," American Association of Petroleum Geologists, Tulsa, Okla. pp. 989–1021.

U.S. Department of the Army. 1966. Calculation Methods for Determination of Depths of Freeze and Thaw in Soils, *Dep. Army Tech. Man.* TM5–852–6.

FOUR

THAW CONSOLIDATION

John F. Nixon and B. Ladanyi

INTRODUCTION

The thaw-settlement phenomena produced by melting of permafrost layers differ only in scale from those which take place in the spring on the ground surface due to melting ice in seasonally frozen ground. In both cases the magnitude of the settlement depends primarily on whether or not the ground freezing permitted the formation of ice layers and/or ice-rich soil. Roads and highways are particularly vulnerable to damage under heavy traffic loads when thawing produces excess water content in the subgrade and base materials. When bodies of clear ice contained in permafrost layers melt due to changes in climatic conditions or man-made changes at the surface, cavities are produced which appear at the ground surface as large depressions.

The development of practical methods for determining the settlement of thawing permafrost and for the prediction of pore pressures generated in thawing soil has been a prerequisite to improved engineering design in cold regions. Prediction of settlement in thawing permafrost makes use of common laboratory tests and simple relationships involving bulk soil density, water content, iceness ratio, and degree of saturation. More detailed information on settlement and excess pore-water pressures is obtained from laboratory thaw-consolidation tests used with thaw-consolidation theory. Details are given in this chapter under the following topics: thaw-settlement prediction, one-dimensional consolidation of thawing soils, residual stress in thawing soils, thaw consolidation in layered systems, and examples of field studies.

4.1 THAW-SETTLEMENT PREDICTION

Permafrost provides adequate bearing capacity for most structures as long as it remains frozen. Engineering problems are caused by thawing of perennially frozen ground containing large quantities of ice. Ice can occur in several forms, ranging from coatings or films on individual soil particles and minute hairline lenses to large inclusions and massive deposits many meters thick. All forms of ice segregation can occur in the same material, including granular soils, and even bedrock cannot be assumed to be ice-free (Pihlainen and Johnston, 1963).

When frozen ground thaws, water is released and settlement develops as the water is squeezed from the ground under the influence of gravity and applied loads. If the rate of water generation exceeds the discharge capacity of the soil, excess pore pressures will develop and can lead to the failure of foundations and slopes. If thawing occurs fast enough, frozen ground may be transformed into a slurry of soil particles and water which is unable to support any significant load. It is therefore important to be able to estimate the amount and the time rate of thaw settlement as well as pore pressures associated with thawing and subsequent consolidation of frozen ground under its own weight and structural loads.

Knowledge of thaw-settlement and consolidation behavior of permafrost is a basic requirement in the design of (1) building foundations (where thaw is permitted or cannot be avoided), (2) buried warm pipelines, (3) water-retaining structures, (4) stability of thawing slopes, and (5) roads and other embankments where only limited permafrost protection is available. In addition, it is needed for estimating possible geotechnical effects of thermal disturbance on permafrost terrain.

Thaw-Settlement Behavior of Soils

When saturated soil is frozen under undrained conditions, i.e., with no change in moisture content, the soil expands in volume by an amount equal to the phase change for the water. When this soil is thawed, it returns to its original volume and consolidates further if drainage is permitted. This additional consolidation due to drainage will be small if the soil was initially in a relatively dense state.

In natural soils this situation occurs only in coarse-grained frozen soils with very little segregated ice. For fine-grained soils some ice segregation will always occur, even under undrained conditions. Slow freezing of frost-susceptible soils such as silts and clayey silts at low stresses with free access to capillary water gives rise to formation of ice lenses and veins. Usually the total moisture content of these frozen soils considerably exceeds the moisture content corresponding to their unfrozen normally consolidated state. Therefore, when such ice-rich soils are thawed under drained conditions, they undergo large settlement under their own weight. As a result, the total thaw settlement for these soils under foundations will originate from three sources: (1) phase change, (2) settlement under their own weight, and (3) settlement under applied loads.

In some very ice-rich soils it is possible to make a rough estimate of the amount of thaw settlement from the thickness of visible ice lenses. For most frozen soils, testing representative samples remains the most reliable procedure for investigating all aspects of the thaw-settlement behavior of soils that are of concern in practice.

Thaw-Consolidation Tests

The earliest reported thaw-consolidation tests were performed by Tsytovich some 40 years ago (Tsytovich and Sumgin, 1937). These tests were made in an ordinary oedometer with a heated loading cap, which permitted a rapid thaw of the sample under different loads. Similar simple equipment is still being used today in connection with some large projects in the United States and Canada. This equipment has been found quite satisfactory for a quick determination of the total thaw settlement of a large number of permafrost specimens. A more detailed description of such tests and equipment can be found in Shuster, 1971; Luscher and Afifi, 1973; Crory, 1973; Speer et al., 1973; Watson et al., 1973b; and Keil et al., 1973.

Since there is no standard procedure for performing thaw-consolidation tests, the sample size, the method of thawing, and the method of load application were arbitrarily selected by the different investigators. Most of these tests were performed on samples with a diameter of 50 to 100 mm and a height-to-diameter ratio of 0.5 : 1.

Usually a small seating load is applied during the thawing period. The sample is subjected to a rapid all-around thawing with no attempt to control the rate and direction of thawing (Crory, 1973). After complete thawing and no further volume changes are observed, the sample is consolidated in the conventional manner used for testing unfrozen soil samples. Figure 4.1 shows schematically a typical result of such a thaw-consolidation test, where the compression curve illustrates the change in void ratio as the frozen soil is initially loaded (point a to b), then allowed to thaw (b to c), and finally to consolidate (c to d) under the application of increasing external pressures. Figure 4.1 also shows that thawing under different pressures does not necessarily lead to the same postthaw behavior of the soil (b' to c' to d'). The most important fact demonstrated by such tests is that the thaw strain (b to c) is usually much greater than the strains due to subsequent consolidation. This fact has been used for developing some simple methods for thaw-settlement evaluation which are included later in this section.

Section 4.2 will show that the thaw-consolidation behavior of soils depends on their thermal and consolidation properties. In general, it is found that very permeable coarse-grained soils consolidate almost completely during thawing; as a consequence, their settlement rate follows closely the rate of advance of the thaw plane. On the other hand, fine-grained soils show only a limited amount of consolidation during thawing; hence at the end of thawing large pore pressures may still remain to be dissipated.

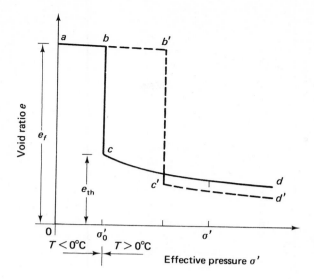

Figure 4.1 Typical thaw-settlement behavior of frozen soils. (*After Tsytovich et al., 1965.*)

A complete study of thaw-consolidation behavior for a frozen soil can be made in a specially designed oedometer like the one described by Morgenstern and Smith (1973) and Nixon and Morgenstern (1974). A diagram of such an apparatus, called a *permode* (permafrost oedometer) by the authors, is given in Fig. 4.2. The permode is basically a standard oedometer with one-way drainage to the top, in which temperatures can be measured at the top, bottom, and at two intermediate points on the side of the soil through the use of thermocouples or thermistors. The Lucite ring of the permode minimizes radial heat flow and enables a one-dimensional thaw-consolidation test to be carried out.

The temperatures at each end of the sample are controlled through the use of thermoelectric elements located (Fig. 4.2) at the base of the permode and in the load cap. The temperature in these elements can be regulated with an accuracy of 0.2°C through the use of temperature controllers. The test is performed by switching the top element to heat (normally +10 to +30°C) and by maintaining the temperature constant throughout the test. During the test, the advance of the thaw plane can be monitored by the thermistors and the pore pressure is recorded as soon as the thaw plane reaches the bottom of the sample. Settlement is observed using a dial guage. This type of oedometer has been used to study the entire thaw-consolidation process in frozen soils. Typical results including comparisons with theory are included in Sec. 4.2 to 4.4.

Methods for Thaw-Settlement Prediction

Thaw-settlement prediction may be based on the settlement diagram or the variation of density on thawing. Both methods are described below.

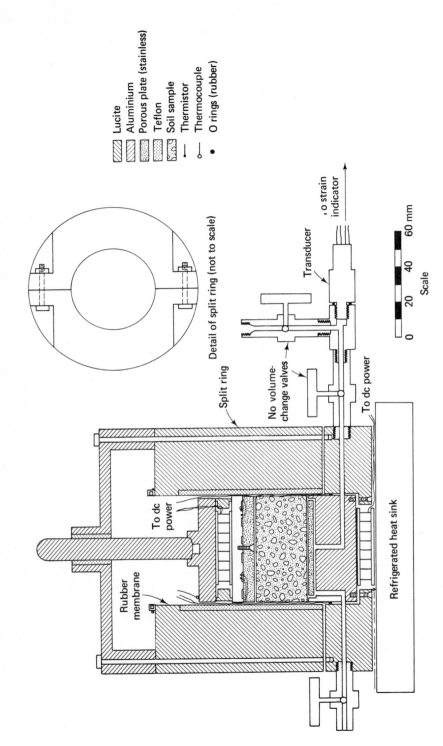

Figure 4.2 Thaw-consolidation apparatus (permode). *(After Morgenstern and Smith, 1973, and Nixon and Morgenstern, 1974.)*

Lucite
Aluminium
Porous plate (stainless)
Teflon
Soil sample
Thermistor
Thermocouple
O rings (rubber)

Detail of split ring (not to scale)

Split ring

No volume-change valves

Transducer

o strain indicator

To dc power

Rubber membrane

To dc power

Refrigerated heat sink

Scale

0   20   40   60 mm

Thaw-settlement diagram As the major portion of thaw settlement of a frozen soil occurs during the thawing stage (Fig. 4.1), Tsytovich (1958) represented the total settlement s as a sum of the thaw settlement s_{th} and the consolidation settlement s_c

$$s = s_{th} + s_c \qquad (4.1)$$

where the original frozen layer thickness H_f is acted upon by the effective pressure σ'. The two components of settlement are given by

$$s_{th} = A_0 H_f \qquad (4.2)$$

and
$$s_c = m_v \sigma' H_f \qquad (4.3)$$

The unit thaw settlement A_0 under an arbitrary pressure σ'_0, lower than σ', can be expressed in terms of the frozen and thawed void ratios of the soil e_f and e_{th}, respectively, as

$$A_0 = \frac{e_f - e_{th}}{1 + e_f} \qquad (4.4)$$

The coefficient of volume change m_v is defined as the volume change per unit volume per unit increase in effective stress. For an increase in effective stress from σ'_0 to σ' if the void ratio of the thawed soil decreases from e_{th} to e, then

$$m_v = \frac{1}{1 + e_{th}} \left(\frac{e_{th} - e}{\sigma' - \sigma'_0} \right) \qquad (4.5)$$

The value of σ'_0 at which the unit thaw settlement A_0 should be measured can be a very light load or a value σ'_0 equal to the effective overburden pressure, as recommended in the last edition of the U.S.S.R. Building Code (1966). For practical purposes, it appears that the most logical test procedure may still be the one originally proposed by Tsytovich (1958) and also used by Watson et al. (1973b). It involves extending the thaw-settlement curve linearly back to the stress origin with A_0 equal to the intercept at the ordinate, i.e., at $\sigma'_0 = 0$, as shown in Fig. 4.3. The value of m_v then equals the slope of the straight line in the same plot.

If the thaw settlement for a total of n layers has to be determined, and if for each layer the corresponding values of A_0 and m_v have been determined in the described manner from the thaw-consolidation tests on representative samples, the total settlement will equal

$$s = \sum_{i=1}^{n} A_{0,i} H_i + \sum_{i=1}^{n} m_{vi} H_i \sigma'_i \qquad (4.6)$$

where σ'_i is the effective stress at the midheight of each layer having an original thickness H_i. Since the effective stress includes σ'_g due to gravity and σ'_z due to the applied pressure,

$$\sigma'_i = \sigma'_{gi} + \sigma'_{zi} \qquad (4.7)$$

Conventional soil-mechanics methods can be used to determine σ'_g and σ'_z.

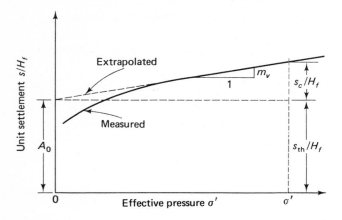

Figure 4.3 Generalized thaw-settlement curve. (*After Watson et al., 1973a.*)

Another, slightly different, thaw-settlement-determination method was proposed by Nixon and Morgenstern (1974), who found that when a frozen soil with a high initial void ratio is thawed under a low effective pressure and then further consolidated, a highly nonlinear pressure-settlement relationship is obtained. When this relationship is plotted on a diagram of e vs. log σ' (Fig. 4.4), the straight-line portion can be extrapolated back to meet a horizontal line drawn through e_f, the initial void ratio of the frozen soil. This intersection corresponds to a small fictitious value of initial stress σ'_0 which serves only for settlement calculation. Its true physical meaning has no importance in this context.

Using conventional soil-mechanics procedure, one can calculate thaw settlement of a layer of thickness H_f when acted upon by the effective stress σ'_1:

$$s = H_f \frac{C_c}{1 + e_f} \log \frac{\sigma'_1}{\sigma'_0} \tag{4.8}$$

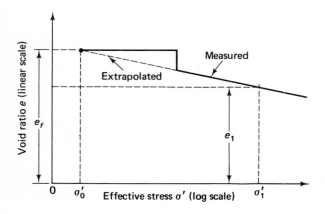

Figure 4.4 A typical e-vs.-σ' relationship on a semilogarithmic plot. (*After Nixon and Morgenstern, 1974.*)

The compression index C_c equals the slope of the linear portion of the plot of e vs. $\log \sigma'$ and is given by

$$C_c = \frac{e_f - e_1}{\log (\sigma'_1/\sigma'_0)} \tag{4.9}$$

As before, for n layers within the depth of thaw $X(t)$, the total settlement will be

$$s = \sum_{i=1}^{n} H_i \frac{C_{ci}}{1 + e_{fi}} \log \frac{\sigma'_i}{\sigma'_0} \tag{4.10}$$

where σ'_i is given by Eq. (4.7).

Variation of density on thawing The unit thaw settlement can be expressed in terms of the dry density of the soil before and after thawing (U.S.S.R. Building Code, 1960; Crory, 1973) as follows:

$$\frac{s}{H_f} = \frac{e_f - e_{\text{th}}}{1 + e_f} = 1 - \frac{\gamma_{df}}{\gamma_{d,\text{th}}} \tag{4.11}$$

where γ_{df} and $\gamma_{d,\text{th}}$ are the frozen and the thawed dry densities of the soil, respectively. As shown by Crory (1973), Eq. (4.11) permits a quick evaluation of the potential settlement of all soils within the thaw depth without requiring thaw-consolidation tests to be run on all the cores obtained from the drill hole.

In some cases it is useful to determine how the unit thaw settlement depends on the basic physical properties of the frozen soil. A complete relationship similar to that shown by Crory (1973) and valid for a zero lateral strain is

$$\frac{s}{H_f} = \frac{w_f(1 + 0.09i_r) - w_{\text{th}}}{S_r/G_s + w_f(1 + 0.09i_r)} \tag{4.12}$$

where w_f and w_{th} are the frozen and thawed total moisture content of the frozen soil, respectively, and i_r is the iceness ratio, defined in terms of the total w_f and unfrozen w_u water contents as

$$i_r = \frac{w_f - w_u}{w_f} \tag{4.13}$$

The total degree of saturation S_r is

$$S_r = \frac{G_s(1.09w_f - 0.09w_u)}{e} \tag{4.14}$$

and G_s is the specific gravity of the soil particles.

In Eq. (4.11) to (4.13) the frozen-soil properties, including e_f, γ_{df}, or w_f, can readily be determined by standard soil-mechanics procedures. Determination of their thawed counterparts, corresponding to a given pressure, requires the use of thaw-consolidation tests. For ice-saturated frozen soils the unit thaw settlement at any given pressure should have a definite correlation with the density of the frozen soil. Luscher and Afifi (1973) obtained a positive correlation between the unit thaw settlement (at a pressure of about 96 kPa) and the dry density of frozen silts, sands, gravels, and dirty gravels taken from several trans-Alaska pipeline system sites. A similar large-scale investigation conducted (Speer et al., 1973) in connection with the Mackenzie Valley Pipe Line Project involved mainly clayey silts and silts. From the large number of tests a correlation was established between the unit thaw settlement (at total overburden pressure) and the frozen bulk density. Using a least-squares fit gave the relationship for the average thaw settlement as

$$\frac{s}{H_f} = 0.736 - 1.018 \ln \gamma_f \pm 0.07 \qquad (4.15)$$

where γ_f is the frozen bulk density of the soil in grams per cubic centimeter.

In a subsequent study of thaw settlements of clayey silts from the same area Watson et al. (1973b) summarized the results of all available data from both investigations and obtained a rather narrow correlation band (Fig. 4.5).

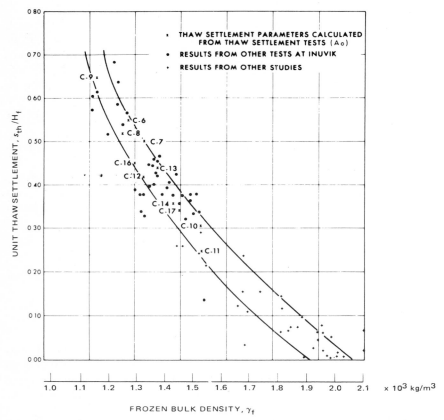

Figure 4.5 Relationship between unit thaw settlement and frozen bulk density. (*After Watson et al., 1973a.*)

The band between the two full lines can be represented by the empirical relationship

$$\frac{s}{H_f} = 0.80 - 0.868\left(\frac{\gamma_f}{\gamma_w} - 1.15\right)^{1/2} \pm 0.05 \qquad (4.16)$$

which is valid for silts and clayey silts within the interval $1.2 < \gamma_f/\gamma_w < 2.0$. For $\gamma_f/\gamma_w = 2$, Eq. (4.16) yields $s/H_f = 0 \pm 0.05$, corresponding to the minimum possible thaw strain of a very dense frozen soil. Since some dense soils between ice lenses swell during thawing (Crory, 1973), the negative sign in the above formula is justified.

This empirical relationship is valid only for the soil types included in the investigation. A similar study on low-plasticity clays from northern Manitoba (Keil et al., 1973) gave a thaw-settlement–vs.–frozen-bulk-density relationship similar to Eq. (4.16) but with the unit thaw settlements about 10 percent higher. For low-plasticity clays this difference can be taken into account by modifying Eq. (4.16) as follows:

$$\frac{s}{H_f} = 0.90 - 0.868\left(\frac{\gamma_f}{\gamma_w} - 1.15\right)^{1/2} \pm 0.05 \qquad (4.17)$$

Dry density of the soil may be used in place of bulk density with the transformation

$$\frac{\gamma_f}{\gamma_w} = \frac{\gamma_{df}}{\gamma_w}\left(1 - \frac{S_r}{G_s}\right) + S_r \qquad (4.18)$$

If we assume $S_r \approx 1$, $G_s = 2.65$ for sands and silts, and $G_s = 2.73$ for clays, Eqs. (4.16) and (4.17) can be written in terms of the dry density of frozen soil γ_{df}. For sands and silts

$$\frac{s}{H_f} = 0.80 - 0.685\left(\frac{\gamma_{df}}{\gamma_w} - 0.241\right)^{1/2} \pm 0.05 \qquad (4.19)$$

and for low-plasticity clays

$$\frac{s}{H_f} = 0.90 - 0.691\left(\frac{\gamma_{df}}{\gamma_w} - 0.236\right)^{1/2} \pm 0.05 \qquad (4.20)$$

Thaw Settlement Due to Undrained Thawing

In connection with laboratory thaw-consolidation investigations it is sometimes necessary to evaluate under undrained conditions the settlement due solely to ice-water phase transformation of the pore ice in a soil. For a soil that does not swell on thawing, the following relationship serves that purpose:

$$\frac{s_u}{H_f} = \frac{0.09 w_f i_r \gamma_{df}}{\gamma_w} \qquad (4.21)$$

or, in terms of water content, degree of saturation S_r, and iceness ratio i_r,

$$\frac{S_u}{H_f} = \frac{0.09 w_f i_r}{1/G_s + (1 + 0.09 i_r) w_f / S_r} \tag{4.22}$$

For a completely frozen saturated soil ($i_r = 1$, $S_r = 1$) Eq. (4.22) reduces to

$$\frac{S_u}{H_f} = \frac{0.09}{1.09 + 1/w_f G_s} \tag{4.23}$$

Thaw Settlement Due to Ice Inclusions

All the methods used for thaw-settlement evaluation assume that a sufficient number of representative frozen-soil specimens can be tested in the laboratory. This requirement can be satisfied only when the ice inclusions in the ground are relatively thin, normally not more than 10 mm. If the soil contains thicker ice lenses, one can either test proportionally larger samples or attempt to evaluate the settlement due to thick ice inclusions separately. The latter method, recommended in the U.S.S.R Building Code (1960), estimated the settlement s_{ii} due to thawing of all ice inclusions thicker than 1 mm within the thaw depth $X(t)$ with the expression

$$s_{ii} = \sum_0^X h_i r_i \tag{4.24}$$

where h_i is the thickness of individual ice inclusions and r_i is a reduction coefficient:

$$r = \begin{cases} 0.4 & h_i < 30 \text{ mm} \\ 0.6 & 30 < h_i < 100 \text{ mm} \\ 0.8 & h_i > 100 \text{ mm} \end{cases}$$

4.2 ONE-DIMENSIONAL CONSOLIDATION OF THAWING SOILS

Industrial development and/or a variety of natural erosion processes will often alter the thermal regime sufficiently to induce melting of the underlying permafrost. Some examples include impounding reservoirs, stripping vegetation, and the effects of building foundations. Seasonal thawing of the near-surface active layer and the loss of vegetation following a forest fire are examples of natural events where thawing of frozen ground may occur. More dramatic are the potential influences of oil pipelines operating at high temperatures in the Arctic (Lachenbruch, 1970).

When thawing occurs at a slow rate, the water generated will flow from the soil at about the same rate as it is produced. No excess pore pressure will be sustained, and settlement will proceed concurrently with thawing. If thawing occurs at a faster rate, excess pore pressures can be generated. If these excess pore pressures are sustained, their implications are severe. Slopes may become unstable, dam foundations may fail, settlements may be impeded, and differential settlements may be aggravated. Many other undesirable effects could be cited. Therefore it is important to investigate the factors controlling pore pressures generated in a thawing soil.

When a mass of frozen soil is subjected to a temperature increase on or near the ground surface, thawing will be controlled by the temperature boundary conditions and the thermal properties of the soil. Analytical solutions to such problems in heat conduction are given by Carslaw and Jaeger (1947) and a variety of numerical methods by Murray and Landis (1959). The movement rate of the freeze-thaw interface, taken here as the 0°C isotherm, is determined accordingly, and attention may be turned to the associated problem of soil consolidation in the thawed soil.

The thaw interface forms the lower boundary of the region of interest in the consolidation problem since the frozen soil does not transmit pore pressures or participate in any significant deformation. On thawing, the soil is subjected to loading caused by its self weight or to a combination of self weight and applied load. In general, the thaw interface moves with time, and hence the consolidation of the soil above it is governed by a moving boundary condition. The Terzaghi consolidation theory models the compressible nature of the soil skeleton. This is extremely important for this type of moving-boundary problem, where the very transient or time-dependent nature of moisture movement within the thawed soil requires that the theory account for the ability of the soil to store or release pore water.

Linear Thaw Consolidation

A one-dimensional configuration (Fig. 4.6) is considered when a step increase in temperature is imposed at the surface of a semi-infinite homogeneous mass of frozen soil. The solution to the heat-conduction problem (Carslaw and Jaeger, 1947) has been reviewed in Chap. 3. The movement of the thaw plane is given by

$$X(t) = \alpha t^{1/2} \tag{4.25}$$

where α = constant determined in solution of heat-conduction problem
X = distance to thaw plane from soil surface
t = time

It is assumed that the soil is compressible in the thawed zone and that the theory of consolidation is valid. Hence, it can be shown that

$$c_v \frac{\partial^2 u}{\partial x^2} = \frac{\partial u}{\partial t} \tag{4.26}$$

where $u(x, t)$ = excess pore pressure
x = depth measured from ground surface
c_v = coefficient of consolidation

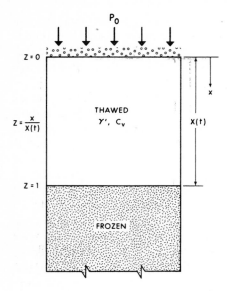

Figure 4.6 One-dimensional thaw consolidation. (*After Morgenstern and Nixon, 1971.*)

Equation (4.26) is valid in the region $0 < x < X$ and for the time $0 < t < \infty$. The upper surface of the soil mass is taken to be free-draining; hence

$$u = 0 \qquad \begin{array}{l} \text{at } x = 0 \\ \text{for } t > 0 \end{array} \qquad (4.27)$$

At the thaw plane, liberated water flows upward if there is any excess pore pressure. For a saturated soil, the boundary condition indicates that any flow from the thaw plane is accommodated by a change in volume of the unfrozen soil. Applying Darcy's law and using a linear effective stress-strain law for the soil skeleton gives the boundary condition at the thaw line

$$P_0 + \gamma' X - u(X, t) = \frac{c_v(\partial u/\partial x)(X, t)}{dX/dt} \qquad \text{at } x = X(t)$$

$$\text{for } t > 0 \qquad (4.28)$$

A derivation of this boundary condition has been given by Morgenstern and Nixon (1971), who assumed that the soil was saturated and that the free water table was maintained at the soil surface. This boundary condition also assumes that the initial effective stress (residual stress) in the thawed soil, for no drainage, is zero and that this is probably true for the more ice-rich soils.

The coefficient of consolidation c_v is related to the coefficient of permeability k and the coefficient of compressibility m_v by

$$c_v = \frac{k}{m_v \gamma_w} \qquad (4.29)$$

Measurement of this parameter will be discussed later.

The solution to Eq. (4.26) subject to the boundary conditions (4.27) and (4.28), obtained by Morgenstern and Nixon (1971), is

$$u(x, t) = \frac{P_0}{\text{erf}(R) + e^{-R^2}/\pi^{1/2}R} \text{ erf } \frac{x}{2(c_v t)^{1/2}} + \frac{\gamma' x}{1 + 1/2R^2} \tag{4.30}$$

It is convenient to introduce the dimensionless variables

$$z = \frac{x}{X(t)} \tag{4.31}$$

and

$$R = \frac{\alpha}{2(c_v)^{1/2}} \tag{4.32}$$

where R is termed the *thaw-consolidation ratio*.

The error function, erf ( ), has been tabulated by Carslaw and Jaeger (1947). The first term on the right-hand side of Eq. (4.30) represents the pore pressures generated under an applied loading P_0. The pore pressures obtained for this loading condition are given in Fig. 4.7. The second term provides the pore pressures maintained in a soil thawing and settling under the action of its own weight. This relation has particular importance in many applications

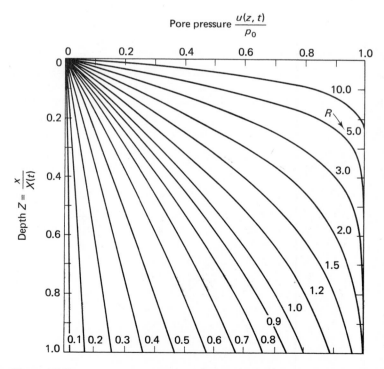

Figure 4.7 Excess pore pressures; $\gamma' = 0$ (weightless material). (*After Morgenstern and Nixon, 1971.*)

described later in this volume and is reproduced for convenience in the form

$$\frac{u(z, t)}{\gamma' X} = \frac{1}{1 + 1/2R^2} \tag{4.33}$$

The pore pressures for this self-loading condition are shown in Fig. 4.8.

For both loading situations the pore pressures increase with increases in the thaw-consolidation ratio R. The dimensionless pore pressures shown in Figs. 4.7 and 4.8 are independent of time. This phenomenon has been observed when the thaw-front motion is proportional to the square root of time [Eq. (4.25)]. The results suggest that when the value of R exceeds unity, the excess pore pressures at the thaw plane approach their maximum value and consequently the effective stress tends toward zero.

For this class of moving-boundary problems we define the average degree of consolidation of the thawed soil as the ratio of the consolidation settlement S_t that has occurred at time t to the total consolidation settlement S_{max} that would occur if thawing were stopped at time t. Settlement associated with the ice-water transformation will be in addition to that considered here and must be treated separately [Eq. (4.23)].

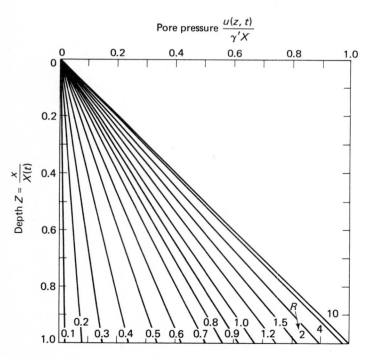

Figure 4.8 Excess pore pressures; $P_0 = 0$ (no applied load). (*After Morgenstern and Nixon, 1971.*)

As in conventional linear-consolidation theory, the degree of consolidation can be obtained by integrating the pore-pressure distribution and for the case of an applied surcharge loading ($\gamma' = 0$) has the form

$$\frac{S_t}{S_{max}} = 1 - \frac{\text{erf}\,(R) + (e^{-R^2} - 1)/\pi^{1/2}R}{\text{erf}\,(R) + e^{-R^2}/\pi^{1/2}R} \tag{4.34}$$

For self-weight loading ($P_0 = 0$)

$$\frac{S_t}{S_{max}} = \frac{1}{1 + 2R^2} \tag{4.35}$$

If thawing is stopped at time t, the total settlement S_{max} equals the soil compressibility m_v multiplied by the effective stress change after completion of consolidation, i.e.,

$$S_{max} = m_v\left(P_0 X + \frac{\gamma' X^2}{2}\right) \tag{4.36}$$

When thawing is taking place, the settlement S_t at time t equals the product of S_{max} and S_t/S_{max}. The settlement ratio S_t/S_{max} has been plotted against the thaw-consolidation ratio in Fig. 4.9.

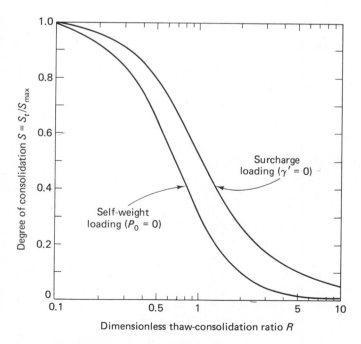

Figure 4.9 Variation of S with R. (*After Morgenstern and Nixon, 1971.*)

For cases where soil is consolidating only under an applied load or only under the influence of self weight, the relationships describing the excess pore-pressure distribution and degree of consolidation are all independent of time. A similar feature was found by Gibson (1958) when considering the pore pressures generated by deposition of material at a rate proportional to the square root of time. The dimensionless thaw-consolidation ratio is a fundamental parameter which, although independent of time, has a role similar to the time factor in more conventional consolidation problems.

Excess pore pressures and the degree of consolidation in thawing soils are dependent principally on the thaw-consolidation ratio R. This parameter is a measure of the relative rates of generation and expulsion of excess pore fluids. As a first approximation, a value of R greater than unity would appear to predict the danger of sustaining substantial pore pressures at the thaw plane and hence the possibility of instability. The magnitude of R is a function of α (the solution to a geothermal calculation) and the coefficient of consolidation c_v. The range of α values likely to occur in practice falls within 0.2 to 1.0 mm/s$^{1/2}$ and can probably be calculated to an accuracy of ± 10 percent (Nixon and McRoberts, 1973). The coefficient c_v may vary from 10 (sandy silts) to 0.01 mm^2/s (clays). A knowledge of the R value is therefore very dependent on our ability to determine the geotechnical properties of the soil material accurately. This problem is explored in detail in Sec. 4.5.

Nonlinear Thaw Consolidation

The assumption of a linear stress-strain law for the soil skeleton is one of the limitations of the linear thaw-consolidation theory. Many frozen soils when thawed have an initial high void ratio, and over the range of stresses of engineering interest the void-ratio–effective stress relationship may be markedly nonlinear. Figure 4.10 compares typical compressibility behavior with the idealized linear assumption adopted earlier. It is important to investigate the influence of this nonlinearity on the consolidation of thawing soil.

The effective stress is denoted by σ_0' for a soil that is thawed with no drainage permitted. If no drainage is permitted under the influence of subsequent loading increments, the void-ratio–effective-stress curve can be found experimentally. Laboratory studies show that a straight-line relationship is obtained when the void ratio e is plotted against the logarithm of effective stress for some thawed soils tested in this manner. This empirical relationship has been incorporated (Davis and Raymond, 1965) into a theory of consolidation for normally consolidated unfrozen soils.

Although the coefficient of permeability k and the slope of the stress-strain curve m_v both change over a range of pressures, it may be assumed, on experimental grounds, that they change in such a way as to maintain the consolidation coefficient c_v approximately constant. Following Davis and

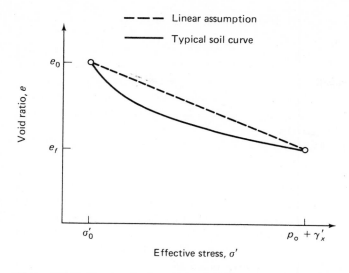

Figure 4.10 Void-ratio–effective-stress relationships. (*After Nixon and Morgenstern, 1973b.*)

Raymond (1965), a constant c_v value has been adopted together with the stress-strain relationship

$$e = e_0 - C_c \log \frac{\sigma'}{\sigma'_0} \tag{4.37}$$

where C_c is the slope of the e–$\log \sigma'$ line (compression index) and σ' is the current effective stress. The general one-dimensional equation of consolidation for a saturated soil is then written

$$-c_v \left[\frac{1}{\sigma'} \frac{\partial^2 u}{\partial x^2} - \left(\frac{1}{\sigma'} \right)^2 \frac{\partial u}{\partial x} \frac{\partial \sigma'}{\partial x} \right] = \frac{1}{\sigma'} \frac{\partial \sigma'}{\partial t} \tag{4.38}$$

This equation is valid in thawed soil regardless of loading type or drainage conditions at the boundaries.

For the same loading conditions the total stresses and the pore-water pressures, respectively, are

$$\sigma = P_0 + \gamma' x + \gamma_w x \tag{4.39}$$

and

$$P_w = u + \gamma_w x \tag{4.40}$$

With the water table at the surface $(x = 0)$, the effective stress is then the difference between these stress components:

$$\sigma' = \sigma - P_w = P_0 + \gamma' x - u \tag{4.41}$$

Substituting the derivative of this expression into Eq. (4.38) gives

$$\frac{\partial u}{\partial t} = c_v\left(\frac{\partial^2 u}{\partial x^2} - \frac{\gamma' - \partial u/\partial x}{P_0 + \sigma'x - u}\frac{\partial u}{\partial x}\right) \tag{4.42}$$

This equation can be linearized for the case where $\gamma' = 0$. This condition, where applied loads dominate the soil consolidation, will be studied here. Numerical methods must be employed to solve a loading combination involving the self-weight condition ($P_0 = 0$).

Setting $\gamma' = 0$ in Eqs. (4.41) and (4.42) and linearizing the resulting equation gives

$$\frac{\partial w}{\partial t} = c_v\frac{\partial^2 w}{\partial x^2} \tag{4.43}$$

where

$$w = \log\frac{P_0 - u}{P_0} \tag{4.44}$$

The boundary condition at the surface now becomes

$$x = 0 \qquad u = 0 \qquad w = 0 \tag{4.45}$$

The boundary condition used previously at the thaw plane [Eq. (4.28)] must now be rederived for consistency. To study the applied loading condition, Nixon and Morgenstern (1973a) derived the boundary condition in terms of $w(x, t)$, the transformed variable:

$$x = X(t) \qquad \log\frac{\sigma'_0}{P_0} - w = \frac{c_v\,\partial w/\partial x}{dX/dt} \qquad t > 0 \tag{4.46}$$

The term $\log(\sigma'_0/P_0)$ is constant, and so Eqs. (4.43), (4.45), and (4.46), in terms of the transformed variable w, are entirely analogous to the corresponding equations derived for the linear theory in terms of $u(x, t)$. Consequently, the solution for the linear thaw-consolidation equation can be applied directly to obtain $w(x, t)$. For thawing based on the square root of time

$$\frac{w(x, t)}{\log(\sigma'_0/P_0)} = \frac{\text{erf}(Rx/X)}{\text{erf}(R) + e^{-R^2}/\pi^{1/2}R} \tag{4.47}$$

Equations (4.47) and (4.44) form the exact solution for a thawing soil with consolidation occurring solely due to an applied load P_0. The soil has an initial void ratio in the thawed state corresponding to an initial effective stress of σ'_0.

The ratio P_0/σ'_0 is a measure of the effective-stress change in the thawing soil and therefore of the nonlinearity of the effective-stress–strain curve. This ratio now enters as an additional dimensionless quantity, and its effect on the excess-pore-pressure distribution in the thawed soil can be investigated. As in the linear theory, the normalized excess-pore-pressure distribution is unchanged throughout the thaw-consolidation process, although it is now dependent on the stress ratio P_0/σ'_0. The degree of settlement in the thawed soil, however, is in-

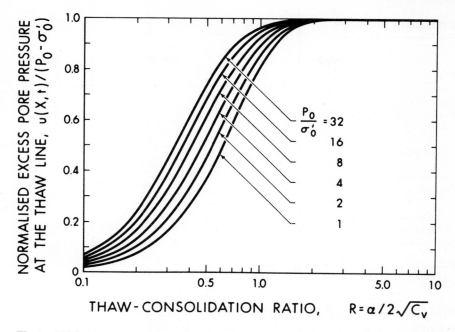

Figure 4.11 Excess pore pressures at the thaw plane for nonlinear theory. (*After Nixon and Morgenstern, 1973a.*)

dependent of time and the ratio P_0/σ_0'. This fact was also recognized by Davis and Raymond (1965) for this type of stress-strain relationship. Consequently, the linear theory can be used equally well for calculating the degree of consolidation settlement.

Figure 4.11 shows the excess pore pressure at the thaw plane as a function of the stress ratio and the thaw-consolidation ratio R. It is seen that as the stress increment ratio increases, the excess-pore-pressure condition at the thaw plane increases to a more critical level.

In cases where high initial void ratios are present in the soil on thawing, the excess pore pressures may be considerably underestimated if only a linear relation between void ratio and effective stress is considered.

Laboratory Thaw-Consolidation Testing

To verify some of the findings of the theory of consolidation for thawing soils, several researchers have conducted laboratory tests under carefully controlled conditions. Procedures employed by these researchers have been described in Sec. 4.1, and some of the results of direct interest in the theory of thaw consolidation are presented here.

Table 4.1 Index properties

Soil	Percentage clay	Liquid limit, %	Plastic limit, %	Specific gravity	Plasticity index
Undisturbed Norman Wells silt	23	29	19	2.65	10
Reconstituted Mountain River clay	55	40	20	2.73	20
Undisturbed Noell Lake clay	40	41	23	2.65	18
Reconstituted Devon silt	23	30	22	2.65	8
Reconstituted Athabasca clay	45	40.8	20.3	2.65	20.5
Reconstituted Lake Edmonton clay	65	70	29	2.76	41
Reconstituted Bentonite clay	94	591	87	2.75	504

Morgenstern and Smith (1973) tested reconstituted samples of various frozen soils (Table 4.1) using thermistors to monitor the position of the 0°C isotherm. The sample was thawed from the top, one-dimensionally. Settlements were monitored during thaw, and when the thaw plane reached the base of the sample, a porous stone and pore-pressure transducer recorded the excess pore pressure u at the sample base. The settlement at the end of thawing S_t, was measured, together with the maximum settlement after thawing S_{max} when consolidation was complete. The value of α was calculated using the time to thaw a given sample depth. The coefficient of consolidation c_v was determined by observing the settlement of the sample after completion of thaw. Consequently, the value of R [Eq. (4.32)] could be calculated for each test.

In general, it was found that the depth of thaw increased in proportion to the square root of time, and the constant α agrees well with existing solutions to this melting problem (Chap. 3). Maximum excess-pore-pressure values measured for these reconstituted frozen soils are summarized in Fig. 4.12. The experimental dependence of the maximum excess pore pressure on the thaw-consolidation ratio R was well demonstrated by this text series. Results for the degree of consolidation obtained during thaw, S_t/S_{max}, show considerable scatter in the data, but the data displayed the same trend as the theoretical curve.

Additional tests by Nixon and Morgenstern (1974) on samples of undisturbed fine-grained permafrost used essentially the same test configuration. Samples with different ice contents were thawed at different rates. The index properties of these soils are also given in Table 4.1. The different values of α and consolidation coefficient c_v, provided a wide variation in the thaw-consolidation ratio R. Results for excess pore pressures are plotted against R in Fig. 4.13. The majority of the test results agreed reasonably well with the prediction offered by the linear theory. Four of the samples contained quantities of ice considerably greater than

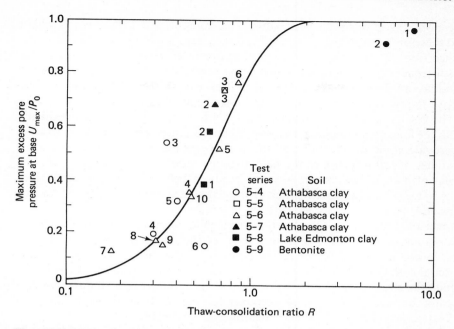

Figure 4.12 Maximum excess pore pressures measured for reconstituted soils. (*After Morgenstern and Smith, 1973.*)

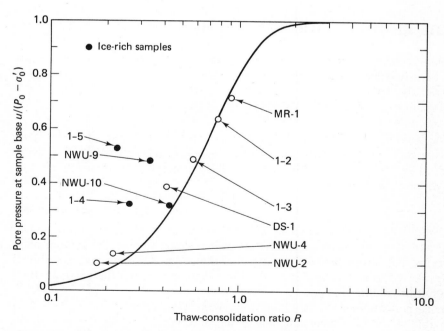

Figure 4.13 Observed and predicted pore pressures for undisturbed permafrost. (*After Nixon and Morgenstern, 1974.*)

those normally present in these soils. The compression of the soil skeleton could therefore be expected to be nonlinear; i.e., large quantities of water would be expelled from the soil with only small increases in effective stress after thawing, and subsequent stress increases would bring successively decreasing amounts of consolidation. The nonlinear theory outlined earlier (Fig. 4.11) was used to improve the pressure prediction of the linear theory shown in Fig. 4.13.

The results of laboratory studies have confirmed, in general, the prediction of both the linear and nonlinear theories of consolidation. Laboratory verification can provide some justification for the use of the theory for design purposes, but studies of soil response in the field, together with experience in applying the concept of thaw consolidation, are also required before theoretical predictions can be made with confidence. Much of the remainder of this chapter is devoted to this end.

Once the theoretical aspects of thaw consolidation have been established, the main parameter of concern is measurement of the consolidation coefficient c_v. If the consolidation coefficient measured directly in a laboratory consolidation test on the thawed soil is employed in the theory, it is also necessary to estimate the stress ratio P_0/σ'_0. This models the nonlinearity of the stress-strain curve for the soil and therefore accounts for the relatively large amounts of consolidation that occur following melting and settlement at lower stresses. An alternative approach for calculating c_v is outlined for a field case history in Sec. 4.5.

4.3 THE RESIDUAL STRESS IN THAWING SOILS

The maintenance of excess pore pressures and the development of settlements are primarily dependent on the thaw-consolidation ratio R. This parameter expresses the balance between the rate of generation of excess pore fluids (melting) and the ability of the thawed soil to expel these fluids from the pore space (consolidation).

The boundary condition at the thaw plane equates flow from the thaw plane with change in volume of the soil. In the linear theory, the volumetric strain of the soil is proportional to the change in effective stress. The change in effective stress at the thaw line $\Delta\sigma'$ is

$$\Delta\sigma' = \sigma'(X, t) - \sigma'_0 \tag{4.48}$$

where $\sigma'(X, t)$ is the effective stress at the thaw plane X, which is a function of time t, and σ'_0 is the effective stress in the soil skeleton thawed under undrained conditions. The initial effective stress in soil thawed under undrained conditions will be referred to as the *residual stress*. Only departures from the residual stress will result in volume changes.

In earlier sections the residual stress was taken equal to zero. This is a reasonable assumption when the soil is rich in ice or has a high void ratio in the thawed, undrained state, but when the stress and thermal histories associated with the formation of a permafrost specimen have been such as to reduce the void ratio of the soil, a significant residual stress may exist in the soil upon thawing.

Before proceeding to a discussion of the physical aspects of residual stress, consider how the parameter is introduced into the theoretical analysis for the consolidation of thawing soils. If the residual stress is considered significant in the analysis, the boundary condition in terms of the excess pore pressure at the thaw plane becomes (Morgenstern and Nixon, 1971)

$$P_0 + \gamma'X - \sigma'_0(x) - u = \frac{c_v \, \partial u/\partial x}{dX/dt} \tag{4.49}$$

Arbitrary functions of $\sigma'_0(X)$ can be employed in this boundary condition. The governing partial differential equation of consolidation is then solved subject to this condition at the moving boundary $x = X(t)$.

Physical Interpretation of Residual Stress

An appreciation of the physical meaning and importance of the residual stress within the context of the theory of thaw consolidation is gained after consideration of the following experiment. A sample of unfrozen fine-grained soil is prepared with a known stress history by consolidating a slurry to a known stress P_0. At this stage the sample has dissipated all excess pore pressures with P_0 an effective stress (Fig. 4.14). The sample is now frozen with no drainage. The average void ratio increases a small amount, point A to B, due to the volume expansion of water to ice in the soil pores. If the sample is now allowed to thaw with no drainage, the void ratio returns to point A. However, an increase is observed in the pore-water pressure, and if the sample has a high enough void ratio, the pore pressure may approach or even equal the total stress on the sample. This implies that the effective stress is greatly reduced and indeed may be zero for all practical purposes. If the sample is now allowed to drain freely, consolidation occurs and the sample regains equilibrium at a much reduced void ratio, point C in Fig. 4.14.

Externally the soil in this sample has undergone a net decrease in volume, represented by AC, under a constant external stress. It is known that negative pore-water pressures build up in fine-grained soils during freezing. It may often be observed that small ice layers, lenses, and other discrete segments of ice form upon freezing, even when freezing has taken place in the absence of free access to water. It must be concluded then that as the total quantity of water in the sample has remained unchanged, the remaining elements of soil are now overconsolidated with respect to the external total stress; i.e., the areas of soil between discrete ice segments have experienced an effective stress greater than P_0. There is an abundance of evidence for the existence of negative pore pressures in fine-grained soils during freezing (e.g., Williams 1966; Wissa and Martin 1968). When a significant clay fraction is present, it is well known that the negative pressures can be exceedingly high.

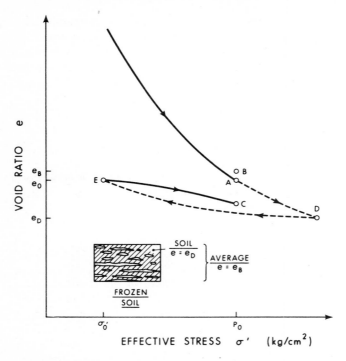

Figure 4.14 Stress path in a closed-system freeze-thaw cycle (schematic). (*After Nixon and Morgenstern, 1973b.*)

On thawing, the overconsolidated elements of the soil possess an effective stress greater than P_0. However, a quantity of free water is available on a local scale from the thawed ice segments, and the soil swells almost instantaneously to absorb the excess water in the macropores that resulted from thawing of the segregated ice. The stress path taken by the soil element is shown by the dotted line *ADE* in Fig. 4.14. If the soil is capable of absorbing all the free water, the remaining effective stress is the residual stress. Alternatively, if the soil swells to a zero-effective-stress condition and free water is still available, the residual stress is zero and excess pore fluids remain in the soil. If free drainage is now permitted at the soil boundaries, the soil reconsolidates to the effective stress P_0 and the reloading behavior is typical of that of an overconsolidated unfrozen soil. The reloading path is represented by the line *EC* in Fig. 4.14.

The net strain from the frozen to the fully thawed consolidated state (*BC*) is sometimes identified as the thaw strain. In this sample experiment, the stress history of the soil was well defined, and it was demonstrated that the thermal history is an extremely important factor in determining the residual stress σ_0' in the thawed soil and the subsequent stress-strain behavior of the soil.

Permafrost behavior is influenced by the stress and thermal histories and the drainage conditions when the soil existed in a thawed state. When a frozen soil sample is removed from the ground, the first measurement in the thawed state is the residual stress. This constitutes the starting point for prediction of the excess pore pressure and settlements in a thawed soil.

If the soil remains undrained for any significant period of time because of fast thaw rates, low coefficient of consolidation, or the lack of a free draining boundary, the residual stress σ_0' will control the initial undrained shear strength of the soil mass. The relationship controlling the undrained strength of a purely frictional thawed soil is

$$\frac{c_u}{\sigma_0'} = \frac{[K_0 + A(1 - K_0)]\sin\phi'}{1 + (2A - 1)\sin\phi'} \qquad (4.50)$$

where c_u = undrained shear strength of thawed soil
   K_0 = ratio between the lateral and vertical effective stresses under conditions of no lateral yield
   A = pore-pressure parameter
   ϕ' = effective angle of shearing resistance for soil mass

The excess pore pressures are controlled by the stress increment $P_0 + \gamma'X - \sigma_0'$ in a soil which is simultaneously thawing and consolidating in a one-dimensional configuration. If the combination of stress and thermal histories were such as to generate high values of σ_0', it is conceivable that σ_0' could be greater than $P_0 + \gamma'X$ and negative pore pressures would result on thawing, accompanied by settlements in this instance smaller than those due to the ice-water transformation alone. This phenomenon has been reported by Crory (1973).

The Measurement of Residual Stress

Special apparatus is needed to measure the residual stress in a thawed soil. Restrictions placed on the test configuration require that no water be allowed to enter or leave the sample during thawing and that no lateral yielding be permitted, so that one-dimensional conditions are satisfied.

With a saturated soil the test may be performed in either of two ways. In the first method the total load σ on the sample is set equal to some constant value, e.g., the effective overburden load that the sample might be subjected to in the field, and after complete thawing the pore-water pressure is measured. The residual stress is calculated by subtracting the pore-water pressure from the total stress. A second procedure, which may be described as a null method, involves thawing the frozen soil and continuously adjusting the total stress σ so that the pore-water pressure is always zero. In this way, on completion of thaw, the residual stress is equal to the total stress on the sample. The second of these methods is preferred since it eliminates all pore-pressure response effects in the soil and in the pore-pressure measuring system.

Measurements of the residual stress have been made on reconstituted samples of Athabasca silty clay from Northern Alberta and on samples of a blue silty clay from the Mountain River, N.W.T. (Nixon and Morgenstern, 1973b). The

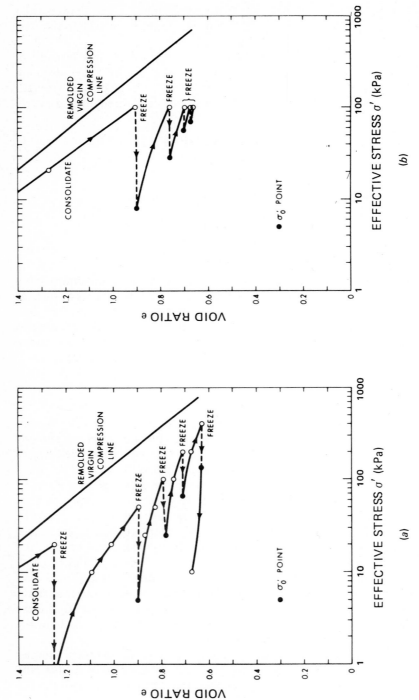

Figure 4.15 Measurement of residual stress for reconstituted Athabasca clay. (*After Nixon and Morgenstern, 1973b.*)

soils were prepared as slurries and deaired. In some cases the slurries were consolidated to a convenient void ratio, and then frozen samples were prepared from the slurry, machined to the correct dimensions, and placed in the apparatus.

In either case, the sample was then thawed and the residual stress measured. For a successful test the void ratio before freezing should be the same as that at the completion of thawing, demonstrating that no drainage occurred during the freeze-thaw cycle. After additional load increments were placed on the thawed soil and the consolidation properties defined, the sample was refrozen without drainage and a new residual stress was measured for the lower void ratio. This procedure was carried out several times, giving a relationship between the thawed void ratio e and σ'_0. This relationship does not represent a stress path taken by the soil but the locus of a series of points taken from a set of stress paths like those indicated in Fig. 4.15a.

In this test series, the soil was remolded and consolidated to a higher stress and refrozen. Upon thawing, the residual stress was measured and the process was repeated, each time consolidating the sample to a higher stress level. To determine the effect of a different stress history on the residual stress, another remolded sample was consolidated to 98.0 kPa, as shown in Fig. 4.15b. It was then frozen and the residual stress measured in the thawed soil. Subsequent measurements of σ'_0 were undertaken by reconsolidating the sample to the same stress of 98.0 kPa.

As freeze-thaw cycling continued in the absence of drainage during freezing, the residual stress increased steadily until it approached the overburden stress. The consolidation which occurred on reloading steadily decreased. This was to be expected, because otherwise the cycling would continue to cause steady

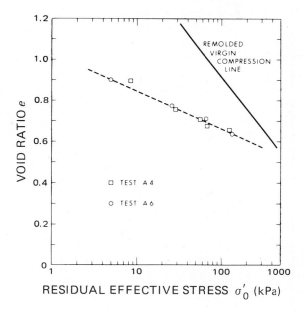

Figure 4.16 Void ratio plotted with residual effect stress for reconstituted Athabasca clay. (*After Nixon and Morgenstern, 1973b.*)

decreases in the void ratio ad infinitum. Furthermore, this test series demonstrated that if the effective overburden stress is close to the residual stress in the thawed soil, subsequent settlements due to consolidation after thaw will be small. The combined results for these tests, summarized in Fig. 4.16, show thawed void ratio plotted against the logarithm of the residual stress σ_0'. Although entirely different stress paths were taken by the two soil samples, approximately the same relationship was found between e and σ_0'. A linear correlation appears to exist between the void ratio of a given thawed soil and the logarithm of the residual stress. This relationship appears to be sensibly independent of the previous stress and thermal history effects, at least for the limited studies undertaken so far.

Implications of Residual Stress

The existence of residual stress in permafrost thawed under undrained conditions has engineering implications. The higher the residual stress in the thawed soil, the smaller the subsequent consolidation settlement, the lower the pore pressures generated during thaw, and the higher the undrained shear strength. If the depositional sequence and the thermal history associated with the formation of a body of permafrost are such that the void ratio decreases significantly with depth, substantial values of the residual stress can be anticipated. Hence, the thawed soil will have a finite shear strength, and problems such as the stability of the thaw bulb around a buried warm-oil pipeline become less acute. The residual stress will generate a finite frictional resistance, and the thawed soil will not behave like a viscous fluid, as suggested by Lachenbruch (1970).

The influence of residual stress is also of concern relative to the effects of thawing permafrost on the behavior of an oil well. The arching of the soil about the well will affect the stresses transferred to the casing which tend to make it buckle. Palmer (1972) has drawn attention to the control of arching by the effective stresses existing in the thawing soil during thaw and subsequent consolidation. He referred to the "extent of initial consolidation," which is related algebraically to the residual stress, and observed that it is a property of the site rather than of the soil type. He further noted that it can only be determined by thaw-consolidation tests on undisturbed cores.

In many cases of foundation design it may be prudent to remove the top few feet of highly compressible ice-rich material in order to limit thaw-induced deformation of the foundation. However, unless the residual stress can be shown to have a significant value compared with the effective overburden stress, serious deformations may still occur as the thaw plane penetrates deeper into the underlying ground. On the other hand, if a stratum with a high residual stress is accessible without excessive excavation, it may be possible to construct flexible structures directly on permafrost without concern for subsequent thaw. For example, oil tanks might be buried in the permafrost rather than placed on the thick insulated and ventilated gravel pads currently used.

4.4 THAW CONSOLIDATION IN LAYERED SYSTEMS

In many cases small differences in soil type with depth may appear unimportant compared with the uncertainty in obtaining the correct geotechnical properties of any fine-grained soil. However, certain changes in the nature of the foundation material are sufficiently clear to justify calculations for nonhomogeneous soil profiles. Examples of sudden changes in material type in permafrost profiles are the surficial layer of organic soil which overlies and protects the frozen mineral soil beneath and the widely varying thicknesses of ice layers which may be found in soil profiles. The occurrence of such gross inhomogeneities is quite commonplace, and it is important to establish how the effects of these features on the engineering behavior of the soil can be assessed.

Two-Layer Soil Problems

The formulation and solution of multilayered systems of thawing soils is somewhat lengthy but by no means complex. A complete problem formulation and description of a numerical solution are given by Nixon (1973). The rate of thaw in a two-layer system has been described in Chap. 3. The governing equations of consolidation can then be solved with the rate of thaw in combination with the boundary condition [Eq. (4.28)] at the thaw plane. An example for a 1.6-m-thick layer of peat overlying clay is given in Fig. 4.17.

A step surface temperature of $+10°C$ is applied at the surface of the peat, which has widely different thermal and consolidation properties from the underlying clay stratum. The rate of thaw and the thaw-plane pore pressures are also computed for the case where the peat layer is removed, and the same surface temperature is applied. In this simple manner, some of the effects of the removal of a surface organic layer on the stability of a thawing soil can be demonstrated theoretically. The thermal and consolidation properties for the two layers are assumed to be as shown in Table 4.2. In this table the submerged densities of

Table 4.2

Property	Peat	Silty clay
Water content w, percent	550	50
Submerged density γ_1, kg/m³	56	
γ', kg/m³	...	720
Depth H, m	1.5	
Latent heat L_1, MJ/m³	298	
L_2, MJ/m³	...	193
Thawed conductivity k_u, J/s m °C	0.377	1.13
Surface temperature T_s, °C	10	
Thaw rate α, m/year$^{1/2}$	0.89	1.93†
Consolidation coefficient c_v, m²/year	20.5	3.3
Permeability K, m/year	40	0.3

† If peat removed.

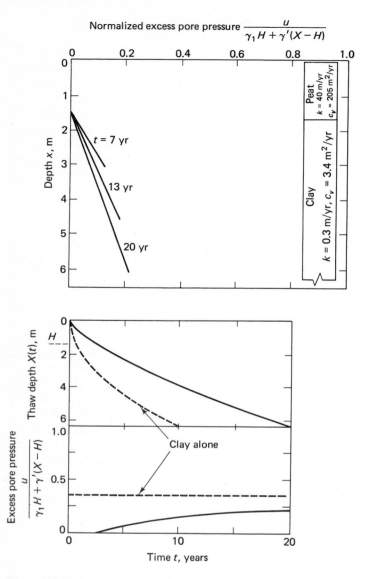

Figure 4.17 Excess pore pressures for peat over clay. (*After Nixon, 1973.*)

the upper and lower layers are widely different and are denoted by γ_1 and γ', respectively. When the thaw plane is in the lower layer, the effective overburden loading due to the peat layer becomes $\gamma_1 H$ if the water table is at the surface. Therefore the final effective stress at any depth x becomes

$$\sigma'_f = \gamma_1 H + \gamma'(X - H) \tag{4.51}$$

(bear in mind that P_0 and σ_0' are taken to be zero in this example). Equation (4.28) is now rewritten at $x = X$ as

$$\gamma_1 H + \gamma'(X - H) - u = \frac{c_v \, \partial u/\partial x}{dX/dt} \qquad (4.52)$$

The excess pore pressure calculated by the numerical procedure can be normalized for convenience by dividing by the final effective stress at the thaw line, $\gamma_1 H + \gamma'(X - H)$.

The excess-pore-pressure profiles at different times for thawing in the two-layer profile are shown in Fig. 4.17. Also shown are the thaw depths with time and the normalized excess pore pressure at the thaw plane. The dotted line shows that the thaw penetration into a given clay layer is decreased by some 50 percent when the peat layer is not removed. More significantly, the buildup of excess pore pressures at the thaw line is such that only about 50 percent of the pressure is attained of that value which would be calculated if no peat layer were present. The presence of the peat layer is, in general, responsible for three effects, all of which serve to make the stability of the underlying thawing layer less critical: (1) a high latent-heat "barrier" is available to impede thawing of the upper layer; (2) after the peat has been thawed, its lower thermal conductivity reduces the rate of thaw in the underlying stratum, reducing the overall thaw penetration and the excess pore pressures in the underlying layer; (3) a relatively free-draining boundary is provided with negligible excess pore pressures maintained at the base of the peat layer.

If the peat is removed and replaced by a layer of gravel, conditions 2 and 3 are still available to improve foundation conditions; however, in all probability the latent-heat barrier described by condition 1 will not be available.

Compressible Soil with Discrete Ice Layers

When a fine-grained soil freezes, a combination of the ambient conditions may prove extremely favorable for the formation of segregated ice. These conditions are often realized near the surface of a deposit of freezing soil. In soils with silt-sized particles, segregated ice in the form of discrete layers, or bands, often occurs. In the finer-grained plastic soils ice banding is also found with the bands oriented perpendicularly to the maximum principal stress. However, vertical ice veins and other ice forms are also found regularly in soils with more clay-sized particles.

To date a complete analysis of the position and magnitude of ice layers or even the amount of distributed ice which may be found in a freezing soil has not been carried out. However, the solution to problems involving the thawing of soils containing horizontal ice bands is rendered considerably simpler by knowing the position and extent of the segregated ice forms at the outset of thawing. A situation involving a layer of saturated compressible soil overlying a single layer of ice will be analyzed.

At the outset, a solution is considered for excess pore pressures in a thawing soil over a layer of ice which extends downward indefinitely. This assumption is made for simplicity at this point, and it will be seen later how the procedure is modified to include any ice layer of finite thickness. It is assumed that a step increase in temperature T_s has been applied at the surface and that the thaw plane is moving through the frozen soil at a rate given by the simple Stefan formula used earlier

$$X = \alpha t^{1/2} = \left[\frac{2k_u(T_s - T_f)}{L_s}\right]^{1/2} t^{1/2} \tag{4.53}$$

where L_s = volumetric latent heat of soil
k_u = thermal conductivity of unfrozen soil
T_f = soil melting temperature

The excess pore pressures developed while the thaw process is still in the soil are given by the linear theory of thaw consolidation. For the case of self-weight loading only, the excess pore pressures exhibit a linear profile with depth and can therefore be written

$$u = B\gamma'x \qquad \text{where } B = \frac{1}{1 + 1/2R^2} \tag{4.54}$$

and B is a constant with time.

When the thaw plane encounters the ice layer, the height of soil solids above the thaw line remains constant with time. If we now assume that the strains in the soil skeleton associated with any increase in excess pore-water pressure (caused by the extra influx of water into the soil) are small, the distance between the soil surface and the thaw plane becomes constant. This assumption is expressed schematically in Fig. 4.18 and implies that the soil is not absorbing any additional meltwater. That this is a reasonable assumption will be seen later from the solution to the problem. If the distance X_0 from the surface to the thaw plane is now a constant, a steady-state temperature distribution exists in the thawed zone, where the temperature is T_s at the soil surface and T_f at the thaw line. Applying the heat-balance equation at the thaw line, which is now in the ice, gives

$$-k_u \frac{\partial \theta}{\partial x} = L_w \frac{dX}{dt} \tag{4.55}$$

where dX/dt is the rate of thaw in the ice layer, L_w is the volumetric latent heat of water, and

$$\frac{\partial \theta}{\partial x} = \frac{-(T_s - T_f)}{X_0} \tag{4.56}$$

The rate of ablation of the ice layer is

$$\frac{dX}{dt} = \frac{k_u(T_s - T_f)}{L_w X_0} \tag{4.57}$$

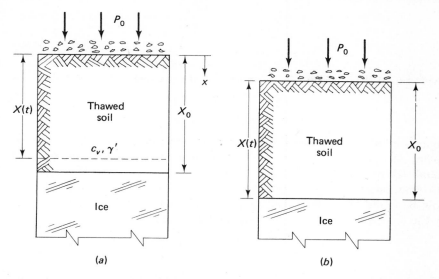

Figure 4.18 Thawing in a soil-ice profile: thaw plane in (*a*) soil and (*b*) ice. (*After Nixon, 1973.*)

This is a constant velocity with time, as distinct from the solution to the heat-transfer problem through soil associated with a step change in surface temperature, where the velocity dX/dt is proportional to $t^{-1/2}$. It is clear that the thaw-front velocity will be reduced when an ice layer is encountered, as L_w is greater than L_s, the latent heat of the frozen soil. At first this might be thought to improve the excess-pore-pressure conditions in the soil above the ice lens. This is not the case since all the meltwater from an ice layer enters the soil as excess pore fluid whereas when thawing through a mixture of soil and ice, only a portion of the meltwater may be thought of as excess pore fluid.

As no new thawed soil is entering the thawed zone, the usual boundary condition for thawing soils expressing the continuity of water at the thaw line is no longer valid and the problem in soil consolidation concerns a fixed height of soil X_0. At the thaw boundary, the surface of the ice layer, the continuity of the mass of water is satisfied as follows:

at $x = X_0$:
$$\gamma_i \frac{dX}{dt} = K \frac{\partial u}{\partial x} \qquad \text{for } t > t_0 \tag{4.58}$$

where $t_0 = X_0^2/\alpha^2 =$ time to thaw soil above ice
$K =$ coefficient of permeability of thawed soil
$\gamma_i =$ unit weight of ice

Substituting the rate of melting of the ice [Eq. (4.57)] gives:

At $x = X_0$:
$$\frac{\partial u}{\partial x} = \frac{\gamma_i}{K} \frac{k_u(T_s - T_f)}{L_w X_0} \tag{4.59}$$

Let

$$z = \frac{x}{X_0} \tag{4.60}$$

and divide Eq. (4.59) by $P_0 + \gamma'X_0$ to normalize the excess pore pressures, giving

$$\frac{1}{P_0 + \gamma'X_0} \frac{\partial u}{\partial z} = \frac{\gamma_i k_u (T_s - T_f)}{K(P_0 + \gamma'X_0)L_w} = D \tag{4.61}$$

The dimensionless excess-pore-pressure gradient at the base of the soil when the thaw plane encounters the ice lens and the dimensionless quantity following the first equal sign in Eq. (4.61) are denoted by D.

The solution for the excess pore pressure $u(z, t)$ above a thawing ice layer can now be found. The linear Terzaghi consolidation equation is assumed to govern the dissipation of excess pore pressures; therefore

$$0 < z < 1 \qquad \frac{\partial u}{\partial T} = \frac{\partial^2 u}{\partial z^2} \qquad T = \frac{c_v t}{X_0^2} > 0 \tag{4.62}$$

where the time t_0 is set equal to zero for simplicity. For the assumptions of the Terzaghi theory, the coefficient of consolidation is an independent constant, and so the value of c_v used here is the same as the value used when the thaw plane is in the soil. The surface is free-draining, and when the boundary condition [Eq. (4.61)] at the thaw plane is used, a solution can be obtained. From here on the case of self-weight loading will be considered because of the simplicity of the initial values. The applied loading condition must be analyzed numerically. The initial values are given by Eq. (4.54), and the excess pore pressures are obtained from Carslaw and Jaeger (1947) in the form

$$\frac{u(z, t)}{\gamma'X_0} = Dz - (D - B) \sum_{n=0}^{\infty} (-1)^n \frac{2}{M^2} \sin(Mz)e^{-M^2 T} \tag{4.63}$$

where $M = (2n + 1)\pi/2$. The dimensionless physical constants D and B are defined by Eqs. (4.54) and (4.61) and express the initial and final excess-pore-pressure gradients in the thawed soil. The solution presented in Fig. 4.19 shows the normalized excess pore pressure at the thaw line plotted with the time factor for different D values. The value of the initial pore-pressure gradient B was taken to be zero, in order to isolate the effects of the thawing of the ice layer alone. The corresponding curves for any other positive value of B are easily evaluated from Eq. (4.63); they can also be obtained from curves for $B = 0$ given in Fig. 4.19 using the relation

$$u|_{B \neq 0} = D - \frac{D - B}{D}(D - u|_{B=0}) \tag{4.64}$$

Here $u|_{B=0}$ represents the normalized pore pressure for $B = 0$ given in Fig. 4.19, and $u|_{B \neq 0}$ represents the required pore pressure for any nonzero value of B. The preceding solution is valid where the ice layer continues indefinitely below the soil.

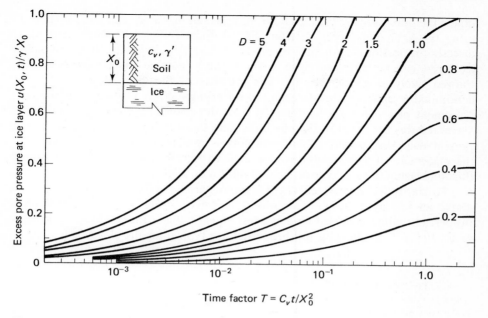

Figure 4.19 Pore pressures at a soil-ice interface. (*After Nixon, 1973.*)

When the ice layer is of finite thickness, as is usually the case, the time to thaw the layer completely is calculated from Eq. (4.57) as

$$t_f = \frac{h_i X_0 L_w}{k_u(T_s - T_f)} \tag{4.65}$$

where h_i is the original thickness of the ice layer and t_f is the time required to thaw the ice layer completely. This time can be converted into a time factor

$$T_F = \frac{c_v t_f}{X_0^2} = \frac{c_v h_i L_w}{k_u(T_s - T_f)X_0} \tag{4.66}$$

When the time factor at final thawing of the ice lens is known, Fig. 4.19 can be used to determine the final (and usually the worst) pore-pressure conditions over the ice layer.

Figure 4.19 shows that if the value of D is less than unity, the normalized excess pore pressure will rise to unity and maintain in the limit a pore pressure numerically equal to this value. If, on the other hand, the D value is greater than unity, stability is assured only for a finite period of time; eventually the excess pore pressures become equal to the effective overburden weight, and complete instability results.

Note that the stability of a compressible soil mass can be attained in two ways. For a D value less than unity some effective stress will be ensured indefinitely at the thaw line. When D is greater than unity, instability results unless the pore pressures never attain their maximum value. This can be checked using the final time factor T_F from Eq. (4.66) and Fig. 4.19. Note that T_F is directly proportional to h_i and inversely to X_0. This indicates that only small ice layers can be tolerated close to the surface and that thicker layers can be thawed safely at greater depths. The presence of the term $P_0 + \gamma'X_0$ in the denominator reinforces this statement of increasing stability with depth. Moreover, placement of a surcharge loading P_0 over the thawing ground containing ice lenses reduces the D value, thereby increasing the stability. If large ice layers are present near the surface, and if instability is predicted at low values of $\gamma'X_0$, the placement of a gravel fill can be used to reduce the D value below unity, thus increasing the stability of the foundation on thawing.

To clarify the relative effects of various parameters on the stability of soil above an ice layer, a sample problem is solved using a set of geotechnical properties similar to those found at a test pipeline site at Inuvik, N.W.T. (Rowley et al., 1973). The following soil properties are typical for the clayey silt:

Permeability $K = 2.5 \times 10^{-4}$ mm/s
Coefficient of consolidation $c_v = 1.1$ mm^2/s
Water content† $w = 40\%$
Submerged unit weight $\gamma' = 0.82$ g/cm^3
Soil latent heat $L_s = 173$ J/cm^3
Thawed conductivity $k_u = 1.05$ J/m s °C

---

† The actual average moisture contents at Inuvik were 80 percent or greater, but for this sample problem a soil layer of 40 percent moisture content is assumed to overlie a pure ice layer.

Two rates of thawing are examined, one corresponding to the fast rate of thawing under a hot pipeline with a surface temperature $T_s = 71$°C and the other corresponding to a natural rate of thaw which might take place in an active layer with a surface temperature $T_s = 12$°C. Using the Stefan solution for the melting problem, we calculate the α values for thawing in the soil to be $\alpha_1 = 0.93$ mm/s$^{1/2}$ for the high T_s and $\alpha_2 = 0.38$ mm/s$^{1/2}$ for the low T_s.

Using Eq. (4.32) with the c_v value provides the two R values, $R_1 = 0.443$ and $R_2 = 0.181$. The pore pressure maintained in the soil, and therefore the initial values for the ice-layer problem, correspond to $B_1 = 0.283$ and $B_2 = 0.061$. The effects of an ice layer in this thawing soil are now considered. For each thawing rate the top of the ice layer was assumed to be at 1 or 3 m below the surface. For $X_0 = 1$ m, the D values for the two rates of thawing are 1.0 and 0.169, respectively. The relationship between the time factor and time can be calculated using Eq. (4.66) for each depth of ice layer X_0. Figure 4.19 and Eq. (4.64) are now used to plot the excess pore pressures at the ice-soil interface with time. Figure 4.20 shows the normalized pore pressure plotted with

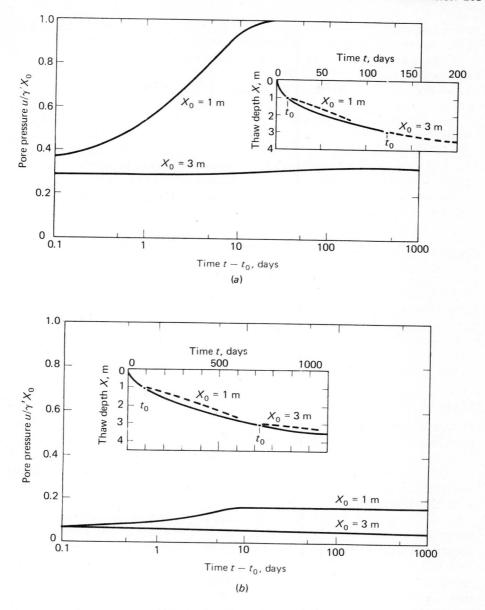

Figure 4.20 Sample solution for pore pressures at a soil-ice interface: (*a*) fast rate of thaw; α in soil = 0.93 mm/s$^{1/2}$; (*b*) slow rate of thaw; α in soil = 0.38 mm/s$^{1/2}$. (*After Nixon, 1973.*)

time in days for the two thaw rates and depth of ice layers. The time-depth history for each thaw interface is also included.

For the fast thaw rate the pore pressure above the 1-m-deep ice layer rises to 94 percent of the maximum effective stress within 10 days. This corresponds to thawing of a 200-mm ice layer. Thawing of the 3-m-deep ice layer produces pore pressures that are similar to those produced by thawing in the soil.

For the slow thaw rate the presence of the 1-m-deep ice layer does not produce pore pressures in the soil which dissipate significantly with time. Note that for the ice layer at the 3-m depth under the same thawing conditions, Fig. 4.20 shows that the pore pressure at the soil-ice interface actually reduces slightly with time. This sample problem suggests that although the settlements are obviously considerable, the pore-pressure conditions in the soil above a thawing ice layer may not be critical with regard to stability.

4.5 FIELD STUDIES

It is important that new methods, including thaw-consolidation theory, be verified on field projects. Comprehensive thaw-settlement studies have recently been performed in connection with new hydroelectric developments and construction of pipelines in Canada and Alaska. Two such field studies will be described here in detail. The first concerns the problem of dikes constructed on discontinuous permafrost. The second is related to the construction of warm pipelines in perennially frozen soils.

Dikes on Discontinuous Permafrost

Performance studies of two major sand dikes constructed on perennially frozen ground were undertaken in connection with the construction of the Kelsey Generating Station on the Nelson River in Manitoba. The station, constructed in 1957 to 1960, is located in the southern fringe area of the permafrost region of Canada, about 684 km north of Winnipeg and 85 km northeast of Thompson in northern Manitoba.

Several relatively small dikes were required to enclose the reservoir. The design and construction of two of the major dikes were influenced greatly by the presence of permafrost. The performance of these two dikes, each about 600 m long and with maximum heights of about 6 m, was of special concern because loss of strength due to thawing of the underlying ice-rich permafrost soils when flooded could cause failure of the foundation. The design and construction procedures for these dikes have been presented by MacDonald (1963), while the terrain studies and all the aspects of settlement prediction and performance monitoring of the dikes have been described by Johnston (1965, 1969) and Brown and Johnston (1970).

The dikes consisted of a compacted sand fill constructed during the winter on a foundation of perennially frozen varved clay in which drainage during consolidation was facilitated by a system of sand drains.

An organic mantle of moss and peat, from 0.3 to 1 m thick, covers the mineral soils at Kelsey, which are predominantly lacustrine, varved clays. The varved materials, which generally become less plastic and more silty with depth, may exceed 7.6 m in thickness. These deposits overlie bedrock or thinly stratified glacial drift.

Permafrost was encountered extensively over the site, occurring as islands or patches of frozen ground which were variable in thickness and area. Extensive ice segregation was found in all perennially frozen varved clays, generally in the form of horizontal lenses varying in thickness up to 200 mm, but the predominant thickness range was from 2 to 25 mm. Ground-temperature measurements at Kelsey indicated that the mean ground temperature in undisturbed areas of permafrost to depths of 6 m was about -0.56 to $-0.28°C$.

It was expected that large differential settlements would occur because of the variable permafrost distribution under the dikes. Preliminary calculations indicated that within a 50-year period the permafrost under the reservoir would thaw completely. It was also estimated that total settlements, due primarily to the thawing of visible ice in the soil, would be of the order of 1.8 m. It was anticipated, providing the free water resulting from thawing of the ice inclusions was able to dissipate rapidly, that consolidation would take place at a rate similar to thawing.

Field observation of temperatures and settlements An extensive system of field observations was organized on the site in order to assess the performance of the dikes. In 1959, thermocouple cables and settlement gauges were installed in the dike and foundation at three locations underlain by permafrost. Frost indicators were placed in holes bored through the dike at the same locations. Ground-temperature observations were made at weekly or bimonthly intervals on all locations. Ground temperatures for East Dike no. 2 are shown in Fig. 4.21a.

Settlement gauges were installed in July 1959 to measure movements at about 1.5-m-deep intervals in the dike fill and foundation at the three main instrumented sections of East Dike no. 2. Details of the gauges and their installation were given by Johnston (1965). In addition to these gauges, settlement points were also placed along the downstream shoulder of the dike crest at about 76-m intervals. Level surveys were made approximately once a month on the settlement gauges. Curves showing movements experienced by each gauge in the fill and foundation are shown in Fig. 4.21b.

Figure 4.21b shows that appreciable settlements were measured at the instrumented locations in the dike. Total settlement of the foundation as of 1967 measured at this location (KS2), where the fill was approximately 4.8 m high, was about 1.5 m. Maximum settlements of nearly 2.1 m occurred at some instrumented sections, but a continuous record of settlement at these locations was not obtained. It is also of interest to note that the observed rate of settlement followed a pattern quite similar to that of the rate of thaw. It was expected that the settlement would continue at a much smaller rate after all ice melting was completed.

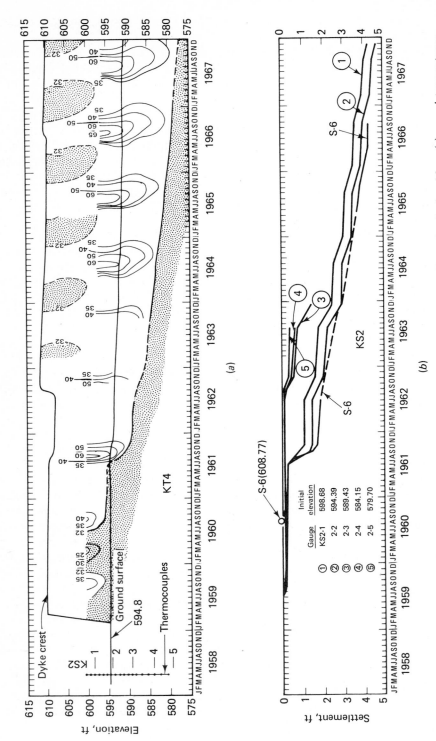

Figure 4.21 Results of ground temperature and settlement observations at East Dike no. 2, Kelsey Generating Station, Man.: (*a*) ground temperatures; (*b*) settlements. Original units (feet and degrees Fahrenheit) retained. (*After Johnston, 1969.*)

204

Comparison of predicted and observed settlements The total settlement of the dike surface at a location underlain by thawing permafrost results from three causes (Johnston, 1969): (1) escape of the water resulting from thawing of the large ice inclusions in the foundation, (2) compression of the thawed soil in the foundation, and (3) compression of the dike sand fill.

The greater part of the total settlement experienced by the Kelsey dikes was due to thawing of the ice inclusions. Settlement due to compression of the fill was estimated to be less than 150 mm. The amount of settlement due to consolidation of the thawed soil layers was not evaluated separately. As far as the amount of total settlement is concerned, Fig. 4.21 shows that at the end of 1967 the maximum settlement attained in one section was about 1.50 m (KS2) when the thaw depth in the same section attained about 5 m (KT4). This corresponds to an average unit thaw settlement of about 30 percent.

Although the basic soil properties that govern the rate of thaw and consolidation of the ground (thermal properties and permeability) had not been directly determined for the soils at the site, Brown and Johnston (1970) successfully estimated the rate of thaw and the amount of total settlement. The authors first developed a formula for calculating the thaw depth which takes into account not only the heat transferred through the soil by conduction but also that carried away by the excess water percolating from the thaw zone. After making reasonable assumptions on the total and unfrozen water content of the soils at the site they found that the rate of thaw should approximately follow the equation $X = 2.07t^{1/2}$, where X is in meters and t is in years. This equation agrees very well with the observations shown in Fig. 4.21a for gauge KT4.

Brown and Johnston (1970) made only a rough estimate of the thaw settlement based on the assumption that the settlement is approximately equal to the total thickness of ice lenses detected by visual inspection of borehole samples. This was in good agreement with the observed settlements since the ice lenses were found to be about one-third by volume.

A more detailed analysis of this settlement follows, using various thaw-settlement formulas presented in Sec. 4.1. The data supplied by Brown and Johnston (1970) show that the silt-clay soils found at Kelsey usually have saturated water contents close to 30 percent, of which about one-half remains unfrozen at temperatures just below freezing. The thaw settlement can be estimated from frozen and thawed dry and bulk densities of the soil using Eq. (4.11).

Assuming that the major portion of settlement was due to thawing of ice lenses, $\gamma_{d,\,\text{th}}$ can be calculated from the saturated water content of the soil between the lenses, i.e.,

$$\gamma_{d,\,\text{th}} = \frac{\gamma_w}{1/G_s + w_{\text{sat}}}$$

For $\gamma_w = 1000$ kg/m^3, $G_s = 2.70$, and $w_{\text{sat}} = 0.30$, one gets $\gamma_{d,\,\text{th}} = 1490$ kg/m^3. For a saturated soil, this corresponds to a porosity of

$$n = \frac{w_{\text{sat}}}{1/G_s + w_{\text{sat}}} = \frac{0.30}{1/2.7 + 0.30} = 0.448$$

To find the value of γ_{df}, with the ice lenses included, first calculate the value of the total water content w_{tot}. Assume that the ice lenses form $\frac{1}{3}$ of the total frozen volume, or $0.9(\frac{1}{3}) = 0.3$ of the excess water after undrained thawing. Now let V equal the total (thawed undrained) soil volume, V_{wl} the volume of excess water due to thawing of ice lenses, V_{wp} the volume of water in soil pores, and $V_{ws} = 0.7V$ the volume of the soil alone. This gives

$$\frac{V_{wl}}{V} = 0.3 \qquad \text{and} \qquad \frac{V_{wp}}{V} = 0.7n = 0.7(0.448) = 0.313$$

The total porosity $n_{tot} = (V_{wl} + V_{wp})/V = 0.3 + 0.313 = 0.613$, from which

$$w_{tot} = \frac{n_{tot}}{G_s(1 - n_{tot})} = \frac{0.613}{2.7(0.387)} = 0.586$$

The total frozen dry density

$$\gamma_{df} = \frac{\gamma_w}{1/G_s + 1.09(w_{tot} - w_u) + w_u}$$

Substituting numerical values gives

$$\gamma_{df} = \frac{1000}{1/2.7 + 1.09(0.586 - 0.15) + 0.15} = 1006 \text{ kg/m}^3$$

The unit thaw settlement [Eq. (4.11)] becomes $s/H_f = 1 - 1006/1490 = 0.325$, which is close to the observed unit settlement of about 0.3.

The statistical-correlation method is another method for predicting the thaw settlement. Equation (4.17) is appropriate because it is based on settlement observations in the same geological area. For γ_f/γ_w Eq. (4.18) gives

$$\frac{\gamma_f}{\gamma_w} = 1.006\left(1 - \frac{1}{2.7}\right) + 1 = 1.634$$

Then from Eq. (4.17), the unit settlement is

$$\frac{s}{H_f} = 0.90 - 0.868(1.634 - 1.15)^{1/2} \pm 0.05 = 0.30 \pm 0.05$$

which corresponds well to the observed value of 0.3.

Another settlement estimate can be made by considering the thawing of the ice inclusions and the pore ice separately. Since the ice inclusions were no thicker than 30 mm, the reduction coefficient r_i in Eq. (4.24) equals 0.4 hence the unit settlement is

$$\frac{S_{ii}}{H_f} = 0.4(\tfrac{1}{3}) = 0.13$$

The frozen bulk density of the soil is

$$\frac{\gamma_f}{\gamma_w} = 1.49\left(1 - \frac{1}{2.7}\right) + 1 = 1.94$$

from which [Eq. (4.17)]

$$\frac{s_{ip}}{H_f} = 0.90 - 0.868(1.94 - 1.15)^{1/2} \pm 0.05 = 0.13 \pm 0.05$$

The total unit settlement is $s/H_f = (s_{ii} + s_{ip})/H_f = 0.26 \pm 0.05$, which is a little less than the observed value.

A Warm-Oil Pipeline in Permafrost

A test section of a warm-oil pipeline was installed near Inuvik, N.W.T., by MacKenzie Valley Pipeline Research Ltd. to provide information on the behavior of permafrost as a foundation material. The test section consisted of a 27-m length of 610 mm pipe through which hot oil at 71°C was circulated. The field test started on July 22, 1971, and the ice-rich permafrost in which the pipeline segment was founded began to thaw. The soil around the pipe was instrumented to measure settlements, temperatures, and pore-water pressures. Undisturbed samples of the permafrost were collected in advance for laboratory testing. The field instrumentation has been described by Slusarchuk et al. (1973) and the experimental data presented by Watson et al. (1973a).

Stability of the thawed zone around a hot pipeline buried on a slope is of considerable interest. Strength of the thawed soil depends on excess pore pressures maintained in the soil during thawing. It was therefore of importance to attempt to predict the pore pressures and the accompanying settlements in a foundation where these quantities have been measured. In this way, the predictive power of available theories could be checked, and a level of confidence established for such theories when applied in the future to heated structures on permafrost.

The test site at Inuvik was overlain by 1.37 m of gravel fill. Thin layers of compressed organic soil, silty clay, and pure ice constituted the first 0.61 m of the soil profile. The base of the pipe was placed at this elevation. Below the pipe, the soil was described as a clayey silt with an ice content that decreased with depth. Approximately 2 m below the initial elevation of the pipe base, a dense gravelly till was present. Although the clayey silt could be expected to be highly compressible in the thawed state, the gravelly till was essentially incompressible due to its high initial density.

Figure 4.22 presents the stratigraphy at the test site, together with the measured water content and bulk density of each layer. The approximate position of the pipe in the configuration is also shown. Other geotechnical properties of the foundation materials can be obtained from Rowley et al. (1973). In order to analyze the thaw-consolidation behavior of the thawing foundation, the consolidation characteristics of the thawed soil must be determined. The coefficient of consolidation c_v has been defined by Eq. (4.29).

On the basis of field tests Rowley et al. (1973) provided permeability values for the thawed soil of between 0.53 and 2.29 μm/s, with an average of 1 μm/s. These values seem high for a soil of this type, and it was suggested that the macrostructure of the freshly thawed permafrost was responsible for the large

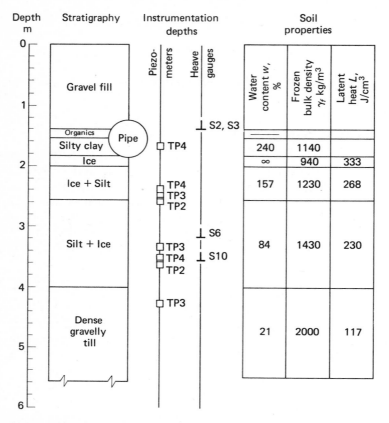

Figure 4.22 Variation of soil properties with depth. (*After Morgenstern and Nixon, 1975.*)

values. The high water levels maintained during the tests may have reduced the effective stress around the tip of the measuring device, possibly causing hydraulic fracture in the soil and thereby greatly increasing the apparent permeability.

Laboratory data on the permeability were obtained from constant-head tests on thawed laboratory samples at different effective stresses. Figure 4.23 summarizes the results plotted as void ratio against the logarithm of effective stress and void ratio against the logarithm of permeability. The permeability for the correct effective-stress range can be determined from a set of tests, as shown in Fig. 4.23.

The other parameter embodied in the consolidation coefficient is the compressibility m_v. This parameter can also be obtained from the laboratory data. As the void-ratio–effective-stress relation for the ice-rich silt appears to be nonlinear, the evaluation of m_v requires the initial and ultimate effective stresses and the corresponding volume change for this effective stress change. In this preliminary assessment, an average value for the increment of effective stress $\Delta\sigma'$

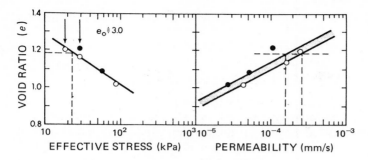

Figure 4.23 Laboratory results for Inuvik clayey silt. (*After Morgenstern and Nixon, 1975.*)

for the compressible clayey silt layers of interest can be calculated by determining the average ultimate effective stress in the silt and subtracting the initial effective stress; that is, $\Delta\sigma' = \sigma'_f - \sigma'_0$, where σ'_0 is clearly very small or zero for this material.

The value of σ'_f, the effective stress when consolidation is completed, was determined from a consideration of the unit weights of the materials involved. The variation in σ'_f can be calculated by assuming that the materials above the base of the pipe (principally gravel) form a surcharge loading P_0. The average submerged density of the soil below the pipe base is denoted by γ'. Values for calculations included $P_0 = 17.4$ kPa and $\gamma' = 434$ kg/m^3. The ultimate effective stress at the top of the ice-rich silt layer was 17.4 kPa, and at the base, 25.8 kPa. A mean of these values gives an average ultimate effective stress of

$$\Delta\sigma' = \sigma'_f = 21.6 \text{ kPa}$$

Laboratory test data for the soil at this effective stress (21.6 kPa) show that the void ratio e_f equals 1.18. The laboratory data and the measured moisture content at the site indicate that the initial void ratio e_0 equals 3.10. The volumetric strain is

$$\frac{\Delta V}{V} = \frac{e_0 - e_f}{1 + e_0} = \frac{3.1 - 1.18}{4.1} = 0.47$$

The coefficient of volume compressibility is

$$m_v = \frac{0.47}{21.6} = 0.0217 \text{ m}^2/\text{kN}$$

The ultimate effective stress in the silt layers was estimated to be 21.6 kPa. Referring again to Fig. 4.23, note that the laboratory permeability values at this effective stress level lie between 0.17 and 0.27 μm/s with an average of 0.22 μm/s.

An average coefficient of consolidation for the layers of interest can now be calculated to be

$$c_v = \frac{k}{m_v \gamma_w} = \frac{0.22 \times 10^{-6} \text{ m/s}}{(0.0217 \text{ m}^2/\text{kN})(9.81 \text{ kN/m}^3)} = 1.03 \times 10^{-6} \text{ m}^2/\text{s} = 0.0103 \text{ cm}^2/\text{s}$$

The movement of the thaw front under the hot pipeline must be considered before going into the geotechnical aspects of the thawing foundation. The symmetry of the problem dictates that for the first few months of thawing, when the thaw depth is of the same order of magnitude as the diameter of the hot pipeline, the heat-flow conditions under the centerline of the pipe are essentially one-dimensional; i.e., temperature gradients in a vertical direction far exceed those in a horizontal plane. Therefore as a first approximation, a one-dimensional mathematical model for heat transfer is used to predict the rate of thaw under the centerline of the pipe.

In an ice-rich foundation of this type, considerable settlement of the pipe will occur as melting proceeds. Hence all observed and predicted thaw depths are defined as the vertical distance from the pipe base to the thaw plane. In predicting the rate of thaw in the foundation, the temperature distribution and the thermal properties in the frozen soil are not accounted for, as they play exceedingly minor roles in thaw calculations when the ground temperatures are close to 0°C (Nixon and McRoberts, 1973).

The simple Stefan solution for the depth of thaw $X(t)$ can be written

$$X = \left(\frac{2k_u T_s}{L}\right)^{1/2} t^{1/2} = \alpha t^{1/2} \tag{4.67}$$

where k_u = thermal conductivity of thawed soil
T_s = suddenly applied constant surface temperature
L = uniform volumetric latent heat of soil
α = constant defined by Eq. (4.67)
t = time

This solution is approximate, and is known to overestimate the thaw rate when the surface temperature is high. It can be improved to a higher order of accuracy however, by a semiempirical factor provided by Nixon and McRoberts (1973), and Eq. (4.67) can be rewritten as

$$X = \left(\frac{2k_u T_s}{L}\right)^{1/2} \left(1 - \frac{\text{Ste}}{8}\right) t^{1/2} \tag{4.68}$$

where $\text{Ste} = c_u T_s/L$ is the Stefan number and c_u is the volumetric heat capacity of the soil.

Since the water content in the soil profile varies considerably (Fig. 4.22), the latent heat and the Stefan number will change considerably with depth. This nonhomogeneity could be accounted for directly by introducing a variable latent heat with depth, but Table 4.3 demonstrates how an average value for these

Table 4.3 Variation of thermal properties with depth

Layer	w, %	L, J/cm³	c_u, J/°C cm³	Ste	H, cm	LH, J/cm²
B (ice)	∞	333	4.2	0.89	20	6,665
C (ice and silt)	157	268	3.7	0.985	75	20,097
D (silt and ice)	84	230	3.5	1.07	125	28,784
D (till)	21	117	2.7	1.74	80	9,378
Total					300	64,924

parameters can be extracted from the soil information. A weighted average L is now obtained by dividing the results from the final two columns, i.e.,

$$L_{av} = \frac{\sum LH}{\sum H} = \frac{64,924}{300} = 216.4 \text{ J/cm}^3 \qquad (4.69)$$

An average value for Ste is found to be 0.98.

The expected thaw strains, based on correlations with frozen bulk density (Sec. 4.1), indicated that the soil in the thawed zone will consolidate to a moisture content of approximately 45 percent. From Kersten's data (1949), a saturated fine-grained soil of this moisture content will have a thermal conductivity of

$$k_u = 0.0106 \text{ J/cm °C s} \qquad (4.70)$$

Since the hot oil in the pipe was maintained at 71°C, this temperature is the surface temperature T_s in the Stefan equation. Substituting these thermal properties into Eq. (4.68) gives

$$X = \left[\frac{2(0.0106)(71)}{216.4}\right]^{1/2}\left(1 - \frac{0.98}{8}\right)t^{1/2} = 0.073t^{1/2} \qquad (4.71)$$

or

$$\alpha = 0.073 \text{ cm/s}^{1/2} = 0.215 \text{ m/day}^{1/2} \qquad (4.72)$$

This predicted relationship between thaw depth and the square root of time can be compared with the corresponding thaw depths observed in the field. The results from Eq. (4.24) and field observations are shown plotted in Fig. 4.24. The results of another prediction (Nixon, 1973), where the variation of the latent heat with depth is taken into account, are included in Fig. 4.24.

The agreement between prediction and field behavior for the first few months of thawing is impressive. The more sophisticated prediction, which accounted for decreasing latent heat with depth, suggests that the rate of thaw should increase somewhat at later times. This was not observed in the thawing foundation and is undoubtedly due to the two-dimensional effects that would tend to retard the propagation of the thaw line at later times. Taking the predicted α and c_v values calculated for the foundation soil in earlier sections gives

$$R = \frac{\alpha}{2}(c_v)^{1/2} = \frac{0.0773}{2(1.03 \times 10^{-2})^{1/2}} = 0.383$$

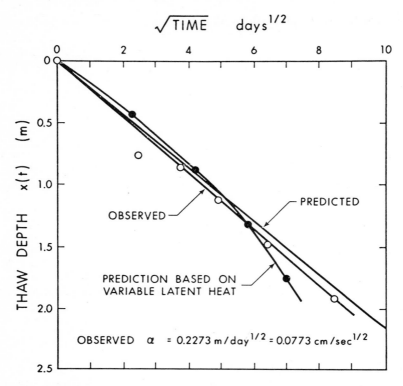

Figure 4.24 Predicted and observed thaw depths. (*After Morgenstern and Nixon, 1975.*)

which is the thaw-consolidation ratio applicable to the thawing foundation for the test pipeline at Inuvik.

Piezometers at the site installed at different depths below the groundwater table provided data on the buildup of excess pore pressures. The excess pore-water pressures in the thawing foundation, in meters of water, can be calculated by subtracting the hydrostatic component (depth from free water table) from the observed pore pressure. The maximum excess pore pressure would normally be expected soon after the thaw plane had passed that piezometer, and the readings can therefore be normalized to obtain $u/(P_0 + \gamma'X)$.

If one knows the R value, a prediction of the normalized excess pore pressures can be made using the solutions given in Sec. 4.2. The predicted values of the excess pore pressure lie between 24 and 25 percent of the terminal or maximum value of the effective stress for each piezometer. The observed values for the normalized excess pore pressure lie between 15 and 39 percent, with an average of 23.7 percent. To put these data in perspective, it is useful to plot the predicted and observed excess pore pressures with depth, as shown in Fig. 4.25. The graph shows some scatter in the data points, but the uniform distribution on either side of the predicted relationship suggests an encouraging correlation between

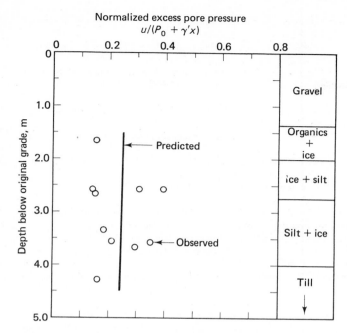

Normalized excess pore pressure
$$u/(P_0 + \gamma'x)$$

Figure 4.25 Predicted and observed thaw-plane pore pressures. (*After Morgenstern and Nixon, 1975.*)

theory and observation. Figure 4.25 also shows the idealized stratigraphy with depth, and it should be noted that the higher excess-pore-pressure readings are located within the ice-rich clayey silt layers, as expected.

The time rate of settlement can be calculated if the thaw depth-time relationship and the settlement ratio S_t/S_{max} are known. This has been reported by Morgenstern and Nixon (1975).

REFERENCES

Brown, W. G., and G. H. Johnston, 1970. Dikes on Permafrost: Predicting Thaw and Settlement, *Can. Geotech. J.*, **7**: 365–371.

Carslaw, H. S., and J. C. Jaeger. 1947. Conduction of Heat in Solids, Clarendon Press, Oxford.

Crory, F. E. 1973. Settlement Associated with the Thawing of Permafrost. *North Am. Contrib. 2d Int. Permafrost Conf., Yakutsk, U.S.S.R.*, National Academy of Sciences, Washington, pp. 599–607.

Davis, E. H., and G. P. Raymond. 1965. A Non-linear Theory of Consolidation, *Geotechnique*, **15**: 161–173.

Gibson, R. E. 1958. The Progress of Consolidation in Clay Layer Increasing in Thickness with Time, *Geotechnique*, **8**: 171–182.

Johnston, G. H. 1965. Permafrost Studies at the Kelsey Hydro-electric Generating Station: Research and Instrumentation, *Natl. Res. Counc. Can. Div. Build. Res. Tech. Pap.* 178 (NRC 7943).

———. 1969. Dykes on Permafrost, Kelsey Generating Station, Manitoba, *Can. Geotech. J.*, **6**: 139–157.

Keil, L. D., N. M. Nielsen, and R. C. Gupta. 1973. Thaw-Consolidation of Permafrost Dyke Foundations at the Long Spruce Generating Station, *26th Can. Geotech. Conf. Toronto, Prepr. Vol.*, pp. 134–141.

Kersten, M. S. 1949. Laboratory Research for the Determination of the Thermal Properties of Soils, *Univ. Minn. Eng. Exp. Stn. Final Rep.*

Lachenbruch, A. H. 1970. Some Estimates of the Thermal Effects of a Heated Pipeline in Permafrost, *U.S. Geol. Surv. Circ.* 632.

Luscher, V., and S. S. Afifi. 1973. Thaw Consolidation of Alaskan Silts and Granular Soils, *North Am. Contrib. 2d Int. Permafrost Conf., Yakutsk, U.S.S.R.*, National Academy of Sciences, Washington, pp. 325–334.

MacDonald, D. 1963. Design of Kelsey Dykes, *Proc. 1st Int. Permafrost Conf., Lafayette, Ind., NAS–NRC, Publ.* 1287, Washington, pp. 492–496.

Morgenstern, N. R., and J. F. Nixon. 1971. One Dimensional Consolidation of Thawing Soils. *Can. Geotech. J.*, **8**, (4): 558–565.

—— and ——. 1975. An Analysis of the Performance of a Warm-Oil Pipeline in Permafrost, Inuvik, N.W.T., *Can. Geotech. J.*, **12**: 199–208.

—— and L. B. Smith. 1973. Thaw-Consolidation Tests on Remoulded Clays., *Can. Geotech. J.*, **10**: 25–40.

Murray, W. D., and F. Landis. 1959. Numerical and Machine Solutions of Transient Heat-Conduction Problems Involving Melting or Freezing, *Trans. Am. Soc. Mech. Eng.*, **81**: 106–112.

Nixon, J. F. 1973. Thaw-Consolidation in Some Layered Systems, *Can. Geotech. J.*, **10**: 617–631.

—— and E. C. McRoberts. 1973. A Study of Some Factors Affecting the Thawing of Frozen Soils, *Can. Geotech. J.*, **10**(3): 439–452.

—— and N. R. Morgenstern. 1973a. Practical Extensions to a Theory of Consolidation for Thawing Soils, *North Am. Contrib. 2d Int. Conf. Permafrost, Yakutsk, U.S.S.R.*, National Academy of Sciences, Washington. pp. 369–377.

—— and ——. 1973b. The Residual Stress in Thawing Soils, *Can. Geotech. J.*, **10**: 571–580.

—— and ——. 1974. Thaw-Consolidation Tests on Undisturbed Fine-Grained Permafrost, *Can. Geotech. J.*, **11**(1): 202–214.

Palmer. A. C. 1972. Thawing and Differential Settlement Close to Oil Wells through Permafrost, *Brown Univ. Div. Eng. Rep.* ARPA E-83.

Pihlainen, J. A., and G. H. Johnston. 1963. Guide to a Field Description of Permafrost for Engineering Purposes, *Natl. Res. Counc. Can. Assoc. Comm. Geotech. Res. Tech. Mem.* 79 (NRC 7576).

Rowley, R. K., G. H. Watson, R. G. Auld, and R. M. Wilson. 1973. Performance of a 48-in Warm-Oil Pipeline Supported on Permafrost., *Can. Geotech. J.*, **10**(2): 282–303.

Shuster, J. A. 1971. Laboratory Testing and Characterization of Permafrost for Foundation Uses, *Proc. Symp. Cold Reg. Eng. Univ. Alaska*, **1**: 73–118.

Slusarchuk, W. A., G. H. Watson, and T. L. Speer. 1973. Instrumentation around a Warm-Oil Pipeline Buried in Permafrost, *Can. Geotech. J.*, **10**: 227–245.

Speer, T. L., G. H. Watson, and R. K. Rowley. 1973. Effects of Ground Ice Variability and Resulting Thaw Settlements on Buried Warm Oil Pipelines, *North Am. Contrib. Proc. 2d Int. Permafrost, Yakutsk, U.S.S.R.*, National Academy of Sciences, Washington, pp. 746–751.

Tsytovich, N. A. 1958. Bases and Foundations on Frozen Soil., *NAS NRS Publ.* 804, *Highw. Res. Board Spec. Rep.* 58, 1960.

—— and M. I. Sumgin. 1937. Principles of Mechanics of Frozen Ground, *USSR Acad. Sci. Press, U.S. Army Cold Reg. Res. Eng. Lab. Trans.* 19, Hanover, N.H.

——, Y. K. Zaretsky, V. G. Grigoryeva, and Z. G. Ter-Martirosyan. 1965. Consolidation of Thawing Soils, *Proc. 6th Int. Conf. Soil Mech. Found. Eng., Montreal*, **1**: 390–394.

U.S.S.R. Building Code. 1960. Technical Considerations in Designing Foundations in Permafrost (SN 91–60), State Construction Publishing House Moscow, *Natl. Res. Counc. Can. Tech. Trans.* 1033, 1963.

——. 1966. Bases and Foundations of Buildings and Structures on Perennially Frozen Soils, Design Standards, SNiP II-B, 6-66.

Watson, G. H., R. K. Rowley, and W. A. Slusarchuk. 1973a. Performance of a Warm-Oil Pipeline Buried in Permafrost., *North Am. Contrib. Proc. 2d Int. Conf. Permafrost, Yukutsk, U.S.S.R.*, National Academy of Sciences, Washington, pp. 759–766.

————, W. A. Slusarchuk, and R. K. Rowley. 1973b. Determination of Some Frozen and Thawed Properties of Permafrost Soils, *Can. Geotech. J.*, **10**(4): 592–606.

Williams, P. J. 1966. Pore Pressures at a Penetrating Frost Line and their Predictions, *Geotechnique*, **16**(3): 187–208.

Wissa, A. E., and R. T. Martin. 1968. Behaviour of Soils under Flexible Pavements: Development of Rapid Frost Susceptibility Tests, M.I.T. *Dep. Civ. Eng.* RR 68–77 *Soils Pub.* 224.

FIVE

MECHANICAL PROPERTIES OF FROZEN GROUND

Orlando B. Andersland, Francis H. Sayles, Jr., and B. Ladanyi

INTRODUCTION†

Placement of a load at or below the frozen soil surface by means of a foundation results in increased stresses in the underlying soil. Relatively large loads can be supported since frozen soil has a strength comparable to that of weak concrete. The foundation will settle as a result of small elastic deformations and time-dependent creep movement. In relatively warm fine-grained frozen soils under high loads settlement may include volume change (consolidation). Engineering design requires that allowable foundation loads be determined and that settlement of the foundation not exceed specified limits during its service life. Any analysis of the frozen-soil behavior depends on the magnitude and distribution of stresses below the foundation. These stresses are closely related to the stress-deformation characteristics of the soil. Constitutive equations are used to describe the stress-strain-time relationships, frozen-soil strength, and the influence of temperature on these relationships. Laboratory tests provide information on frozen-soil parameters needed for the constitutive equations.

The strength of frozen ground develops from cohesion, interparticle friction, and particle interlocking, much as in unfrozen soils. Cohesive forces are attributed

---

† Notation is listed at the end of the chapter.

to adhesion between soil particles and the ice in the soil voids and to surface forces between particles. At low solids concentrations (ice-rich soils) the strength and mechanical behavior may approximate that for ice. For ice-rich soils the long-term strength will approach zero since ice creeps under extremely small stresses. At high solids concentrations (ice-poor soils) interparticle friction and dilatancy play a major part in determining the soil strength. The great difference in strength between frozen and unfrozen soils is derived from the ice component. The presence of unfrozen water films on soil particles reduces the ice content and results in a more plastic behavior during deformation. The frozen-soil strength is sensitive to strain rate, temperature, confining pressure, particle size, particle orientation and packing, and impurities (air bubbles, salts, or organic matter) in the water-ice matrix.

For the prefailure state the compressive stresses at which deformations begin to be important are an order of magnitude lower than those required to cause the frozen soil to fail in a short duration test. Stresses between soil particles and the ice at points of contact cause pressure melting of the ice. Differences in water surface tensions move the unfrozen water to regions of lower stress, where it refreezes. The process of ice melting and water movement is accompanied by a breakdown of the ice and the bonds with the soil grains, resulting in plastic deformation of the pore ice and a readjustment in particle arrangement. The result is the time-dependent deformation of frozen soil called *creep*. Frozen soil exhibits substantial deformation under sustained loading, the magnitude and creep rate being dependent on stress, stress history, temperature, and composition. Engineering design requires that the stresses not only be small enough to avert failure but that the deformations that develop during the service life also be within tolerable limits. The theories presented in this chapter to describe the mechanical properties will be used later for solving problems where the stresses are essentially constant with time. The effects of normal pressure, temperature, and soil composition on experimental parameters required for the theory are included.

5.1 CREEP OF FROZEN SOILS

The dominant creep characteristics under sustained stress and the marked rate dependence of strength are special features of the mechanical properties of frozen soils. The rate effects are temperature- and stress-dependent and vary with the amount of ice present in the frozen soil. When a frozen soil sample is subjected to a load, it will respond with an instantaneous deformation and a time-dependent deformation; if the load is high enough, it will display a limiting strength. Several typical creep curves are shown in Fig. 5.1a. For step loading under uniaxial stress conditions and at constant temperature the type of creep curve shown in Fig. 5.1b is common for frozen soils and a large number of other materials. Figure 5.1c shows the corresponding creep rate $-d\varepsilon/dt$ vs. time. The basic creep curve consists of three periods of time during which the creep rate

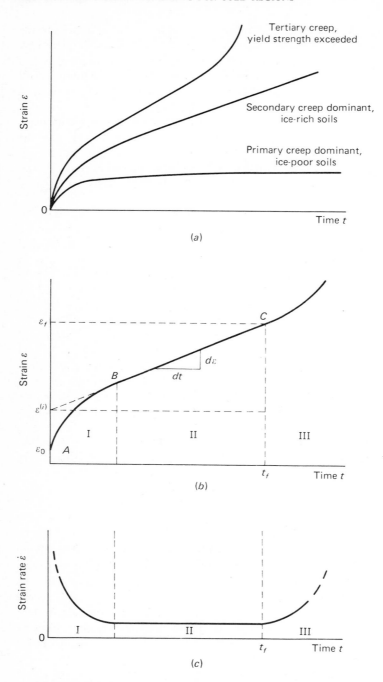

Figure 5.1 Constant-stress creep test: (*a*) creep-curve variations; (*b*) basic creep curve; (*c*) true strain rate vs. time.

is, in order: period I, decreasing; period II, remaining essentially constant; and period III, increasing. These are often called periods of primary, secondary, and tertiary creep. For stresses less than the long-term strength of the frozen soil the second period, with the minimum creep rate, and the third period, with increasing creep rates, may not develop.

The shape of creep curves for frozen soils is influenced not only by temperature but also by the magnitude of the applied stress, the soil type, and its density. Ice-saturated medium to high-density sands and silts will exhibit the creep behavior illustrated in Fig. 5.1*b* and *c* for a given constant temperature and medium to high stress levels. For low stress levels these same soils will display only primary creep and will asymptotically approach some limiting deformation, as shown for ice-poor soils in Fig. 5.1*a*. In contrast, ice-rich silts and clays exhibit an abbreviated primary creep period and a prolonged secondary-creep stage, and tertiary creep may never be attained, as shown by the intermediate curve in Fig. 5.1*a*. Some fine-grained soils can display primary-creep deformations with strains exceeding 20 percent.

For engineering applications where the performance of a structure depends upon the strength and deformation characteristics of the in situ frozen soil, creep behavior must be determined by tests on undisturbed soil samples under stress and temperature conditions which are expected to prevail during the life of the structure. Alternatively, field testing may be required when considerable variability exists in the natural permafrost. With the creep behavior of the frozen soil determined, an appropriate theory or curve-fitting procedure will be used to give a constitutive equation suitable for use in the analysis and prediction of the foundation performance. Both engineering theories and empirical curve-fitting methods are given in later sections.

When dealing with creep of laboratory test samples it must be recognized that both the increase in area and the strain can become very large. For unfrozen soils common practice allows for increase in area for compressive loads; hence the true stress σ is defined by

$$\sigma = \frac{P}{A} \tag{5.1}$$

where A is the actual area of the cross section corresponding to the load P. Strain is generally computed as the conventional or engineering strain ϵ, which refers the change in length dL to an original length L_0 and is given by

$$\epsilon = \int_{L_0}^{L} \frac{dL}{L_0} = \frac{L}{L_0} - 1 \tag{5.2}$$

True strain differs from conventional strain in that each increment of strain is based on the actual length at the time of the increment instead of the original length. The true strain ε is given by

$$\varepsilon = \int_{L_0}^{L} \frac{dL}{L} = \ln \frac{L}{L_0} \tag{5.3}$$

For both unfrozen and frozen soils most geotechnical problems involve compressive strains which are negative when Eq. (5.3) is used. For convenience define compressive strain as positive and write Eq. (5.3) in the form

$$\varepsilon = -\ln\frac{L}{L_0} = \ln\frac{L_0}{L} = \ln\frac{1}{1 - \Delta L/L_0} = \ln\frac{1}{1 - \epsilon} \tag{5.4}$$

The creep rate immediately after application of the load is usually very high. The magnitude of the instantaneous strain ε_0 will often depend on the type of test equipment used. Special care is required to perform the loading in a well-defined instantaneous manner for frozen soils. When the proposed service life of the structure is considerably larger than the primary-creep period, the strain developed during the primary-creep period under design loads is small compared with the amount of strain developed during the secondary-creep period. In this case the creep curves can be approximated by straight lines, as shown in Fig. 5.2. These creep curves, obtained at a constant temperature, were step-loaded to different uniaxial stress levels, $\sigma_1 < \sigma_2 < \sigma_3 < \sigma_4$. The tangents of the straight parts of the creep curves are extended to time zero, giving the intercepts shown in Fig. 5.2. Engineering design now requires constitutive equations suitable for calculating stresses, strains, and strain rates for the frozen soil subject to creep.

Research on the creep of frozen soils has followed two paths over the years. One path considers the physical theory capable of describing creep phenomena in terms of established concepts of physics. The aim has been to describe the basic mechanism of creep in terms of established properties of matter. Progress in this field has been substantial. The other approach seeks an engineering

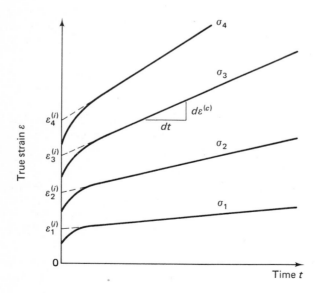

Figure 5.2 Linearized creep curves. (*After Hult, 1966.*)

theory of creep to be used in engineering design. The engineering theory of creep can be considered as a collection of laws which, by experience, are known to describe the creep behavior of frozen soils adequately. Emphasis here will be placed on the engineering theory, much of the material being drawn from work by Hult (1966), Ladanyi (1972), Sayles (1968, 1973), and Vyalov (1959, 1962, 1963) on creep of frozen soils.

5.2 STRESS-STRAIN-TIME RELATIONSHIPS

The creep curves shown in Fig. 5.1 are common to ice and frozen soils. Generally the amount of strain developed during the secondary-creep period is large compared with the strain developed during primary creep. In such a case the creep curves can be approximated by straight lines extending back to time equal to zero, as shown in Fig. 5.2. Predictions to be derived using these straight lines will be in error during the first phase of the creep process, but the error will decrease steadily during continued creep. When the proposed lifetime of the structure is of the duration of the primary-creep period of the frozen soil, the consitutive equation must describe the decrease in creep rate during period I. The decelerating creep of period I requires a more elaborate model than the steady-state creep of period II. Both secondary and primary-creep models are presented in subsequent sections.

It should be remembered that once creep has entered the secondary stage, it is just a matter of time before failure will occur, either through excessive deformation or by entering tertiary creep. Also, for temporary construction loads, considerable accuracy may be lost if the primary creep is ignored since some soils will remain in the primary-creep stage for several months, especially when small loads are applied.

Secondary Creep

For the creep curves shown in Fig. 5.2, Hult (1966) has described a convenient method for establishing the constitutive equation of the material. The creep curves are approximated by straight lines having intercepts shown. At constant stress and temperature, the strain in the secondary creep is given by

$$\varepsilon = \varepsilon^{(i)} + \varepsilon^{(c)} \tag{5.5}$$

where the pseudoinstantaneous strain $\varepsilon^{(i)}$ is governed by

$$\varepsilon^{(i)} = F(\sigma, T) \tag{5.6}$$

and the creep strain $\varepsilon^{(c)}$ by the creep law

$$\frac{d\varepsilon^{(c)}}{dt} = G(\sigma, T) \tag{5.7}$$

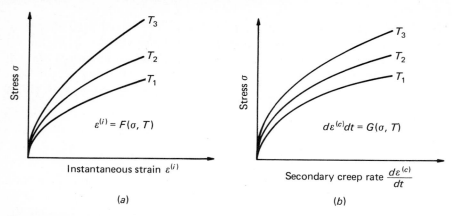

Figure 5.3 Constant-temperature curves: (a) instantaneous strain vs. stress; (b) creep rate vs. stress. (*After Hult, 1966.*)

The form of the functions $F(\sigma, T)$ and $G(\sigma, T)$ is determined by plotting the intercepts $\varepsilon^{(i)}$ and the slopes $d\varepsilon^{(c)}/dt$ against the applied stresses, as in Fig. 5.3. Suitable mathematical expressions are fitted to the experimental curves with temperature as a parameter.

When the mathematical form of the functions F and G have been determined, the total strain after time t in a creep-test step loaded to a stress σ at a constant temperature is [Eqs. (5.5) to (5.7)] given by

$$\varepsilon = F(\sigma, T) + tG(\sigma, T) \tag{5.8}$$

When the load is increased in steps, σ and T being constant for each step, the strain in the creep process can be predicted by a summation procedure, as shown schematically in Fig. 5.4. The total strain at any time t is then a function of the complete loading and temperature history of the process. When σ and T vary continuously with time, the total strain is given by

$$\varepsilon = F(\sigma, T) + \int_0^t G(\sigma, T)\, dt \tag{5.9}$$

Differentiation with respect to time gives the rate of strain

$$\frac{d\varepsilon}{dt} = \frac{d}{dt} F(\sigma, T) + G(\sigma, T) \tag{5.10}$$

The pseudoinstantaneous strains shown in Fig. 5.2 can be written

$$\varepsilon^{(i)} = \varepsilon^{(ie)} + \varepsilon^{(ip)} \tag{5.11}$$

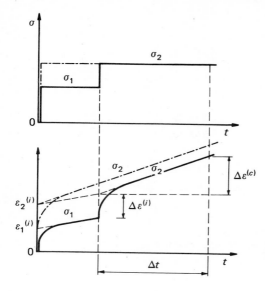

Figure 5.4 Creep curve for step loading. [*After Ladanyi, 1972, reproduced by permission of the National Research Council of Canada from the Canadian Geotechnical Journal*, **9:** 63–80 (1972).]

where $\varepsilon^{(ie)}$ is an elastic (reversible) portion and $\varepsilon^{(ip)}$ is a plastic (irreversible) portion. The elastic portion can be expressed as

$$\varepsilon^{(ie)} = \frac{\sigma}{E(T)} \tag{5.12}$$

where $E(T)$ is a fictitious Young's modulus. It is smaller than the instantaneous elastic modulus because $\varepsilon^{(ie)}$ also contains the delayed elasticity effect. For the plastic portion Ladanyi (1972) has written $\varepsilon^{(ip)}$ as a power expression

$$\varepsilon^{(ip)} = \varepsilon_k \left[\frac{\sigma}{\sigma_k(T)} \right]^{k(T)} \tag{5.13}$$

where σ_k plays the role of a temperature-dependent deformation modulus. The exponent $k > 1$ is usually little affected by the temperature while ε_k is an arbitrary small strain value introduced for convenience in calculation and plotting of data. For test data at a constant temperature, the numerical values of σ_k and k are obtained from a log-log plot of $\varepsilon^{(ip)}$ vs. σ. For the case of loading the total pseudoinstantaneous strain now takes the form

$$\varepsilon^{(i)} = \varepsilon^{(ie)} + \varepsilon^{(ip)} = \frac{\sigma}{E} + \varepsilon_k \left(\frac{\sigma}{\sigma_k} \right)^k = F(\sigma, T) \tag{5.14}$$

The second term should be deleted in the case of unloading since $\varepsilon^{(ip)}$ is an irreversible strain quantity.

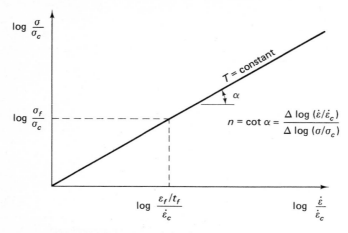

Figure 5.5 Creep exponent n [Eq. (5.15)] and creep-strength determination [Eq. (5.57)].

The creep law $G(\sigma, T)$ can be written as a simple power expression (Hult, 1966; Odqvist, 1966; Ladanyi, 1972):

$$\frac{d\varepsilon^{(c)}}{dt} = \dot{\varepsilon}^{(c)} = \dot{\varepsilon}_c \left[\frac{\sigma}{\sigma_c(T)}\right]^{n(T)} \tag{5.15}$$

where $\sigma_c(T)$ and $n(T)$ are creep parameters, both dependent on temperature. The proof stress σ_c (Hult, 1966) is the uniaxial stress for an arbitrarily selected creep rate $\dot{\varepsilon}_c$, which is introduced into Eq. (5.15) to put it into normalized form. For frozen soils $\dot{\varepsilon}_c$ is often taken as 10^{-5} min^{-1}. For a constant temperature the numerical value of n is obtained from a log-log plot of $\dot{\varepsilon}^{(c)}/\dot{\varepsilon}_c$ vs. σ/σ_c, as shown in Fig. 5.5.

For a given material the experimentally determined functions $F(\sigma, T)$ and $G(\sigma, T)$ are substituted into Eq. (5.9) to give the constitutive equation. In its integrated form Eq. (5.9) becomes

$$\varepsilon = \frac{\sigma}{E} + \varepsilon_k \left(\frac{\sigma}{\sigma_k}\right)^k + t\dot{\varepsilon}_c \left(\frac{\sigma}{\sigma_c}\right)^n \tag{5.16}$$

Vyalov (1959) provided experimental data showing that for time intervals greater than about 24 h the two instantaneous strain terms together become less than 10 percent of the total creep strain. For engineering applications where time intervals are greater than 1 day, use of the third term only in Eq. (5.16) gives good approximations of the total strains.

Example 5.1 Creep data from Fig. 5.6 with additional creep rates for frozen Callovian sandy loam at $-20°$C in uniaxial compression are summarized in

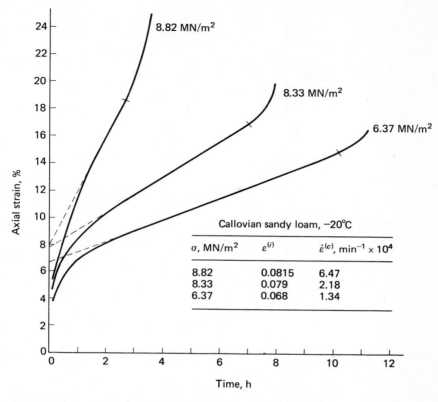

Figure 5.6 Creep curves for frozen Callovian sandy loam at $-20°C$ in uniaxial compression. (*Data from Vyalov, 1962.*)

Table 5.1. Determine the creep parameters k, σ_k, n, and σ_c needed to write the total strain equation

$$\varepsilon = \varepsilon_k \left(\frac{\sigma}{\sigma_k}\right)^k + \dot{\varepsilon}_c \left(\frac{\sigma}{\sigma_c}\right)^n t$$

Table 5.1†

σ, MN/m^2	$\dot{\varepsilon}^{(c)}$, min^{-1}
8.82	6.47×10^{-4}
8.33	2.18×10^{-4}
6.37	1.34×10^{-4}
6.18	7.02×10^{-5}
6.13	2.50×10^{-5}

† Data from Vyalov, 1962, Fig. 28.

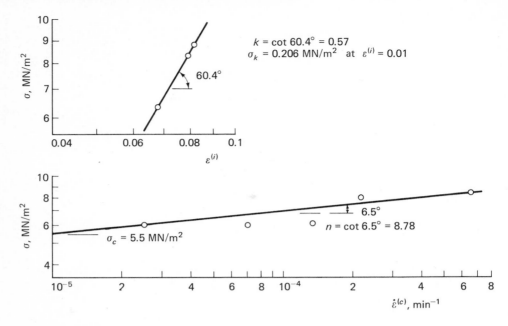

Figure 5.7 Log-log plot of $\varepsilon^{(i)}$ and $\dot{\varepsilon}^{(c)}$ vs. applied stress for the Callovian sandy loam (data from Fig. 5.6).

SOLUTION Find the intercepts $\varepsilon^{(i)}$ for the straight-line extensions shown in Fig. 5.6. Estimate the creep rates $\dot{\varepsilon}^{(c)}$ from the creep curves or for this example use the values given in Table 5.1. Plot the logarithm of $\varepsilon^{(i)}$ and $\dot{\varepsilon}^{(c)}$ against the logarithm of applied stress, as shown in Fig. 5.7. Draw the best-fit straight lines and from the slopes determine $k = \cot 60.4° = 0.57$ and $n = \cot 6.5° = 8.78$. For convenience select $\varepsilon_k = 10^{-2}$ and $\dot{\varepsilon}_c = 10^{-5} \ \mathrm{min}^{-1}$. From the straight-line extensions read $\sigma_k = 0.206 \ \mathrm{MN/m^2}$ and $\sigma_c = 5.5 \ \mathrm{MN/m^2}$.

Primary Creep

When the lifetime of the structure is approximately equal to the duration of primary creep for the frozen soil, the constitutive equation must describe the decrease in creep rate shown in period I, Fig. 5.1b. The instantaneous strain ε_0 develops immediately upon load application, followed by the gradual development of the creep strain $\varepsilon^{(c)}$. According to Hult (1966), ε_0 contains an elastic and a plastic deformation. It is difficult to determine the plastic deformation accurately, and for small stresses this deformation can usually be neglected. Then

$$\varepsilon_0 \approx \frac{1}{E_0(T)} \sigma \tag{5.17}$$

The creep strain $\varepsilon^{(c)}$ is some function of stress σ, time t, and temperature T, so that

$$\varepsilon^{(c)} = f(\sigma, t, T) \tag{5.18}$$

To arrive at an incremental-strain theory take the time derivative of Eq. (5.18), giving

$$\frac{d\varepsilon^{(c)}}{dt} = g(\sigma, t, T) \tag{5.19}$$

where $g = \partial f / \partial t$ with σ and T assumed constant. Elimination of t between Eq. (5.18) and (5.19) yields

$$\frac{d\varepsilon^{(c)}}{dt} = h(\sigma, \varepsilon^{(c)}, T) \tag{5.20}$$

For constant σ and T Eqs. (5.18) to (5.20) are fully equivalent. In the primary-creep period the decrease of creep rate is generally termed *hardening*. Since Eq. (5.19) contains time t, it is often termed a time-hardening creep law, as compared with Eq. (5.20), which defines a strain-hardening creep law. Hult (1966) does not recommend the time-hardening theory for cases where large stress redistributions occur.

The primary creep of ice and frozen soils at constant stress can often be described by the creep law

$$\varepsilon^{(c)} = K\sigma^n t^b \qquad b < 1 \tag{5.21}$$

where K, n, and b are temperature-dependent material constants. Differentiation with respect to time, with stress constant, and elimination of t yields the strain-hardening creep law

$$\frac{d\varepsilon^{(c)}}{dt} = K^{1/b} b \sigma^{n/b} (\varepsilon^{(c)})^{-(1-b)/b} \tag{5.22}$$

which for convenience can be written

$$\frac{d}{dt}(\varepsilon^{(c)})^{1/b} = \frac{\dot{\varepsilon}_c}{b}\left(\frac{\sigma}{\sigma_c}\right)^{n/b} \tag{5.23}$$

where b, n, and σ_c are material creep parameters and $\dot{\varepsilon}_c$ is an arbitrary, conveniently selected creep rate. For a constant-stress creep test, it follows from Eq. (5.23) that the creep strain becomes

$$\varepsilon^{(c)} = \left(\frac{\dot{\varepsilon}_c}{b}\right)^b \left(\frac{\sigma}{\sigma_c}\right)^n t^b \tag{5.24}$$

For convenience in determining the creep parameters Eq. (5.24) can be written as

$$\varepsilon^{(c)} = Ct^b \tag{5.25}$$

where

$$C = \left(\frac{\dot{\varepsilon}_c}{b}\right)^b \left(\frac{\sigma}{\sigma_c}\right)^n \tag{5.26}$$

Equation (5.25) can be written as

$$\log \varepsilon^{(c)} = \log C + b \log t \tag{5.27}$$

which permits evaluation of b and C if the experimental creep strain and time data linearize on a plot of $\log \varepsilon$ vs. $\log t$ (Fig. 5.8). For $t = 1$, $\varepsilon = C = F(\sigma)$. For different values of σ, the corresponding values of C can be read from Fig. 5.8. Plotting the $\log C$ vs. $\log \sigma$ (Fig. 5.8) permits the evaluation of n and σ_c since

$$\log C = \log C_0 + n \log \sigma \tag{5.28}$$

where the intercept

$$\log C_0 = b \log \frac{\dot{\varepsilon}_c}{b} - n \log \sigma_c \tag{5.29}$$

For $\sigma = 1$ note that $C = C_0$ in Fig. 5.8. Using Eq. (5.29), we now obtain the creep modulus σ_c from the relation

$$\sigma_c = \left[\frac{(\dot{\varepsilon}_c/b)^b}{C_0} \right]^{1/n} \tag{5.30}$$

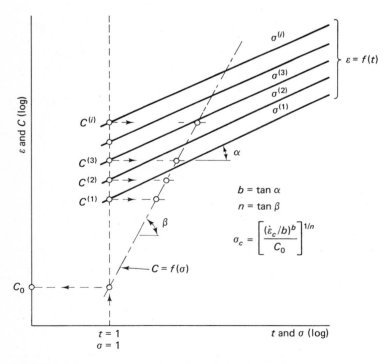

Figure 5.8 Primary-creep parameters from time–creep-strain data.

For the multiaxial state of stress replace σ and ε with the equivalent stress σ_e and the equivalent creep strain ε_e, respectively; thus Eq. (5.24) can be written

$$\varepsilon_e^{(c)} = \left(\frac{\dot{\varepsilon}_c}{b}\right)^b \left(\frac{\sigma_e}{\sigma_c}\right)^n t^b \qquad (5.31)$$

The equivalent (or generalized) stress, strain, and strain rate are given below in terms of the principal stresses, strains, and strain rates, respectively.

$$\sigma_e^2 = \tfrac{1}{2}[(\sigma_1 - \sigma_2)^2 + (\sigma_2 - \sigma_3)^2 + (\sigma_3 - \sigma_1)^2] \qquad (5.32)$$

$$\varepsilon_e^2 = \tfrac{2}{9}[(\varepsilon_1 - \varepsilon_2)^2 + (\varepsilon_2 - \varepsilon_3)^2 + (\varepsilon_3 - \varepsilon_1)^2] \qquad (5.33)$$

$$\dot{\varepsilon}_e^2 = \tfrac{2}{9}[(\dot{\varepsilon}_1 - \dot{\varepsilon}_2)^2 + (\dot{\varepsilon}_2 - \dot{\varepsilon}_3)^2 + (\dot{\varepsilon}_3 - \dot{\varepsilon}_1)^2] \qquad (5.34)$$

The primary-creep parameters can also be determined from time and creep-rate data of the form summarized in Fig. 5.9 for frozen Ottawa sand. From

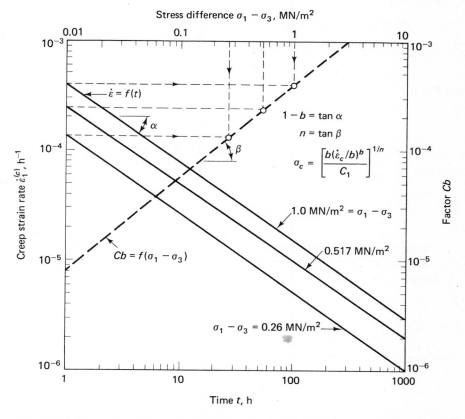

Figure 5.9 Primary-creep parameters from time–creep-strain-rate data for Ottawa sand. (*Data from Sayles, 1973.*)

Eq. (5.25) the creep-rate–vs.–time relationship becomes

$$\dot{\varepsilon}^{(c)} = \frac{d\varepsilon^{(c)}}{dt} = Cbt^{b-1} \tag{5.35}$$

with C and b defined as before. For triaxial test conditions $\sigma = \sigma_e = \sigma_1 - \sigma_3$ and $\dot{\varepsilon} = \dot{\varepsilon}_e = \dot{\varepsilon}_1$. Writing Eq. (5.35) in the form

$$\log \dot{\varepsilon}_e^{(c)} = \log Cb - (1 - b) \log t \tag{5.36}$$

gives the equation for a straight line with

$$1 - b = \frac{\Delta \log \dot{\varepsilon}_e^{(c)}}{\Delta \log t} = \tan \alpha \tag{5.37}$$

For $t = 1$ h, $\dot{\varepsilon}_e^{(c)} = Cb = f(\sigma_e)$. The plot of $\log Cb$ vs. $\log \sigma_e$ also linearizes (Fig. 5.9), permitting an evaluation of n and σ_c. Multiplying Eq. (5.26) by b, replacing σ with σ_e, and taking the logarithm of both sides gives the straight-line relationship

$$\log Cb = (1 - b) \log b + b \log \dot{\varepsilon}_c - n \log \sigma_c + n \log \sigma_e \tag{5.38}$$

which can be used to obtain the intercept

$$\log C_1 = (1 - b) \log b + b \log \dot{\varepsilon}_c - n \log \sigma_c \tag{5.39}$$

From Fig. 5.9 obtain

$$n = \frac{\Delta \log Cb}{\Delta \log \sigma_e} = \tan \beta \tag{5.40}$$

For $\sigma_e = 1$ MN/m^2, $Cb = C_1$ from Fig. 5.9. Using Eq. (5.38), we now obtain the creep modulus σ_c from

$$\sigma_c = \left[\frac{b(\dot{\varepsilon}_c/b)^b}{C_1} \right]^{1/n} \tag{5.41}$$

Example 5.2 Time and creep-rate data for frozen Ottawa sand at a constant temperature are summarized in Fig. 5.9. (a) Determine the material creep parameters b, n, and σ_c needed for the primary-creep-rate equation

$$\dot{\varepsilon}_1^{(c)} = Cbt^{b-1} = b\left(\frac{\dot{\varepsilon}_c}{b}\right)^b \left(\frac{\sigma_1 - \sigma_3}{\sigma_c}\right)^n t^{b-1}$$

(b) Transform this equation into the steady-state-creep form assuming that steady-state creep starts at $t_0 = 6000$ h.

SOLUTION (a) From the slope of $\log \dot{\varepsilon}_1$ vs. $\log t$ (Fig. 5.9) obtain $1 - b = \tan \alpha = 0.7$ and $b = 0.3$. Plot the Cb values ($\dot{\varepsilon}_1^{(c)}$ at $t = 1$ h) against $\sigma_1 - \sigma_3$. The resulting straight line represents $Cb = f(\sigma_1 - \sigma_3)$ with a slope giving $n = \tan \beta = 0.87$. For $\sigma_1 - \sigma_3 = 1$ MN/m^2 obtain $C_1 = 4 \times 10^{-4}$ h^{-1}.

Assuming that $\dot{\varepsilon}_c \doteq 10^{-8}\,\text{h}^{-1}$ and using Eq. (5.41), obtain $\sigma_c = 5.32\,\text{MN/m}^2$. Hence

$$\dot{\varepsilon}_1^{(c)} = 0.3\left(\frac{10^{-8}}{0.3}\right)^{0.3}\left(\frac{\sigma_1 - \sigma_3}{5.32}\right)^{0.87}t^{-0.7}$$

with stresses in meganewtons per square meter and time in hours.

(b) Transformation of primary to steady-state creep at $t = t_0$ involves Eq. (5.35) in the form

$$\dot{\varepsilon}_e^{(c)} = \dot{\varepsilon}_1^{(c)} = \dot{\varepsilon}_c'\left(\frac{\sigma_1 - \sigma_3}{\sigma_c}\right)^n$$

where

$$\dot{\varepsilon}_c' = b\left(\frac{\dot{\varepsilon}_c}{b}\right)^b t_0^{b-1} = 3.88 \times 10^{-6}\,\text{h}^{-1}$$

and

$$\varepsilon_e^{(i)} = \varepsilon_1^{(i)} = t_0\,\frac{1-b}{b}\,\dot{\varepsilon}_c'\left(\frac{\sigma_1 - \sigma_3}{\sigma_c}\right)^n = 5.44 \times 10^{-2}\left(\frac{\sigma_1 - \sigma_3}{5.32}\right)^{0.87}$$

The steady-state creep strains are then given (for $t \geq t_0$) by

$$\varepsilon_e = \varepsilon_1 = \varepsilon_1^{(i)} + \dot{\varepsilon}_1^{(c)}t = \left(\frac{\sigma_1 - \sigma_3}{5.32}\right)^{0.87}(3.88 \times 10^{-6})(14{,}000 + t)$$

with t in hours and stresses in meganewtons per square meter.

Vyalov's Equation

Vyalov (1962) has proposed that the theory of nonlinear hereditary creep be used to describe the time-dependent deformation behavior of frozen soil. This theory is quite flexible and is based on the assumption that deformation at any time and temperature depends upon both the applied stress and history of any prior deformation. The total strain can be expressed as

$$\varepsilon = \varepsilon_0 + \varepsilon(t) = \varepsilon_0 + \varepsilon_1 + \varepsilon_2 + \varepsilon_3 \tag{5.42}$$

where $\varepsilon(t) = \varepsilon_1 + \varepsilon_2 + \varepsilon_3$ includes primary, secondary, and tertiary creep, respectively. The initial deformation ε_0 is elastic and fully recoverable, ε_1 includes both elastic and plastic deformation, and ε_2 and ε_3 are nonrecoverable. The deformation at time $t > 0$ consists of elastic deformation linearly related to stress and plastic deformation which is nonlinear. The relationship of stress to strain can be expressed as

$$\varepsilon_i = \frac{\sigma}{E_i} + \left(\frac{\sigma}{A_i}\right)^{1/m} \tag{5.43}$$

where E_i and A_i are moduli of linear and nonlinear deformation, respectively. The entire stress range can be described by

$$\varepsilon_i = f(\sigma) \qquad \text{or} \qquad \sigma = f(\varepsilon_i) \tag{5.44}$$

As strain increases with time, each period of time is characterized by its own curve, which is sometimes called an *isochronous curve* or an *isocurve*. The initial strain for $t = 0$ represents the elastic deformation while the final deformation $(t = \infty)$ corresponds to continuous, unlimited duration of load σ.

Experimental data (Vyalov, 1962) show that the deformation curves for various time periods (isocurves) are similar and can be described by a power law. The functions in Eq. (5.44) can be expressed as

$$\varepsilon = \left[\frac{\sigma}{A(t)} \right]^{1/m} \qquad \text{or} \qquad \sigma = A(t)\varepsilon^m \tag{5.45}$$

where $A(t)$ is the modulus of total deformation. Its value changes with respect to load duration, beginning with an initial A_0 and ending with an ultimate and continuous A_∞. This modulus depends on the frozen-soil temperature, and when $m \leq 1$, it is the strengthening factor, independent of time and temperature.

The stress-strain state, while changing with time, can be described by a rheological equation of state, including stress, strain, their rates, and time. Development of the above equations (Vyalov, 1962) in compliance with the theory of nonlinear hereditary creep leads to the expression

$$\varepsilon^m = \frac{\sigma}{A_0} (1 + at^\lambda) \tag{5.46}$$

The temperature effect on the frozen soil is accounted for by the equation

$$A_0 = w(\theta + 1)^k \tag{5.47}$$

where $\theta°C = 273 - T$ K and w and k are soil parameters. If the small initial deformation ε_0 is neglected, the total strain given by Eq. (5.46) can be expressed as

$$\varepsilon = \left[\frac{\sigma t^\lambda}{\omega(\theta + 1)^k} \right]^{1/m} \tag{5.48}$$

where $\omega = w/a$. The parameters ω, λ, k, and m are constants representative of the frozen soil. This equation conceals the fact that the 1 in $\theta + 1$ has units of temperature. For this reason Assur (1963) suggested that Eq. (5.48) be written

$$\varepsilon = \left[\frac{\sigma t^\lambda}{\omega(\theta + \theta_c)^k} \right]^{1/m} = \left[\frac{\sigma t^\lambda}{\omega\theta_c^k(\theta/\theta_c + 1)^k} \right]^{1/m} \tag{5.49}$$

Here the numerical values of m and λ do not vary with the units employed, but ω and θ_c^k do. Vyalov assumed $\theta_c = 1°C$, a constant reference temperature greater than zero, so that $\log(1 + \theta)$ has meaning at $\theta = 0$. Typical values for the constants m, λ, ω, and k are given in Table 5.2 for several soil types.

Table 5.2 Constants for Vyalov's deformation equation (after Sayles and Haines, 1974)

Soil	m	λ	ω for $\theta_0 = 1°C$, MPa $\cdot$ h$^\lambda$/°C^k	k
Suffield clay	0.42	0.14	0.73	1.2
Bat-Baioss clay†	0.40	0.18	1.25	0.97
Hanover silt	0.49	0.074	4.58	0.87
Callovian sandy loam†	0.27	0.10	0.88	0.89
Ottawa sand‡ (20/30 mesh)	0.78	0.35	44.72	1.0
Manchester fine sand‡ (40/200 mesh)	0.38	0.24	2.29	1.0

† Data from Vyalov (1962).
‡ Data from Sayles (1968).

Example 5.3 Experimental creep data for saturated Ottawa sand, porosity equal to 37 percent, are summarized in Fig. 5.10a and b (Sayles, 1968). Straight lines have been assumed on the log-log plot of stress vs. strain. Determine, for the Ottawa sand, the parameters m, λ, ω, and k in Eq. (5.49).

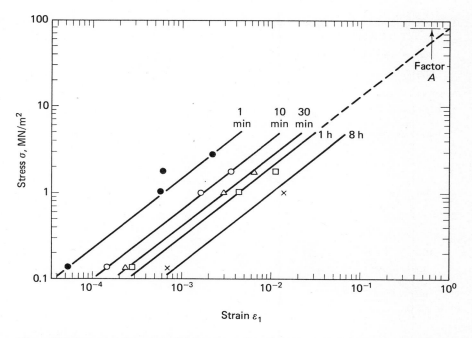

Figure 5.10 Saturated Ottawa sand: (a) stress, strain and time, $-0.56°C$. (*Data from Sayles; 1968*)

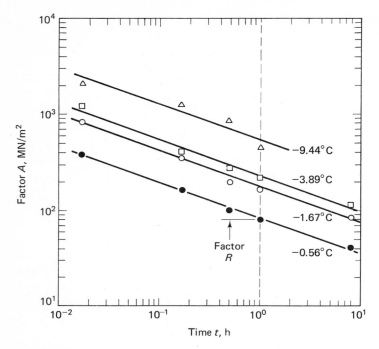

Figure 5.10 (*b*) time, factor *A*, and temperature.

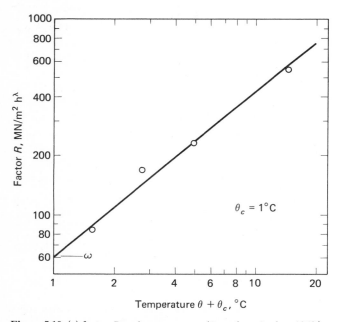

Figure 5.10 (*c*) factor *R* and temperature. (*Data from Sayles; 1968.*)

SOLUTION Write Eq. (5.49) in the form $\sigma = A\varepsilon^m$. The straight-line relationships shown in Fig. 5.10a are now represented by $\log \sigma = \log A + m \log \varepsilon$ with slope $= m = (\Delta \log \sigma)/(\Delta \log \varepsilon) = \tan \alpha = 0.79$ and intercepts for $\varepsilon_1 = 1$ equal to the factor A ($\log A = \log \sigma$) with units of meganewtons per square meter. Each line corresponds to a different time. Since $A = \omega(\theta + \theta_c)^k t^{-\lambda} = Rt^{-\lambda}$ the straight lines in Fig. 5.10b are represented by $\log A = \log R - \lambda \log t$. The slope $= -\lambda = (\Delta \log A)/(\Delta \log t) = 0.36$. The intercept for $t = 1$ h equals the factor R with units of MPa $\cdot$ h$^\lambda$. Each temperature provides a different R factor. Next $R = \omega(\theta + \theta_c)^k$, and the straight line in Fig. 5.10c is represented by $\log R = \log \omega + k \log (\theta + \theta_c)$. The slope $= k = (\Delta \log R)/[\Delta \log (\theta + \theta_c)]$ $= 0.85$, and the intercept for $\theta + \theta_c = 1°C$ gives $\omega = 61$ MPa $\cdot$ h$^\lambda$/°C^k.

5.3 STRENGTH OF FROZEN SOILS

The strength of frozen soils may take on different meanings depending on the engineering problem. It includes both the concept of rupture and that of excessive deformation. Both have application to frozen-soil engineering. In frozen soils, deformation may result from slippage between soil particles and plastic flow in the ice component. When deformation occurs in a restricted zone or along some localized surface in the soil mass, it is common to call this a *slip surface*. In an element of the soil mass this slip surface is referred to as a *failure plane*. The shearing resistance may be defined as the shear stress on the failure plane at failure. In other cases deformation may occur simultaneously along many surfaces, and a failure plane is undefined. For this case it is convenient to define failure in terms of the maximum principal stresses which can be mobilized. These concepts do not change when considering frozen vs. unfrozen soils.

The concept of excessive deformation takes on special meaning for frozen soils since these materials exhibit a slow deformation within certain ranges of stress and temperature. Most field problems in permafrost involve temperatures only a few degrees below the melting point of ice. Pressure melting of ice at points of contact with soil particles contributes to plastic deformation of the pore ice and readjustment in particle arrangement. The result is a time-dependent deformation of frozen soil. Hence, the engineering problem becomes one of predicting the frozen-soil deformation under given loads over the service life of the structure. This section provides two methods for predicting the available strength of a frozen soil for a specified time or service life. Measurement of frozen-soil properties is presented in a later section.

Creep Strength

The creep strength of frozen soils is defined as the stress level, after a finite time, at which rupture, instability leading to rupture, or extremely large deformations without rupture occur. In compression creep tests on frozen soils at constant stress the creep strength may be identified with the beginning of an increasing creep rate (tertiary creep), point C in Fig. 5.1b. Frozen fine-grained soils at temperatures near 0°C can experience extremely large deformations without rupture, especially when they are subjected to triaxial stresses. Strength for these soils must be defined in relation to the maximum deformation which a given structure can tolerate. In laboratory testing, axial strains of 20 percent are often arbitrarily considered to be failure. The creep strength is defined as the stress level producing this strain after a finite time interval.

The creep strength can be determined experimentally by testing several duplicate specimens at a given temperature with each specimen at a different stress level. When that stress level and the time to reach tertiary creep for each specimen are used, a curve of creep strength vs. time can be plotted, as shown for Ottawa sand in Fig. 5.11. Tests of this kind are limited by the time available, normally much less than the service life of a structure. The creep theory can be extended to permit computation of the creep strength. The method outlined below is applicable to soils where secondary creep is dominant.

Creep-strength prediction consists of finding a relationship between the creep strength σ_f, time to failure t_f, secondary- or minimum-creep rate $\dot{\varepsilon}^{(c)}$, failure strain ε_f, and temperature T. A constant-stress creep curve (Fig. 5.1b) shows that

$$\varepsilon_f = \varepsilon^{(i)} + t_f \dot{\varepsilon}^{(c)} \tag{5.50}$$

from which

$$t_f = \frac{\varepsilon_f - \varepsilon^{(i)}}{\dot{\varepsilon}^{(c)}} \tag{5.51}$$

The design engineer may specify an acceptable maximum strain which equals the failure strain. In this case the numerator in Eq. (5.51) will be constant, and

$$t_f = \frac{C}{\dot{\varepsilon}^{(c)}} \tag{5.52}$$

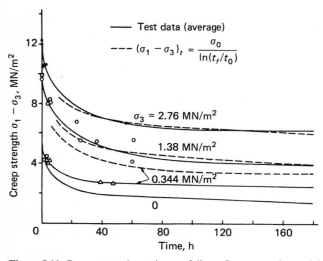

Figure 5.11 Creep strength vs. time to failure, Ottawa sand at $-3.85°C$. (*After Sayles, 1973.*)

This relationship between time to creep failure and secondary- or minimum-creep rate has been adopted as the basis for a number of creep-rupture criteria (Garofalo, 1965). The steady-state or minimum-creep rate $\dot{\varepsilon}^{(c)}$, in turn, can be related to the applied stress and temperature. For large creep-rate intervals it is observed that the numerator in Eq. (5.51) is not a constant but is some function of strain, creep rate, and temperature. A more general form of Eq. (5.52) is

$$t_f = \frac{F(\varepsilon, \dot{\varepsilon}, T)}{\dot{\varepsilon}^{(c)}} \tag{5.53}$$

Compression creep of frozen soils often shows that the amount of permanent strain at the end of steady-state creep is approximately constant for a given temperature and type of test (Sayles and Epanchin, 1966; Vyalov, 1962). This behavior suggests that instability occurs when the total damage done by straining reaches a certain value. Hence there is some experimental justification for using a constant permanent strain as a basis for the creep-failure criterion in frozen soils. This criterion is convenient for problem solving and is acceptable to the design engineer who wishes to limit the total strain to values acceptable for the structure.

For this approach the numerator in Eq. (5.51) is not constant but is some function of the pseudoinstantaneous plastic strain $\varepsilon^{(ip)}$. If we neglect the instantaneous elastic strain $\varepsilon^{(ie)}$, Eq. (5.51) becomes (Ladanyi, 1972)

$$t_f = \frac{\varepsilon_f - \varepsilon^{(ip)}}{\dot{\varepsilon}^{(c)}} \tag{5.54}$$

Substitution, using Eqs. (5.13) and (5.15), for $\varepsilon^{(ip)}$ and $\varepsilon^{(c)}$ gives

$$t_f = \frac{\varepsilon_f - \varepsilon_k(\sigma/\sigma_k)^k}{\dot{\varepsilon}_c(\sigma/\sigma_c)^n} \tag{5.55}$$

According to Eq. (5.55), the creep strength approaches zero when t tends to infinity. For frictional materials the secondary-creep rate approaches zero when the applied stress is lower than some finite stress value σ_{lt} equal to the long-term strength (Vyalov, 1962). This behavior is accounted for when Eq. (5.54) is written as

$$t_f = \frac{\varepsilon_f - \varepsilon_k(\sigma/\sigma_k)^k}{\dot{\varepsilon}_c[(\sigma - \sigma_{lt})/\sigma_c]^n} \tag{5.56}$$

For high-ice-content soils and large time intervals the pseudoinstantaneous plastic strain can be neglected relative to the time-dependent portion; hence Eq. (5.55) becomes

$$t_f = \frac{\varepsilon_f}{\dot{\varepsilon}_c(\sigma/\sigma_c)^n} \tag{5.57}$$

which is analogous to Eq. (5.52). Since Eq. (5.57) has the same form as Eq. (5.15), the time to failure t_f and the creep strength σ_f can be obtained directly from the plotted creep law, as shown in Fig. 5.5. For this purpose $\dot{\varepsilon}_f$ has been written as

$$\dot{\varepsilon}_f = \frac{\varepsilon_f}{t_f} \tag{5.58}$$

The creep strength after a long time interval and a constant temperature T, based on Eq. (5.57) and (5.58), is given by

$$\sigma_f \approx \sigma_c(T) \left(\frac{\dot{\varepsilon}_f}{\dot{\varepsilon}_c} \right)^{1/n} \tag{5.59}$$

Example 5.4 Using the creep parameters from Example 5.1 and observing that the failure strain ε_f was close to 15 percent for the frozen Callovian sandy loam (Fig. 5.6), estimate the 10-year strength at $-20°C$ using the creep-strength equation in the form

$$\sigma_f \approx \sigma_c \left(\frac{\varepsilon_f}{\dot{\varepsilon}_c t_f} \right)^{1/n}$$

SOLUTION For $t_f = 10$ years $= 5.25 \times 10^6$ min, $\varepsilon_f = 0.15$, $\dot{\varepsilon}_c = 10^{-5}$ min^{-1}, $\sigma_c = 5.5$ MN/m^2, and $n = 8.78$ compute the 10-year strength

$$\sigma_f \approx 5.5 \left[\frac{0.15}{10^{-5}(5.25 \times 10^6)} \right]^{1/8.78} = 2.8 \text{ MN/m}^2$$

Vyalov's Long-Term Strength

Tests on a series of frozen-soil specimens with different but constant stress for each specimen show that the lower the stress the longer the time required for failure. The test data for the curves shown in Fig. 5.11 were obtained by plotting failure stresses vs. time. For compression, rupture occurs only in low-moisture, dense frozen soils. Ice-saturated soils with low density exhibit deformations that are plastic in character and which end in flattening the specimen without loss of its continuity. The criterion of strength is considered to be some selected critical value of deformation which initiates progressive flow, i.e., point C in Fig. 5.1b. Long-term strengths reported by Vyalov (1962) ranged from 18 to 37 percent of the instantaneous cohesion for a frozen sandy silt.

Vyalov (1959) suggested that the variation of strength of frozen soils with time can be represented by

$$\sigma_f = \frac{\sigma_0}{\ln \left[(t_f + t^*)/t_0 \right]} \approx \frac{\sigma_0}{\ln (t_f/t_0)} \tag{5.60}$$

where σ_0, t_0 = parameters which depend on soil type and temperature
t_f = time to failure
σ_f = long-term strength

The value t^* equals $t_0 \exp(\sigma_0/\sigma_i)$, where σ_i is the initial instantaneous strength. For long-term strengths Vyalov (1963) stated that the quantity t^* may be neglected. This equation appears to be applicable to frozen soils where either primary or secondary creep dominates the deformation behavior.

Equation (5.60) with t_f equal to infinity results in a long-term strength equal to zero, which is not consistent with the idea of continuous strength at some finite time. Vyalov (1963) stated that the idea is purely conventional, but in practice, after some long period of time, the additional strength reduction is so

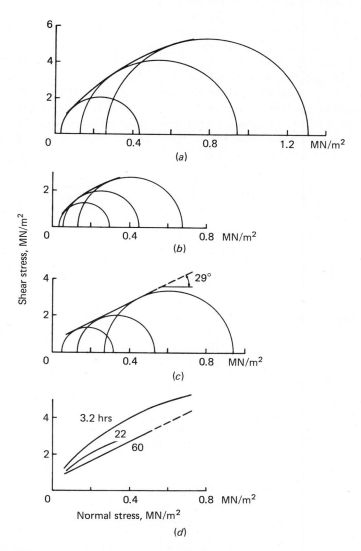

Figure 5.12 Mohr envelopes based on creep strength of Ottawa sand at $-3.85°C$: (*a*) 3.2 h, (*b*) 22 h, (*c*) 60 h, (*d*) composite. (*After Sayles, 1973.*)

insignificant and so low that this additional strength reduction can be neglected in engineering calculations.

Sayles (1973) has modified Vyalov's (1959) equation for long-term strength to allow for triaxial stress conditions as follows:

$$\sigma_f \approx (\sigma_1 - \sigma_3)_f \approx \frac{\sigma_0}{\ln (t_f/t_0)} \tag{5.61}$$

where σ_0 and t_0 are parameters determined by short-term creep tests under the stress and temperature conditions anticipated for the design problem. The strength variations with time predicted by Eq. (5.61) are represented by dashed lines in Fig. 5.11 for comparison with test data from relatively short-term creep tests.

Mohr-Coulomb envelopes representing creep strengths of Ottawa sand for different times after load application of constant axial stresses are shown in Fig. 5.12. The curved envelopes for the shorter periods of time suggest that the ice behavior dominates the strength before friction between sand particles develops. The envelope for the 60-h period at reduced axial stress approaches a straight line with an angle of internal friction close to 29°. This friction angle was close to that for the unfrozen Ottawa sand. These envelopes show that at lower applied stresses time is available for the ice to creep from between the sand grains and allow the development of frictional resistance between the sand particles. The frictional resistance of the sand grains thus tends to dominate the strength of the frozen sand over long periods of time.

Example 5.5 The reciprocal of creep strength is plotted against the logarithm of time in Fig. 5.13, giving straight lines for the Suffield clay. Determine the parameters σ_0 and t_0 at $-1.67°C$ for Eq. (5.60).

SOLUTION Rearrange the equation into the form

$$\frac{1}{\sigma_f} = \frac{1}{\sigma_0} \ln \frac{t_f}{t_0} = \frac{1}{\sigma_0} 2.303 \log \frac{t_f}{t_0}$$

where the slope of the straight lines equals $2.303(1/\sigma_0)$. From Fig. 5.13 for $T = -1.67°C$ obtain

$$\text{Slope} = 2.303 \frac{1}{\sigma_0} = \frac{1.66 - 1.24}{\log 10 - \log 1}$$

Solve for $\sigma_0 = 5.48$ MN/m². For $t = 1$ h read from the intercept $1/\sigma_1 = 1.24$ (MN/m²)$^{-1}$ at $-1.67°C$. Now solve for t_0 using

$$2.303 \log \frac{1}{t_0} = \frac{\sigma_0}{\sigma_1} = 5.48(1.24)$$

or $t_0 = 1.12 \times 10^{-3}$ h.

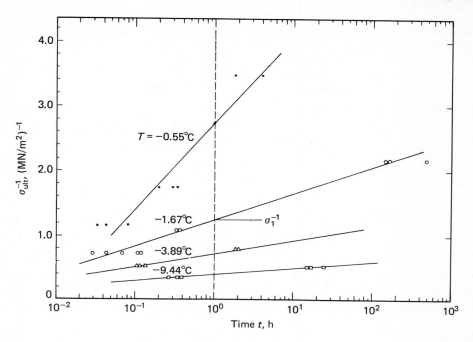

Figure 5.13 Reciprocal of creep strength vs. logarithm of time for Suffield clay. (*After Sayles and Haines, 1974.*)

5.4 TEMPERATURE EFFECT ON CREEP RATE AND STRENGTH

Experimental creep data on both unfrozen and frozen soils (Mitchell et al., 1968; Andersland and AlNouri, 1970) suggest that thermal activation is involved in the deformation processes and that these processes show a rate dependence on temperature through the factor $\exp(-U/RT)$, where U is the apparent activation energy for the rate-controlling mechanisms, R is the universal gas constant, and T is the absolute temperature. The temperature dependence of the creep rate when other factors are constant becomes

$$\dot{\varepsilon}^{(c)} = A \exp\left(-\frac{L}{T}\right) \tag{5.62}$$

where $L = U/R$ with units of temperature. The values of A and L in Eq. (5.62) for different temperatures can be found by plotting the natural logarithm of the observed creep rates against the reciprocal of the absolute temperature.

Using Eq. (5.62) together with the power-creep law [Eq. (5.15)], as has been done for ice (Glen, 1955; Gold, 1970), one can write

$$\dot{\varepsilon}^{(c)} = \dot{\varepsilon}_c \left(\frac{\sigma}{\sigma_{c\theta}}\right)^n = A \exp\left(-\frac{L}{T}\right) \tag{5.63}$$

To eliminate A, Ladanyi (1972) let the proof stress $\sigma_{c\theta}$ at a temperature T equal the proof stress σ_{c0} at $T = 273$ K. Then

$$\dot{\varepsilon}^{(c)} = \dot{\varepsilon}_c \left(\frac{\sigma}{\sigma_{c0}} \right)^n = A \exp \left(-\frac{L}{273} \right) \tag{5.64}$$

Dividing Eq. (5.63) by (5.64) gives

$$\left(\frac{\sigma_{c\theta}}{\sigma_{c0}} \right)^{-n} = \frac{\exp(-L/T)}{\exp(-L/273)} \tag{5.65}$$

and

$$\sigma_{c\theta} = \sigma_{c0} \exp \frac{L(273 - T)}{273nT} \equiv \sigma_{c0} f_1(T) \tag{5.66}$$

Equations (5.63) and (5.66) give

$$\dot{\varepsilon}^{(c)} = \dot{\varepsilon}_c \left(\frac{\sigma}{\sigma_{c0}} \right)^n \exp \frac{-L(273 - T)}{273T} \tag{5.67}$$

The term $\dot{\varepsilon}_c (\sigma/\sigma_{c0})^n$ represents the creep rate at a temperature close to the melting point ($T \approx 273$ K). Equation (5.67) can be simplified by using θ defined as the absolute value of the negative temperature in degrees Celsius:

$$\theta°C = 273 - T \qquad \text{K} \tag{5.68}$$

Then Eq. (5.67) can be written

$$\sigma_{c\theta} = \sigma_{c0} \exp \frac{L\theta}{273n(273 - \theta)} \equiv \sigma_{c0} f_1(\theta) \tag{5.69}$$

For most practical frozen-soil problems θ is much smaller than $273°C$; hence Eq. (5.69) can be approximated as

$$\sigma_{c\theta} \simeq \sigma_{c0} \exp \frac{L\theta}{(273)^2 n} \equiv \sigma_{c0} f_2(\theta) \tag{5.70}$$

where the term $(273)^2 n/L$ is a constant with units of temperature. The parameters σ_{c0} and L can be determined by first plotting the logarithm of σ against the logarithm of $\dot{\varepsilon}$, as shown in Fig. 5.14. Next, the intercept values $\sigma_{c\theta}$ from Fig. 5.14 are plotted against θ, as shown in Fig. 5.15, giving an intercept equal to σ_{c0}.
From Eq. (5.70)

$$\frac{L}{(273)^2 n} = \frac{\Delta \ln \sigma_{c\theta}}{\Delta \theta} \tag{5.71}$$

and using the slope of the line in Fig. 5.15, we get

$$L \approx 2.303(273)^2 n \frac{\Delta \log \sigma_{c\theta}}{\Delta \theta} \qquad °C \tag{5.72}$$

The apparent activation energy is given by

$$U = RL \tag{5.73}$$

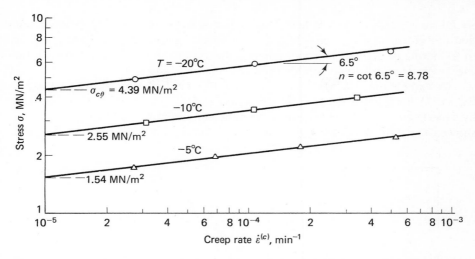

Figure 5.14 Creep rate vs. stress for Callovian sandy loam at temperatures of -5, -10, and $-20°C$. (*Data from Vyalov, 1962.*)

where the universal gas constant R equals 8.32 J/mol °C. Hoekstra (1969) has noted that the activation energy, computed above, does not correspond to its physical definition, since in frozen soil a gradual phase change occurs in addition to the thermal energy involved in moving particles of atomic size from one

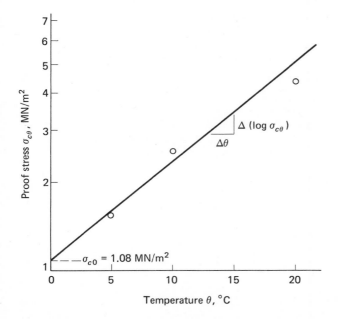

Figure 5.15 Temperature dependence of $\sigma_{c\theta}$ for Callovian sandy loam (data from Fig. 5.10).

equilibrium position to another. Andersland and Douglas (1970) pointed out that movement of a soil particle is a mechanically activated process in contrast to a thermally activated process; hence the observed or apparent activation energy may involve some combination of these processes.

An exponential increase of creep strength is predicted by the same theory, Eq. (5.67), for a linear decrease in temperature. This is only partially supported by experimental results (Fig. 5.16). The data summarized by Sayles (1966, 1968) showed that this form of strength variation is limited to clays. For the silts and

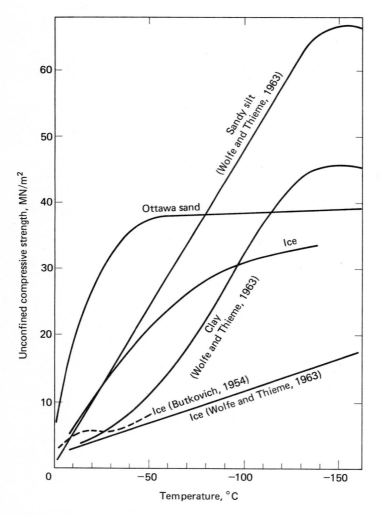

Figure 5.16 Temperature dependence of unconfined compressive strength for several frozen soils and ice. (*After Sayles, 1966.*)

sands the observed strength increase with decrease in temperature ranges from almost linear to parabolic, leveling off at the colder temperatures. The latter type of strength variation with temperature is also shown in Vyalov's work (1962). Hence there may be some justification for using Vyalov's power relationship to account for temperature. Assur (1963) has written this power relationship in normalized form [see also Eq. (5.49)]

$$\sigma_{c\theta} = \sigma_{c0}\left(1 + \frac{\theta}{\theta_c}\right)^{\omega} \equiv \sigma_{c0}\, f_3(\theta) \tag{5.74}$$

where θ_c is an arbitrary temperature, say 1°C, and θ is defined by Eq. (5.68). The exponent ω in Eq. (5.74) is obtained by plotting $\log \sigma_{c\theta}$ vs. $\log(1 + \theta/\theta_c)$, as in Fig. 5.17. Then from the slope of the straight line we have

$$\omega = \frac{\Delta \log \sigma_{c\theta}}{\Delta \log(1 + \theta/\theta_c)} = \tan \alpha \tag{5.75}$$

For small temperature intervals $\omega \approx 1$ and the power law [Eq. (5.74)] reduces to

$$\sigma_{c\theta} \simeq \sigma_{c0}\left(1 + \frac{\theta}{\theta_0}\right) = \sigma_{c0}\, f_4(\theta) \tag{5.76}$$

A linear plot of Eq. (5.76), given in Fig. 5.18, shows the temperature intercept θ_0.

The uniaxial-creep strength at a temperature T is obtained by substituting σ_{c0} for $\sigma_c(T)$ in Eq. (5.59) and multiplying by any of the functions $f_1(\theta)$ to $f_4(\theta)$, giving

$$\sigma_f = \sigma_{c0}\left(\frac{\dot{\varepsilon}_f}{\dot{\varepsilon}_c}\right)^{1/n} f(\theta) \tag{5.77}$$

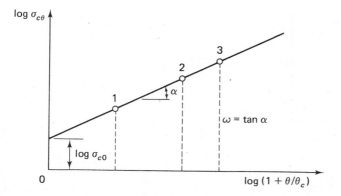

Figure 5.17 Temperature dependence of $\sigma_{c\theta}$ as given by Eq. (5.74). [*After Ladanyi, 1972, reproduced by permission of the National Research Council of Canada from the Canadian Geotechnical Journal,* **9**: *63–80 (1972).*]

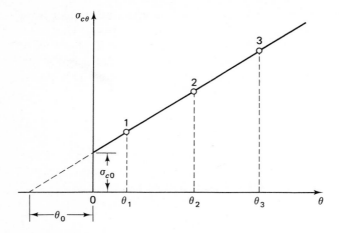

Figure 5.18 Temperature dependence of $\sigma_{c\theta}$ as given by Eq. (5.76). [*After Ladanyi, 1972, reproduced by permission of the National Research Council of Canada from the Canadian Geotechnical Journal,* **9:** *63–80 (1972).*]

Example 5.6 The temperature dependence of the proof stress is shown in Fig. 5.15 for Callovian sandy loam. Compute the apparent activation energy for this frozen soil and determine the value of the function $f_2(\theta)$ for a temperature correction to $-5°C$.

SOLUTION Computation of the apparent activation energy requires use of Eqs. (5.72) and (5.73) in the form

$$U = RL \approx R(2.303)(273)^2 n \, \frac{\Delta \log \sigma_{c\theta}}{\Delta \theta}$$

For the Callovian sandy loam $n = 8.78$ (Fig. 5.14), and the gas constant $R = 8.32$ J/mol °C. Hence

$$U = 8.32(2.303)(273)^2(8.78) \, \frac{\log 1.6 - \log 2.35}{5 - 10}$$

or $U = 8.32(50,318) = 418.6$ kJ/mol. The function $f_2(\theta) = \exp[L\theta/(273)^2 n]$, where $L = U/R$; hence

$$f_2(\theta) = \exp \frac{50,318(5)}{(273)^2(8.78)} = 1.47$$

5.5 STRENGTH ANALYSIS

The behavior of frozen soils subjected to multiaxial total stresses is similar to that for unfrozen soils. The strength for ice-rich fine-grained soils can be relatively independent of changes in total stress, hence the name *nonfrictional soil* ($\phi = 0$).

These frozen soils usually exhibit negligible volume change during deformation. The strength for frozen cohesionless soils, where internal friction develops, will increase with an increase in confining pressure. Sliding friction, particle reorientation, and dilatancy contribute to the strength for the frictional soils ($\phi > 0$). Depending on the degree of ice saturation and the development of steady-state creep, measured angles of internal friction ϕ can approach values for the unfrozen soils at the same dry density. These material descriptions, nonfrictional and frictional soil, are convenient for use in extending the engineering creep theory for use with the multiaxial stress states.

Nonfrictional Soil

Ladanyi (1972) assumed validity of the von Mises plasticity rule and volume constancy for all plastic deformations when the power laws describing the uniaxial case [Eqs. (5.13) and (5.15)] are generalized for the multiaxial state. These power laws, expressed in terms of equivalent (or generalized) stresses σ_e, strains ε_e, and strain rates $\dot{\varepsilon}_e$, are

$$\varepsilon_e^{(ip)} = \varepsilon_k \left(\frac{\sigma_e}{\sigma_{ku}} \right)^k \tag{5.78}$$

and

$$\dot{\varepsilon}_e^{(c)} = \dot{\varepsilon}_c \left(\frac{\sigma_e}{\sigma_{cu}} \right)^n \tag{5.79}$$

The subscript u has been added to the stress parameters σ_k and σ_c to denote reference to the uniaxial state of stress. In terms of principal stresses, strains, and strain rates the equivalent (or generalized) terms σ_e, ε_e, and $\dot{\varepsilon}_e$ are defined by Eqs. (5.32), (5.33), and (5.34), respectively. For the axially symmetric state of stress ($\sigma_1 > \sigma_2 = \sigma_3$), Eqs. (5.13) and (5.15) become

$$\varepsilon_1^{(ip)} = \varepsilon_k \left[\frac{\sigma_1 - \sigma_3}{\sigma_{ku} f(\theta)} \right]^k \tag{5.80}$$

and

$$\dot{\varepsilon}_1^{(c)} = \dot{\varepsilon}_c \left[\frac{\sigma_1 - \sigma_3}{\sigma_{cu} f(\theta)} \right]^n \tag{5.81}$$

For the plane-strain condition, i.e., for σ_1, $\sigma_2 = \frac{1}{2}(\sigma_1 + \sigma_3)$, σ_3 and ε_1, $\varepsilon_2 = 0$, $\varepsilon_3 = -\varepsilon_1$, Eqs. (5.13) and (5.15) become

$$\varepsilon_1^{(ip)} = \left[\frac{(3)^{1/2}}{2} \right]^{k+1} \varepsilon_k \left[\frac{\sigma_1 - \sigma_3}{\sigma_{ku} f(\theta)} \right]^k \tag{5.82}$$

$$\dot{\varepsilon}_1^{(c)} = \left[\frac{(3)^{1/2}}{2} \right]^{n+1} \dot{\varepsilon}_c \left[\frac{\sigma_1 - \sigma_3}{\sigma_{cu} f(\theta)} \right]^n \tag{5.83}$$

The temperature effect is accounted for by the function $f(\theta)$, which may take any of the forms expressed in Sec. 5.4. The creep-proof stress σ_{cu0} corresponds to the uniaxial compression value extrapolated to 0°C. For prefailure conditions, constant loading, and a constant temperature, Eq. (5.81) can be integrated to give the total strain

$$\varepsilon_1 \approx \varepsilon_1^{(c)} = \dot{\varepsilon}_c t \left[\frac{\sigma_1 - \sigma_3}{\sigma_{cu0}\, f(\theta)} \right]^n \tag{5.84}$$

For time intervals greater than about 24 h, experimental data indicate that the instantaneous portion of strain becomes less than 10 percent and can be neglected (Vyalov, 1959).

At failure Ladanyi and Johnston (1974) assumed that the frictionless frozen soil behaved according to the von Mises criterion, which for the axial-symmetric case reduces to

$$\sigma_1 - \sigma_3 = \sigma_{fu} \tag{5.85}$$

where σ_1 and σ_3 are the major and minor principal stresses, respectively, and σ_{fu} is the time- and temperature-dependent uniaxial strength. The cohesion c, common to unfrozen soils, becomes

$$c(t, \theta) = \tfrac{1}{2}\sigma_{fu}(t, \theta) \tag{5.86}$$

When the time to failure t_f, for example, the service life of the structure, and the average creep failure strain ε_f are known, and where secondary creep dominates, the value of ε_{fu} can be expressed in terms of time and temperature on the basis of Eq. (5.77):

$$\sigma_{fu}(t, \theta) = \sigma_{cu0} \left(\frac{\varepsilon_f}{t\dot{\varepsilon}_c} \right)^{1/n} f(\theta) \tag{5.87}$$

In cases where primary creep dominates the deformation behavior, Vyalov's long-term strength, Eq. (5.60), appears to be more appropriate.

Frictional Soil

Frozen frictional soils, tested for strength by a given procedure, provide data for which Mohr envelopes can be prepared. Each envelope corresponds to a given period of time to reach failure (Fig. 5.12). This time will equal the time to reach peak strength in a constant-strain-rate test or the time to reach the onset of tertiary creep in a creep test. The deviator stress at failure increases with increase in confining pressure. This increase becomes progressively smaller as the air voids are compressed. The failure envelope for constant-strain-rate tests and short-term creep tests, expressed in terms of total stresses, is thus nonlinear and can be quoted for specific ranges of normal stress and time to failure. Experimental data (Sayles, 1973) support the concept that the long-term Mohr's-strength envelope for frozen granular soils approaches that for the unfrozen condition at the same dry density. The value of the temperature-dependent uniaxial creep strength σ_{fu}, shown in Fig. 5.19, is given by Eq. (5.87) in terms of the time to failure t_f, the average creep failure strain ε_f, the proof stress in uniaxial compression σ_{cu0}, the temperature function $f(\theta)$, and the creep parameters $\dot{\varepsilon}_c$ and n.

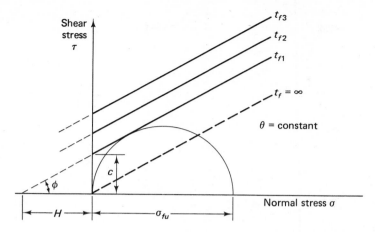

Figure 5.19 Straight-line approximation of the failure envelopes. [*After Ladanyi, 1972, reproduced by permission of the National Research Council of Canada from the Canadian Geotechnical Journal,* **9:** *63–80 (1972)*]

For practical purposes, it is convenient to approximate the failure envelopes by straight lines (Fig. 5.19) within the range of expected normal pressures. The resulting Mohr-Coulomb envelopes are then defined by

$$\tau = c(t, \theta) + \sigma \tan \phi \tag{5.88}$$

or

$$\tau = [H(t, \theta) + \sigma] \tan \phi \tag{5.89}$$

where

$$H(t, \theta) = c(t, \theta) \cot \phi \tag{5.90}$$

and

$$c(t, \theta) = \frac{\sigma_{fu}(t, \theta)}{2(N_\phi)^{1/2}} \tag{5.91}$$

The flow value N_ϕ is defined by

$$N_\phi = \frac{1 + \sin \phi}{1 - \sin \phi} \tag{5.92}$$

In terms of principal stresses the stress difference at failure is

$$(\sigma_1 - \sigma_3)_f = \sigma_{fu}(t, \theta) + \sigma_3(N_\phi - 1) \tag{5.93}$$

The angle of internal friction ϕ depends little on time and temperature within the range of practical interest, and the effect appears to be primarily concentrated in the value of the creep-failure stress in uniaxial compression σ_{fu}. For a constant temperature and different times to failure, a set of Mohr-Coulomb envelopes corresponding to Eq. (5.88) is shown in Fig. 5.19. Based on Eq. (5.93), a set of creep strength curves for different confining pressures and a constant temperature is shown schematically in Fig. 5.20. This analytical form, for a very slow creep rate, gives a finite value of frictional strength which agrees with experimental data for soil materials.

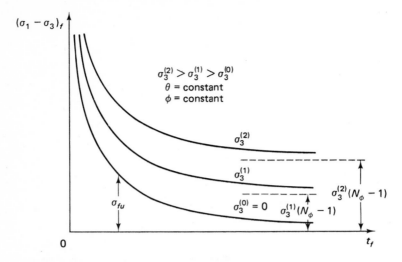

Figure 5.20 Dependence of creep strength on confining pressure [Eq. (5.93)] [*After Ladanyi, 1972, reproduced by permission of the National Research Council of Canada from the Canadian Geotechnical Journal,* **9**: 63–80 (1972).]

Experimental data on frozen frictional soils show that confining pressures influence not only the strength but also the stress–strain–strain-rate behavior in the prefailure state. Assuming that the Mohr-Coulomb theory is reasonably valid in the prefailure state, the dependence of strain and strain rate on normal pressure can be deduced from Eqs. (5.87) and (5.93) as follows:

$$\sigma_1 - \sigma_3 = \sigma_{cu0}\left(\frac{\dot{\varepsilon}^{(c)}}{\dot{\varepsilon}_c}\right)^{1/n} f(\theta) + \sigma_3(N_\phi - 1) \tag{5.94}$$

from which the secondary creep rate is

$$\dot{\varepsilon}^{(c)} = \dot{\varepsilon}_c \left[\frac{\sigma_1 - N_\phi \sigma_3}{\sigma_{cu0} f(\theta)}\right]^n \tag{5.95}$$

and the creep strain at time t becomes

$$\varepsilon^{(c)} = \dot{\varepsilon}_c t \left[\frac{\sigma_1 - N_\phi \sigma_3}{\sigma_{cu0} f(\theta)}\right]^n \tag{5.96}$$

For the flow value $N_\phi = 1$, Eq (5.95) reduces to Eq. (5.15) and coincides with Eq. (5.81). The stress-strain curves implied by Eq. (5.96) for prefailure and for the failure state by Eq. (5.93) are shown schematically in Fig. 5.21.

Equation (5.95) does not cover the whole region of prefailure strain rates in that nonzero strain rates are given at zero stress difference for a constant flow value N_ϕ. This limits application of Eq. (5.95) to strains close to failure or to those contained within a narrow range of internal friction mobilization, the latter

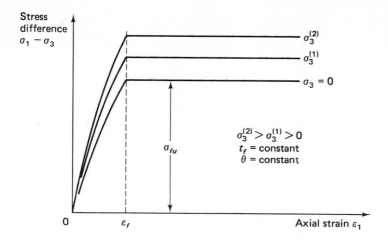

Figure 5.21 Stress-strain curves based on Eqs. (5.93) and (5.96). [*After Ladanyi, 1972, reproduced by permission of the National Research Council of Canada from the Canadian Geotechnical Journal,* **9:** *63–80 (1972).*]

having corresponding reduced values of N_ϕ. According to Ladanyi (1972), this limitation is overcome by writing in place of Eq. (5.94)

$$\sigma_1 - \sigma_3 = \left(\frac{\dot{\varepsilon}^{(c)}}{\dot{\varepsilon}_c}\right)^{1/n} [\sigma_{cu0} f(\theta) + \sigma_3(N_\phi - 1)] \qquad (5.97)$$

from which

$$\dot{\varepsilon}^{(c)} = \dot{\varepsilon}_c \left[\frac{\sigma_1 - \sigma_3}{\sigma_{cu0} f(\theta) + \sigma_3(N_\phi - 1)}\right]^n \qquad (5.98)$$

Equation (5.98) yields zero strain rate at $\sigma_1 = \sigma_3$; however, at failure the stress difference becomes

$$(\sigma_1 - \sigma_3)_f = \sigma_{fu}(t, \theta) + \sigma_3(N_\phi - 1)\left(\frac{\dot{\varepsilon}_f}{\dot{\varepsilon}_c}\right)^{1/n} \qquad (5.99)$$

which implies a time-dependent angle of internal friction if ε_f remains constant or an ε_f increasing linearly with time if ϕ is made independent of time. For the former assumption, N_ϕ in Eq. (5.98) denotes the flow value at the strain rate $\dot{\varepsilon}_f = \dot{\varepsilon}_c$. Available experimental data on the behavior of frozen sand in triaxial compression (Sayles, 1973; Alkire and Andersland, 1973) showed that ε_f increases with an increase in σ_3.

A simpler form can be obtained if only the strength and not the entire stress-strain behavior is made dependent on normal pressure. Experimental data reported by Sayles (1973) and Alkire and Andersland (1973) show that doubling or tripling σ_3 does not have a marked effect on the shape of the prefailure portion of the stress-strain curves. When the effect of confining pressure on the creep rate in the prefailure state is neglected, the analysis uses Eq. (5.81) in place of

Eq. (5.98) for describing the secondary-creep rate. This leads to the following constitutive equation for describing the behavior of a frictional frozen soil in the prefailure state:

$$\varepsilon = \dot{\varepsilon}_c t \left[\frac{\sigma_1 - \sigma_3}{\sigma_{ca0}\, f(\theta)} \right]^n \tag{5.100}$$

where σ_{ca0} is an average creep-proof stress resulting from a series of confined creep tests at an average confining pressure $\sigma_{3,\,av}$ representative of the range to be expected in the problem under consideration.

Example 5.7 Data shown in Figs. 5.22 and 5.23 represent the first peak (cohesion) strengths for saturated Ottawa sand in triaxial-strain-rate controlled tests. Confining pressures ranged from 0 to 8.0 MN/m². The Ottawa sand had a porosity of 37 percent and was tested at a temperature of $-3.85°C$. Use these data to determine the parameters n, N_ϕ, and $\sigma_{cu\theta}$ for the stress interval $0 \leq \sigma_3 \leq 8$ MN/m² (average line) in the creep-strength equation

$$(\sigma_1 - \sigma_3)_f = \left(\frac{\dot{\varepsilon}}{\dot{\varepsilon}_c} \right)^{1/n} \left[\sigma_{cu\theta} + \sigma_3(N_\phi - 1) \right]$$

SOLUTION Using the slope of the line in Fig. 5.23, $n = \cot 6.0° = 9.5$. Use the line labeled $\dot{\varepsilon} = 0.0044$ min^{-1} in Fig. 5.22 for determining N_ϕ and $\sigma_{cu\theta}$. The

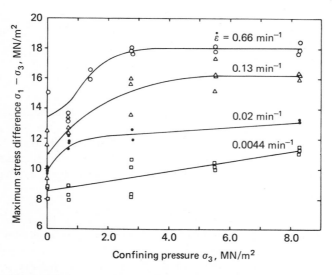

Figure 5.22 Strength vs. confining pressure for Ottawa sand at $-3.85°C$. (*After Sayles, 1973.*)

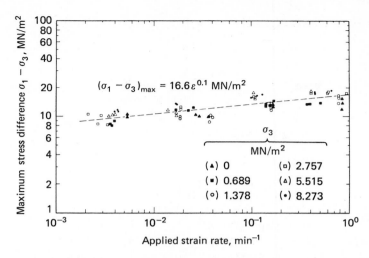

Figure 5.23 Strength vs. applied strain rate for Ottawa sand. (*After Sayles, 1973.*)

intercept gives $\sigma_{cu\theta} = 8.5$ MN/m^2 and

$$N_\phi - 1 = \frac{\sigma_1 - \sigma_3}{\sigma_3} = \frac{11.0 - 8.5}{8.0} = 0.3125$$

with $\qquad N_\phi = \dfrac{1 + \sin \phi_c}{1 - \sin \phi_c} = 1.3125 \qquad$ and $\qquad \phi_c = 7.75°$

(for $\dot{\varepsilon}_c = 0.0044$ min^{-1}). The creep-strength equation becomes

$$(\sigma_1 - \sigma_3)_f = \left(\frac{\dot{\varepsilon}}{0.0044}\right)^{0.1} (8.5 + 0.3125\sigma_3)$$

with σ in MN/m^2 and $\dot{\varepsilon}$ in min^{-1}.

CHECK For $\dot{\varepsilon} = 0.02$ min^{-1},

$$\sigma_1 - \sigma_3 = \begin{cases} 9.9 \text{ MN/m}^2 \\ 12.8 \text{ MN/m}^2 \end{cases} \quad \text{for} \quad \sigma_3 = \begin{cases} 0 \\ 8.0 \text{ MN/m}^2 \end{cases}$$

Example 5.8 The ultimate (second-peak) strengths are shown in Figs. 5.11 and 5.12 for the same Ottawa sand of Example 5.7. Determine the strength equation representative of the curves in Fig. 5.11. The second peak occurred at about $\varepsilon_f = 0.12$ with $n = 9.5$ as before.

SOLUTION From the Mohr-Coulomb plot (Fig. 5.12), for $t_f = 60$ h, observe that $\phi_c = 29.0°$ and $c = 0.6$ MN/m^2. These values correspond to an average strain rate

$$\dot{\varepsilon}_c = \frac{\varepsilon_f}{t_f} = \frac{0.12}{60} = 0.002 \text{ h}^{-1}$$

Using $\phi_c = 29°$, we have $N_\phi = (1 + \sin \phi_c)/(1 - \sin \phi_c) = 2.88$; then

$$\sigma_{cu\theta} = 2c(N_\phi)^{1/2} = 2(0.6)(2.88)^{1/2} = 2.04 \text{ MN/m}^2$$

gives

$$(\sigma_1 - \sigma_3)_f = \left(\frac{60}{t_f}\right)^{0.1} (2.04 + 1.88\sigma_3)$$

with stresses in meganewtons per square meter and t_f in hours.

CHECK For $\sigma_3 = 2.76 \text{ MN/m}^2$,

$$(\sigma_1 - \sigma_3)_f = 7.24 \left(\frac{60}{t_f}\right)^{0.1}$$

and $\qquad (\sigma_1 - \sigma_3)_f = \begin{cases} 8.07 \text{ MN/m}^2 \\ 7.24 \text{ MN/m}^2 \\ 6.55 \text{ MN/m}^2 \end{cases}$ for $\quad t_f = \begin{cases} 20 \text{ h} \\ 60 \text{ h} \\ 160 \text{ h} \end{cases}$

where t_f is time to failure.

5.6 ICE-CONTENT AND SOIL-COMPOSITION EFFECTS

When water freezes, its volume increases about 9 percent, giving ice with a density close to 917 kg/m³. For a closed system the soil volume will increase in proportion to the amount of pore water which freezes. The freezing point of fresh water is 0°C whereas the freezing point of water in the soil pores will be depressed depending on particle surface forces and any solutes present in the water. Ice formation will depend on the rate and direction of heat flow and the amount of water available to the freezing front. The mechanical properties of the frozen soil are influenced by the size and shape of the soil particles, their concentration and type, and the degree of saturation. Emphasis here will be placed on the influence of ice content and soil composition on creep behavior and strength of the frozen soil.

Ice Content

The volume concentration of dispersed soil particles in ice may range from zero to the maximum dry density of the soil. Ice has no long-term strength; i.e., it flows under very small loads. When a constant external load is applied to an ice specimen, the deformation curve is characterized by an instantaneous elastic deformation followed by a creep curve, which eventually shows a steady state. When the load is removed, an instantaneous elastic recovery takes place, followed by an elastic aftereffect which corresponds to the recovery of the transient creep. A permanent deformation represents the plastic flow which took place during the time the stress was applied. Ice can be treated as an elastic material provided that the rate of stress application is fast enough or low stresses are involved for short periods of time.

The addition of dispersed soil particles to the ice matrix alters sample behavior in several ways. For low volume fractions of sand the increase in shear strength is a linear relation to the relative proportion of sand and ice, as shown in Fig. 5.24. This increase in strength appears to be related to faster deformation in the smaller ice matrix volume needed to accommodate overall sample deformation. Hooke et al. (1972) suggested that sand grains in deforming ice may be surrounded by clouds of dislocations which impede passage of primary glide dislocations. These dislocations may contribute to the decrease in secondary-creep rates as the volume fraction of sand is increased, in agreement with higher strengths (Fig. 5.24) reported for a given deformation rate.

When a critical volume fraction of sand, about 42 percent, is reached, a rapid increase in shear strength is observed in Fig. 5.24. At this point friction between sand particles and dilatancy begin to contribute to the shear strength. Dilatancy must act against the cohesion of the ice matrix and the adhesion between sand grains and ice, thus creating an effect analogous to higher effective stresses. Larger contact stresses between sand grains permit a greater mobilization of the frictional resistance. Chamberlain (1973) has reported that dilation is completely suppressed in a saturated frozen Ottawa sand for confining pressures of 52 MN/m^2 and greater.

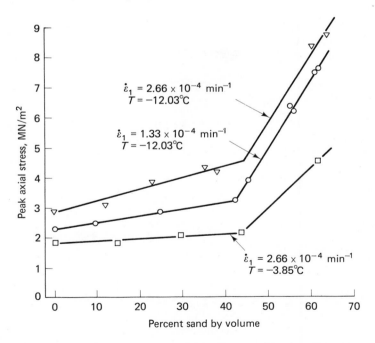

Figure 5.24 Volume concentration of Ottawa sand and peak strength. (*After Goughnour and Andersland, 1968.*)

The influence of relative amounts of ice on the maximum compressive strength of Manchester fine sand has been shown by Kaplar (1971). The unconfined dry sand with very small amounts of ice and a low volume ratio of ice to sand has very low strengths. On reaching a ratio close to 0.2 the strength increases rapidly, reaching a maximum at a ratio close to 0.58. The strength now decreases rapidly, presumably approaching some value representative of the ice. The higher ratios of ice volume to soil volume correspond to the low sand volumes in Fig. 5.24.

A comparison of the stress-strain curves in Fig. 5.25 shows a reduced stress difference for sand-ice samples with a reduced ice saturation (ratio of ice volume to sand-pore volume). Data reported by Alkire and Andersland (1973) suggested that this reduction in stress is in proportion to the volume of ice in the sand voids and is primarily due to a decrease in cohesion of the ice matrix. The Young's modulus for the sand-ice samples in Fig. 5.25 decreased with a decrease in ice saturation. Vyalov (1962) pointed out that soil freezing under a closed system (no expansion or squeezing out of water) leads to a stronger material than when soil freezes under conditions of free expansion with no outside supply of water available. This closed-system condition may be encountered in nature under special conditions where water is trapped in pockets surrounded by impervious materials.

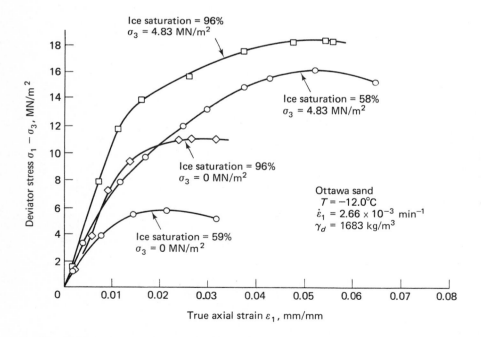

Figure 5.25 Stress-strain curves for two levels of ice saturation. (*Data from Alkire, 1972.*)

Soil Composition

Frozen-soil behavior depends on particle size, grain-size distribution, and density, as well as mineralogical composition of the soil particles. For frozen granular soils the relative density influences soil behavior, including shearing resistance, in a manner similar to that of unfrozen granular soils. Superimposed on this behavior are the cohesive effects of the ice matrix. Small changes in density (or void ratio) have a significant effect on the stress-strain curves for Ottawa sand, as shown in Fig. 5.26. The initial deformation of these frozen-sand samples was dominated by the ice matrix followed by development of frictional resistance with increase in axial strain. Data reported by Sayles (1973) showed that increased confining pressures appear to prolong the primary-creep stage. The confining pressure seems to enhance strain-hardening creep and prevents opening of cracks that might lead to instability and failure of the frozen soil. Failure strain for the Ottawa sand increased with lower sample densities (Fig. 5.26) and with larger confining pressures (Fig. 5.25). For frozen soils with granules of ice uniformly distributed throughout the mass, Vyalov (1962) stated that the shear zone may avoid the ice crystals and pass through weaker areas, which include the contacts between the particles and the ice lenses.

The stress-strain behavior of the Ottawa sand is contrasted with that of frozen Sault Ste. Marie clay in Fig. 5.27. Lower ice contents and a thin layer of unfrozen water (about one to two molecules thick) on the clay particles contributed to a plastic type failure at close to 12 percent axial strain. The Ottawa

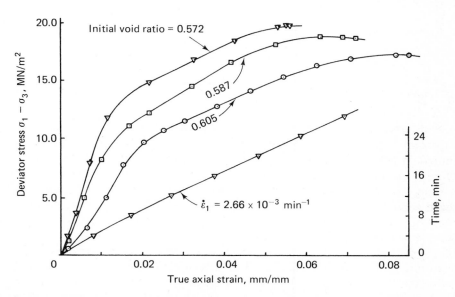

Figure 5.26 Influence of void ratio on the stress-strain behavior for Ottawa sand; ice saturation ≈ 97 percent, $\sigma_3 = 4.83$ MN/m^2, $T = -12.0°$C. (*After Alkire and Andersland, 1973, reproduced from the Journal of Glaciology by permission of the International Glaciological Society.*)

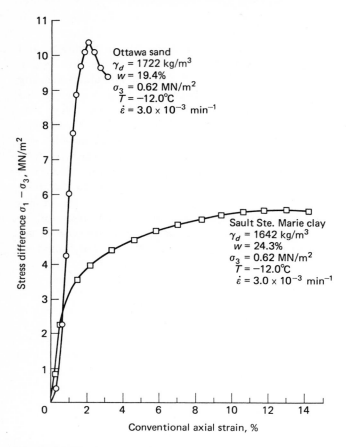

Figure 5.27 Comparison of stress-strain curves, Ottawa sand vs. Sault Ste. Marie clay. (*Data from AlNouri, 1969.*)

sand, with essentially no unfrozen water, shows a brittle-type failure at close to 2 percent axial strain. For high confining pressures (60 to 115 MN/m^2) Chamberlain (1973) has shown that the sand structure collapses during shear, resulting in pressure melting of the pore ice and an increase in pore pressure. This brings on a decrease in shear strength which approaches that for the unfrozen condition at pressures close to 115 MN/m^2. For pressures higher than 115 MN/m^2, greater compressibility of the pore water compared with the solids allows a slow increase in the frictional component of shear strength.

Being intermediate in particle size, frozen silts should demonstrate a behavior between that of the sand and the clay. The stress-strain behavior of frozen peat (MacFarlane, 1968) appears to be intermediate to that of the sand and clay, the peak strength in uniaxial compression occurring at about 2 to 3 percent. Creep curves for frozen-peat samples show a time-dependent behavior similar to that of frozen inorganic soils.

Fine-grained soils frozen with a directional temperature gradient often develop ice lenses, giving the appearance of a laminated structure. Vyalov (1962) stated that the bond strength between soil particles and the ice matrix is greater than between particles and adjacent ice lenses. For very rapid loading the ice behaves like a brittle material with strengths greater than that of fine-grained frozen soils. In contrast, for long-term loads the ice deforms continuously with no limiting long-term strength. For rapid shear the laminated frozen-soil texture shows the greatest strength when the shearing zone intersects the ice lenses and the least strength when the shear zone runs along the contact between the ice lens and the frozen soil (Vyalov, 1962).

Solutes in the pore water alter the ice content of frozen soils at given temperatures and in turn reduce the available strength. The solutes may be added to the soil (drilling mud) or may occur naturally in the soil. Ruedrich and Perkins (1974) ran a series of uniaxial-compression tests on recompacted samples of Prudhoe Bay sand in which the salt concentration in the pore water was varied. For a given axial strain rate a large reduction in the available maximum uniaxial strength was shown. Ruedrich and Perkins (1974) also showed that a linear relationship exists between the logarithm of the maximum uniaxial strength and the logarithm of strain rate for strain rates as low as 3×10^{-9} min^{-1}.

5.7 DEFORMATION AND COMPRESSIBILITY OF FROZEN SOIL

A frozen-soil element located below the centerline of a vertically loaded footing will experience an increase in both vertical and lateral stresses. Stress changes are determined using Boussinesq's theory and methods common to unfrozen soils. The soil element will respond by deforming and with large stresses may fail. Safety against failure (bearing capacity) of footings in frozen soils is covered in the following chapter. The total vertical strain in the soil element involves both shape change and volume change. Shape change may include shear (or elastic) settlement and time-dependent creep settlement. Volume change involves consolidation (decrease in mass) of the frozen soil by flow of unfrozen water and pressure melting with migration of water to regions of lower pressure. In the past, volume change was considered to be negligible. Work reported by Vyalov (1959) and Brodskaia (1962) showed that this was true only for relatively cold frozen soils containing little or no unfrozen water. Consolidation can be substantial in warm frozen soil containing significant amounts of unfrozen water.

Ladanyi (1975) outlined two possible approaches for predicting time-dependent settlements for frozen soils: (1) consider the frozen soil as a quasi-single-phase medium with mathematically well-defined creep properties, neglecting the fact that one portion of the deformation is due to volume change or (2) consider the consolidation and creep as two simultaneous but separate phenomena whose relative amounts of deformation depend on the applied loads and elapsed time. The second approach would clearly be the more appropriate, but basic data needed for using this method are still lacking. Hence the first method for predicting delayed deformations of frozen soils has been used almost exclusively in practice. The following sections briefly summarize elastic deformations, creep settlement, and compression settlement.

Elastic Deformation

The elastic properties of frozen soils can be characterized by Young's modulus E and Poisson's ratio μ. Young's modulus is many times greater for frozen soils than for unfrozen soils. It depends on soil composition, void ratio, ice content, temperature, and external pressures. Stiffness increases with decreasing void ratio (higher density), and the modulus for frozen soils is greater than or equal to that of ice. Frozen granular soils give the largest E values and plastic frozen clays the smallest. Silts are intermediate in value. Unfrozen water contents contribute to lower E values in frozen clay soils. The soil modulus will vary from a maximum at 100 percent ice saturation to a minimum at 0 percent saturation (same soil unfrozen). Comparative Young's moduli are given in Fig. 5.28 for three soil types at temperatures ranging from 0 to $-10°C$. The cyclic load tests used were repeated until elastic deformations became constant.

Poisson's ratio for the same three soils is summarized in Table 5.3. Values reported by Tsytovich (1975) are based on direct measurements of longitudinal and transverse deformations. The values were checked by

$$\mu = \frac{E}{2G} - 1 \qquad (5.101)$$

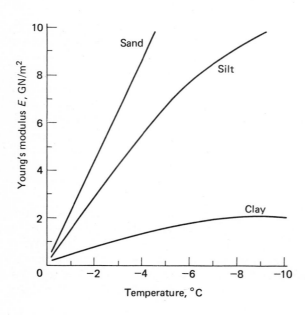

Figure 5.28 Average Young's moduli E from a large number of cyclic load tests on frozen sand, silt, and clay. Sand: 93 percent larger than 0.25 mm, 5.6 percent from 0.25 to 0.05 mm, 1.4 percent smaller than 0.05 mm, average total water content of 17 to 19 percent (dry-weight basis); silt: 35.6 percent larger than 0.05 mm, 9.2 percent smaller than 0.005 mm, total water content of 26 to 29 percent; clay: 50 percent smaller than 0.005 mm, total water content about 47 percent. (*After Tsytovich, 1975.*)

Table 5.3 Poisson's ratio for frozen soils (after Tsytovich, 1975)

Soil type	Water content, %	Temperature, °C	Stress, kN/m^2	Poisson's ratio
Sand (7% pass 0.25 mm,	19.0	−0.2	196	0.41
1.4% pass 0.05 mm)	19.0	−0.8	588	0.13
Silt (64.4% pass 0.05 mm,	28.0	−0.3	147	0.35
9.2% pass 0.005 mm)	28.0	−0.8	196	0.18
	25.3	−1.5	196	0.14
	28.7	−4.0	588	0.13
Clay (50 + % pass 0.005 mm)	50.1	−0.5	196	0.45
	53.4	−1.7	392	0.35
	54.8	−5.0	1176	0.26

using measured Young's moduli from compression tests and shear moduli from torsion tests on cylindrical frozen specimens. The data show that temperature has a significant influence on Poisson's ratio. The value of μ approaches 0.5 as temperatures approach 0°C. Additional values of Poisson's ratio are reported by Stevens (1973) for three soils: 20/30 Ottawa sand, Manchester silt, and Goodrich clay.

Tsytovich (1975) described experiments on horizontal layered strata of frozen ground and how to arrive at the total vertical elastic deformation. The conclusion was that the average elastic modulus of the stratified frozen soil can be determined by equating the total elastic deformation to the sum of the elastic deformations of individual layers. Thus

$$E_{av} = \frac{\sum h_i}{\sum (h_i/E_i)} \tag{5.102}$$

where h_i is the thickness and E_i the elastic moduli for the individual layers of frozen ground. Use of Eq. (5.102) with ice layers present gave predicted deformations within 2.5 percent of experimental values.

Creep Settlement

Settlement due to creep of the frozen soil can be estimated on the basis of Eq. (5.98) for circular footings with axial symmetry when it is recognized that $\varepsilon^{(i)} \ll \varepsilon^{(c)}$ for the long time intervals involved. For continuous footings approximating the plane-strain condition Eq. (5.98) becomes

$$\varepsilon_1 = \left[\frac{(3)^{1/2}}{2} \right]^{n+1} \dot{\varepsilon}_c t \left[\frac{\sigma_1 - \sigma_3}{\sigma_{cu0} \, f(\theta) + \sigma_3(N_\phi - 1)} \right]^n \tag{5.103}$$

For both equations the flow value N_ϕ corresponds to the average strain rate $\dot{\varepsilon}_1 = \dot{\varepsilon}_c$. An alternate creep relationship involves Eq. (5.49). Consider a circular footing on permafrost where stresses and temperatures are known with depth. When increments of depth Δz_i below the center of the footing are used, the creep settlement ρ_i for layer i after a time t_1 will equal

$$\rho_i = \Delta z_i \varepsilon_{1i} = \Delta z_i \dot{\varepsilon}_c t_1 \left(\frac{\Delta\sigma_z - \Delta\sigma_r}{\sigma_c}\right)^n \qquad (5.104)$$

where $\Delta\sigma_z$ and $\Delta\sigma_r$ represent the increase in vertical and radial stresses due to the surface load and the creep modulus σ_c is given as $\sigma_c = \sigma_{cu0} f(\theta) + \sigma_3(N_\phi - 1)$. The total settlement ρ_T at time t_1 is obtained by summing the incremental settlements for each layer:

$$\rho_T = \sum\rho_i = \sum \Delta z_i \varepsilon_{1i} \qquad (5.105)$$

The temperature change with depth is accounted for by using any of the functions $f_1(\theta)$ to $f_4(\theta)$ given in Sec. 5.4.

Compression Settlement

Compression or consolidation of frozen soils involves flow of unfrozen water from the soil pores under a pressure gradient due to surface loads. Pressure melting at points of particle-ice contact followed by migration of water to regions of lower stress contributes to this moisture movement. In a fine-grained soil, such as clay, more than one-half the water may still be unfrozen at $-1°C$. Brodskaia (1962) observed compression of frozen-soil samples by determination of changes in total water content. This compression occurs primarily during the initial period of loading and comprises a steadily smaller fraction of the total as time passes. Tsytovich (1975) reported that compression constitutes no more than one-third of the settlement, the remainder being due to creep. Methods are not yet available for predicting the time rate of compression settlement.

The total compression settlement can be estimated using the coefficient of volume compressibility m_v, which has been determined from laboratory compression tests on samples of frozen soil. Measured values of m_v reported by Tsytovich (1975) on several frozen soils are summarized in Table 5.4, along with total and unfrozen water content, bulk density, and soil temperature. For one-dimensional compression m_v is defined as

$$m_v = \frac{\Delta H/H_0}{\Delta\sigma} \qquad (5.106)$$

where ΔH is the decrease in thickness for a frozen soil element of initial height H_0 and $\Delta\sigma$ is the increase in stress. The compression settlement ρ_i for a frozen-soil-layer thickness Δz_i is given by

$$\rho_i = \Delta z_i \Delta\sigma_{zi} m_v \qquad (5.107)$$

Next, a summation over the total soil depth for which there is a significant change in stress gives the total settlement.

Table 5.4 Coefficient of volume compressibility for various frozen soils (after Tsytovich, 1975)

Soil type	Total moisture content, %	Unfrozen water content, %	Bulk density, kg/m³	Soil temperature °C	Pressure interval, kN/m² Coefficient of volume compressibility, $m_v \times 10^2$ m²/MN				
					0–98	98–196	196–392	392–588	588–785
Medium-grained sand	21	0.2	1990	−0.6	1.22	0.92	0.61	0.41	0.31
	27	0.0	1870	−4.2	1.73	1.33	1.02	0.71	0.51
	27	0.2	1860	−0.4	3.26	2.65	1.43	0.81	0.51
Silty sand with massive texture	25	5.2	1900	−3.5	0.61	1.43	1.84	2.24	2.36
	27	8.0	1880	−0.4	2.45	2.96	2.65	1.84	1.43
Medium silty clay, with massive texture	35	12.3	1830	−4.0	0.81	1.53	2.65	2.86	2.45
	32	17.7	1840	−0.4	3.67	4.28	3.77	2.14	1.43
with reticular texture	42	11.6	1710	−3.8	0.51	1.02	1.84	4.28	3.26
	38	16.1	—	−0.4	5.71	6.02	3.98	2.45	1.63
with stratified texture	104	11.6	1360	−3.6	5.51	5.51	6.02	3.67	3.47
	92	16.1	1430	−0.4	19.47	13.97	7.55	3.67	1.84
Varved clay	36	12.9	1840	−3.6	1.53	2.24	2.65	2.35	1.94
	34	27.0	1870	−0.4	3.26	3.06	2.55	2.04	1.63

5.8 MEASUREMENT OF FROZEN-SOIL PROPERTIES

Laboratory tests to investigate strength and creep-deformation properties of frozen soils are performed both on natural undisturbed and artificially prepared frozen-soil samples. While certain procedures for frozen-soil sampling, handling, and preparation coincide with those usually applied in testing unfrozen soils, there are a number of additional requirements to be satisfied in order to obtain good quality frozen-soil samples. As no standard procedures for testing frozen soils have as yet been established, this section will give only a short review of procedures used by various investigators for sample preparation and testing for strength and deformation properties.

Sample Preparation

This section deals only with the preparation of frozen-soil specimens for uniaxial and triaxial testing. A detailed description of procedures for taking undisturbed frozen-soil samples in the field, their handling, and transportation to the laboratory will be given in Chap. 9.

The strength and deformation properties of frozen soils, as shown by Figs. 5.10 and 5.16, are strongly affected by the soil temperature as well as by the content and distribution of ice within the soil (Figs. 5.24 and 5.25). All procedures for handling and preparation of soil samples for testing are therefore designed to minimize thermal disturbance, sublimation and evaporation of ice and to produce samples with minimum ice segregation during freezing.

Undisturbed block and core samples of frozen soil must be protected from thawing and loss of moisture from the time they are taken from the ground until they are tested. This is necessary because the soil structure may be completely changed if the sample is thawed and then refrozen. Relatively small temperature fluctuations can cause moisture redistribution and some changes in the unfrozen water content within the sample (Baker, 1976). For this reason it is usually recommended that undisturbed samples be stored under the same thermal and moisture conditions as those existing at the time of sampling. Methods for achieving these conditions are described in Chap. 9.

Artificially frozen soil samples should be prepared in such a manner that the principal physical properties affecting the mechanical behavior of the soil, including density, moisture content, homogeneity, and ice distribution, are controlled as closely as possible. This can be achieved in the laboratory by using special molds and a controlled method of freezing.

The steps to be followed in the preparation of laboratory-frozen soil specimens (Baker, 1976) include (1) assembly of the mold, (2) compaction of the soil sample, (3) saturation of the sample, (4) freezing, (5) disassembly of the mold and removal of the sample, (6) trimming and placement for testing.

The geometry of the mold is determined by the desired shape of the test specimen. Since unidirectional freezing of the specimen is usually desirable, the mold is fabricated from, and/or surrounded with, materials having good insulating properties. Use of split molds and coating of all interfacing surfaces of the mold with a silicone grease facilitate specimen removal after freezing.

Conventional soil-mechanics procedures, e.g., compaction in layers and vibratory techniques, are used for preparing samples of soil with a given density and water content. When saturated samples are required, saturation under vacuum is recommended. A detailed description of the saturation procedure has been given by Sayles and Haines (1974) and Baker (1976).

Goughnour and Andersland (1968) and Hooke et al. (1972) prepared sand-ice specimens by uniformly mixing natural snow or powdered ice with a selected proportion of precooled sand. This mixture was compacted in the mold, and precooled water at 1°C was admitted under pressure. This method permitted preparation of frozen-sand specimens with large ice content and randomly spaced soil particles.

Vyalov et al. (1966) reported that frozen-soil samples with no ice segregation can be obtained by rapidly freezing samples at temperatures below −30°C. Rapid freezing has been used by Sayles and Haines (1974) to eliminate ice lensing in samples of Hanover silt and Suffield clay prepared for creep testing. The specimens were frozen in an open system by removing the top cover of the mold and connecting the bottom of the mold to a deaired water supply. In this arrangement the bottoms of the soil specimens were exposed to a 4.4°C temperature with a free water supply, and the tops were exposed to cold circulating freezing air. Hanover silt samples were frozen within 48 h by exposing their tops to −29°C air. The tops of the Suffield clay samples were exposed to −79°C air, causing the specimens to freeze within 24 h.

It is clear that remolded soil samples can be frozen in cold rooms, refrigerated cabinets, and constant-temperature baths, depending on test requirements. Good practice involves freezing soil samples at temperatures at least 3°C below test temperature to minimize the influence of temperature history on unfrozen water contents (Andersland and AlNouri, 1970).

Very accurate control of soil freezing, without the use of a cold room, can be obtained by using a thermoelectric cooling plate which operates by the Peltier effect. The design of a cooling plate and the potential use of the method in uniaxial strength testing have been described by Williams (1968).

Frozen-soil specimens prepared in molds are usually kept sealed in the molds until preparation for testing. When they are removed in advance, they should be sealed in rubber membranes and stored in sealed plastic bags with crushed ice to reduce sublimation. Before testing, all specimens should be stored at the test temperature for a minimum of 24 h. Data reported by Sayles and Haines (1974) showed that 24 h was a sufficient tempering time for specimens 76 mm in diameter and 152 mm high.

Preparation of specimens from blocks of natural or artifically frozen soils involves trimming, for which a diamond saw seems to be the best tool. The diamond saw produces a very clean cut in coarse-grained soils. Clayey soils present a problem in that they tend to stick to the saw blade and reduce the efficiency. The blade must be cleaned regularly when cutting such specimens (Baker, 1976).

Cylindrical specimens required for triaxial tests can be machined on a metal lathe or carefully cut with a coring tube in the laboratory. Machining roughly cut and trimmed specimens on a lathe gives very good results for fine-grained soils. Cylindrical samples of frozen sands and gravels can be cored from block samples in the laboratory using a diamond-set core barrel and a large industrial drill press (Shuster, 1971). Special care is required when machining natural permafrost samples if they contain large ice inclusions, which tend to be very brittle and easily chipped (Baker, 1976). It is important that the ends of the specimens be cut square to the sample axis in order to minimize eccentric loading and seating errors. Gloves should be used when handling soil samples, and all tools should be kept in the cold room to avoid sample damage by localized thawing.

Test Equipment

Equipment used for testing the mechanical properties of frozen soils is essentially of the same type as that used for testing unfrozen soils and rocks. Some modifications are usually necessary to adapt the equipment to the particular requirements of low-temperature testing.

Since frozen-soil strength may vary within fairly large limits and is a function of soil type, temperature, strain rate, and confining pressure, the loading system must be able to cover loads ranging from those required for unfrozen soils up to those required for weak rocks. In addition, the loading system should be able to maintain a well-controlled rate of deformation for constant-strain-rate tests and should be able to maintain a given stress constant for long periods of time for creep tests.

The temperature of the frozen specimen should be held nearly constant ($\pm 0.05°C$) during the entire test. This is particularly important when the test is made at freezing temperatures close to 0°C. According to Vyalov et al. (1966), the maximum acceptable temperature tolerances in the tests vary from ± 0.5 percent when the test temperature is higher than $-2°C$ and up to ± 1 percent when the test temperature is below $-10°C$.

For long-term creep tests, proper measures must be taken to protect the specimen from sublimation. This is usually accomplished by covering the specimen with a rubber membrane or some protective coating. The method selected will depend on the specific test requirements and the type of test.

Various types of hydraulic and electromechanical presses, many of them used to test unfrozen soils and rocks, have been used for uniaxial and triaxial compression tests on frozen soils. Short-term tests are usually conducted with hydraulic and electromechanical presses; creep tests are carried out with lever presses, dead-load systems, air-pressure jacks, or electrically controlled closed-loop systems; all of them permit a constant load to be maintained for long periods of time. Some of the methods used by various investigators for performing short- and long-term tests on frozen soils are summarized in the following paragraphs.

Triaxial-compression tests carried out on artificially frozen soil samples at Michigan State University (Andersland and Akili, 1967; Goughnour and Andersland, 1968; Andersland and AlNouri, 1970; Alkire and Andersland, 1973) used the triaxial cell illustrated in Fig. 5.29. The frozen-soil samples were enclosed in rubber membranes and mounted in the cell, which was immersed in an equal-part mixture of ethylene glycol and water coolant. The coolant was maintained at a constant temperature by circulation through a portable refrigerated bath. Temperatures adjacent to the sample were measured by a thermistor and varied by no more than $\pm 0.05°C$. Axial loads were measured by means of a force transducer mounted in the base of the triaxial cell (Fig. 5.29). Axial deformations, determined by means of a displacement transducer, were recorded with an accuracy of ± 0.1 mm. Confining pressures were applied to test samples by means of pressurized nitrogen acting on the coolant liquid in the triaxial cell. In unconfined compression tests volume changes as small as 0.001 cm^3 were estimated using a burette with 0.01-cm^3 subdivisions and a flexible tube connected to the triaxial cell (Fig. 5.29). Immersion of the burette and tube in the coolant bath avoided volume change related to temperature change. In order to make the specimen deform uniformly, the load was applied to the specimen through lucite disks and friction reducers. The friction reducers consisted of aluminum foil coated on the sample side with silicone grease and powdered graphite and covered with a thin polyethylene film.

Constant-axial-strain-rate tests were performed by applying constant axial-deformation rates to the loading ram of the triaxial cell by means of a variable-speed mechanical loading system. In constant-axial-stress-creep tests, axial loads were applied to the specimen by using a load frame supporting a dead load of lead bricks. Upon sample deformation, a constant stress was maintained by adding lead shot to the dead weights to compensate for the small increase in sample area. Constant sample volume was assumed for this correction.

In tests conducted at the U.S. Army Cold Regions Research and Engineering Laboratory by Sayles (1968) and Sayles and Haines (1974), four types of loading equipment were used to accommodate the different strength and deformation characteristics of frozen soils. The instantaneous- (conventional) compressive-strength tests were performed on a mechanically driven universal testing machine. Short-term creep tests to determine the strength of frozen soils with relatively high resistance were performed on an 89-kN (20,000-lb) capacity air-actuated hydraulic press capable of maintaining a vibration-free constant load within 2 percent of the applied load for long periods of time. A constant-stress apparatus (Sayles, 1968) was used for creep tests in which large deformations occur. This press featured a programmed cam that maintained constant axial stress within 1 percent of the initial applied stress during the tests. A lever-type press was used to test specimens that experience small deformations over long periods. Test temperatures were controlled by heating and circulating air within insulated test enclosures located in walk-in cold rooms. During normal operations, air-temperature variations within the plastic enclosures did not exceed $\pm 0.05°C$.

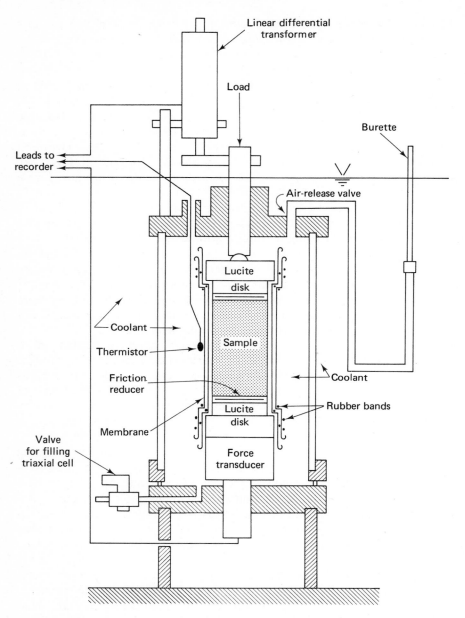

Figure 5.29 Schematic diagram of a triaxial cell for frozen-soil testing, with volume-change measuring system. (*After Goughnour and Andersland, 1968.*)

In more recent investigations performed at the same laboratory by Haines et al. (1975), a series of strain-rate-controlled compression and tension tests on a frozen silt were carried out in a closed-loop electrohydraulic testing machine equipped with a cold cabinet in which tests can be run at prescribed temperatures.

Types of Tests

A number of tests can be used to determine the time-dependent properties of frozen soil. Only three types will be described here. Each of these tests provides data suitable for determining the functions or constants appearing in the stress-strain-time relations given earlier in the chapter. The advantage of one test over another depends upon the frozen soil and test equipment available.

Creep test In a creep test a specimen of the frozen soil, initially unstressed, is subjected instantaneously to a homogeneous stress state that is then maintained constant. The material deforms, and the resulting strain-time data give a creep curve similar to that shown in Fig. 5.1b. This curve is the starting point for the analytical description of the creep properties of the frozen soil. Tests of uniaxial compression, uniaxial tension, indirect tension, triaxial compression, direct shear, torsion, and torsion plus axial compression have been used for obtaining this information (Scott, 1969). Usually a large number of creep tests are necessary to define the behavior of a frozen soil in terms of time, temperature, and the deviatoric and hydrostatic components of the stress tensor. In some cases incremental-loading procedures have been used to reduce the number of tests. Examples of a stress-reduction method have been reported by Andersland and Akili (1967) and Alkire and Andersland (1973).

Relaxation test In this test the specimen, initially unstressed, is rapidly loaded to some prescribed strain. This strain is maintained, and the stress response is measured as a function of time. The resulting stress-time data give a relaxation curve which can be used for estimating the creep parameters in an appropriate creep equation. This method, although well known in creep literature, has as yet been very little used for testing frozen soils.

Constant-strain-rate test The constant-strain-rate test is common to unfrozen soils and is readily adaptable to frozen soils. For this test a constant strain rate linearly increasing with time is imposed upon the frozen-soil specimen. The measured output is the resulting stress as a function of strain. Typical results are shown in Figs. 5.25 to 5.27. The advantage of this test is the reduction in dynamic effects consequent upon the sudden initial stress conditions required with the creep and relaxation tests (Scott, 1969) and the relatively short test duration.

Creep-testing Procedure

When planning a series of creep tests, it is first necessary to determine the instantaneous or conventional strength of the frozen soil at each selected test temperature. The instantaneous strength is a short-term strength corresponding to an arbitrarily selected strain rate or time to failure. For example, Sayles and Haines (1974) defined an "instantaneous" strength as the maximum resistance determined by loading the test specimen at a constant rate of strain of about 0.15 min^{-1}, while Vyalov et al. (1966) recommended a time to failure of about 30 s for obtaining this strength.

With the instantaneous strength known, a series of creep tests are performed at reduced stress levels. Some typical creep curves are shown in Fig. 5.6. Special care in sample loading is required to obtain values of $\varepsilon^{(i)}$ which are consistent between duplicate samples. In a study of creep behavior of frozen silt and clay, Sayles and Haines (1974) carried out with each of two soils four series of creep tests, each at a different temperature. Each series included constant-load compression tests performed at stress levels of approximately 60, 40, 20, 10, and 5 percent of the average instantaneous strength. Whether constant-stress or constant-load tests were performed depended upon the magnitude of the applied stress and the expected deformation. Constant-load tests were used for high and low stress levels, where small deformations were expected, while constant-stress tests were performed at intermediate stress levels, where the deformations were expected to grow continuously with time to large values.

Creep curves may show all three phases of creep illustrated in Fig. 5.1b, or, as often happens, secondary creep can be very short or tertiary creep may not be attained. For the latter case a useful alternative way of plotting the creep curves is shown in Fig. 5.1c, in which creep rates from the curve in Fig. 5.1b have been plotted against total strain. Such a plot enables the minimum creep rate and the beginning of tertiary creep to be easily determined. When the secondary-creep portion or at least the minimum creep rate can be clearly distinguished, the creep parameters can be determined from the creep curves as described in Sec. 5.2.

If, on the other hand, only primary creep is of interest, or if secondary creep has not been attained, it is preferable to plot, in a log-log plot against time, either the creep strains, as in Fig. 5.8, or the creep-strain rates, as in Fig. 5.9, and use either of the two plots to determine the primary-creep parameters, as described in Sec. 5.2.

In order to reduce the number of tests to a minimum, several successive incremental loads are often applied to a single specimen and the corresponding instantaneous and creep strain are recorded. This procedure, which is common to field loading tests, can give satisfactory results in laboratory creep tests only if the total strains remain relatively small, so that there are no substantial structural changes in the sample during the test. As this is usually difficult to achieve when the load is increased in steps, it may be preferable to carry out this kind of test by a successive stress-reduction technique, as done by Andersland and Akili (1967) or Alkire and Andersland (1973).

Constant-strain-rate Test Procedure

Constant-strain-rate tests can easily be performed using conventional soil-testing equipment with a variable-speed mechanical-loading system. Some typical results of such tests are shown in Figs. 5.25 and 5.27. These curves can be used for determining both the time-dependent deformation modulus (defined as the slope

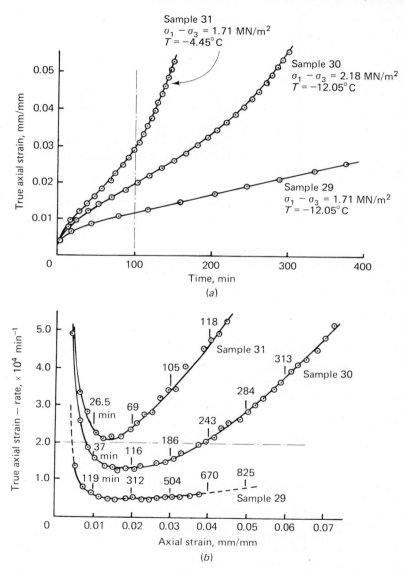

Figure 5.30 Creep tests on polycrystalline ice: (a) axial strain vs. time; data adjusted for system error and elastic strain; $\sigma_3 = 0$; (b) axial strain rate vs. axial strain. (*After Goughnour and Andersland, 1968.*)

of the tangent of the stress-strain curves at the origin) and the time-dependent strength. For the latter, the peak strength is usually plotted either against time, as in Fig. 5.11, or against the applied strain rate, as in Fig. 5.23. This latter plot is equivalent to the relationship between the secondary- or minimum-creep rate and the applied stress obtained in creep tests, and both can be described by the same empirical equation, (5.59).

It is interesting to note that the relationship between the constant-stress creep tests and the constant-strain-rate tests can be visualized directly from Fig. 5.30b. It is apparent that the horizontal section across the plot, e.g., that at 2.0×10^4 min^{-1} in the figure, corresponds to a particular constant-strain-rate test. The corresponding stress-strain curve for a given rate can be directly deduced from such a section by reading stresses as a function of strains at all intersection points with the curves. It is clear that such a stress-strain curve deduced from creep data is quite different from an isochronous curve, or isocurve, which corresponds to total strains attained at a given time. Such a curve is obtained by making a vertical section on the creep curves at a given time, as shown at 100 min in Fig. 5.30a.

NOTATION

A	area; a constant; moduli of nonlinear deformation in Vyalov's equation
b	exponent in creep equation
C	a constant
c	cohesion intercept
E	Young's modulus
$F(\ )$	function
$f(\ )$	function
$G(\ )$	function
H	$c \cot \phi$
k	exponent in Vyalov's creep equation
m	exponent in Vyalov's creep equation
n	exponent in creep equation
t	time
t_f	time to failure
t_0	soil parameter in Vyalov's strength equation
K	creep parameter
L	U/R, or length
L_0	initial length
N_ϕ	flow value $= (1 + \sin \phi)/(1 - \sin \phi)$
P	load
R	universal gas constant $= 8.32$ J/mol °C
T	temperature
U	apparent activation energy
ϵ	conventional or engineering strain[†]
ε	true or logarithmic strain $= \ln [1/(1 - \epsilon)]$[†]

[†] Dot over strain symbols denote time rate.

$\varepsilon^{(c)}$	creep strain
$\varepsilon^{(i)}$	pseudoinstantaneous (intercept) strain
$\varepsilon^{(ie)}$	elastic portion of $\varepsilon^{(i)}$
$\varepsilon^{(ip)}$	plastic portion of $\varepsilon^{(i)}$
ε_e	equivalent or generalized strain
ε_f	creep failure strain (at onset of tertiary creep)
ε_k	arbitrary strain in stress-strain equation
ε_0	instantaneous strain
$\varepsilon_1, \varepsilon_2, \varepsilon_3$	principal normal strains
θ	absolute value of negative temperature (°C) equal to $273 - T$ K
θ_c	arbitrary temperature (positive)
θ_0	temperature intercept
λ	exponent in Vyalov's equation
μ	Poisson's ratio
σ	uniaxial normal stress
σ_c	proof stress in the creep equation
σ_{c0}	σ_c for a freezing temperature close to 0°C
$\sigma_{c\theta}$	σ_c for a temperature θ
σ_{cu}	σ_c for creep in uniaxial compression
σ_{cu0}	σ_{cu} for a freezing temperature close to 0°C
$\sigma_{cu\theta}$	σ_{cu} for a temperature θ
σ_e	equivalent or generalized stress
σ_f	creep failure stress
σ_{fu}	σ_f in uniaxial compression
σ_k	proof stress in pseudoinstantaneous stress-strain equation
σ_{lt}	long-term strength
σ_0	soil parameter in Vyalov's strength equation
$\sigma_1, \sigma_2, \sigma_3$	principal normal stresses
τ	shear stress
ϕ	angle of internal friction
ω	soil parameter in Vyalov's creep equation

REFERENCES

Alkire, Bernard D., 1972. Mechanical Properties of Sand-Ice Materials, unpublished Ph.D thesis, Michigan State University, East Lansing.

——, and Orlando B. Andersland. 1973. The Effect of Confining Pressure on the Mechanical Properties of Sand-Ice Materials. *J. Glaciol.*, **12**(16): 469–481.

AlNouri, Ilham. 1969. Time-dependent Strength Behavior of Two Soil Types at Lowered Temperatures, unpublished Ph.D thesis, Michigan State University, East Lansing.

Andersland, O. B., and W. Akili. 1967. Stress Effect on Creep Rates of a Frozen Clay Soil, *Geotechnique*, **17**(1): 27–39.

——, and Ilham AlNouri. 1970. Time-dependent Strength Behavior of Frozen Soil, *J. Soil Mech. Found. Div. Am. Soc. Civ. Eng.*, **96**(SM4): 1249–1265.

——, and A. G. Douglas. 1970. Soil Deformation Rates and Activation Energies, *Geotechnique*, **20**(1): 1–16.

Assur, A. 1963. Discussion on Creep of Frozen Soils, *North Am. Contrib. Proc. 1st Int. Conf. Permafrost, Lafayette, Ind., NAS-NRC Publ.* 1287, pp. 339–340.

Baker, T. H. W. 1976. Transportation, Preparation, and Storage of Frozen Soil Samples for Laboratory Testing, *ASTM Spec. Tech. Publ.* 599, pp. 88–112.

Brodskaia, A. G. 1962. Compressibility of Frozen Ground, Engl. trans. U.S. Dep. *Commerce, Natl. Tech. Inf. Ser.* AD715087.

Butkovich, T. R. 1954. Ultimate Strength of Ice, *U.S. Army Res. Rep.* 11.

Chamberlain, Edwin. 1973. Mechanical Properties of Frozen Ground under High Pressure, *North Am. Contrib. 2d Int. Conf. Permafrost, Yakutsk, U.S.S.R.*, National Academy of Sciences, Washington, pp. 295–305.

Garofalo, F. 1965. "Fundamentals of Creep and Creep Rupture in Metals," Macmillan, New York.

Glen, J. W. 1955. The Creep of Polycrystalline Ice, *Proc. R. Soc. (Lond.)*, **A228:** 519–538.

Gold, L. W. 1970. The Failure Process in Columnar Grained Ice, unpublished Ph.D thesis, McGill University, Montreal.

Goughnour, Roy R., and O. B. Andersland. 1968. Mechanical Properties of a Sand-Ice System, *J. Soil Mech. Found. Div. Am. Soc. Civ. Eng.*, **94**(SM4): 923–950.

Haines, F. D., J. A. Karalius, and J. Kalafut. 1975. Strain Rate Effect on the Strength of Frozen Silt, *U.S. Army Cold Reg. Res. Eng. Lab. Res. Rep.* 350, Hanover, N.H.

Hoekstra, P. 1969. The Physics and Chemistry of Frozen Soils, *Highw. Res. Board Spec. Rep.* 103, pp. 78–90.

Hooke, Roger LeB., Brian B. Dahlin, and Michael T. Kauper. 1972. Creep of Ice Containing Dispersed Fine Sand, *J. Glaciol.*, **11**(63): 327–336.

Hult, Jan A. H. 1966. "Creep in Engineering Structures," Blaisdell, Waltham, Mass.

Kaplar, C. W. 1971. Some Strength Properties of Frozen Soil and Effect of Loading Rate, *U.S. Army Cold Reg. Res. Eng. Lab. Spec. Rep.* 159, Hanover, N.H.

Ladanyi, Branko. 1972. An Engineering Theory of Creep of Frozen Soils, *Can. Geotech. J.* **9**(1): 63–80.

——. 1975. Bearing Capacity of Strip Footings in Frozen Soils, *Can. Geotech. J.*, **12**(3): 393–407.

——, and G. H. Johnston. 1974. Behavior of Circular Footings and Plate Anchors in Permafrost, *Can. Geotech. J.*, **11**(4): 531–553.

MacFarlane, I. C. 1968. Strength and Deformation Tests on Frozen Peat, *Proc. 3d Int. Peat Cong., Quebec*, pp. 143–149.

Mitchell, J. K., R. G. Campanella, and A. Singh. 1968. Soil Creep as a Rate Process, *J. Soil Mech. Found. Div. Am. Soc. Civ. Eng.*, **94**(SM1): 231–253.

Odqvist, Folke K. G. 1966. "Mathematical Theory of Creep and Creep Rupture," Oxford Mathematical Monograph, Oxford University Press, London.

Ruedrich, R. A., and T. K. Perkins. 1974. A Study of Factors Influencing the Mechanical Properties of Deep Permafrost, *J. Pet. Technol.*, **26**: 1167–1177.

Sayles, F. H. 1966. Low Temperature Soil Mechanics, *U.S. Army Cold Reg. Res. Eng. Lab. Tech. Note*, Hanover, N.H.

——. 1968. Creep of Frozen Sands. *U.S. Army Cold Reg. Res. Eng. Lab. Tech. Rep.* 190, Hanover, N.H.

——. 1973. Triaxial and Creep Tests on Frozen Ottawa Sand, *North Am. Contrib. 2d Int. Conf. Permafrost, Yakutsk, U.S.S.R.*, National Academy of Sciences, Washington.

——, and N. V. Epanchin. 1966. Rate of Strain Compression Tests on Frozen Ottawa Sand and Ice, *U.S. Army Cold Reg. Res. Eng. Lab. Tech. Note*, Hanover, N.H.

——, and Duane Haines. 1974. Creep of Frozen Silt and Clay, *U.S. Army Cold Reg. Res. Eng. Lab. Tech. Note* 252, Hanover, N.H.

Scott, R. F. 1969. The Freezing Process and Mechanics of Frozen Ground, *U.S. Army Cold Reg. Eng. Lab. Monogr.* 2-D1, Hanover, N.H.

Shuster, J. A. 1971. Laboratory Testing and Characterization of Permafrost for Foundation Uses, *Proc. Symp. Cold Reg. Eng. Univ. Alaska*, **1**: 73–118.

Stevens, Henry W. 1973. Viscoelastic Properties of Frozen Soil under Vibratory Loads, *North Am. Contrib. 2d Int. Conf. Permafrost, Yakutsk, U.S.S.R.*, National Academy of Sciences, Washington, pp. 400–409.

Tsytovich, N. A. 1975. "The Mechanics of Frozen Ground," McGraw-Hill Book, New York.

Vyalov, S. S. 1959. Rheological Properties and Bearing Capacity of Frozen Soils, *U.S. Army Cold Reg. Res. Eng. Lab. Trans.* 74, Hanover, N.H.

—— (ed.). 1962. The Strength and Creep of Frozen Soils and Calculations for Ice-Soil Retaining Structures, *U.S. Army Cold Reg. Res. Eng. Lab. Trans.* 76, Hanover, N.H.

————. 1963. Rheology of Frozen Soils. *Proc. 1st Int. Conf. Permafrost, Lafayette, Ind., NAS-NRC Publ.* 1287, pp. 332–337.

———— S. E. Gorodetskii, V. F. Ermakov, A. G. Zatsarnaya, and N. K. Pekarskaya. 1966. Methods of Determining Creep, Long-Term Strength and Compressibility Characteristics of Frozen Soils, Nauka, Moscow, *Natl. Res. Counc. Can. Tech. Trans.* 1364, Ottawa, 1969.

Williams, P. J. 1968. Thermoelectric Cooling for Precise Temperature Control of Frozen and Unfrozen Soils, *Can. Geotech. J.* **5**(4): 264–266.

Wolfe, L. H., and J. O. Thieme. 1967. Physical and Thermal Properties of Frozen Soil and Ice, *Soc. Pet. Eng. J.*, **4**(1): 67–72.

SIX

FOUNDATIONS FOR COLD REGIONS

Arvind Phukan and Orlando B. Andersland

INTRODUCTION†

The basic function of foundations is to transfer and distribute all loads acting on the superstructure to the supporting ground in such a way that the stability of the structure is maintained within the required limits during the design life of the structure. Since the behavior of every foundation will depend primarily on the engineering characteristics of the underlying soil and rock deposits, the foundation engineer must have adequate knowledge of various foundation materials, their principal constituents, physical and mechanical properties, and other relevant factors affecting the strength of the foundation soils.

Cold regions include both seasonal and permanently frozen ground. Seasonal frost penetration in the northern United States (excluding Alaska) can involve depths of 2.5 m or more. The upper layer of these soils undergo a freeze and a thaw cycle which reduces soil strength. These phase changes produce various phenomena, e.g., frost heave, subsidence, and differential settlement, which may jeopardize the stability of foundations and cause serious damage to the structure. Thus, the design of foundations in cold regions requires an evaluation of temperature changes, the distortion or deformation of soils for the various conditions related to the thawing and freezing cycle, and the long-term strength of foundation soils for the expected ground temperatures. Nevertheless, the foundation must perform its function while providing a margin of safety against

† Notation is listed at the end of the chapter.

collapse of the structure, and settlement must be below limits determined by conditions of practical use as well as by structural, psychological, and aesthetic considerations.

Foundation design generally proceeds in three steps. (1) One must select the most economical foundation which will provide a reasonable factor of safety against failure of the ground under the anticipated loads. When suitable soil strata for supporting the structure are located at a relatively shallow depth, the foundations from which the engineer may choose include spread footings, raft foundations, or deep foundations such as posts or piers. Seasonal freezing or changes in the active layer may determine footing depths. When the upper soil strata are too weak, the loads must be transferred to more suitable soils at greater depth by means of pile foundations. (2) Deformation, thaw, and/or consolidation settlement which may develop under the service loads during the design life of the structure are calculated. If the predicted settlement is in excess of the allowable, the foundation design must be modified and checked again for stability. (3) The final step involves the feasibility of the foundation design and its construction in relation to any special conditions such as increase in ground temperatures and possible thawing of permafrost, surface drainage and groundwater conditions, and topography. The thermal interaction between the structure and the ground (Chap. 3) must be maintained at the level which is needed for the long-term stability of the foundation. For cold regions, these special conditions may have such a dominant influence on the foundation choice that they are taken into consideration from the beginning.

6.1 DESIGN CONSIDERATIONS

Foundation design for cold regions may be divided into two broad sections. One deals with the rheological aspects which define the effects of stress upon the foundation material. These effects will be temperature-dependent when the foundation material consists of frozen soils. The other section considers the thermal aspects, consisting of heat flow and thermal analysis. Both studies are essential for the stability of foundations, but engineering judgments must be applied to the ultimate design of safe as well as economical foundations.

In cold regions, foundations are generally placed below the frost-penetration depth, or active layer. Major factors which are to be considered for the depth selection include depth of soil strata suitable for supporting the foundation load, the temperature profile, the level at which changes in moisture content cause appreciable shrinkage and swelling of the soil, surface drainage and groundwater which may thaw the permafrost, and the presence of large ice masses, adjacent structures, property lines, excavations, and future construction. Emphasis here will be given to items not usually covered in textbooks on foundation engineering.

Seasonal Frozen Ground

In areas of seasonal ground freezing, foundations, pavement structures, and depth of water lines are planned to allow for frost penetration. In frost-susceptible soils the volume increase during freezing can be many times more than that which would be expected from a volume increase of the pore water when it changes into ice. The formation of segregated ice which results in significant heaving of the soil is conditional on three requirements: (1) below-freezing temperatures must penetrate into the ground, (2) the soil must meet certain grain-size requirements to be frost-susceptible, and (3) a source of water must be available to the freezing soil. Frost susceptibility and its determination for various soils have been discussed in Chap. 2.

Foundations are protected against the effects of frost heave by placing the footings below the level of ground freezing. Water pipes are placed below the level of frost penetration for protection from freezing. Partial or total freeze-up of water in pipes located in the annual frost zone depends on the freezing index at the pipe depth. Since normal water usage involves both flowing and nonflowing intervals, the usage pattern must be considered in estimating possible freeze-up.

Foundations do not always have to be placed at or below the known depth of frost penetration to avoid damage. In rock and coarse sandy soils ice lenses do not form; hence there is no danger of excessive volume changes on freezing. Also, the maximum depth of frost penetration will rarely be found near heated buildings, and a depth of two-thirds or three-quarters of the maximum recorded depth of frost penetration is generally quite adequate. Local experience is the best guide, and many local building codes specify minimum limits for foundation depths to provide frost protection. For unheated buildings or garden walls, deeper foundations do not eliminate the possibility of frost damage to the structure. It is possible for the entire structure to be lifted off its foundation by heaving of the adjacent soil when adfreeze bonds between the footing or wall and frozen soil transmit the heave to the structure. If such a structure is planned in a soil which is particularly susceptible to frost heave, the problem can be eliminated by use of non-frost-susceptible granular fill around the structure or any suitable chemical compound which will preclude adhesion of the structure to the surrounding soils.

Calculation of the frost-penetration depth is often based on the modified Berggren equation (Aldrich and Paynter, 1953)

$$X = \lambda \left(\frac{7200 k T_s t}{L} \right)^{1/2} \tag{6.1}$$

where X = frost penetration, m
$\quad k$ = thermal conductivity (generally taken as average for frozen and unfrozen state), J/s m °C
$\quad L$ = latent heat of fusion of soil, J/m^3
$\quad t$ = time, h

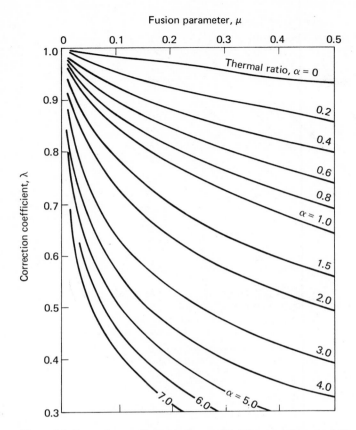

Figure 6.1 Correction coefficient in the modified Berggren formula. (*After Aldrich and Paynter, 1953.*)

The dimensionless correction coefficient λ is given in Fig. 6.1 as a function of two dimensionless parameters, α and μ. The thermal ratio $\alpha = T_m/T_s$ and the fusion parameter $\mu = (c/L)T_s$ depend on the mean annual surface temperature T_m (°C), the mean surface temperature during the freezing period T_s (°C), the volumetric heat capacity c (J/m³ °C), and the latent heat of fusion of the soil L (J/m³). When computing the maximum depth of frost penetration for nonuniform or multilayer soils, use of the modified Berggren equation requires the use of approximate computation techniques. A semiempirical adaptation of the formula is illustrated in Example 6.1.

Adequate thickness of non-frost-susceptible backfill must be used behind walls and retaining structures to protect against lateral heave. The thickness of non-frost-susceptible backfill required to prevent frost penetration into the frost-susceptible soil retained by the wall is shown in Fig. 6.2. The curves are based on a sinusoidal temperature variation at the face of the wall giving the freezing index at its back. The modified Berggren equation was used to determine the frost penetration into the backfill material.

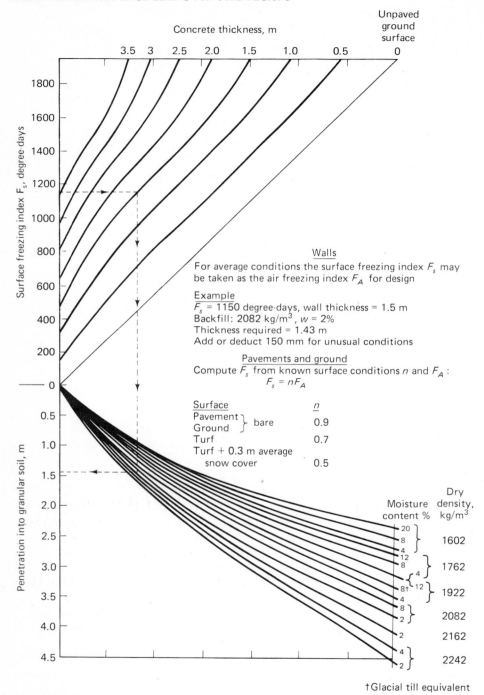

Figure 6.2 Frost penetration through concrete into granular soils and till. (*Adapted from Sanger, 1969.*)

Table 6.1

Layer	Thickness, m	Thermal conductivity,† J/s m °C	Volumetric heat capacity,† MJ/m³ °C	Latent heat of fusion, MJ/m³
Bituminous concrete	0.100	1.38	1.88	0
Base course	0.150	1.73	1.54	31.6
Subbase	0.460	2.25	1.68	44.7
Subgrade	...	2.94	1.81	108.0

† Average values for the frozen and unfrozen states.

Example 6.1 Determine the frost penetration below the bituminous concrete pavement described in Table 6.1. The pavement is kept free of snow. The mean annual temperature is 7.8°C, the surface freezing index is 818 degree-days, and the freezing period is 98 days.

SOLUTION Select an estimated trial frost-penetration depth $X = 1.4$ m. Compute an effective $(L/k)_{\text{eff}}$ ratio

$$
\left(\frac{L}{k}\right)_{\text{eff}} = \frac{2}{X^2}\left[\frac{d_1}{k_1}\left(\frac{L_1 d_1}{2} + L_2 d_2 + \cdots + L_n d_n\right)\right.
$$

$$
\left. + \frac{d_2}{k_2}\left(\frac{L_2 d_2}{2} + L_3 d_3 + \cdots + L_n d_n\right) + \cdots + \frac{d_n}{k_n}\frac{L_n d_n}{2}\right]
$$

$$
= \frac{2}{(1.4)^2}\left\{\frac{0.1}{1.38}\left[0 + 31.6(0.15) + 44.7(0.46) + 108(0.69)\right] \times 10^6\right.
$$

$$
+ \frac{0.15}{1.73}\left[\frac{31.6(0.15)}{2} + 44.7(0.46) + 108(0.69)\right] \times 10^6 + \frac{0.46}{2.25}
$$

$$
\left[\frac{44.7(0.46)}{2} + 108(0.69)\right] \times 10^6 + \frac{0.69}{2.94}\left[\frac{108(0.69)}{2}\right] \times 10^6\right\}
$$

$$
= 42.617 \times 10^6
$$

Compute the weighted values of c and L within the estimated depth of frost penetration:

$$
c_{wt} = \frac{c_1 d_1 + c_2 d_2 + \cdots + c_n d_n}{X}
$$

$$
= \frac{1.88(0.10) + 1.54(0.15) + 1.68(0.46) + 1.81(0.69)}{1.4}
$$

$$
= 1.74 \text{ MJ/m}^3 \text{ °C}
$$

$$L_{wt} = \frac{L_1 d_1 + L_2 d_2 + \cdots + L_n d_n}{X}$$

$$= \frac{0(0.10) + 31.6(0.15) + 44.7(0.46) + 108(0.69)}{1.4} = 71.3 \text{ MJ/m}^3$$

Compute the effective values of the thermal ratio α and the fusion parameter μ:

$$\alpha = \frac{T_m t}{F} = \frac{7.8(98)}{818} = 0.93$$

$$\mu = \frac{c_{wt} F}{L_{wt} t} = \frac{1.74(818)}{71.3(98)} = 0.20$$

Determine the correction coefficient $\lambda = 0.79$ from Fig. 6.1. Compute the depth of frost penetration:

$$X = \lambda \left[\frac{7200 T_s t}{(L/k)_{\text{eff}}} \right]^{1/2} = \lambda \left[\frac{7200 F}{(L/k)_{\text{eff}}} \right]^{1/2} = 0.79 \left[\frac{7200(24)(818)}{42.617 \times 10^6} \right]^{1/2} = 1.44 \text{ m}$$

Since the original estimate of $X = 1.4$ m is close to 1.44 m, no additional trial calculations are needed. The frost-penetration depth will be about 1.44 m.

Permafrost

A zone of permanently frozen ground develops below the active layer in regions where the mean annual surface temperature falls below 0°C. The permafrost zone is divided into continuous and discontinuous zones. In the continuous zone, permafrost occurs everywhere beneath the ground surface except in newly deposited unconsolidated sediments, where the climate has just begun to impose its influence on the ground thermal regime. The thickness of permafrost varies from about 60 m at the southern limit of the continuous zone to depths over 300 m in the northern areas. The active layer generally varies from about 1 m in the southern areas to about $\frac{1}{2}$ m in the north. These permanently frozen soils present unique foundation problems.

Frozen ground would normally present excellent foundation support, since the ice forms a strong bond between the soil particles. The difficulties are caused by creep below foundations in ice-rich soils and with warmer temperatures the development of a very wet condition in the upper layer of the permafrost which cannot drain through the underlying foundation material. The following items summarize the design approaches which are commonly applied to the design of structures in the arctic and subarctic (Table 6.2).

Retaining permafrost in its frozen state
Allowing permafrost to thaw after construction
Improvement of site conditions
Disregarding the permafrost

Table 6.2 Foundation design approach for the arctic and subarctic

I. Unfavorable foundation materials when permafrost has thawed (fine-grained soils or rock containing ground ice)
  A. Maintain existing thermal regime (applies to continuous and discontinuous permafrost zones)
    1. Permanent construction
       a. Piling
       b. Spread footings
       c. Posts and pads
       d. Ducted foundation
       e. Artificial refrigeration
       f. Rigid structural base
    2. Temporary construction
       a. Posts and pads
       b. Sills
       c. Slabs or rafts
  B. Accept thermal-regime changes caused by construction (applies to continuous and discontinuous permafrost zones)
    1. Permanent construction
       a. End-bearing piles, caissons, or footings to stable stratum
       b. Rigid structural base (for small structures only)
    2. Temporary construction
       a. Piling
       b. Perimeter sills
  C. Modify foundation conditions before construction (applies primarily to discontinuous permafrost zone)
    1. Permanent and temporary construction: use designs applicable for conditions resulting after:
       a. Prethaw and preconsolidation of unfavorable materials
       b. Replacement of unfavorable materials
II. Favorable foundation materials when permafrost has thawed (clean, granular soils or rock without ground ice): use designs applicable to temperate zone

Thermal ground disturbances are caused mainly by the change of surface conditions related to construction activity or operation and heat input from structures into the ground. The vegetative cover or the surficial organic layer typically overlying permafrost soils acts as an effective insulator and reduces the seasonal temperature variations experienced by the underlying soil. When this surficial organic layer is removed or disturbed by construction activities, more heat input is given to the ground, resulting in a deeper thaw bulb. Especially in areas where the ground temperature is close to 0°C, a slight thermal imbalance causes significant thermal degradation of deep-thawed zones. The other source is heat from a structure, which if allowed to enter the frozen ground, will cause a deep thaw bulb to form. From analytical models it is possible to prediet the anticipated thaw bulb under different boundary conditions (Chap. 3). Standard techniques described later in this section can also be used to determine the thaw depth.

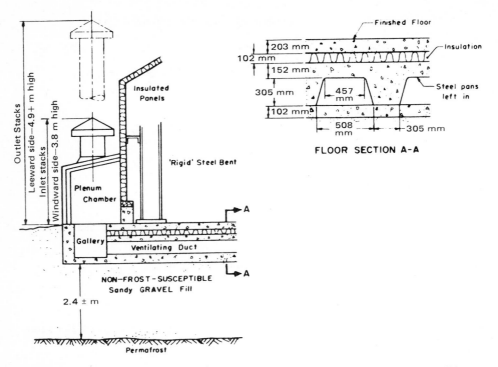

Figure 6.3 Pan-slab foundation showing plenum chamber and ventilation duct; site conditions: annual frost zone = 0.3 to 1.5 m, permafrost: silty, sandy, gravel (temperature = − 11 to 0°C), mean thawing index = 388 degree-days, mean freezing index = 4444 degree-days, mean annual temperature = − 11.1°C, temperature range = − 40 to 15°C, annual precipitation = 101 mm (plus 381 mm snow). (*Adapted from Sanger, 1969.*)

Retaining permafrost in its frozen state This concept is generally applied to unheated structures where the bearing soil layer is kept frozen throughout the year. Freezing and thawing of the active layer may still occur. This design principle may be applied by various methods, including a ventilated air space (Fig. 6.3), which retains a temperature between the building and the ground surface typically near the local ambient outside temperature. This air space will reduce or prevent heat input to the ground from the building. Another measure is a mechanical refrigeration system consisting of a grid of cooling pipes through which the refrigerated fluid is circulated to maintain the frozen soil, but this system is complex as well as expensive. It requires reasonably complicated mechanical equipment, a steady fuel supply, and a monitoring procedure to check the mechanical system as designed to ensure that the refrigeration load does not exceed the design capacity.

A recently developed self-powered thermal device is the thermal pile used on the trans-Alaska pipeline to keep the ground frozen. The pile is equipped with heat pipes and radiators, as shown in Fig. 6.4. The thermal devices work only

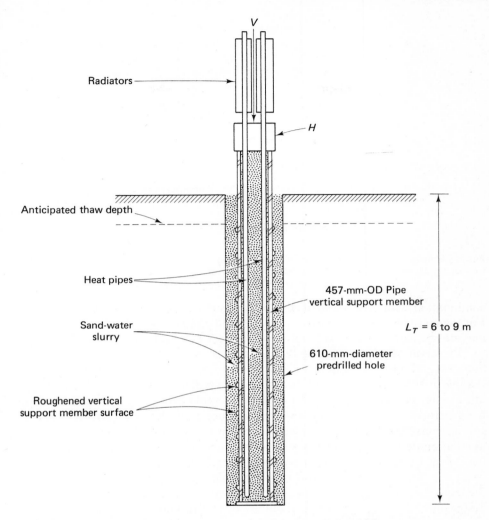

Figure 6.4 Thermal vertical-support member used on the trans-Alaska pipeline.

in the winter, when air temperatures are lower than ground temperatures. These devices remove heat from the ground by a two-phase convective process: thin-film liquid evaporation occurs along the length of the embedded portion of the pile, and the resulting vapor rises to the upper portion, where it releases heat to the air through a radiator section. Similar systems, known as the Long pile and air-convection piles, have been reported by Long (1963) and Reed (1966).

Alternative foundations may prove economical where pile installation is difficult, as in gravelly soils. For small, low-cost buildings which can tolerate some movement, insulation may be used to prevent or reduce thawing of the underlying frozen material. This is achieved by placing a gravel blanket in

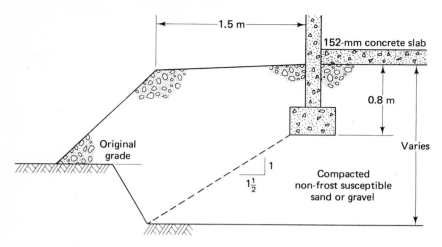

Figure 6.5 Typical foundation design for unheated building over frost-susceptible soil in deep seasonal frost or permafrost areas. (*Adapted from U.S. Army/Air Force Draft.*)

combination with cork or foamed glass as part of the floor-insulation system. For the construction of highways, railways, and airstrips, where other techniques may not be feasible, the insulation method must be relied on.

Preservation of the existing thermal regime is chosen when conditions are not ideal and other techniques are uneconomical and/or undesirable. This system is applicable to continuous and discontinuous permafrost zones. Proper drainage must be provided to prevent accumulation of water which can thaw the underlying permafrost. The flow of water may cause heat flow by convection, and special consideration must be given to granular soils on a slope. The typical foundation design shown in Fig. 6.5 can be used under any building in seasonal frost areas or under any fully ventilated, unheated building in a permafrost area when the thickness of the non-frost-susceptible mat is modified as required by the local climate. Where non-frost-susceptible material is scarce or expensive, the design shown in Fig. 6.5 can be modified by use of underslab insulation or by use of a structural floor supported by footings or piles far enough above the ground to provide a ventilated air space between the floor and the ground surface.

Most geotechnical problems in permafrost areas require the engineer to make an estimate of the depth and rate of thaw for a construction site or proposed foundation based on a given thaw index and melting period or known building temperatures. The modified Berggren equation provides one means of calculating the thaw depth. Nixon and McRoberts (1973) have used the Stefan solution to predict movement of the interface between the thawed and frozen zones. The Stefan solution may be written as

$$X = \left(\frac{2k_u T_s}{L}\right)^{1/2} t^{1/2} = \alpha t^{1/2} \tag{6.2}$$

where X = thaw depth

k_u = thermal conductivity of thawed soil

T_s = suddenly applied constant surface temperature equal to thaw index divided by period of thaw

L = volumetric latent heat of soil

t = time

α = constant defined by Eq. (6.2)

Temperatures in the frozen soil are ignored. This solution is approximate and is known to overestimate the thaw rate when the surface temperature is high. It can be improved to a higher order of accuracy by a semiempirical factor provided by Nixon and McRoberts (1973). Thus Eq. (6.2) can be rewritten

$$X = \left(\frac{2k_u\,T_s}{L}\right)^{1/2}\left(1 - \frac{c_u\,T_s}{8L}\right)t^{1/2} \tag{6.3}$$

where c_u is the volumetric heat capacity of the thawed soil.

For a surface soil layer of thickness H and thermal conductivity k_1 overlying a soil of infinite depth with properties k_2, L_2, movement of the thaw interface in the lower layer can also be computed. Chapter 3 outlines the procedure for computation of the time to thaw the overlying soil layer, the depth of thaw in the second layer, and the interface temperature between the two layers.

Example 6.2 Estimate the depth of thaw penetration at the site of a proposed building project where the mean annual air temperature is $-2.8°C$, the design air-thaw index equals 1833 degree-days, and the thaw period lasts 160 days. Assume that $n = 1.0$ (elevated building with air space between the building floor and the ground surface). Soil data for the site are given in Table 6.3.

Table 6.3

Depth, m	Group symbol	Soil description	Physical and thermal properties
0.0			
	OL	Organic, sandy silt, unfrozen	
0.61			
	ML Nbe	Black, slightly organic, sandy silt, frozen; no visible segregation but bonded	γ_d = 1361 kg/m³ γ = 1842 kg/m³ w = 33% k_u = 1.18 J/s m °C k_f = 2.08 J/s m °C
7.62			
	SP-Nbn	Brown, uniform medium sand; no visible segregation but bonded	γ_d = 1682 kg/m³ w = 20% k_f = 3.46 J/s m °C
18.29			
		Bedrock	

SOLUTION 1 Assume that the 0.61-m organic layer is replaced with silt. For the silt backfill compute the volumetric latent heat of fusion

$$L = 333.7\gamma_d \frac{w}{100} = (333.7 \text{ kJ/kg})(1361 \text{ kg/m}^3)(\tfrac{33}{100}) = 149.9 \text{ MJ/m}^3$$

and the average volumetric heat capacity

$$c_{av} = \frac{\gamma_d}{\gamma_w}\left(0.18 + 0.75 \frac{w}{100}\right) c_w = \frac{1361}{1000}\left[0.18 + 0.75\left(\frac{33}{100}\right)\right] 4.18$$

$$= 2.4 \text{ MJ/m}^3 \text{ °C}$$

Compute values for the thermal ratio α and the fusion parameter μ:

$$\alpha = \left|\frac{T_0 t}{I}\right| = \left|\frac{-2.8(160)}{1833}\right| = 0.24$$

$$\mu = \frac{T_s c_{av}}{L} = \frac{I c_{av}}{tL} = \frac{1833(2.4)}{160(149.9)} = 0.18$$

Determine the correction coefficient $\lambda = 0.91$ from Fig. 6.1. Aldrich and Paynter (1953) recommended using an average thermal conductivity $k_{av} = \frac{1}{2}(k_u + k_f) = \frac{1}{2}(1.18 + 2.08) = 1.63$ J/s m °C. Compute the depth of thaw

$$X = \lambda\left(\frac{7200knI}{L}\right)^{1/2} = 0.91\left(\frac{7200(24)(1.63)(1.0)(1833)}{149.9 \times 10^6}\right)^{1/2} = 1.69 \text{ m}$$

SOLUTION 2 Assume that the 0.61-m organic surface layer is replaced with silt. For the silt backfill compute the volumetric latent heat of the soil equal to 149.9 MJ/m³, the same as in solution 1. Compute the volumetric heat capacity of the thawed soil

$$c_u = \frac{\gamma_d}{\gamma_w}\left(0.18 + 1.0 \frac{w}{100}\right) c_w = \frac{1361}{1000}\left[0.18 + 1.0\left(\frac{33}{100}\right)\right] 4.18 = 2.90 \text{ MJ/m}^3 \text{ °C}$$

The equivalent step temperature change is

$$T_s = \frac{nI}{t} = \frac{1.0(1833)}{160} = 11.5\text{°C}$$

Using the improved Stefan solution [Eq. (6.3)], compute the depth of thaw

$$X = \left[\frac{2(1.18)(11.5)}{149.9 \times 10^6}\right]^{1/2}\left[1 - \frac{(2.9 \times 10^6)(11.5)}{8(149.9 \times 10^6)}\right][160(24)(60)(60)]^{1/2}$$

$$= 1.54 \text{ m}$$

Allowing permafrost to thaw after construction For this concept, the soil is permitted to thaw under the thermal-regime changes caused by construction. This concept is used only if the thawing soil maintains adequate shear strength and the total settlement or differential settlement due to thaw is within allowable limits. This principle can be applied to thaw-stable soils, but the definition of thaw stability must be defined in relation to allowable differential settlements. For example, for a precision microwave antenna whose tolerance to differential settlements is small, the thaw stability would be narrowly defined. The thaw stability under a flexible steel warehouse or low-rise residential construction would have less strict requirements.

Extensive site investigation with settlement predictions based on thaw-consolidation theory (Chap. 4) makes alternate foundation options possible. For dams and dikes constructed on permafrost, the thawing effect of water becomes particularly critical. The rate at which thawing will occur and the depth to which thaw will penetrate the water-retaining structures are of prime importance in the design of their foundations. Field observations and prediction of thaw settlement of sand dikes at the Kelsey Generating Station on the Nelson River in Manitoba, were summarized in Chap. 4.

Improvement of site conditions In this method, which is generally applicable to discontinuous permafrost zones, the site condition is improved by prethawing followed by compaction if necessary or by excavation and backfill. For the prethawed design, the site is thawed by suitable means in advance of construction. Sanger (1969) quoted a Russian criterion in which prethaw was used when the thickness of the frozen layer was less than 60 percent of the computed thaw penetration in 10 years. Prethawing precludes much of the thaw settlements and avoids the condition of lowest shear strength near the structure.

Disregarding the permafrost Where the permafrost foundation material consists of sound bedrock or dense thaw-stable granular soils which are not affected by frost action, conventional design techniques as applied in nonpermafrost zones may be used.

6.2 FOUNDATION TYPES AND METHODS OF CONSTRUCTION

Depending on the foundation soils and loading conditions, a wide range of foundation types is suitable for cold regions. The simplest foundations for small dwellings, single-story houses, farm structures, barns, etc., are ground sills, spread surface footings on gravel berms, and individual shallow footings. Complex foundations, e.g., deep footings, piles and piers, caissons and raft or mat foundations, may be used for heated structures which liberate heat and for cold structures. Powerhouses, kilns, furnaces, warm-oil pipelines, rolling mills, steel plants, and industrial buildings can be classified as heated structures, whereas ice rinks, cold storage, and chilled-gas pipelines can be categorized as cold structures. A few typical foundations for various structures are presented in Figs. 6.3 to 6.7. These foundation types are discussed in Secs. 6.4 and 6.5. Tower pad

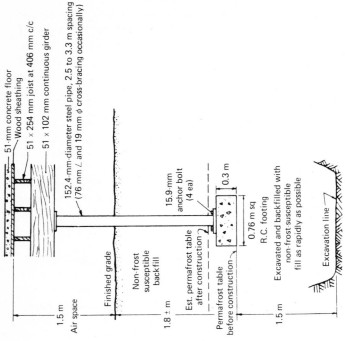

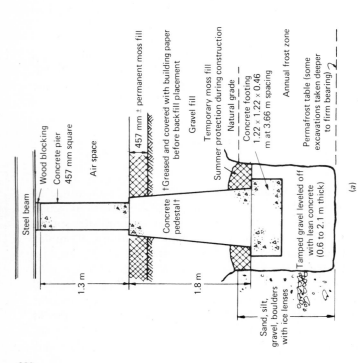

Figure 6.6 Footings on permafrost. (*a*) Pedestal and footing; site conditions: annual frost zone 0.76 to 1.83 m, depending on thickness of organic cover; permafrost: sand and silt interspersed with gravel and boulder (0.6 m diameter) (temperature, −3.3 C); mean thawing index 1078 degree-days (16-year average); mean freezing index 3778 degree-days (16-year average); mean annual temperature −7.78°C (30-year record); temperature range −49.4 to 35.5°C (mean range −2.78 to 17.8°C); annual precipitation 241 mm rain (plus 1397 mm snow); bearing pressure (estimated) 143.6 kN/m². (*Adapted from Sanger, 1969.*)

(*b*) Steel pipe and footing; site conditions: marginal permafrost area; annual frost zone: OL, ML, SP, SM, (thickness ≈1.8 m); permafrost: silty sand (temperature −2.2 to 0°C); mean thawing index 1500 degree-days; mean freezing index 2222 degree-days; mean annual temperature −1.1°C; temperature range −46.7 to 32.2°C; annual precipitation 483 mm (plus 1.27 m of snow); bearing pressure 143.6 kN/m². (*Adapted from Sanger, 1969.*)

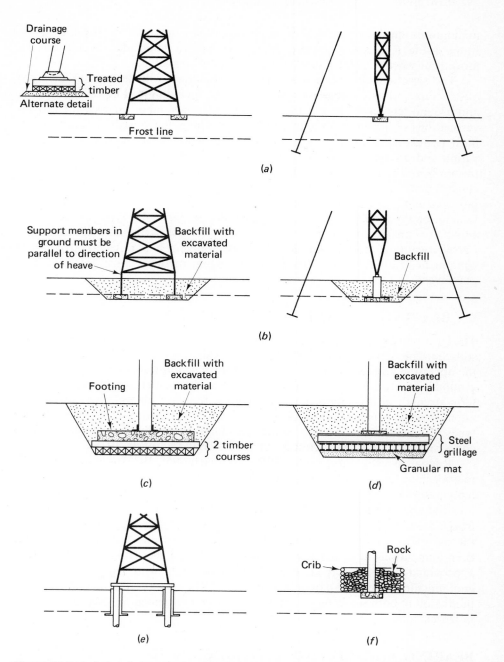

Figure 6.7 Foundation designs employing minimum or no non-frost-susceptible granular material: (*a*) non-frost-susceptible foundation with shallow footings; (*b*) frost-susceptible foundation with footings below frost line; (*c*) and (*d*) alternate foundation details; (*e*) pile foundation; (*f*) crib foundation. (*After U.S. Army/Air Force Draft.*)

foundations employing minimum or no non-frost-susceptible material are illustrated in Fig. 6.7. Larger gravel pads may be used to reduce detrimental vertical movement when non-frost-susceptible material is available.

The selection of a particular type of foundation will depend on the type of structure and its purpose; subsoil conditions, including soil types, ice content, and ground temperature; and the available materials, labor, and cost. Field investigations of frozen ground are presented in Chap. 9. Construction techniques must be related to the nature of the frozen ground. In permafrost areas, excavation and grading should be limited to the actual required construction zone to minimize the thermal degradation in the adjacent areas. Summer or winter construction must be planned according to the local soil types, groundwater position, and climatic conditions. Methods employed for construction of various foundation types will depend on the availability of particular types of equipment which are considered economical and effective for the particular soil conditions. Extreme caution must be employed before applying a new technique or new equipment in areas where standard construction methods have not been used previously.

6.3 BEARING CAPACITY OF FROZEN GROUND

The term *bearing capacity* may be defined as the allowable pressure on foundation soils limiting settlement or deformation to values which do not interfere with the operation and safety of the superstructure. The allowable pressure for frozen ground is generally dependent on time as well as the temperature-dependent long-term strength of the supporting soils. Unlike the case for unfrozen soils, there are no specific values of allowable pressure which can be prescribed for different types of frozen soils. However, some guidelines are available from the Russian codes and the published literature (Sanger, 1969); Tsytovich, 1975).

Russian investigators (Vyalov, 1959; Tsytovich, 1958, 1975) used semiempirical relationships for solving bearing-capacity problems by substituting the time- and temperature-dependent strength and deformation parameters of the frozen soil into the appropriate formulas borrowed from bearing-capacity theories for unfrozen soils. Ladanyi and Johnston (1974) and Ladanyi (1975) have extended the use of a cavity-expansion model to solving creep and failure problems for deep foundations in frozen ground. In their solution the frozen-soil behavior is approximated by a linear viscoelastic-plastic medium with time-, temperature-, and pressure-dependent strength properties. The theory provides a basis for prediction of both safety against failure and creep settlement of deep foundations in frozen soils.

BEARING CAPACITY OF UNFROZEN SOIL

Computation of the ultimate bearing capacity for a shallow footing resting on unfrozen soil represents a problem of elastic-plastic equilibrium. Rigorous methods are not generally available for computing the bearing capacity of real

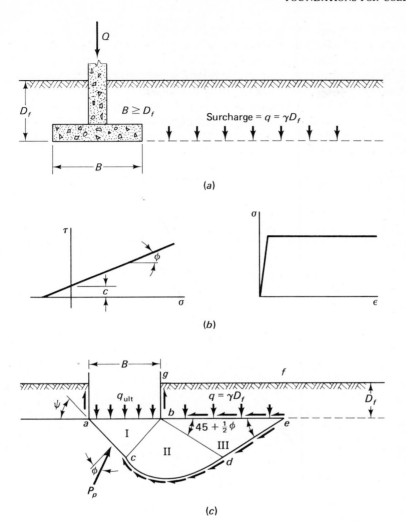

Figure 6.8 Bearing capacity of shallow footings: (*a*) conditions for a shallow foundation; (*b*) Mohr envelope and stress-strain curve for the soil; (*c*) simplified boundaries for the shear zones and the forces acting to prevent failure.

soils having weight and in general exhibiting both cohesion and friction. The major difficulty in finding acceptable solutions lies in the selection of a constitutive relationship describing the stress-strain-time behavior of the soil. Available theories on bearing capacity are mostly limited to solutions developed for a rigid plastic solid. This solid is assumed to exhibit no deformation before shear failure and a plastic flow at constant stress after failure. The prediction of the ultimate loads is limited to relatively incompressible soils or to the general shear-failure mode. In practice it is common to use the available solutions for compressible soils as well with a reduction for the effects of compressibility. Based on the theory of plasticity, basic solutions (Prandtl, 1921; Reissner, 1924) for the bearing-capacity problem are formulated for the conditions shown in Fig. 6.8. Assume a continuous footing of width B resting on an unfrozen soil at a depth D_f. The soil mass is considered to be homogeneous and has infinite depth. The soil has an effective unit weight γ and shear-strength parameters cohesion c and angle of internal friction ϕ defined by the straight-line Mohr envelope and a stress-strain curve representing a rigid-plastic body (Fig. 6.8b).

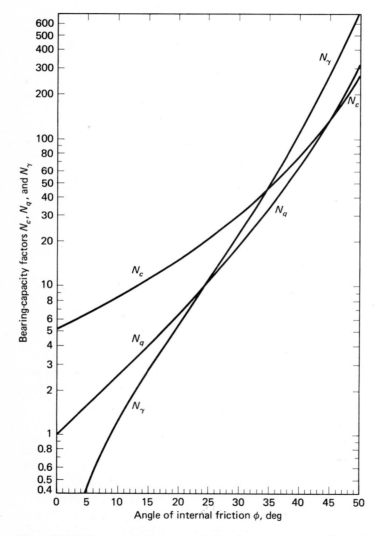

Figure 6.9 Bearing-capacity factors for shallow footings as computed from Eqs. (6.5), (6.6), and (6.8).

To solve the problem, several assumptions are generally made: (1) the footing length is assumed to be much greater than the width (continuous footing); (2) the shearing resistance of the overburden soil (along *ef*, Fig. 6.8c) is disregarded; and (3) the friction between the overburden soil and the foundation (along *bg*, Fig. 6.8c) as well as between the overburden and supporting soil (along *be*, Fig. 6.8c) is disregarded. These assumptions permit replacement of the overburden soil by a uniformly distributed surcharge $q = \gamma D_f$. The continuous footing permits the assumption of plane-strain conditions. Assumption 1 is justified when the footing length is greater than 10B. Assumptions 2 and 3 are usually justified and are always on the safe side.

Approximate solutions for the problem shown in Fig. 6.8 are given by Terzaghi (1943). When the bearing capacity of a real footing is exceeded, the failure pattern is similar to the three zones shown. The elastic zone I acts if it were part of the footing and penetrates the soil like a wedge, pushing against a zone of radial shear II. The passive Rankine zone III is moved in an upward and outward direction. The lower boundary *acde* of the displaced soil mass is composed of two straight lines inclined at $45 + \frac{1}{2}\phi$ and $45 - \frac{1}{2}\phi°$, respectively, to the horizontal. The shape of the connecting curve *cd* is approximated by a logarithmic spiral. For a nonfrictonal soil ($\phi = 0$) the curve *cd* becomes a circle.

The bearing capacity per unit area for a weightless soil ($\gamma = 0$) has been found to be (Prandtl, 1921; Reissner, 1924)

$$q_{ult} = cN_c + qN_q \tag{6.4}$$

where N_c and N_q are dimensionless bearing-capacity factors, defined by

$$N_q = [\tan^2 (45° + \tfrac{1}{2}\phi)] \exp (\pi \tan \phi) \tag{6.5}$$

and

$$N_c = (N_q - 1) \cot \phi \tag{6.6}$$

These values are shown graphically in Fig. 6.9 and are tabulated in Table 6.4.

For a cohesionless soil without overburden ($c = 0$, $q = 0$) Terzaghi (1943) showed that

$$q_{ult} = \tfrac{1}{2}\gamma B N_\gamma \tag{6.7}$$

where N_γ is again a dimensionless bearing-capacity factor, which varies sharply with the angle ψ (Fig. 6.8c). The numerical values in Fig. 6.9 are from an analysis by Caquot and Kerisel (1953) using a value of ψ equal to $45 + \frac{1}{2}\phi°$. Vesić (1970) has shown that N_γ can be approximated with an error on the safe side (less than 10 percent for $15° < \phi < 55°$ and less than 5 percent for $20° < \phi < 40°$) by the expression

$$N_\gamma \approx 2(N_q + 1) \tan \phi \tag{6.8}$$

The N_γ values based on Eq. (6.8) are presented in Table 6.4 and Fig. 6.9. For intermediate cases, where $c \neq 0$, $q \neq 0$, and $\gamma \neq 0$, Eqs. (6.4) and (6.7) can be

Table 6.4 Bearing-capacity factors computed from Eqs. (6.5), (6.6), and (6.8)

ϕ	N_c	N_q	N_γ	ϕ	N_c	N_q	N_γ
0	5.14	1.00	0.00				
1	5.38	1.09	0.07	26	22.25	11.85	12.54
2	5.63	1.20	0.15	27	23.94	13.20	14.47
3	5.90	1.31	0.24	28	25.80	14.72	16.72
4	6.19	1.43	0.34	29	27.86	16.44	19.34
5	6.49	1.57	0.45	30	30.14	18.40	22.40
6	6.81	1.72	0.57	31	32.67	20.63	25.99
7	7.16	1.88	0.71	32	35.49	23.18	30.22
8	7.53	2.06	0.86	33	38.64	26.09	35.19
9	7.92	2.25	1.03	34	42.16	29.44	41.06
10	8.35	2.47	1.22	35	46.12	33.30	48.03
11	8.80	2.71	1.44	36	50.59	37.75	56.31
12	9.28	2.97	1.69	37	55.63	42.92	66.19
13	9.81	3.26	1.97	38	61.35	48.93	78.03
14	10.37	3.59	2.29	39	67.87	55.96	92.25
15	10.98	3.94	2.65	40	75.31	64.20	109.41
16	11.63	4.34	3.06	41	83.86	73.90	130.22
17	12.34	4.77	3.53	42	93.71	85.38	155.55
18	13.10	5.26	4.07	43	105.11	99.02	186.54
19	13.93	5.80	4.68	44	118.37	115.31	224.64
20	14.83	6.40	5.39	45	133.88	134.88	271.76
21	15.82	7.07	6.20	46	152.10	158.51	330.35
22	16.88	7.82	7.13	47	173.64	187.21	403.67
23	18.05	8.66	8.20	48	199.26	222.31	496.01
24	19.32	9.60	9.44	49	229.93	265.51	613.16
25	20.72	10.66	10.88	50	266.89	319.07	762.89

combined to give

$$q_{ult} = cN_c + qN_q + \tfrac{1}{2}\gamma BN_\gamma \qquad (6.9)$$

which is known as Terzaghi's (1943) equation.

Foundation Shape Factors

Terzaghi's equation is limited to long rectangular or continuous footings. Adaptation to other foundation shapes has been developed on the basis of comparative-loading tests. Equation (6.9) can be written in a more general form (Vesić, 1970) as

$$q_{ult} = cN_c\zeta_c + qN_q\zeta_q + \tfrac{1}{2}\gamma BN_\gamma\zeta_\gamma \qquad (6.10)$$

Table 6.5 Shape factors for shallow foundations (after De Beer, 1967; modified by Vesić, 1970)

Shape of footing	ζ_c	ζ_q	ζ_γ
Strip	1.00	1.00	1.00
Rectangle	$1 + \dfrac{B}{L}\dfrac{N_q}{N_c}$	$1 + B/L \tan \phi$	$1 - 0.4\dfrac{B}{L}$
Circle and square	$1 + \dfrac{N_q}{N_c}$	$1 + \tan \phi$	0.60

where N_c, N_q, and N_γ are the same bearing-capacity factors as for the continuous footing. The shape factors ζ_c, ζ_q, and ζ_γ are dimensionless parameters (Table 6.5) which permit computation of the bearing capacity for rectangular, square, and circular footings. These shape factors take into account the angle of internal friction ϕ of the soil and the geometrical form of the foundation.

Local Shear Failure

The general shear failure illustrated in Fig. 6.8c does not develop unless the soil is fairly dense or stiff. For more compressible soils, the footing sinks into the ground before the state of plastic equilibrium spreads beyond point d in Fig. 6.8c. An approximate solution for continuous footings on such soils is given by Terzaghi (1943), who proposed the use of the same bearing-capacity equation and factors with reduced-strength parameters c' and ϕ' defined as

$$c' = \tfrac{2}{3}c \tag{6.11}$$

$$\phi' = \tan^{-1}\left(\tfrac{2}{3}\tan\phi\right) \tag{6.12}$$

The angle of shearing resistance becomes ϕ' instead of ϕ, and the bearing-capacity factors assume values of N'_c, N'_q, and N'_γ which can be obtained from Table 6.4 or Fig. 6.9 using the new ϕ' value. This approach provides acceptable answers for some soils but may be on the unsafe side for other soils. A more rational method of handling local shear failure is needed. Vesić (1975) has presented a tentative approximate analysis which permits the engineer to assess numerically the order of magnitude of expected reduction of bearing capacity caused by the more compressible soils. Since application to frozen soils is not known, it is omitted here.

Inclined and Eccentric Loads

Inclined and eccentric loads introduce a horizontal component to the vertical loads considered in the previous discussion. The bearing-capacity problem now becomes more complicated in that the footing can fail by general shear of the underlying soil or by sliding along its base. The vertical component Q of the footing reaction is related to the horizontal component P at the verge of sliding by

$$P_{max} = Q \tan \delta + A'c_a \tag{6.13}$$

where c_a = adhesion between footing and soil
δ = angle of friction between footing and soil
A' = effective contact area of footing

Data presented by Schultze and Horn (1967) suggest that $\delta = \phi_f$ and that the undrained shear strength of soft clays may be used for the adhesion in soft clays.

An analysis similar to that for vertical loads must be performed to determine the ultimate vertical component Q_{ult} required to cause a general shear failure. Failure zones disclosed by such an analysis are illustrated in Fig. 6.10. Investigations by De Beer (1949) and Meyerhof (1953) have shown that it is on the safe side to account for the eccentricity by use of an effective width $B' = B - 2e$ of the footing. The effect of the load inclination is now taken into account by introducing the inclination factors ζ_{ci}, ζ_{qi}, and $\zeta_{\gamma i}$ (Schultze, 1952; Hansen, 1961) into Eq. (6.10):

$$q_{ult} = \frac{Q_{ult}}{B'L} = cN_c \zeta_c \zeta_{ci} + qN_q \zeta_q \zeta_{qi} + \tfrac{1}{2}\gamma BN_\gamma \zeta_\gamma \zeta_{\gamma i} \tag{6.14}$$

where $L = L - 2e_L$ is the effective length of the footing and e_L is the eccentricity of the load in the longitudinal direction. The ratio B/L and the direction of the inclined load have an effect on the inclination factors. Vesić (1970) has proposed the following expressions for the inclination factors:

$$\zeta_{qi} = \left(1 - \frac{P}{Q + B'L'c \cot \phi}\right)^m \tag{6.15}$$

$$\zeta_{\gamma i} = \left(1 - \frac{P}{Q + B'L'c \cot \phi}\right)^{m+1} \tag{6.16}$$

$$\zeta_{ci} = 1 - \frac{mP}{B'L'cN_c} \tag{6.17}$$

where m is given by

$$m_B = \frac{2 + B/L}{1 + B/L} \tag{6.18}$$

when the load inclination is in the direction of the shorter side B of the footing. When the load inclination is in the direction of the longer side L of the footing, m becomes

$$m_L = \frac{2 + L/B}{1 + L/B} \tag{6.19}$$

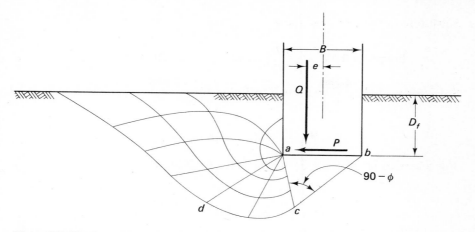

Figure 6.10 Plastic zone for inclined and eccentric loads. Effective footing width $B' = B - 2e$.

When the load makes an angle θ_n with the long side L of the footing, Vesić (1970) recommended interpolation between the values m_L and m_B; hence

$$m_n = m_L \cos^2 \theta_n + m_B \sin^2 \theta_n \tag{6.20}$$

Example 6.3 Determine the bearing capacity q_{ult} for a vertical load on a square footing placed at a 3.7-m depth in permafrost. Available test data include a conventional unconfined compressive strength $q_u = 4.62$ MN/m^2 at $-1.67°$C. Data from two creep tests at the same temperature include the following:

Load, % of q_u	Applied creep stress, MN/m^2	Time to failure, h
60	2.76	0.027
40	1.86	0.240

Use the soil data given in Example 6.2 and neglect any internal soil friction ($\phi = 0$). Consider the service life of the footing equal to 50 years.

SOLUTION Using Eq. (5.60) gives

$$\sigma_f = \frac{\sigma_0}{\ln (t_f/t_0)} = \frac{\sigma_0}{\ln t_f - \ln t_0}$$

Solve for

$$\ln t_0 = \ln t_f - \frac{\sigma_0}{\sigma_f}$$

Substitute in the creep-test data

$$\ln t_0 = \ln 0.027 - \frac{\sigma_0}{2.76} \quad \text{and} \quad \ln t_0 = \ln 0.240 - \frac{\sigma_0}{1.86}$$

Solve for σ_0 and t_0. Substitute into Eq. (5.60)

$$\sigma_f = \frac{12.46}{\ln t_f + 8.13}$$

For a service life of 50 years $= 4.38 \times 10^5$ h compute

$$\sigma_f = \frac{12.46}{\ln (4.38 \times 10^5) + 8.13} = 0.59 \text{ MN/m}^2$$

Compute the 50-year cohesion value $c = \frac{1}{2}\,\sigma_f = \frac{1}{2}(0.59) = 0.295$ MN/m^2. Use Eq. (6.10) with $N_c = 5.14$, $N_q = 1.00$, $N = 0$, $\zeta_c = 1.2$, and $\zeta_q = 1.00$. Now compute

$$q_{ult} = cN_c\zeta_c + \gamma D_f N_q \zeta_q$$

$$= 0.295(5.14)(1.2) + \frac{18.06(3.7)}{1000}\,1.00(1.00) = 1.89 \text{ MN/m}^2$$

Cavity-Expansion Theory

Since the early work on bearing capacity of foundations by Gibson (1950) and Meyerhof (1951), where this mathematical model was first mentioned in the geotechnical literature, the theory of cavity expansion has been applied with success to the problem of bearing capacity of deep foundations in various types of soil by several authors (Skempton et al., 1953; Ladanyi, 1961, 1963, 1967, 1973; Vesić, 1973). Compared with some other mathematical models used in soil mechanics, the theory of cavity expansion offers the advantage of considering a highly symmetric problem, thus permitting relatively simple analytical solutions to be obtained, even for a rather complex soil behavior such as the nonlinearity of both the failure envelope and the stress-strain relationship of the soil.

In the field of mechanics of frozen soils, Ladanyi and Johnston (1974) and Ladanyi (1975) have shown how the theory of cavity expansion could be used for predicting creep settlements and time-dependent bearing capacity of deep circular and strip foundations. According to the authors, in frozen soils this particular failure model seems to be more justified than the usual one based on Prandtl's theory, since the available experimental evidence obtained both in shallow and deep plate-load tests in frozen soils (Vyalov, 1959; Ladanyi and Johnston, 1974) failed to show any trace of distinct failure surfaces of the Prandtl type.

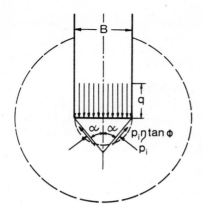

Figure 6.11 Transformation of a cavity expansion to a deep footing problem. [*After Ladanyi and Johnston, 1974, reproduced by permission of the National Research Council of Canada from the Canadian Geotechnical Journal,* **11**: *531–553 (1974).*]

The cavity-expansion model, however, can be considered to represent approximately the soil behavior under a deep circular or strip footing only at some distance from the footing. In order to take into account the change in direction of stresses and strains in the vicinity of the footing, several assumptions are necessary. For transformation of stresses Ladanyi and Johnston (1974) assumed, as did Gibson (1950), that during penetration of a footing into the soil a rigid soil cone (for a circular footing) or wedge (for a strip footing) is formed at the base of the footing. This cone or wedge is acted upon by a uniformly distributed soil pressure equal to the cavity-expansion pressure p_i (Fig. 6.11). The cavity would be spherical under a circular footing and cylindrical under a long rectangular footing. Both for the cone and the wedge, statical considerations at failure give the expression

$$q_{as} + H = (p_{ias} + H)(1 + \tan \phi \cot \alpha) \tag{6.21}$$

where q_{as} = average pressure acting on footing at failure

p_{ias} = asymptotic (ultimate) value of cavity-expansion pressure acting on cone (or wedge) with angle 2α at tip

ϕ = angle of internal friction

and
$$H = c \cot \phi \tag{6.22}$$

with c the time- and temperature-dependent frozen-soil cohesion. From theoretical considerations supported by some experimental evidence (Ladanyi and Johnston, 1974), the angle α may be close to $45°$ under a circular footing and about $45 - \phi/2°$ under a strip footing. Hence, for a circular footing, Eq. (6.21) can be written as

$$q_{as} \approx p_{ias}(1 + \tan \phi) + c \tag{6.23}$$

During prefailure the shear strength along the soil cone or wedge may not be fully mobilized, and Eq. (6.21) can be written (Ladanyi and Johnston, 1974) as

$$q + H = (p_i + H)(1 + \eta \tan \phi \cot \alpha) \tag{6.24}$$

where q is the actual footing pressure, p_i is the corresponding cavity-expansion pressure, and η is a dimensionless coefficient representing the degree of mobilization of shear strength along the cone or wedge for a given settlement. Ladanyi and Johnston (1974) indicated that in frozen soils, as in stiff clays, the ultimate load is reached at a total settlement s close to one-tenth of the footing diameter or width B. They then suggested that $\eta = 10s/B$ if $s < 0.1B$ and $\eta = 1$ if $s \geq 0.1B$.

On the other hand, for transforming cavity-expansion displacements into footing settlements, Ladanyi and Johnston (1974) and Ladanyi (1975) equalized the displaced volumes in both cases, which yielded

$$\frac{s}{B} = \frac{1}{3}\left[\left(1 - \frac{u_i}{r_i}\right)^{-3} - 1\right] \tag{6.25}$$

for a circular footing and

$$\frac{s}{B} = \frac{\pi}{8}\left[\left(1 - \frac{u_i}{r_i}\right)^{-2} - 1\right] \tag{6.26}$$

for a strip footing, where $r_i = B/2 + u_i$ is the current radius of the cavity and u_i is the radial cavity expansion under internal pressure p_i.

For solving the cavity-expansion problem, Ladanyi and Johnston (1974) and Ladanyi (1975) assumed for frozen soil a power-law dependence between the stresses and the strain rates, such as given by Eq. (5.15) or (5.79). In the same manner, the strength of frozen soil is defined by Eq. (5.86) and (5.87). From the first equations the authors deduced the relationship between the creep-settlement rate and the applied pressure. On the other hand, using the creep equation in integrated form and adding the failure condition, which results in nonlinear isocurves of the form shown in Fig. 5.21, enabled the authors to calculate creep settlements during formation of the plastic zone and the bearing-capacity factors. A brief summary of the assumptions on frozen-soil behavior used by Ladanyi and Johnston (1974) and Ladanyi (1975) together with the most important results of their study are summarized below.

The basic stress–vs.–steady-state-strain-rate relationship assumed for frozen soil in the theory is

$$\dot{\varepsilon}_e = A\sigma_e^n \tag{6.27}$$

where $\dot{\varepsilon}_e$ and σ_e are the equivalent creep strain rate and the equivalent stress, as in Eq. (5.79), $n \geq 1$ is the creep exponent, and

$$A = \frac{\dot{\varepsilon}_c}{\sigma_{cu\theta}^n} \tag{6.28}$$

where $\sigma_{cu\theta}$ is the unconfined compression-creep modulus defined as the stress corresponding to the reference strain rate $\dot{\varepsilon}_c$ and the temperature θ, as in Eqs. (5.74) or (5.76). In order to take into account the effect of the confining pressure on the creep rate, Ladanyi and Johnston (1974) proposed to replace $\sigma_{cu\theta}$ by $\sigma_{ca\theta}$, which is an average value of the creep modulus for the considered range of confining pressure. In addition, as shown in Chap. 5, any solution based on the steady-state creep law [Eq. (6.27)] can be transformed into a time-hardening creep case by replacing, in the solution, the time t by t^b and the reference strain rate $\dot{\varepsilon}_c$ by $(\dot{\varepsilon}_c/b)^b$, where $b \le 1$ denotes the time-hardening creep exponent.

As far as creep-failure conditions are concerned, it is assumed that a frozen soil undergoing creep in unconfined compression will fail, or pass into a tertiary-creep phase, when, as in Eq. (5.87),

$$\sigma_{fu} = \sigma_{cu\theta} \left(\frac{\varepsilon_f}{\dot{\varepsilon}_c\,t} \right)^{1/n} \tag{6.29}$$

where ε_f is the failure strain of the frozen soil under triaxial-test conditions.

From Eq. (6.29), the ordinary triaxial-test cohesion for a nonfrictional ($\phi = 0$) soil is equal to

$$c = \tfrac{1}{2}\sigma_{fu} \tag{6.30}$$

and for a frictional ($\phi > 0$) soil, with a ϕ value independent of strain rate and temperature, it is

$$c = \frac{\sigma_{fu}}{2(N_\phi)^{1/2}} \tag{6.31}$$

where the flow value is

$$N_\phi = \frac{1 + \sin\phi}{1 - \sin\phi} \tag{6.32}$$

The theory developed by Ladanyi and Johnston (1974) and Ladanyi (1975) covers both circular and strip footings. Ladanyi (1975) also gives empirical transformation formulas for the effects of footing shape and free surface, respectively. However, since the most important field of application of this kind of solution is that of deep footings, which usually have a circular or square base, only the portion of the solution valid for deep circular footings (Ladanyi and Johnston, 1974) will be shown here.

The total settlement s of a deep circular footing in frozen soil is equal to the sum of the instantaneous settlement s_{inst}, to be determined by conventional soil-mechanics methods using a temperature-dependent modulus of elasticity of the soil, and the creep settlement s_c, which can be determined by the spherical-cavity-expansion theory. For total settlements not exceeding about 20 percent of the footing diameter or side dimension, the following equation for creep settle-ment can be used:

$$S_c = \frac{B}{3}\left\{\left[1 - \frac{At}{2}\left(\frac{3}{2n}\right)^n (q - p_0 - \eta c)^n\right]^{-3} - 1\right\} \tag{6.33}$$

or

$$S_c \approx \frac{At}{2}\left[\frac{3}{2n}(q - p_0 - \eta c)\right]^n \tag{6.34}$$

which corresponds to a steady settlement rate of

$$\dot{S}_c = \frac{ds_c}{dt} = \frac{A}{2}\left[\frac{3}{2n}(q - p_0 - \eta c)\right]^n \tag{6.35}$$

These equations can be transformed into a time-hardening form by using the transformation rule described earlier.

On the other hand, cavity-expansion theory permits values of the bearing-capacity factors to be calculated for a frozen soil which has undergone steady-state creep and reached creep failure (start of tertiary creep). The rate of creep is a power function of stress. Since these bearing-capacity factors are based on isochronous curves of the shape shown in Fig. 5.21, they are valid both for nonlinear elastic-plastic and nonlinear viscoelastic-plastic materials.

According to cavity-expansion theory, the ultimate pressure q_{as} under which deep circular footings will pass into the tertiary creep stage and eventually fail is given by

$$q_{as} = p_0 N_q + c N_c \tag{6.36}$$

where p_0 is the average original total pressure at the footing level, c is the time- and temperature-dependent cohesion, given by Eq. (6.31), and N_q, N_c are the bearing-capacity factors defined by

$$N_q = 1 \tag{6.37}$$

and

$$N_c = 1 + \frac{4}{3}\left(n + \ln\frac{2}{3\varepsilon_f}\right) \tag{6.38}$$

Equations (6.37) and (6.38) are for nonfrictional soils ($\phi = 0$). The variation of N_c [Eq. (6.38)] for $1 \leq n \leq 10$ and for four values of ε_f are shown in Fig. 6.12. For a frictional frozen soil ($\phi > 0$) these bearing-capacity factors are

$$N_q = (1 + \tan\phi)\left(1 - \frac{n}{k}\right)^{(n/k)-1}(\tfrac{2}{3})^{1/k}(kI_r \tan\phi)^{n/k} \tag{6.39}$$

$$N_c = (N_q - 1)\cot\phi \tag{6.40}$$

where ε_f is the average failure strain, n is the exponent in the power creep law [Eq. (6.27)], while

$$k = \frac{3N_\phi}{2(N_\phi - 1)} = \frac{3}{4}\left(\frac{1}{\sin\phi} + 1\right) \tag{6.41}$$

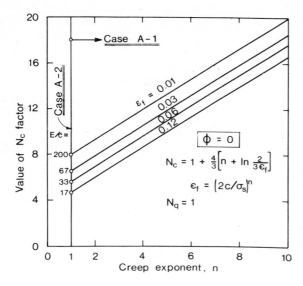

Figure 6.12 Bearing-capacity factor N_c for a deep circular footing, valid for a frozen soil with $\phi = 0$ and with linear ($n = 1$) and nonlinear ($n > 1$) creep behavior. [*After Ladanyi and Johnston, 1974, reproduced by permission of the National Research Council of Canada from the Canadian Geotechnical Journal,* **11**: *531–553* (*1974*).]

and I_r is a rigidity index for an incompressible nonlinear soil, defined by

$$I_r = \frac{4(N_\phi)^{1/2}}{3\varepsilon_f^{1/n}[1 + (p_0/c)\tan\phi]} \tag{6.42}$$

Figure 6.13 shows the variation of N_c with I_r based on Eqs. (6.39) and (6.40) for $n = 1$, 3, and 5 and for ϕ ranging from zero to ϕ_{max}. The limit of validity for Eq. (6.39) occurs at ϕ_{max} when $n = k$. For the values of n greater than k, the nonlinearity is such that the failure region does not develop.

All the above formulas are valid for deep circular footings for which the effect of the free surface on bearing capacity can be neglected. For footings that are closer to the frozen-soil surface, Ladanyi (1975) proposed to multiply the bearing-capacity factors N_q and N_c [Eqs. (6.37) and (6.40)], which are valid for a deep footing, by reduction factors d'_q and d'_c, respectively. The values of the two reduction factors, deduced from an empirical formula originally proposed by Hansen (1961), are given by

$$d'_c = \frac{D/B + [f(\phi) + 0.35]^{-1}}{D/B + [f(\phi)]^{-1}} \tag{6.43}$$

and

$$d'_q = d'_c - \frac{d'_c - 1}{N_q} \tag{6.44}$$

where D is the depth of embedment of the footing (or pile) in the frozen soil and

$$f(\phi) = \frac{0.6}{1 + 7\tan^4\phi} \tag{6.45}$$

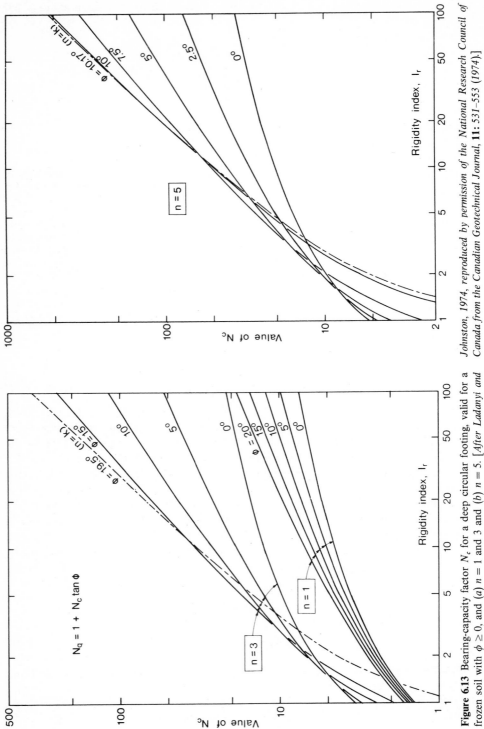

Figure 6.13 Bearing-capacity factor N_c for a deep circular footing, valid for a frozen soil with $\phi \geq 0$, and (a) $n = 1$ and 3 and (b) $n = 5$. [After Ladanyi and Johnston, 1974, reproduced by permission of the National Research Council of Canada from the Canadian Geotechnical Journal, **11**: 531–553 (1974).]

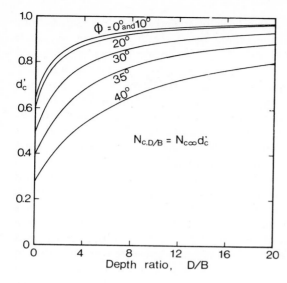

Figure 6.14 Depth factor d_c'. [*After Ladanyi, 1975, reproduced by permission of the National Research Council of Canada from the Canadian Geotechnical Journal,* **12**: *393–407, (1975).*]

The variation of d_c' with D/B is shown in Fig. 6.14 for six values of ϕ ranging from 0 to 40°. Note that $d_q' \approx d_c'$ for $\phi \geq 25°$. Use of the cavity-expansion theory is illustrated by the following example, from Ladanyi and Johnston (1974).

Example 6.4 Estimate the bearing capacity 40 h after load application for a deep circular footing embedded in frozen silt. The average total ground pressure at the footing level is 0.06 MPa. The frozen silt at a temperature of $-0.3°C$ has creep parameters $\sigma_{cu\theta} = 0.476$ MPa (for $\dot{\varepsilon}_c = 10^{-4}$ min^{-1}) and $n = 2.095$. Strength parameters include $\phi = 15°$ and $\varepsilon_f = 0.10$.

SOLUTION Using Eqs. (6.29) and (6.31), compute the cohesion after 40 h ($= 2400$ min) to be 0.120 MN/m². Using Eq. (6.42), compute $I_r = 4.596$, and from Eqs. (6.39) and (6.40) compute $N_q = 3.866$ and $N_c = 10.70$. Obtain the ultimate pressure q_{as} with Eq. (6.36):

$$q_{as} = 0.06(3.866) + 0.12(10.70) = 1.516 \text{ MN/m}^2$$

6.4 SHALLOW FOUNDATIONS

Shallow foundations are generally used when suitable subsoil conditions are encountered at shallow depths or when the design load of the superstructure does not require deep foundations. They are normally defined as footings having a width B equal to or greater than their depth D_f (Fig. 6.8a). They are placed immediately beneath the lowest part of the superstructure at a depth governed by either the frost-penetration or active layer discussed in Sec. 6.1. Satisfactory foundation performance requires that three basic requirements be satisfied: (1) proper foundation location with respect to any future factors which could adversely affect its performance, (2) a stable foundation including adequate bearing capacity of the underlying soil strata, and (3) acceptable immediate and long-term settlements which do not damage the structure or impair its usefulness. The first requirement involves factors discussed in Sec. 6.1. The second requirement is specific. The third requirement can refer to total or differential settlements caused by frost heaving, thaw consolidation, creep, or other factors. Each requirement must be satisfied for an acceptable foundation.

Shallow foundations may be placed directly in contact with the frozen ground for suitable subsoil conditions. General procedures required to maintain thermal equilibrium in the frozen ground dictate that shallow foundations be placed on a gravel berm or a layer of suitable sandy soil with or without insulation (Figs. 6.5 and 6.6). The placement of such shallow concrete footings must meet two requirements: (1) the temperature of the concrete must be warm enough to permit curing in a reasonable time without freezing, and (2) the placement of concrete must not cause thawing of the frozen supporting soils. As such, the placement of shallow concrete footings over frozen ground is limited by the footing size, the temperature of the foundation soils, and the time of construction. It is general practice to excavate and construct shallow foundations in the fall. This allows the cold winter temperatures to freeze back the disturbed subsoil area, and the superstructure can be built in winter under temporary cover.

Selection of Footing Type

Various foundation types suitable for different structures were discussed in Sec. 6.3. In areas of seasonally frozen ground, footing types are based on structural needs and the requirement that the footing transmit the load to the soil strata at a pressure suited to the soil properties. The footings must extend below the level of deepest frost penetration over the service life of the structure. Recent experience (Robinsky and Bespflug, 1973) has shown that insulated foundations can be used for both heated and unheated structures to prevent frost penetration. Design curves provide reasonable guidelines for selection of the necessary foundation insulation for structures on clayey or silty soils. In some regions, the depth can be determined by the thickness of the active layer in which seasonal changes in moisture content may cause appreciable volume changes in the soil. There are many factors, such as pressure distribution from adjacent structures, existence of highly compressible organic soil or peat, etc., which must be considered in selecting the footing depth. Standard design methods, available in foundation engineering textbooks (Leonards, 1962; Bowles, 1968), are omitted here.

Footings on permanently frozen ground are designed to minimize thermal degradation of the supporting soils, whose strength must not be permitted to deteriorate during the design life of the structure. Heat flow from heated structures must be diverted from the frozen ground. A common approach is to use an air space under the building through which the cold winter air passes and refreezes the ground thawed during the summer. The shading effect of the building plus the use of sunshades or an unheated overhang along the edges reduces the thawing index and the thickness of the active layer below the building. Movement of air must not be restricted in any way by the shades. Footings using the air space for control of ground temperatures are illustrated in Fig. 6.6. It is common to excavate several feet down into the permafrost and backfill with non-frost-susceptible materials. The excavation should be completed quickly so as to alter ground temperatures as little as possible. The backfill material protects the permafrost from heat released during hydration and hardening of the concrete footing. In Fig. 6.6 a temporary moss fill has been used as an insulating material for protection during summer construction. A permanent moss fill is shown near the top of the concrete pedestal.

An alternate approach involves the use of a gravel mat with or without an air space. For one-story structures an acceptable pad of non-frost-susceptible materials is placed on top of the natural cover. Stripping of the area should not be permitted. Depth of thaw can be computed using the modified Berggren equation or the Stefan solution with the pad thickness modified as needed. Normally the gravel must be about $1\frac{1}{2}$ times the thickness of the undisturbed active zone and extend at least 1.5 m beyond the edges of the building (Fig. 6.5). A small slope for runoff takes surface water away from the building. It is good practice to protect the pad with vegetation when it will grow in the area.

For larger structures with high live loads (warehouses, workshops, garages, hangars, and powerplants) a simple air space is not economical to construct. A gravel pad and raft support with ventilated pan ducts for cold winter air circulation is needed. Figure 6.3 shows a pan-slab foundation including a plenum chamber and details on the ventilation ducts. Cold air passing through the ducts gains heat from the duct walls and increases in temperature. The outlet duct air temperature must be cold enough to counteract the thawing index and ensure freezeback of the gravel pad during the winter season. Natural draft created by a chimney or forced draft created by mechanical ventilation using commercial blowers of low pressure and high discharge have been used on projects. Maintenance and problems created by possible equipment breakdown are responsible for use of mechanical ventilation only under special circumstances, e.g., degrading permafrost consisting of ice-rich fine-grained soils. Tobiasson (1973), reporting on the performance of the Thule hangar soil-cooling system, emphasized the need for considering several factors in design and operation of the system. Manifolds and ducts should be large enough to permit entry of maintenance personnel for inspection and removal of blockages. The system should be airtight. Provisions should be incorporated to minimize the amount of snow infiltration and to remove any drift snow that enters the soil-cooling ducts. The ends of exhaust stacks should be located 1 m or more above the roof rather than on the lee side of the building, where snow eddies develop. If dampers are installed, they should be installed only on upwind stacks, which allow convection currents to remove warm air from ducts even with the upwind damper closed.

An example design of a foundation involving ventilated pads was given in Chap. 3. A modified version of the design procedure for natural draft created by a chimney followed by the U.S. Army/Air Force (1966a) in the design of a pan-duct system first involves selection of a pad thickness which will contain the seasonal thaw penetration. The thaw depth is computed using either the modified Berggren equation or the improved Stefan solution. Next the chimney or stack height needed to create the natural draft is selected on the basis that the duct outlet air temperature satisfies freezeback requirements for the pad. The heat flow from the floor and the pad must equal the heat removed by the duct air, i.e.,

$$Qld = V A_d \rho c_p T_R \tag{6.46}$$

where Q = total heat flow to duct, J/m^2 s
l = duct length, m
d = duct spacing, m
V = velocity of duct air, m/s
A_d = duct cross-sectional area, m^2
ρ = air density, kg/m^3
c_p = specific heat of air at constant pressure, J/kg °C
T_R = temperature rise in duct air, °C

The required airflow obtained by the chimney effect is related to the stack height. The stack height is determined by the relation (ASHRAE, 1963)

$$h_d = h_v + h_f \tag{6.47}$$

where h_d = natural draft, mmH$_2$O
h_v = velocity head, mmH$_2$O
h_f = friction head, mmH$_2$O

The natural draft (ASHRAE, 1963) is

$$h_d = \frac{\rho \varepsilon H (T_c - T_0)}{T_c + 273.1} \qquad \text{mmH}_2\text{O} \tag{6.48}$$

where ρ = air density† at average duct temperature, kg/m^3
ε = efficiency of stack system ≈ 0.80 (ASHRAE, 1963)
H = stack height, m
T_c = stack air temperature, °C
T_0 = average outside air temperature, °C

† Air density (kg/m^3) = ρ = $1.2929(1 + 0.00367T)^{-1}$, where T equals the temperature in degrees Celsius.

The velocity head (ASHRAE, 1963) is

$$h_v = \left(\frac{V}{4.033}\right)^2 \quad \text{mmH}_2\text{O} \tag{6.49}$$

where V is the duct air velocity in meters per second. The friction head (ASHRAE, 1963) is

$$h_f = f' \frac{l_e}{D_e} h_v \quad \text{mmH}_2\text{O} \tag{6.50}$$

where f' = dimensionless friction factor
$\quad l_e$ = equivalent duct length, m
$\quad D_e$ = equivalent duct diameter (m) = 4 times area (m^2) divided by perimeter (m)

The equivalent duct length includes the actual duct length plus 65 diameters for each right-angle bend and 10 diameters for each entry and exit.

The friction factor f' is a function of Reynolds number N_R and the ratio e/D_e. Sanger (1969) gave a value for e equal to 0.0003 m based on field observations. The Reynolds number is given as

$$N_R = \frac{V(a' + 0.25D_e)}{v} \tag{6.51}$$

where a' is the shortest duct dimension in meters and v is the kinematic viscosity† of air in square meters per second at the average duct temperature. The friction factor (ASHRAE, 1963) is

$$f' = 0.0055 \left[1 + \left(20{,}000 \frac{e}{D_e} + \frac{10^6}{N_R}\right)^{1/3}\right] \tag{6.52}$$

With all the variables in Eq. (6.47) determined, the stack height is

$$H = \frac{h_d(T_c + 273.1)}{\rho\varepsilon(T_c - T_0)} \tag{6.53}$$

This first estimate of H can be incorporated into a new equivalent duct length for a recalculated stack height. Increasing the thickness of insulation in the floor (Fig. 6.3) will reduce the required stack height.

Example 6.5 A ventilated pan-duct system is to be designed for a 67-m-wide building with an average floor temperature of 15.5°C. The floor section includes a 203-mm concrete slab, 102 mm of insulation, a 152-mm concrete slab, 0.3-m-high ducts as shown in Fig. 6.3, and a 102-mm concrete slab on gravel fill. The non-frost-susceptible pad below the floor will consist of gravel

---

† Kinematic air viscosity (m^2/s) = $v = 1.708 \times 10^{-5} \rho_T^{-1}(T/273.15)^{1/2}$, where ρ_T is the air density in kilograms per cubic meter at the temperature T in Kelvins.

with a dry density of 2000 kg/m³ and a water content of 2.5 percent. The mean annual temperature of the pad at the duct outlet is about 0°C. The building site has a minimum freezing index of 2222 degree-days and a freezing season of 215 days. The thermal conductivity of the concrete and the insulation are, respectively, 1.73 and 0.057 W/m°C. Determine the pad thickness required to ensure negligible thaw penetration into the subgrade and the required stack height (Fig. 6.3) to ensure freezeback of the gravel pad.

SOLUTION Determine the pad thickness assuming that the ducts are closed for $365 - 215 = 150$ days each year. The floor thaw index $I_f = 15.5(150) = 2325$ degree-days. The depth of thaw is given by the modified Berggren equation

$$X = kR_f \left[\left(1 + \frac{7200\lambda^2 I_f}{kLR_f^2} \right)^{1/2} - 1 \right]$$

where the average thermal conductivity of the gravel $k = \frac{1}{2}(1.21 + 1.73) = 1.47$ W/m°C, the thermal resistance of the floor system is

$$R_f = \sum \frac{X_i}{k_i} = \frac{203 + 152 + 102}{1000(1.73)} + \frac{305}{1000(1.73)} + \frac{102}{1000(0.057)} = 2.23 \text{ m}^2 \text{ °C/W}$$

the correction coefficient $\lambda = 0.97$, and the latent heat of the gravel $L = 333.7$ $\gamma_d w/100 = 333.7(2000)(2.5/100) = 16.68$ MJ/m³. Compute the depth of thaw

$$X = 1.47(2.23) \left\{ \left[1 + \frac{7200(24)(0.97)^2(2325)}{1.47(16.68 \times 10^6)(2.23)^2} \right]^{1/2} - 1 \right\} = 3.36 \text{ m}$$

and the required pad thickness equals 3.36 m.

The total amount of heat to be removed from the gravel pad by cold-air ventilation during the freezing season with ducts open equals the latent plus sensible heat contained in the thawed pad. The heat content per square meter of pad is $3.36(16.68) = 56$ MJ/m². Allowing 10 percent for sensible heat gives a total $= 56 + 0.1(56) = 61.7$ MJ/m². This heat must be withdrawn by cold-air ventilation during the freezing season (215 days); hence the average rate of heat flow from the gravel pad is $61.7/215(24) = 11.95$ kJ/m² h.

The average thawing index at the surface of the pad is

$$I_t = \frac{LX^2}{7200\lambda^2 k} = [(16.68 \times 10^6)(3.36)^2][7200(24)(0.97)^2(1.47)]^{-1}$$

$$= 788 \text{ degree-days}$$

This thawing index must be compensated by an equal freezing index at the duct outlet to assure freezeback. The average pad surface temperature at the duct-outlet end equals (required freezing index)/(length of freezing season) = $-788/215 = -3.7°C$. The inlet air during the freezing season has an average temperature equal to (air freezing index)/(length of freezing season) $= -2222/215 = -10.3°C$. Therefore, the average permissible temperature rise in the ducts, assuming that the outlet air temperature is about the same as that of the pad, is $T_R = -3.7 - (-10.3) = 6.6°C$.

Heat flow from the floor surface to the duct during the freezing season equals the temperature difference between the floor and the duct air divided by the thermal resistance between them. The thermal resistance $R = X_c/k_c + X_i/k_i + 1/h_{rc} = (203 + 152)/1000(1.73) + 102/1000(0.057) + 1/5.68 = 2.17$ m^2 °C/W (note that $h_{rc} = 5.68$ W/m^2 °C, the surface transfer coefficient between duct wall and duct air, represents the approximate combined effect of convection and radiation). The average heat flow between the floor and inlet duct air equals $[15.5 - (-10.3)]/2.17 = 11.9$ W/m^2 and between the floor and outlet duct air equals $[15.5 - (-3.7)]/2.17 = 8.8$ W/m^2, giving an average rate of heat flow from the floor $\frac{1}{2}(11.9 + 8.8) = 10.35$ W/m^2. Including heat flow from the pad, the total equals $10.35 + 3.15 = 13.5$ W/m^2. The heat flow to the duct air must equal the heat removed by the duct air [Eq. (6.46)]. The average duct air velocity is

$$V = \frac{Qld}{A_d \rho c_p T_R} = \frac{(13.5 \text{ J/m}^2 \text{ s})(67 \text{ m})(0.81 \text{ m})}{(0.147 \text{ m}^2)(1.33 \text{ kg/m}^3)(1000 \text{ J/kg °C})(6.6°C)} = 0.56 \text{ m/s}$$

The required airflow produced by the stack or chimney effect is related to the stack height. The stack height is determined by the available natural draft [Eq. (6.47)]. Compute the equivalent duct diameter $D_e = (4 \times \text{area})/\text{perimeter} = 0.372$ m. Assume an inlet length of 1.5 m and an outlet length of 4.5 m, giving an estimated length of straight duct equal to $1.5 + 67 + 4.5 = 73$ m. Estimate the equivalent duct length $l_e = 73 + 0.372[2(65 + 10)] = 128.8$ m. The kinematic viscosity of air $v = 1.708 \times 10^{-5} \rho_T^{-1}(T/273.15)^{1/2} = [(1.708 \times 10^{-5})/1.33](266/273.15)^{1/2} = 1.27 \times 10^{-5}$ m^2/s at $-7.0°C$, and the shortest duct dimension is $a' = 0.3$ m. Compute the Reynolds number [Eq. (6.51)]

$$N_R = \frac{V(a' + 0.25D_e)}{v} = \frac{(0.56 \text{ m/s})[(0.3 \text{ m}) + 0.25(0.372 \text{ m})]}{1.27 \times 10^{-5} \text{ m}^2/\text{s}} = 17,329$$

Compute the friction factor [Eq. (6.52)]

$$f' = 0.0055\left\{1 + \left[\frac{20,000(3 \times 10^{-4})}{0.372} + \frac{10^6}{17,329}\right]^{1/3}\right\} = 0.0285$$

Compute the friction head

$$h_f = f' \frac{l_e}{D_e} h_v = 0.0285 \frac{128.8}{0.372} h_v = 9.87 h_v$$

Compute the draft head $h_d = h_v + h_f = 10.87h_v = 10.87(0.056/4.036)^2 = 0.209$ mmH$_2$O. Compute the stack height required to produce this draft [Eq. (6.53)]

$$H = \frac{h_d(T_c + 273.1)}{\rho\varepsilon(T_c - T_0)} = \frac{0.209(-3.7 + 273.1)}{1.33(0.80)[-3.7 - (-10.3)]} = 8.0 \text{ m}$$

Shallow Foundation Design

Because the mechanical properties of frozen ground are temperature-dependent, the ground-temperature profile is one of the primary factors considered in the design of shallow foundations. Mechanical properties of the frozen soils are determined from laboratory tests on undisturbed samples or from in situ tests. Details on the ground thermal regime were given in Chap. 3, laboratory measurement of frozen soil behavior was covered in Chap. 5, and field investigations are covered in Chap. 9. Design decisions now involve the foundation performance with reference to its service life and its tolerance to deformations. Based on preliminary design philosophy and cost limitations, a specific foundation type may often be adopted before any alternatives are assessed.

Design procedures used for footings involve the following steps: (1) select the footing depth based on various factors discussed in the previous section, (2) estimate the warmest temperatures below the footing for use in selection of soil properties, (3) select a footing size using bearing-capacity theory to give the desired factor of safety, (4) prepare a settlement analysis using the appropriate time-deformation relationships for the anticipated foundation soil, and (5) modify the footing size to reduce bearing pressures when settlements are intolerable. Thaw penetration and frost depth have been discussed in Sec. 6.1 with typical examples.

Ground temperatures Temperature at the permafrost boundary is 0°C. Below this level the warmest permafrost temperatures can be estimated using the expression

$$T(z) = -A_0\left\{1 - \exp\left[-z\left(\frac{\pi}{\alpha P}\right)^{1/2}\right]\right\} \tag{6.54}$$

where $T(z)$ = temperature at depth z

A_0 = temperature difference between top of the permafrost and depth of no influence

α = thermal diffusivity

P = period of 365 days.

Since maximum ground temperatures do not occur simultaneously at all depths, this temperature profile is conservative. For layered soils temperature corrections can be made using equivalent soil layers, as illustrated in Example 6.6. Use of the warmest permafrost temperatures for selection of soil properties will be on the conservative side. Temperatures computed using Eq. (6.54) represent the upper limit of the trumpet curves described in Chap. 1.

Example 6.6 Determine the warmest permafrost temperatures below a footing placed at the 2.44-m depth in Example 6.2. The 2.44-m depth allows for some variation in the future thaw depth. Use the soil data from Example 6.2. The surface temperature of the permafrost is 0°C, and the temperature at a depth below the influence of annual temperature fluctuations is -2.78°C.

SOLUTION The thermal conductivity of the frozen sandy silt (from Example 6.2) is $k_f = 2.08$ J/s m °C, and the volumetric heat capacity

$$c_f = \frac{\gamma_d}{\gamma_w}\left(0.18 + 0.5\,\frac{w}{100}\right) c_w = \frac{1361}{1000}\left[0.18 + 0.5\left(\frac{33}{100}\right)\right] 4.18 = 1.9 \text{ MJ/m}^3 \text{ °C}$$

The thermal diffusivity

$$\alpha = \frac{k_f}{c_f} = \frac{2.08(60)(60)(24)}{1.9 \times 10^6} = 0.094 \text{ m}^2/\text{day}$$

The temperature difference $A_0 = 0 - (-2.78) = 2.78$°C, and the temperature at depth z [Eq. (6.54)] equals

$$T(z) = -2.78\left(1 - \exp\left\{-z\left[\frac{\pi}{0.094(365)}\right]^{1/2}\right\}\right)$$

$$= -2.78 + 2.78 \exp(-0.3026z)$$

Temperature computations are summarized in Table 6.6. This temperature profile is conservative since the maximum temperatures do not occur simultaneously at all depths. Corrections for the layered soil system are made by converting the sand to an equivalent silt layer, where

$$\alpha_{\text{silt}} = 0.094 \text{ m}^2/\text{day}$$

$$c_{f,\text{ sand}} = \frac{1682}{1000}\left[0.18 + 0.5\left(\frac{20}{100}\right)\right]4.18 = 1.9 \text{ MJ/m}^3 \text{ °C}$$

$$\alpha_{\text{sand}} = \frac{k_f}{c_f} = \frac{}{1.9 \times 10^6} = 0.16 \text{ m}^2/\text{day}$$

$$\text{Diffusivity ratio} = \left(\frac{\alpha_{\text{silt}}}{\alpha_{\text{sand}}}\right)^{1/2} = \left(\frac{0.094}{0.16}\right)^{1/2} = 0.77$$

Table 6.6

Depth, m	z,[†] m	exp$(-0.3026z)$	2.78 exp$(-0.3026z)$	$T(z)$, °C
1.83	0	1.000	2.78	0
2.13	0.3	0.913	2.54	-0.2
2.43	0.6	0.833	2.32	-0.5
2.83	1.0	0.738	2.05	-0.7
3.33	1.5	0.635	1.76	-1.0
3.83	2.0	0.546	1.52	-1.3
4.33	2.5	0.469	1.30	-1.5
4.83	3.0	0.403	1.12	-1.7
5.33	3.5	0.347	0.96	-1.8
5.83	4.0	0.298	0.83	-1.9
6.83	5.0	0.220	0.61	-2.2
7.83	6.0	0.163	0.45	-2.3
8.83	7.0	0.120	0.33	-2.4

† Datum taken at the permafrost surface.

Table 6.7

	Depth, m	z_{silt},[†] m	z_{sand}, m	$\exp(-0.3026z)$	$2.78\exp(-0.3026z)$	$T(z)$, °C
Silt	4.83	3.0	...	0.403	1.12	−1.7
	5.33	3.5	...	0.347	0.96	−1.8
	5.83	4.0	...	0.298	0.83	−1.9
	6.83	5.0	...	0.220	0.61	−2.2
	7.62	5.79	...	0.1734	0.48	−2.3
Sand	9.33	7.11	7.5	0.103	0.29	−2.5
	10.33	7.88	8.5	0.076	0.21	−2.57
	11.83	9.03	10.0	0.048	0.13	−2.64
	14.00	10.70	12.17	0.025	0.07	−2.71

† Datum taken at the permafrost surface

Thus 1 m of sand is equivalent to 0.77 m of silt with reference to temperatures under transient conditions. Computations for the temperature distribution in the sand using the correction for α_{sand} are summarized in Table 6.7. The computed temperatures are plotted in Fig. 6.15*b*.

Footing size The bearing capacity of frozen ground can be predicted using Terzaghi's equation or expressions based on cavity-expansion theory, both given in Sec. 6.4. The footing size is then computed on the requirement that there be adequate safety against failure for the dead load plus maximum live loads. The safe or allowable soil pressure q_a is defined as

$$q_a = \frac{q_{ult}}{F_s} \tag{6.55}$$

where F_s is a safety factor and q_{ult} is the ultimate bearing capacity of the frozen soil. For frozen soils, no generally accepted consistent criteria for assessment of adequate safety have been adopted for engineering design. Common practice has been to use factors of safety which assess the reliability of all parameters entering into the design, including loads, strength and deformation characteristics of the frozen soil mass, serviceability and economy of the structure, and the probability and consequences of failure. The approach used for unfrozen soils in the selection of safety factors F_s, outlined in Table 6.8, has received a certain amount of acceptance for foundation design in general.

The design philosophy given by Vyalov (1959) and Tsytovich (1975) should be considered in selection of a safety factor. When the long-term bearing capacity corresponding to the service life of the structure is divided by a factor of safety equal to 1.5, failure will not occur. In hard frozen soils settlement will be negligible; however, in plastic frozen soils substantial creep settlement may occur and should be considered in design. When the design-bearing capacity equals or exceeds the long-term strength based on the service life of the structure,

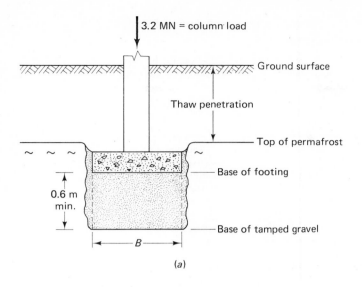

(a)

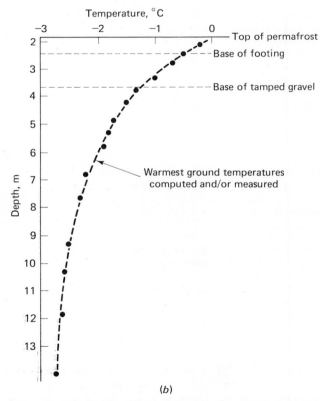

(b)

Figure 6.15 Footing design: (a) loads and general data; (b) warmest ground temperatures.

Table 6.8 Minimum safety factors for design of shallow foundations on unfrozen soil (after Vesić, 1970)

Preliminary note: The selection of safety factors for design cannot be made properly without assessing the degree of reliability of all other parameters that enter into design, such as design loads, strength and deformation characteristics of the soil mass, etc.; in view of this, each case is to be considered separately by the designer; the following table may be used as a guide for permanent structures in reasonably homogeneous soil conditions

Category	Typical structures	Characteristics of the category	Soil exploration Thorough, complete	Limited
A	Railway bridges, warehouses, blast furnaces, hydraulic, retaining walls, silos	Maximum design load likely to occur often; consequences of failure disastrous	3.0	4.0
B	Highway bridges, light industrial and public buildings	Maximum design load may occur occasionally; consequences of failure serious	2.5	3.5
C	Apartment and office buildings	Maximum design load unlikely to occur	2.0	3.0

Remarks:
1. For temporary structures these factors can be reduced to 75% of the above values. However, in no case should safety factors lower than 2.0 be used.
2. For exceptionally tall buildings, such as chimneys and towers, or generally whenever progressive bearing-capacity failure may be feared, these factors should be increased by 20 to 50%.
3. The possibility of flooding of foundation soil and/or removal of existing overburden by scour or excavation should be given adequate consideration.
4. It is advisable to check both the short-term (end-of-construction) and long-term stability unless one of the two conditions is clearly less favorable.
5. It is understood that all foundations will be also analyzed with respect to maximum tolerable total and differential settlement. If settlement governs the design, higher safety factors must be used.

use of a factor of safety in terms of stress is not appropriate, and instead the design should be based on a permissible rate of settlement or the combined factors of total allowable settlement and the planned service life of the structure.

This approach requires complete information on the creep behavior of the foundation soils, as given in Chap. 5.

Example 6.7 Determine the footing size for a column load of 3.2 MN using soil data from Examples 6.2 and 6.3 with temperature data from Example 6.6.

SOLUTION A footing depth of 2.44 m, selected in Example 6.6 on the basis of frost-penetration calculations, and 1.22 m of tamped gravel, placed below the footing to prevent any thaw of the permafrost during hydration and hardening of the concrete, give an effective footing depth of 3.66 m. Assume that the tamped gravel acts as an extension to the footing. Calculate the footing size based on the bearing capacity of the frozen silt at the 3.66-m depth. The average temperature, close to $-1.67°C$ (Fig. 6.15b), permits use of q_{ult} computed in Example 6.3. The net load on the permafrost equals the weight of footing + gravel + column − weight soil removed + column load $= 1000[(1.83)^2(0.61)(23.56) + (1.83)^2(1.22)(21.99) + 3.05(0.76)^2(23.56) - (1.83)^2(1.83)(18.06) - 1.83(0.76)^2(18.06)] + 3.2 \times 10^6 = 3.25$ MN. When we use a factor of safety equal 2.0 (Table 6.8) and q_{ult} from Example 6.3, the allowable soil pressure is

$$q_a = \frac{q_{ult}}{F_s} = \frac{1.89}{2.0} = 0.95 \text{ MN/m}^2$$

which requires a square footing dimension

$$B = \left(\frac{\text{load}}{q_a}\right)^{1/2} = \left(\frac{3.25}{0.95}\right)^{1/2} = 1.85 \text{ m}$$

Settlement analysis Settlements due to creep and compressibility of frozen soils have been discussed in Chap. 5. A knowledge of the stress distribution under the foundation will be essential for determining these settlements. The settlement on frozen soils will be mainly from creep deformation, but the settlement due to compressibility must also be determined for warm frozen soils to check whether it is of significance to the total settlement. Frozen soils with considerable ice may undergo significant settlement due to volume compressibility, which can be calculated by using Eqs. (5.106) and (5.107). Data from Table 5.4 can be used for the estimation of volume compressibility m_v, or special tests are conducted. Tsytovich (1975) indicated that this contribution to the total settlement of the layer is no more than one-third, the remainder resulting from creep deformation.

Since consolidation in frozen soils occurs simultaneously with creep, questions about the relative contribution from each of the phenomena remain. Considering the lack of experimental data on these separate phenomena, Ladanyi (1975) concluded that time-dependent settlements can best be predicted assuming that the frozen soil is a quasi-single-phase medium with mathematically well-defined

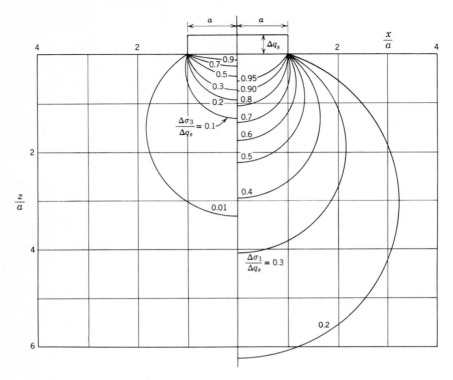

Figure 6.16 Principal stresses under a strip load. (*After Lambe and Whitman, 1969.*)

creep properties. In this approach the frozen-soil creep behavior is investigated within a given region of stresses and temperatures and the results are put into the form of a general constitutive equation, which then serves as the basis for calculating foundation settlements in frozen soils.

Settlement due to creep can be predicted on the basis of Eq. (5.98) for circular footings with axial symmetry, recognizing that $\varepsilon^{(i)} \ll \varepsilon^{(c)}$ for the long time intervals involved. For continuous footings approximating the plane-strain condition Eq. (5.98) becomes Eq. (5.103). For both equations the flow value N_ϕ corresponds to the average strain rate $\dot{\varepsilon}_1 = \dot{\varepsilon}_c$. An alternate creep relationship involves Vyalov's deformation equation described in Sec. 5.2. Consider now a circular footing on permafrost where stresses and temperatures are known with depth. Details given in Sec. 5.7 show how the incremental settlements for each layer are summed up to give the total settlement, Eq. (5.105). The temperature change with depth is accounted for by the use of any of the functions $f_1(\theta)$ to $f_4(\theta)$ given in Eqs. (5.69), (5.70), (5.74), and (5.76). Stresses induced within the frozen soil by the footing loads are generally determined on the assumption that the soil approximates a linear elastic medium. Analytical solutions for stresses in linearly elastic solids for a wide variety of geotechnical problems have been

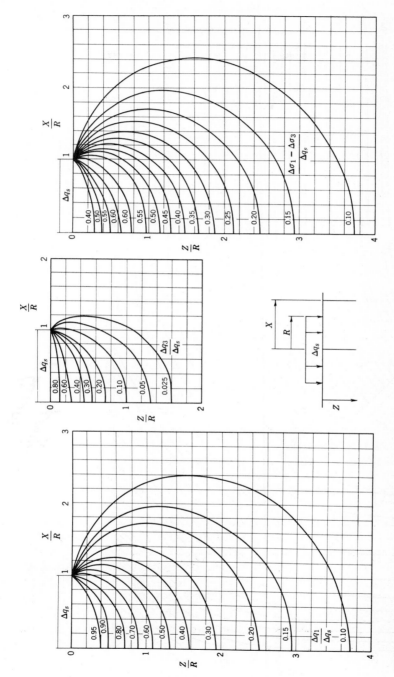

Figure 6.17 Stresses under a uniform load on a circular area. (*After Lambe and Whitman, 1969.*)

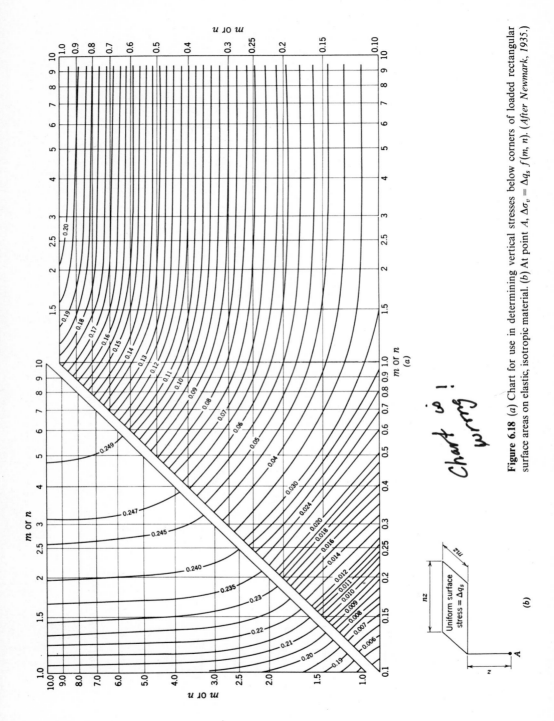

Figure 6.18 (*a*) Chart for use in determining vertical stresses below corners of loaded rectangular surface areas on elastic, isotropic material. (*b*) At point *A*, $\Delta\sigma_v = \Delta q_s\ f(m, n)$. (*After Newmark, 1935.*)

322

summarized by Poulos and Davis (1974) and are omitted here. Available solutions in graphical form are given in Fig. 6.16 for principal stresses below a strip load and Fig. 6.17 for stresses under a uniformly loaded circular area; Fig. 6.18 permits computation of vertical stresses below a rectangular loaded area.

Stresses computed using the theory of elasticity are, in general, some function of Poisson's ratio μ. The exception includes vertical stresses resulting from normal stresses applied to the ground surface and stresses caused by a strip load. Hence the solutions presented in Figs. 6.16 and 6.18 are independent of Poisson's ratio. The solution in Fig. 6.17 corresponds to $\mu = 0.45$. Experimental data on Poisson's ratio for frozen soils, summarized in Table 5.3, show a major dependence on temperature. Tsytovich (1975) reported that μ approaches 0.5 as the soil temperature increases to 0°C. For the same soils Young's modulus varied significantly depending on soil composition, ice content, freezing temperature, and confining pressures.

Example 6.8 Determine the creep settlement of the square footing described in Fig. 6.15a using soil data from Example 6.2, temperatures from Example 6.6, and net load and footing dimension from Example 6.7. Neglect creep in the 1.22 m of tamped gravel.

SOLUTION Use Eq. (5.49) with constants for the silt from Table 5.2, which include $\theta_c = 1°C$, $m = 0.49$, $\lambda = 0.074$, $k = 0.87$, $\omega = 4.58$ MPa $\cdot$ h^2/°C^k, where Pa = N/m^2 has been used for convenience, and $\theta = (0 - \text{soil temperature})°C$. Compute the load at the base of the tamped gravel = (net load)/B^2 = (3.25 MN)/(1.85 m)^2 = 0.95 MN/m^2. The vertical stresses below the footing, from Fig. 6.18, are given in Table 6.9. Soil temperatures from Example 6.6 are included with the tabulation of settlement calculations in Table 6.10.

Footing Size

Table 6.9

Depth, m	Layer thickness, m	$f(m, n)$	$\Delta\sigma_v = \Delta q_s\, f(m, n)$	Average
			Vertical stress, kN/m^2	
3.66		1.00	950	
	0.61			883.5
4.27		0.86	817	
	0.61			679
4.88		0.57	541	
	1.22			375
6.10		0.22	209	
	1.53			150.6
7.63		0.097	92	

3.66 equals the effective depth of footing = includes tamped gravel pad

Δq_s = load $\times$ Area function of Depth and Footing size

Table 6.10

Depth, m	Layer thickness, m ①	Soil type	Average θ, °C	Vertical stress, kN/m²	Strain† $\varepsilon_1(t) = \left[\dfrac{\sigma t^\lambda}{[\omega(\theta+\theta_c)]^k}\right]^{1/m}$	Strain ② for $t = 10$ years $= 87{,}600$ h (m/m)	Deformation, m (1×2)
3.66							
	0.61	Silt	1.35	883.5	$\left[\dfrac{883.5 \times 10^3 t^{0.074}}{(4.58 \times 10^6)(1.35+1)^{0.87}}\right]^{1/0.49}$	0.04256	0.02596
4.27							
	0.61	Silt	1.60	679	$\left[\dfrac{679 \times 10^3 t^{0.074}}{(4.58 \times 10^6)(1.60+1)^{0.87}}\right]^{1/0.49}$	0.02078	0.01267
4.88							
	1.22	Silt	1.83	375	$\left[\dfrac{375 \times 10^3 t^{0.074}}{(4.58 \times 10^6)(1.83+1)^{0.87}}\right]^{1/0.49}$	0.005323	0.006494
6.10							
	1.53	Silt	2.20	150.6	$\left[\dfrac{150.6 \times 10^3 t^{0.074}}{(4.58 \times 10^6)(2.20+1)^{0.87}}\right]^{1/0.49}$	0.0006652	0.001018
7.63							$\sum = 0.04618$‡

† Neglect ε_0.

‡ Total creep settlement for 10-year period = 46 mm. Increased footing size would reduce the stresses and therefore the settlement.

6.5 PILE FOUNDATIONS

Pile foundations are most commonly used in permafrost to support and transfer both vertical and lateral loads to a depth where volume changes, as well as loss of shear strength, are minimal due to change of temperature. They provide an effective means of minimizing disturbances to the thermal regime. In addition, seasonal frost heave and subsidence movements of the thawing zone are isolated from the structures by the use of adequate embedment length of piles. Pile foundations offer many advantages where construction difficulties are encountered in areas of deep seasonal frost penetration or frost-susceptible soils or permafrost with ice-rich soils. Piles with ventilated air spaces between the ground surface and the heated structures have proved to be an effective foundation type for particularly troublesome ice-rich fine-grained frozen soils.

The load-carrying capacity of piles in permafrost is attained by the adfreeze bond developed between the soil or backfill (slurry) and the pile surface. If firm strata are encountered at suitable depths, the load can also be supported by the end-bearing capacity of the piles. The adfreeze bond and corresponding load capacity of piles in permafrost is temperature-dependent. The warmer the permafrost temperature, the lower the adfreeze bond between the pile surface and the surrounding soils. The end-bearing capacity of piles is counted only where the supporting materials consist of either hard bedrock or dense thaw-stable sands and gravels. In fine-textured soils having a high ice content, the end-bearing value is negligible. In marginal permafrost areas adequate adfreeze-bond strength is maintained by the use of various thermal pile designs without degradation of the thermal regime.

Pile Types

Pile materials may consist of timber, steel, concrete, or composite material of concrete and steel. The selection of a particular pile type will depend on various factors such as initial costs, placement costs, loads to be carried, transportation, resistance to corrosion, difficulty in splicing, etc.

Timber piles Timber piles up to 10 m long are usually 150 to 250 mm in diameter at the top and 300 to 350 mm at the butt. They are normally less expensive than other types, easy to handle, and readily available in lengths from 10 to 20 m. Local timber—generally spruce, douglas fir, or western pine—is commonly used. Protection of the wood from deterioration was recommended by Linell and Johnston (1973). At Inuvik, N.W.T., wood piles installed for 10 years showed superficial soft rot occurring mainly within the annual thaw zone. For local timber, preservative can be brushed on for the length extending above the permafrost. When pressure creosoting is used, the process requires that the entire pile be treated. Since the creosote coating reduces the adfreeze bonds below that which can develop for bare wood, in design the tangential adfreeze working stresses must be reduced.

Steel piles Pipe piles and H piles are the most common types of steel piles, although other types like box sections and angles have been used. For steel piles installed for 8 to 11 years at the U.S. Army Cold Regions Research and Engineering Laboratory, Alaskan field station, Linell and Johnston (1973) reported essentially no steel corrosion in the permafrost and only insignificant amounts of corrosion in the active layer. Laboratory tests should be made on the soils and water in which steel piles will be exposed to determine whether corrosion will be a problem. Pipe piles filled with concrete or sand may be used to provide high load capacity. Pipe piles close-ended or capped at the bottom may be placed in preaugered holes but cannot be driven in permafrost as displacement piles. Open-ended steel-pipe and H piles can be driven in relatively warm permafrost to great lengths and can carry high loads. The average compressive stress on steel pipe and H piles under the design load should not exceed 62 MN/m^2.

Concrete piles Concrete piles are not generally used where frost-heave forces may produce tensile stresses sufficient to crack the piles and expose the steel to corrosion. Pretensioned precast piles (round, square, or double T's) can be used advantageously if handling, transporting, and cutoff do not create a problem. Cast-in-place concrete piles have been used only occasionally in permafrost areas. The problem of thawing the permafrost or freezing the concrete must be considered when cast-in-place piles are used.

Special pile types These self-refrigerated or thermal piles serve not only to carry structural loads but also to remove heat from the ground surrounding the embedded portion of the pile and move it up to the surface, where it is dissipated to the atmosphere. In the two-phase system, which operates on an evaporation and condensation cycle analogous to a steam-heating system with gravity condensate return, the pile is charged with propane, carbon dioxide, or other suitable evaporative material (Long, 1963, 1973). Evaporation of this material by heat from the ground and its condensation in the portion of the pile exposed to cold temperatures above the ground surface provide the heat-transfer mechanism. Fixed radiation surfaces are commonly used above ground. Condensate returns by gravity to the liquid reservoir at the lower end of the pile. These piles automatically cease operation when air temperatures become warmer than those around the lower part of the pile.

Pile Placement

In the past, local timber piles were installed in steam- or water-thawed holes to a depth around 7 m. Now, modern driving or drilling techniques are available to minimize permafrost thermal disturbances. Pile-placement methods are selected on the basis of ground temperatures, the type of soil anticipated, the required depth of embedment, the type of pile, and the cost of mobilizing the required equipment and personnel at the site. Crory (1963) listed the following installation methods: (1) steam thawing: prethawing a hole in permafrost followed by driving the pile in place; (2) bored hole: rotary drilled holes followed by driving in undersized holes or by placement in oversized holes with a soil-slurry backfill; (3) dry augering: similar to 2, with either undersized or oversized holes; the method can make holes 1 m in diameter to depths in excess of 20 m; (4) driving: conventional or modified temperate-zone pile-driving techniques without hole preparation; (5) various combinations or modifications of the above.

Crory (1963) stated that artificial refrigeration may be required when using steam thawing or slurry backfill in relatively warm permafrost. The positive artificial freezeback can usually be accomplished in less than 2 days by circulating suitable fluids or gases through tubing attached to the piles. Careful control of the slurry temperature and water content is required. Sanger (1969) provided the following preferred grading for a sand slurry and an annulus opening greater than 13 mm:

Sieve size†	Percent finer by weight
9.52 mm	100
No. 4	93–100
No. 10	70–100
No. 40	15–57
No. 200	0–17

† U.S. standard series

The sand slurry is formed by mixing sand with a minimum of water (about a 150-mm slump), and it is placed at a temperature between 1 and 4°C. The slurry is normally placed by direct backfilling by wheelbarrow on small jobs or by the use of concrete buckets with cranes on larger jobs. Tremie pipes or direct pumping may be used, but operations during cold weather may cause major trouble because of freezing. Generally the pile is centered, the hole is pumped, and slurry is backfilled in one continuous operation. The material must be vibrated with a small-diameter concrete spud vibrator in such a way that no bridging or voids are left along the pile. Also, timber piles often rise or float when the holes are backfilled with silt-water slurries; these piles must be weighted or restrained. An annular coating of ice may form on the hole wall or the pile surface for slurries with a high water content (45 percent for silt). This ice layer may control the available tangential shear strength which supports the pile. Installation of slurried piles in marginal permafrost areas during the spring months (March through June) takes advantage of the reserve cold in the ground and can often eliminate the need for artificial refrigeration. Linell and Johnston (1973) stated that refrigeration is not required where the mean annual ground temperature is −4°C or colder.

Holes for the piles can also be made by rotary or churn drilling using different bits. However, dry augering techniques are much preferred as they introduce a minimum amount of heat. For fine-grained soils with significant amounts of unfrozen water, steel pipe and H piles can be driven with vibratory or other heavy hammers. The smallest H section to be considered for driving in frozen soil should normally not be smaller than 10 BP 42, and the rated hammer energy should not be less than 34 kJ. Field driving tests of acceptability should be performed before construction starts.

Pile Load Capacity

Pile design for permafrost is normally based on the long-term adfreeze bond between the pile surface and the adjacent frozen slurry and/or soil. There are two alternative design approaches: (1) the applied shear stress along the pile surface must be below some acceptable strength for the site soil conditions, or (2) the continuous-settlement rate must be less than acceptable rates based on the service life and total allowable settlement of the pile. End bearing is considered only when the pile tip is driven to rock or dense sands or gravels. Some movement is generally required to mobilize end bearing in the other soils. Dynamic pile-driving formulas are not suitable for piling in permafrost because time- and temperature-dependent soil and ice properties rather than the initial driving resistance of the pile govern the long-term pile capacity.

The capacity of single piles in permafrost, subjected to static vertical loads, depends upon (1) the warmest or average permafrost temperature profile at the site; (2) adfreeze strength of the pile in permafrost as a function of temperature; (3) the length of embedment to carry structural loads, resist downdrag and frost-heaving forces; (4) the type, size, and construction procedure for the piling; and (5) complete freezeback before loads are applied. Exploratory and verification pile tests along with a check on time settlements are used to establish the pile capacity. Nomenclature used to describe the forces and dimensions needed for design of single piles in permafrost are shown in Fig. 6.19. Both the summer and winter loading conditions are considered. The required length of embedment is governed by summer design conditions. The available adfreeze bond in the permafrost must carry both the structural load and any load caused by the consolidating thawed surface soils. The soils in the active layer freeze and bond to the pile during the colder winter months. Any heaving forces which develop for silt and clay soils in the active layer must be resisted by the adfreeze bond in the permafrost and skin friction of the consolidating soils below the active layer. The forces to be resisted and the resisting forces include those shown in Table 6.11. End bearing is normally excluded from design considerations for tip diameters less than 150 mm (U.S. Army/Air Force, 1967) because of the greater movements required to mobilize p_b in comparison with much smaller movements for adfreeze failure. The right sides of Eqs. (6.56) and (6.57) are conservative since the end bearing p_b is neglected.

Values for the adfreeze bond strength must be selected before Eqs. (6.57) and (6.59) can be used in practice. Average values for the ultimate adfreeze bond strength reported by Sanger (1969) are shown in Fig. 6.20 for saturated fine

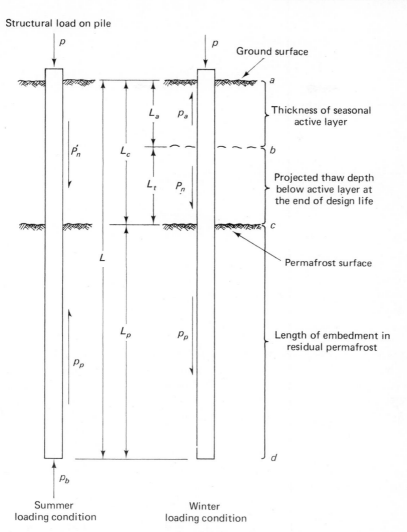

Structural load on pile

Figure 6.19 Nomenclature for pile design in permafrost. All lengths shown consist of several soil strata designated by subscript i so that $L_p = \sum L_{p_i}$. Forces are p = applied structural load, p_a = heave force exerted by adfreeze of seasonally frozen strata, p_n = downdrag exerted by consolidating thawed strata, p_p = developed adfreeze bond in permafrost, p_b = end bearing.

sands, saturated silts with ice lenses, and ice. Sanger (1969) cautioned that these values should be checked by field tests for final design.

As with footings, allowable loadings of piles in frozen ground are mainly determined by creep deformation, which occurs under constant load at stress levels well below the rupture levels measured in relatively rapid tests to failure. Creep occurs in the adfreeze bond zone at the contact surface between the pile

Table 6.11

Forces to be resisted		Resisting forces	Eq.
		Summer loading	
$p + p_n$	<	p_p	(6.56)
$p + \pi d \sum \tau_{n_i} L_{c_i}$	<	$\pi d \sum \tau_{p_i} L_{p_i}$	(6.57)
		Winter loading	Eq.
p_a	<	$p + p_n + p_p$	(6.58)
$\pi d \sum \tau_{a_i} L_{a_i}$	<	$p + \pi d \sum \tau_{n_i} L_{t_i} + \pi d \sum \tau_{p_i} L_{p_i}$	(6.59)

and the surrounding frozen soils. For the ice-rich soils, the pile capacity may best be estimated on the basis of an allowable total displacement during the service life of the structure.

Example 6.9 A 178-kN-capacity pile is required in a deep, ice-rich silt deposit which is frozen well below the depth explored by drilling. Average moisture content is 35 percent, and the mean annual thawing index is 1222 degree-days. An air space is to be provided below the floor of the structure, and spruce will be used for the piling. Determine the required pile diameter and embedment.

SOLUTION Using the pile capacity of 178 kN and the strength of spruce equal to 5.17 MN/m², we get the required pile diameter

$$D = \left(\frac{4}{\pi} \frac{\text{load}}{\text{strength}} \right)^{1/2} = \left(\frac{4}{\pi} \frac{178}{5170} \right)^{1/2} = 0.209 \text{ m} = 209 \text{ mm}$$

Specify a minimum 210-mm-diameter pile to carry the structural load. The piles will be slurried into 300-mm-diameter predrilled holes and allowed to freeze back. Measured ground temperatures show the permafrost table at 1.52 m (Fig. 6.21). Specific surface area per meter of pile length equals $210\pi/1000 = 0.66$ m²/m. Computations showing the pile capacity are given in Table 6.12. When a factor of safety of 2 (Table 6.8) is used on the sustained load, the design load becomes 356 kN. Using Fig. 6.21, we see that the data show a required embedment length of 7.0 m with the pile to be placed in a 9-m hole. For a sustained load and the 7.0-m embedment, heaving is only a remote possibility.

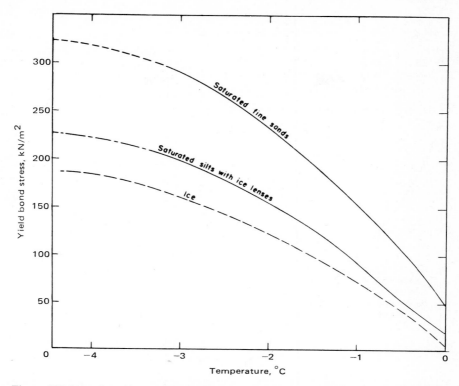

Figure 6.20 Tentative ultimate adfreeze bond strength in creep for saturated soils. (*Adapted from Sanger, 1969.*)

Pile Freezeback

Freezeback of backfill slurry may be permitted to occur naturally when there is a sufficient reserve of cold in the ground. This reserve of cold is greatest in the spring, when permafrost temperatures are at their lowest values. When permafrost temperatures are high and/or the time available for freezeback is not available,

Table 6.12

Embedment, m	Adfreeze strength, kN/m²	×	ΔA, m²/m	×	ΔL, m	=	ΔP	Cumulative capacity, kN
0–1.2	28.7		0.66		1.2		22.73	22.73
1.2–2.0	57.5		0.66		0.8		30.36	53.09
2.0–3.5	76.6		0.66		1.5		75.83	128.92
3.5–6.0	95.8		0.66		2.5		158.07	286.99
6.0–9.2	114.9		0.66		3.2		242.67	529.66

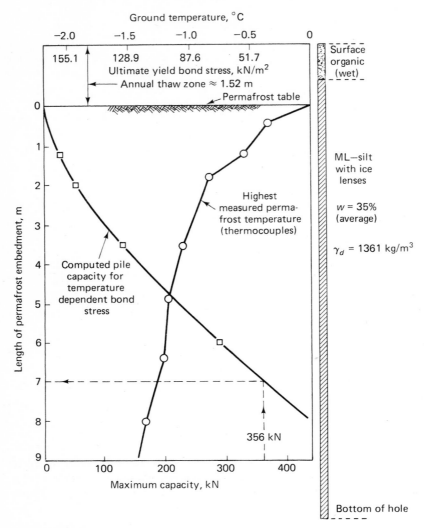

Figure 6.21 Pile-capacity analysis.

freezeback by refrigeration is used. Specifications usually require that slurry temperatures below a critical depth not rise above the ambient temperature 24 h after refrigeration has been turned off. Freezing coils are spirals of copper tubing for nondriven piles and are protected straight pipes running parallel to the pile axis for driven piles.

Both latent and sensible heat are conducted into the permafrost surrounding a drilled or augered hole when the annulus around the pile is backfilled with a soil-water slurry. When the water content of the slurry is known, the sensible

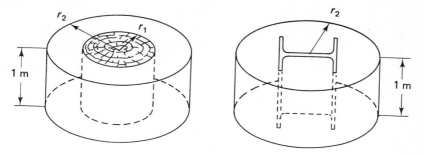

Figure 6.22 Volumetric latent heat of slurry backfill [see Eq. (6.60)]. (*After Crory, 1963.*)

heat of the soil, water, and pile can be computed. Present practice is to place the slurry at temperatures slightly above freezing so that the sensible heat is less than 7.5 MJ/m³. This value is small enough to be approximated and added to the latent heat. The latent heat requires information on the volume of slurry, the water content w, and the dry density of the slurry γ_d. For each meter of pile embedment the latent heat is given as (Fig. 6.22)

$$Q = \pi L(r_2^2 - r_1^2)w\gamma_d = L(\pi r_2^2 - A)w\gamma_d \tag{6.60}$$

where L is the latent heat of the slurry in joules per cubic meter, A is the pile cross-sectional area in square meters, and other symbols are as before. Good construction control of the slurry dry density and the annulus dimensions helps to reduce the heat input.

To select the optimum installation period for pile freezeback, plots of temperature vs. depth are required for the site. Present computational methods assume the slurried pile to be a finite cylindrical heat source inside a semi-infinite medium. Placement of the slurry represents a suddenly applied constant warmer-temperature source from which heat dissipates radially into the permafrost. The general solution to the natural freezeback problem (Fig. 6.23), adapted from Carslaw and Jaeger (1959) and Lee (1962), permits computation of the time required for freezeback at different temperatures. A specific solution to the freezeback problem is presented in Example 6.10.

The solutions presented for the pile-freezeback problem assume that heat is conducted only radially away from the pile and slurry. This solution gives acceptable values for minimum pile spacing. The actual heat flow is always toward the colder areas, as shown in Fig. 6.24. During late winter, freezeback occurs fastest near the colder surface as heat dissipates outward and upward from the pile. During late summer, freezeback depends on the cold reserve of the permafrost below the thawed active layer. Crory (1963) recommended that thermocouple assemblies be installed to verify the freezeback times before loading the piles.

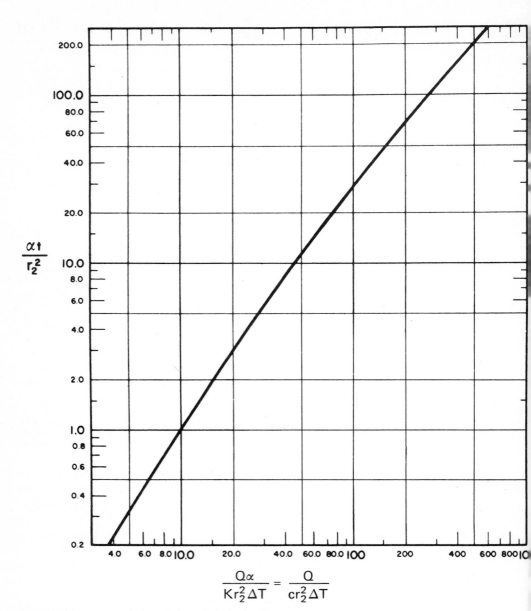

$$\frac{\alpha t}{r_2^2}$$

$$\frac{Q\alpha}{Kr_2^2\,\Delta T} = \frac{Q}{cr_2^2\,\Delta T}$$

Figure 6.23 General solution of slurry freezeback, where

t = freezeback time, s
K = thermal conductivity of permafrost, J/m s °C
c = volumetric heat capacity of permafrost, J/m³ °C
α = diffusivity of permafrost, m²/s, = K/C
Q = volumetric latent heat of slurry per meter of pile length, J/m
ΔT = initial temperature of permafrost, °C below freezing
r_2 = radius of pile hole, m

334   (*After U.S. Army/Air Force, 1966.*)

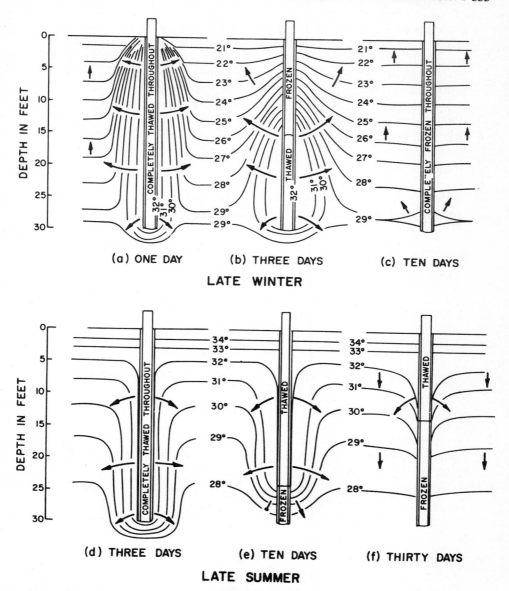

Figure 6.24 Natural freezeback of piles in permafrost during winter and summer. Original units (feet and degrees Fahrenheit) retained; (a) 1 day, (b) 3 days, (c) 10 days, (d) 3 days, (e) 10 days (f) 30 days. (*After Crory, 1963.*)

Example 6.10 (*a*) Determine the minimum spacing of piles in Example 6.9 that will permit natural freezeback without allowing permafrost temperatures to exceed $-0.5°C$. Additional data include an average permafrost temperature of $-0.8°C$, dry density of 1361 kg/m³, thermal conductivity of 2.08 W/m °C, and a water content of 35 percent. The backfill slurry has a maximum temperature of 4.5°C, water content of about 40 percent, and dry density of 1200 kg/m³. The pile diameter equals 210 mm with a hole diameter of 300 mm. (*b*) Check the freezeback time for an early spring condition with an average permafrost temperature of $-1.67°C$, using the general solution shown in Fig. 6.23.

SOLUTION (*a*) Computation of the minimum pile spacing requires use of the volumetric heat capacity and latent heat of the slurry:

$$c_{slurry} = \gamma_d\left(0.71 + 4.19\,\frac{w}{100}\right) = 1200[0.71 + 4.19(\tfrac{40}{100})] = 2.86 \text{ MJ/m}^3 \text{ °C}$$

$$L_{slurry} = 333.7\gamma_d\,\frac{w}{100} = 333.7(1200)(\tfrac{40}{100}) = 160.2 \text{ MJ/m}^3$$

Compute the volumetric heat capacity of the frozen silt:

$$c_{silt} = \gamma_d\left(0.71 + 2.1\,\frac{w}{100}\right) = 1361[0.71 + 2.1(\tfrac{35}{100})] = 1.97 \text{ MJ/m}^3 \text{ °C}$$

Compute the volume occupied by the slurry. The annulus area equals

$$\pi\,\frac{(0.3)^2 - (0.21)^2}{4} = 0.036 \text{ m}^2$$

or 0.036 m³ of slurry per meter of pile embedment. It is assumed that the cylindrical volume of permafrost surrounding each pile, diameter S, gains the heat lost by the slurry; hence

$$Q = 0.036\{160.2 \times 10^6 + [4.5 - (-0.5)](2.86 \times 10^6)\}$$

$$= \frac{\pi S^2[-0.5 - (-0.8)](1.97 \times 10^6)}{4}$$

and $S = [6.282(4)/\pi(0.591)]^{1/2} = 3.68$ m. This indicates that a pile spacing of 4 m is marginal. Two alternatives include (1) placement of piles when the permafrost is at its coldest (spring) temperature or (2) use of refrigeration to assist in freezeback of the piles. A colder permafrost temperature of $-1.67°C$ gives a spacing of 1.9 m, which is more reasonable for structural needs.

(*b*) Estimate the freezeback time for the $-1.67°C$ temperature using the latent heat of slurry equal to 160.2 MJ/m³ resolved to a unit length of pile embedment (including heat capacity)

$$Q = 0.036[160.2 \times 10^6 + 5(2.86 \times 10^6)] = 6.282 \text{ MJ/m}$$

Next compute

$$\frac{Q}{cr_2^2 \Delta T} = \frac{6.282 \times 10^6}{(1.97 \times 10^6)\left(\dfrac{0.3}{2}\right)^2 (1.67)} = 84.9$$

and from Fig. 6.23 read $\alpha t/r_2^2 \approx 22$. Solve for the freezeback time

$$t \approx \frac{22\left(\dfrac{0.3}{2}\right)^2}{2.08/(1.97 \times 10^6)} = 469 \text{ ks} = 5.4 \text{ days}$$

Example 6.11 The average volume of slurry backfill for a group of piles is 0.88 m³ each. The slurry is placed at an average temperature of 8°C and must be frozen to −5°C. The silt-water slurry with a dry density of 1281 kg/m³ and 40 percent water content is used as backfill material, and an available refrigeration unit is capable of removing 65.94 kJ/s. Calculate the length of time required to freezeback a group of 20 piles.

SOLUTION The volumetric latent heat of the backfill slurry is

$$L = 333.7\gamma_d \frac{w}{100} = 333.7(1281)(\tfrac{40}{100}) = 171 \text{ MJ/m}^3$$

The volumetric heat capacity of the frozen backfill is

$$c_f = \gamma_d\left(c_s + c_i \frac{w}{100}\right) = 1281[0.71 + (2.1)(\tfrac{40}{100})] = 1.98 \text{ MJ/m}^3 \text{ °C}$$

The volumetric heat capacity of the thawed backfill is

$$c_u = 1281[0.71 + (4.19)(\tfrac{40}{100})] = 3.06 \text{ MJ/m}^3 \text{ °C}$$

Heat required to depress the slurry temperature to the freezing point equals $3.06(0.88)(8.0) = 21.54$ MJ per pile. Heat required to freeze the slurry equals $0.88(171) = 150.48$ MJ per pile. Heat required to depress the slurry temperature from the freezing point to −5°C equals $1.98(0.88)(5.0) = 8.71$ MJ per pile. The total heat to be removed from the slurry equals $20(21.54 + 150.48 + 8.71) = 3614.64$ MJ. Time required for artificial freezeback, excluding allowances for system losses, equals $3,614,640/65.94 = 54,817$ s $= 15.2$ h.

Pile-Load Tests and Settlement Prediction

Pile-load tests may be required to obtain data needed for design, to verify design assumptions, and/or to evaluate various alternative designs. Although pile-load tests in permafrost are expensive, a redesign or repair of the foundation may be more expensive. Hence pile-load tests are carried out at the site of important projects at known temperatures to provide information on load-displacement rates and the ultimate adfreeze strengths needed for design. In addition to the direct pile-load capacity, considerable useful information on freezeback times, ease of pile placement, and supplementary foundation-soil data can be obtained.

Test-pile lengths are estimated from laboratory creep data for the soil conditions at the site. Generally, field tests are conducted when the permafrost has its lowest bond strength and least resistance to creep. This occurs in late fall or early winter, when the permafrost is at its highest temperature. Temperature-profile measurements (Chap. 9) must be made at the test site with thermocouples at depth intervals of not more than 1.5 m. Dial-gauge and other instrumentation must be stable and protected from external disturbances, including sunlight, precipitation, and frost-heave forces. Test piles are preferably of the same type and are placed under the same conditions as anticipated for the job. Where appropriate, several alternatives may be investigated to permit refinement in design.

The load is usually applied in small increments by means of a hydraulic jack reacting against a dead weight or against a reaction beam fastened to a pair of anchor piles. This load must be maintained for several days, a procedure different from standard ASTM procedures for pile testing in thawed ground.

Small load increments, each held for several days, will yield load-settlement data useful for predicting the ultimate and working stress levels. Only long-term tests, for a year or more, can define the true creep behavior. From various pile-load-test results Crory (1963, 1968, 1973) has recommended that the pile be unloaded or rebounded only after reaching the sustained load-carrying capacity with no further settlement. This load is determined by closing off the jack and allowing the pile to seek a point at which downward movement has stopped. For normal piles the maximum displacement under test should be limited to a maximum of 50 mm. Generally, the adfreeze bond of normal-length piles is broken after only 3 mm displacement.

Settlement-time curves, plotted in Fig. 6.25a, provide minimum rates of settlement for each load increment. For this typical test, 89-kN load increments were applied at 24-h intervals, and dial-gauge readings were taken as needed to obtain continuous curves. In Fig. 6.25b the minimum rates of settlement are plotted against load on both semilogarithmic and arithmetic scales. Using the semilogarithmic plot a rate of settlement close to 3.8 mm/year corresponds to a 178-kN load for the ground temperatures at the time of test. Data needed for correlating the rate of settlement with temperature are usually not available. If the pile tests are conducted during the period of warmest permafrost conditions (late fall or early winter), colder temperatures during other periods will give lower settlement rates. A rigid pile cap can be used to minimize differential settlements between piles.

Laterally Loaded Piles

Pile foundations designed for lateral loading due to earth pressures or wind and earthquake effects are generally tested with the anticipated lateral loads to verify the design assumptions. In unfrozen soils, Beresantsev et al. (1961) recommended that vertical piles be used when the angle between the resulting force and the vertical is less than 5°. Batter piles are recommended for angles

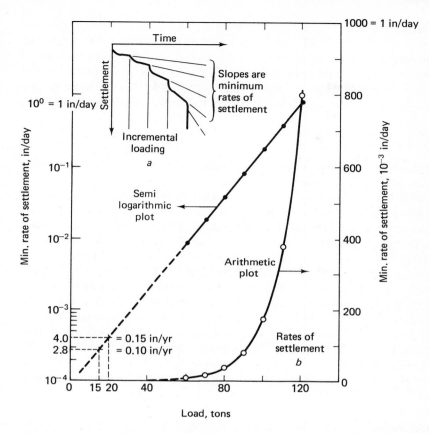

Figure 6.25 Load and minimum rate of settlement for a test pile. Original units (days, inches, and tons) retained. (a) incremental loading. (b) rates of settlement. (Adapted from Crory, 1968).

between 5 and 15° and anchor plates for angles greater than 15°. Two design approaches may be used to determine the lateral load capacity of piles in permafrost. The ultimate lateral soil resistance per linear meter of pile can be determined from Broms' (1965) model formulated as $9Ds_u$, where D is the pile diameter and s_u is the undrained shear strength of the soil (for frozen soils the creep strength corresponding to the service life is used). The other method considers the design of beams on an elastic foundation (Matlock and Reese, 1962). To use this method, the load-deflection relationship of the foundation soil is required. As this relationship for permafrost is temperature- and time-dependent, lateral-load pile tests should be used to confirm the design assumptions. The time- and temperature-dependent behavior of permafrost has been considered by Rowley et al. (1975) in their prediction of pile performance under lateral loads. Their analysis showed that in ice-rich permafrost the basic data needed for the design of laterally loaded piles can be deduced from the results of pressuremeter creep tests (Chap. 9). The pressuremeter data can be given either in the form of time- and temperature-dependent pressure-deflection curves to be used as a basis for computer design or, alternatively, as time- and temperature-dependent values of the lateral subgrade modulus K to be used in the conventional method of design (Kezdi, 1975). Rowley et al. (1975) noted that their work was limited to an ice-rich permafrost and to one method of pile installation, frozen backfill, and that additional research is needed in this area.

Anchors in Frozen Ground

Anchors are used in frozen ground for various types of structures, including guyed towers and buried pipelines. Anchor design requires an evaluation of the resistance of frozen soil to uplift forces and creep displacements associated with long-term loads. Various anchor types include piling, anchor plates, grouted rod anchors, and plate or power-installed screw anchors. Pile anchors are seldom used because of excessive costs and lack of any clear advantage over the other types. Anchor plates consisting of a block of concrete, timber, or steel buried in the soil with an attached rod or cable are normally effective and dependable. They are used where lateral loading permits the anchor to act against a large volume of undisturbed soil. They do require excavation of a major nature, which in permafrost areas introduces problems of excavation, backfill control, and thawing in the disturbed soil. When applied vertical loads are resisted only by poorly compacted backfill, the vertical load-displacement characteristics are often very poor. Johnston and Ladanyi (1972, 1974) have presented an analysis of field behavior of grouted rod anchors and power-installed screw anchors which can be used for design. This material is summarized in the next two sections.

Grouted rod anchors Grouted rod anchors, described by Johnston and Ladanyi (1972), are similar to short small-diameter cast-in-place concrete piles. An expansive portland cement grout provides the best compromise between performance and cost for grouted rod anchors installed in all types of frozen and unfrozen soils and rock. Under load the grouted rod anchors show instantaneous and creep displacements at low loads and slip at loads close to failure in either unfrozen or frozen soils. The creep displacements in frozen soils are a large part of the total displacement and must be accounted for in design. For frozen soils, temperature change alters the shear strength at the anchor-soil interface; hence it becomes a design parameter.

For the grouted rod anchors (Fig. 6.26) the ultimate pulling capacity P_{ult} can be expressed by

$$P_{ult} = 2\pi a L \tau_{a,\,ult} + W_p \qquad (6.61)$$

where $\tau_{a,\,ult}$ = shear strength at anchor-soil interface
a = pile radius
L = length of anchor embedded in frozen soil
W_p = effective weight of anchor

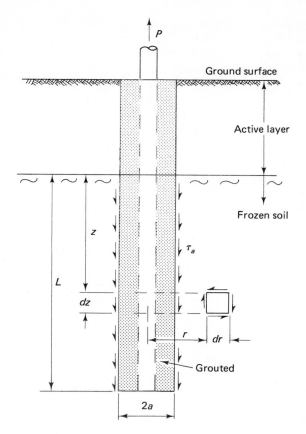

Figure 6.26 Grouted rod anchor. (*After Johnston and Ladanyi, 1972.*)

Field tests reported by Johnston and Ladanyi (1972) showed a typical creep behavior for anchors embedded in frozen soil. For design purposes, prediction of displacements in the secondary-creep stage are required. Creep failure, by definition, occurs at the onset of tertiary creep.

Displacements during secondary creep are given by

$$s(t) = s_i + \dot{s}t \qquad (6.62)$$

where $s(t)$ = time-dependent displacement of anchor
  s_i = pseudoinstantaneous displacement corresponding to $\varepsilon^{(i)}$ in Fig. 5.2.
$\dot{s} = ds/dt$ = secondary-displacement rate
  t = time

The applied shear stress at the anchor-soil interface τ_a determines the magnitude of s_i and $\dot{s}$ at a given temperature. Prediction of the pile displacement under a constant load requires the experimental determination of $s_i = F(\tau_a)$ and $\dot{s} = G(\tau_a)$. These functions are analogous to Eqs. (5.6) and (5.7). To determine the functions

F and G, Johnston and Ladanyi (1972) made the following assumptions: (1) the grouted rod anchor is cylindrical, (2) the shear stress is distributed uniformly over the anchor length buried in the frozen soil, (3) the frozen soil in contact with the anchor is uniform and at a constant temperature, and (4) gravity forces can be ignored in the computations. Assumption 2 becomes reasonable when one considers that the anchor is much less deformable than the soil and that initial nonuniform displacements at the anchor-soil interface tend to equalize due to stress relaxation for the long time intervals involved with creep. When soil properties or temperatures vary along the anchor, the analysis can be extended to account for these changes.

The analysis used by Johnston and Ladanyi (1972) established that the functions F and G can be expressed in the form

$$\dot{s} = G(\tau_a) = \dot{\gamma}_c a(n-1)^{-1} \left(\frac{\tau_a}{\tau_c}\right)^n \tag{6.63}$$

and

$$s_i = F(\tau_a) = \gamma_k a(k-1)^{-1} \left(\frac{\tau_a}{\tau_k}\right)^k \tag{6.64}$$

where τ_c, n = creep parameters
$\dot{\gamma}_c$ = arbitrary shear strain rate
τ_k, k = experimental parameters
γ_k = arbitrary shear strain

In agreement with Eq. (5.104) and assumption 1, the applied shear stress τ_a at the anchor-soil interface becomes

$$\tau_a = \frac{P - W_p}{2\pi a L} \tag{6.65}$$

Substitution of Eqs. (6.63) and (6.64) into Eq. (6.62) gives

$$s(t) = s_k \left(\frac{\tau_a}{\tau_k}\right)^k + \sum_0^t \dot{s}_c \left(\frac{\tau_a}{\tau_c}\right)^n \Delta t \tag{6.66}$$

where s_k and $\dot{s}_c$ denote, respectively,

$$s_k = \frac{\gamma_k u}{k-1} \tag{6.67}$$

$$\dot{s}_c = \frac{\dot{\gamma}_c a}{n-1} \tag{6.68}$$

The experimental parameters k, τ_k, n, and τ_c are obtained by plotting s_i and $\dot{s}$ values, respectively, against the applied shear stress in a log-log plot analogous to the procedure used in Example 5.1.

A slip between the anchor and the frozen soil occurs after some finite time. By definition, this slip or failure takes place at the onset of tertiary creep which for the field tests occurred at a total displacement of from 25 to 50 mm

(Johnston and Ladanyi, 1972). These displacements are similar to the maximum vertical movements which can be tolerated in rigid, self-supporting transmission-line towers. Using s_f as the total allowable anchor displacement, Johnston and Ladanyi (1972) defined time to failure t_f in terms of s_i and $\dot{s}$ as

$$t_f = \frac{s_f - s_i}{\dot{s}} \tag{6.69}$$

Substituting s_i and $\dot{s}$ from Eq. (6.63) and (6.64) into Eq. (6.69) gives

$$t_f = \frac{s_f - s_k(\tau_a/\tau_k)^k}{\dot{s}_c(\tau_a/\tau_c)^n} \tag{6.70}$$

where s_k and $\dot{s}_c$ are given by Eqs. (6.67) and (6.68). For times greater than 2 or 3 days, s_i becomes less than 10 percent of the total displacement, and Eq. (6.70) can be written as

$$t_f \approx \frac{s_f}{\dot{s}_c}\left(\frac{\tau_c}{\tau_a}\right)^n \tag{6.71}$$

For a design service life t and an allowable displacement s_{all} Eq. (6.71) can be used with Eq. (6.65) to compute an allowable load P_{all}:

$$P_{\text{all}} = 2\pi a L \tau_c \left(\frac{s_{\text{all}}}{\dot{s}_c t}\right)^{1/n} + W_p \tag{6.72}$$

Example 6.12 Transmission-tower specifications require that anchor movement not exceed 25 mm vertically over the 25-year service life. Field pullout tests on 150-mm-diameter grouted anchors in permafrost gave the data in Table 6.13. For similar soil and temperature conditions determine the allowable bond stress for use in anchorage design for the proposed transmission line.

SOLUTION Assume that instantaneous displacements equal zero since tower anchor lines are retensioned several times before being put into service. Select an arbitrary displacement rate $\dot{s}_c = 0.01$ mm/h. From a plot of log $\dot{s}_a$ vs. log τ_a with $\dot{s}_c = 0.01$ mm/h read the intercept $\tau_c = 97$ kN/m^2. The slope of the log

Table 6.13

Anchor number	Applied stress τ_a, kN/m^2	Steady-state creep-displacement rate $\dot{s}_a$, mm/h
1	117.8	0.0437
2	132.1	0.1102
3	161.8	0.5639
4	186.7	1.7831

$\dot{s}_a$–vs–log τ_a plot equals $1/n = (\log\ 186.7 - \log\ 117.8)/(\log\ 1.7831 - \log\ 0.0437)$; hence $n = 8.05$. Compute the allowable bond stress τ_a with Eq. (6.71):

$$t_f \approx \frac{s_f}{\dot{s}_c}\left(\frac{\tau_c}{\tau_a}\right)^n = \frac{25}{10^{-2}}\left(\frac{97}{\tau_a}\right)^{8.05} = 2.19 \times 10^5\ \text{h} = 25\ \text{years}$$

Solve for $\tau_a = 55.6\ \text{kN/m}^2$ for the 25-year service life.

Power-installed screw anchors Either single- or multiple-helix configurations may be used for power-installed screw anchors. For multiple helix, each helix is normally of increasing diameter up to the shaft of the anchor. For warm-temperature frozen fine-grained soils these anchors are installed by screwing them down into the ground to a specified depth. They are not suitable for frozen coarse-grained soils because of problems related to installation. Proof testing of power-installed screw anchors is not indicative of their capacity because displacements and ultimate pullout loads are related to the time- and temperature-dependent behavior of the frozen soil.

The report by Johnston and Ladanyi (1974) on field tests of deep power-installed screw anchors installed in permafrost provides an understanding of their behavior for vertical pullout loads and suggests a method for predicting their ultimate capacity. The screw anchors were installed to a depth where their failure approximated that for a deep footing of similar size. When this condition is satisfied, the uplift capacity Q_{ult} (Johnston and Ladanyi, 1974) will be approximated by

$$Q_{\text{ult}} = \frac{\pi B^2}{4}\ q_{\text{ult}} + W \tag{6.73}$$

where B = plate diameter
   q_{ult} = ultimate bearing capacity
   W = weight of lifted soil mass plus weight of anchor

The ultimate bearing capacity is now given by Eq. (6.36), where the soil-weight term is neglected because of depth. Time to failure or anchor displacements for a given period of loading can be computed using the cavity-expansion theory (Ladanyi and Johnston, 1974; Ladanyi, 1975) outlined in Sec. 6.3.

6.6 FROST-HEAVE FORCES ON FOUNDATIONS

Various investigators (Crory and Reed, 1965; Hoekstra, 1969; Penner, 1974a, 1974b) have described the phenomenon of frost-heave forces on foundations and have reported measurements of frost-heave forces for different soil conditions. Frost-action effects are illustrated in Fig. 6.27 relative to the upward thrust on overlying structural elements, lateral thrust behind a retaining wall, and the

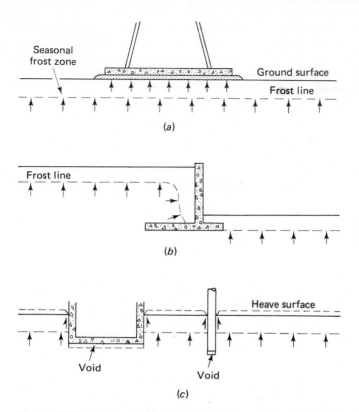

(a)

(b)

(c)

Figure 6.27 Frost-action effects: (a) heaving of soil in seasonal frost zone, causing direct upward thrust on overlying structural elements; (b) freezing of frost-susceptible soil behind walls, causing thrust perpendicular to freezing front; (c) force at base of freezing interface tends to lift entire frozen slab, applying jacking forces to lateral surfaces of embedded structures and creating voids underneath. Structures may not return to their original positions on thawing. (*After U.S. Army/Air Force Draft.*)

jacking forces to lateral surfaces of embedded structures. Frost heave is caused mainly by the volumetric expansion of in situ pore water upon freezing, as well as by ice lenses from the freezing of water that migrates to the freezing front. The former component is usually small compared with the latter, which is also termed ice-segregation heave. Three conditions required for frost heave include (1) a freezing temperature that changes water to ice, (2) availability of water, which moves to the freezing front due to capillary forces, and (3) frost-susceptible soils. When the ice growth is unrestricted by confining pressures, the soil surface and footing rise unless special precautions are taken to prevent movement. This phenomenon is called frost heave. Field data reported by Aitken (1963) showed that frost heave of a fine-grained soil is reduced by a surcharge load. As the pressure was increased, a condition existed whereby the water would no longer migrate toward the freezing front but was expelled from it. Frost-heave rates can be measured in the laboratory under simulated field conditions, but such values are often overconservative; i.e., the estimated values may be much greater than observed for field conditions. This difference is due to difficulties in simulating the various factors including the characteristics of the freeze front, variation of overburden pressure, the rate of heat removal, soil consolidation, and flow of water. However, analytical models combined with the finite-element method (Hwang et al., 1972) show promise for prediction of frost-heave rate under different boundary conditions. Heave forces are perhaps best considered in terms of vertical forces on a horizontal surface, tangential forces on a vertical surface, and anchorage against heave.

Vertical Forces on a Horizontal Surface

To avoid frost-heave forces, footings are generally placed below the active layer. However, if frost penetrates below the footing in frost-susceptible soils, heave forces resulting from ice segregation may lift the footing, as shown in Fig. 6.27c. The upward thrust may exceed the footing pressure. The magnitude of these pressures depends on temperatures of the ice lens and is theoretically limited by the phase transition of ice to water. Hoekstra (1969) indicated that these pressures may vary between 20 kPa for a sand soil to 300 kPa for a silt soil when ice lenses form at the freezing front and when there is no water migration in the frozen soil. Small footing movements (heave) or deformation in the frozen soil would reduce these heave forces. Thermodynamic models proposed to explain the heave phenomena have not been developed to the stage where they can be used in design. Work reported by Penner (1974a, 1974b) on frost-heaving forces in Leda clay showed that the main heaving activity appears to be located at the interface between the frozen and unfrozen soil. Field measurements showed little heaving activity above the freezing plane within the frozen soil.

Tangential Forces on a Vertical Surface

As shown in Figs. 6.19 and 6.27c, when the active layer is slowly frozen during the winter, tangential stresses which are due to heaving and which jack out the pile or foundation are generated against the vertical surface. These stresses can be measured for field conditions. In the absence of experimental field data, the design values recommended by Vyalov and Porkhaev (1969) are 78.5 kPa for regions having soil temperatures of $-3°C$ or higher and 58.8 kPa for regions with soil temperatures below $-3°C$. A possible increase in tangential forces resulting from heaving is taken into account by an overload coefficient, for which a higher value is taken if the layer of seasonal freezing does not merge with permafrost. When preliminary explorations indicate unfavorable conditions, Vyalov and Porkhaev (1969) recommended that the tangential stresses be determined directly from field tests. The actual tangential forces on a vertical surface are governed by the soil type, moisture or degree of saturation of the soil, and permafrost temperatures. For Fairbanks silt, Crory and Reed (1965) have reported that the maximum rate of heave occurs early in the winter months at relatively shallow depths (1 m) and that the maximum pile heave force (about 275 kPa) occurs during periods of active frost generation with a very cold near-surface ground temperature. Relatively high maximum heave forces were also produced after complete freezeback of the seasonal thaw zone during periods of extreme cold.

Anchorage against Heave

Pile embedment must be sufficient to resist uplift forces by frost heave. The Tsytovich rule was that the embedment should be at least 2 to 3 times the thickness of the normal active zone. Such an empirical rule should not be applied without proper tests or design analysis. As given in Eq. (6.59), the effective embedment length should be calculated using the adfreeze strength of the pile and soil at the anticipated temperature corresponding to the maximum frost-heave forces. An increased dead weight is a convenient method of anchoring against frost-heave forces, and granular backfill may be used for anchoring footings. Design concepts of anchors in frozen ground, discussed in the previous section, may also be used to consider uplift forces caused by frost heave.

Measures against Frost Heave

Design measures to preclude frost-heave forces include use of surcharge loading, replacement of frost-susceptible soils with frost-stable material, increased depth of foundations, lowering the water table, and use of materials to isolate the structure from the active layer. Where unheated structures are built on frost-susceptible soil in regions of seasonal frost, they will be exposed to frost heave, which can be mitigated by use of non-frost-susceptible backfill material.

Heave-force isolation can be accomplished by casing the pile or foundation member and filling the annulus between the pile and casing with an oil-wax mixture having a thick consistency (Fig. 6.28). To avoid the costs and problems involved with a casing, the U.S. Army/Air Force Draft reported that a premixed backfill of soil, oil, and wax can be used to reduce frost-heave thrust on the upper sections of a pile to acceptably low values (Fig. 6.28b). The U.S. Army/Air Force Draft method for permanent bench marks involves use of the oil-wax mixture with the casing extending up to 1 m below the predicted annual frost-zone depth. The datum rod, with a welded flat plate on the bottom, extends a sufficient distance below the casing to ensure stability.

Various methods of providing additional shear strength or anchorage in permafrost (including notching the pile, driving railroad spikes in timber piles, and welding angle-iron flanges to steel piles) have been only partially effective

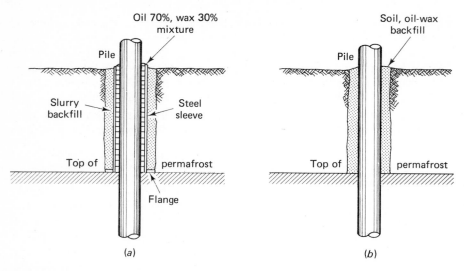

Figure 6.28 Heave isolation (*a*) with and (*b*) without sleeve. (*After U.S. Army/Air Force Draft.*)

in eliminating frost heaving of lightly loaded piles (U.S. Army/Air Force Draft). Thermal piles offer increased anchorage against frost heaving by more rapid lowering of pile surface temperatures in the permafrost during the fall and winter. Self-refrigerating thermal piles reduce the depth of summer thaw and furnish heat to that portion of the pile in contact with the active zone, thereby reducing the adfreeze bond involved in the frost-jacking process. The net effect is reduced jacking forces.

6.7 PAVEMENT STRUCTURES FOR COLD REGIONS

Pavement design in seasonal frost as well as in permafrost areas depends on the types of subgrade soil. The main concern is the limitation of the surface deformation resulting from frost action during the freezing period or the adequacy of bearing capacity during the seasonal thawing period. In permafrost areas, additional consideration must be given to the influence of construction on the existing ground thermal balance. Changes in the ground thermal regime may cause degradation of the permafrost, resulting in total or differential settlement and reduction in the bearing capacity of the pavement structure. Thus when pavement design is considered for permafrost areas, it is of utmost importance to recognize the significant influence of thermal variations on the soil and pavement properties. In addition, identification of frozen-ground features and susceptibility of the soil to thermal disturbances are critical design factors.

Pavement Design under Seasonal Frost Action

Pavement structures located in cold regions are subjected to (1) frost heaving of subgrade soils as a result of ice segregation during freezing, (2) a reduction in bearing capacity during the melting periods, and (3) cracking resulting from shrinkage of the pavement and base under the extreme low temperatures. Other related detrimental effects include development of surface roughness, restriction of drainage by the frozen substrata, and the influence of fatigue damage under repetitive stressing as a result of changes in stiffness characteristics of the subgrade soil, base course, and pavement surface. The potential for frost damage to the pavement structure depends on the presence of frost-susceptible soils, freezing and thawing temperatures in the soil, and the availability of water to the freezing soil. For uniform conditions, heaving will be uniform, and the pavement surface will remain relatively smooth with no effect on pavement serviceability as long as the frozen and heaved condition lasts. For irregular conditions, differential heaving will occur, causing surface roughness and possible cracking at points of severe distortion. Permanent roughness will develop from the cumulative effects of traffic loads during the period of frost heave.

Thawing and reduction in pavement bearing capacity may occur during relatively mild winters and during the spring. The spring thaw, proceeding almost entirely from the surface downward, leads to extremely poor drainage conditions. Frozen soil below blocks downward drainage. Lateral drainage may be restricted due to still frozen shoulders resulting from the insulating effect of snow and/or different thermal conductivity and surface reflectivity characteristics. Lack of drainage combined with excess water in the base course and thawed subgrade will greatly reduce the bearing capacity. Thaw-consolidation theory (Chap. 4) helps explain the phenomenon occurring in the base course and subgrade soils. The magnitude of the reduced subgrade strength becomes a major part of the design process and is discussed in a later section.

Several methods available for reducing thaw penetration beneath highway or runway pavements in permafrost areas include the placement of non-frost-susceptible base materials, use of insulating layers as part of the subbase materials, and/or painting the pavement surface white. The required thickness of non-frost-susceptible materials is based on the seasonal thaw penetration. This approach is effective when sufficient non-frost-susceptible materials are available. It is often used in combination with the other alternatives. The insulation may include foamed-in-place polyurethane or factory-produced polystyrene boards. The thickness of insulation required to protect the subgrade soil for various freezing indexes is discussed in NCHRP (1974). White painted pavement surfaces have a high reflectivity, which reduces the amount of shortwave radiation absorbed at the pavement surface, giving lower surface temperatures. Experimental data (Berg and Aitken, 1973; Fulwider and Aitken, 1962) indicated that the total thickness required for confinement of thaw penetration within a non-frost-susceptible base course can be reduced by as much as 35 percent. The effects of traffic and maintenance procedures govern the loss in effectiveness of the painted surface in reducing thaw penetration. About 26 percent loss in reflectivity was observed for one season at the Thule Air Force Base (Fulwider and Aitken, 1962).

Two types of pavement cracking are associated with frost or low temperatures. The first, with random orientation and spacing, is caused by differential frost heaving and develops at points of severe distortion. It occurs in both flexible and rigid pavements. The second form of cracking results from thermal contraction and appears as transverse cracks penetrating the entire pavement structure and extending into the shoulders of the road. This type of crack occurs at freezing temperatures when the entire pavement structure contracts as the temperature drops. When the tensile strength is exceeded, the crack develops. Problems arise when water enters the cracks, forming an ice lens, which produces an upward lip at the crack edges, or when deicing solution enters the cracks and causes localized thawing of the base, resulting in a pavement depression adjacent to the crack. Approaches used by various highway organizations in handling this problem are discussed in NCHRP (1974).

Corps of Engineers Design

Design of pavement structures in seasonal frost or permafrost areas is based on two alternative concepts (Linell et al., 1963; Lobacz et al. 1973; Hennion and Lobacz, 1973): (1) pavement surface deformation resulting from frost action or seasonal thaw-freeze cycles must be controlled, or (2) bearing capacity of the pavement structure must be sufficient during the adverse climatic period. The first concept requires that the combined thickness of pavement and non-frost-susceptible base eliminate or limit to an acceptable amount the frost or thaw penetration and any consequences thereof. This approach can be labeled the *complete protection method*. The depth of frost or thaw penetration can be estimated based on the design air-freezing or air-thawing index, respectively. The second concept anticipates reduced strength of the subgrade during the melting period and ignores the reduced heave which will occur.

Using these concepts, the Corps of Engineers has developed three design methods including (1) complete protection, (2) limited subgrade frost penetration, and (3) reduced subgrade strength. The design methods vary slightly depending on whether the pavement is located in a seasonal frost or permafrost area. Hennion and Lobacz (1973) excluded the second method for most subartic areas because high freezing-index values require thickness in excess of practical and economical limitations. Exceptions may include cases where insulation is used to limit subgrade frost penetration. Each method described in the following sections concerns only the design needed to allow for seasonal frost or permafrost conditions. The design for normal (nonfrost) conditions can be found in Yoder and Witczak (1975).

Complete protection The complete-protection method will limit seasonal frost penetration or thaw to the non-frost-susceptible base course. This protection prevents the underlying frost-susceptible soils from freezing in seasonal frost areas or the frozen soil from thawing in permafrost areas. The required thickness of the base course can be computed by either of the methods outlined in Sec. 6.1. The lower 100 mm of the base must be designed as a filter. Use of high-moisture-retaining non-frost-susceptible soils, such as uniform sands, in permafrost areas decreases the required base-course thickness. The higher latent heat of these soils gives them a higher resistance to thaw penetration. Use of insulation beneath the base course to prevent subgrade freezing or thawing has been described in an earlier section.

Limited subgrade frost penetration The limited-subgrade-frost-penetration method attempts to confine deformations to small acceptable values by use of a combined thickness of pavement and non-frost-susceptible base course which limits the subgrade frost penetration. Added thickness may be needed in some cases to keep pavement heave and cracking within tolerable limits based on local experience and field data. Linell et al. (1963) recommended this method in seasonal frost areas for the following soils: (1) all silts, (2) very fine silty sands containing more than 15 percent finer than 0.02 mm by weight, (3) clays with plasticity indexes of less than 12, and (4) varved clays and other fine-grained banded sediments. Exceptions include extremely variable subgrade conditions for which the complete-protection method must be used or when some nonuniform heave and cracking are not considered detrimental for flexible paved areas.

The design method uses an average air-freezing index for the three coldest years in a 30-year period (or for the coldest winter in 10 years of record) to determine the combined thickness of pavement and base required to limit subgrade frost penetration. Determine the base thickness required for zero frost penetration by subtraction. The ratio r equals the water content of the subgrade divided by the water content of the base. Enter Fig. 6.29 with the base thickness for zero frost penetration into the subgrade and, using the r value, read the design base thickness on the left-hand scale and the allowable frost penetration shown on the right-hand scale. The r value is limited to a maximum of 2.0 because part of the moisture in fine-grained soils remains unfrozen. The bottom 100 mm of base should consist of non-frost-susceptible sand, gravelly sand, or similar material designed as a filter. When the combined design thickness of pavement and base exceeds 1.8 m, Linell et al. (1963) recommended consideration of the following alternatives: (1) limit the total combined thickness to 1.8 m and use steel reinforcement to prevent cracks in rigid pavements; (2) limit slab dimensions to 4.6 m without use of reinforcement; (3) reduce the required combined thickness by use of a base of non-frost-susceptible uniform fine sand with high moisture retention in the drained condition in lieu of more free-draining material.

Reduced subgrade strength The reduced-subgrade-strength method is based on the anticipated reduced subgrade strength during the frost melting period, and the amount of heave is neglected. Linell et al. (1963) and Hennion and Lobacz (1973) recommended this method for both seasonal frost and permafrost

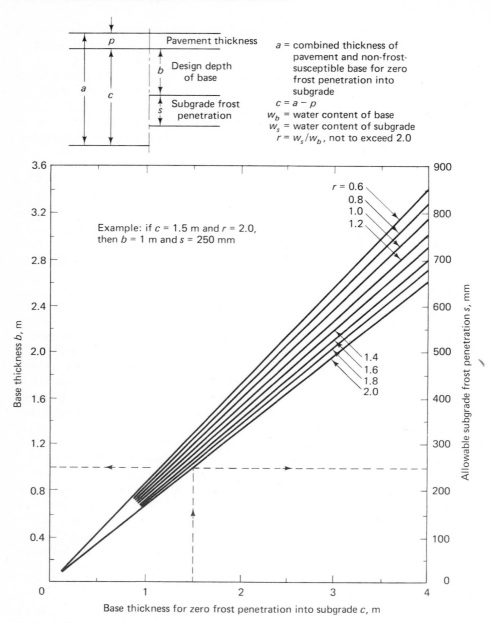

Figure 6.29 Thickness of non-frost-susceptible base for limited subgrade frost penetration. (*Adapted from Lobacz et al., 1973.*)

Table 6.14 Frost-susceptible soils (after Linell et al., 1963)

Group	Description
F1	Gravelly soils containing between 3 and 10% finer than 0.02 mm by weight
F2	(*a*) Gravelly soils containing between 10 and 20% finer than 0.02 mm by weight; (*b*) sands containing between 3 and 15% finer than 0.02 mm by weight
F3	(*a*) Gravelly soils containing more than 20% finer than 0.02 mm by weight; (*b*) sands, except very fine silty sands, containing more than 15% finer than 0.02 mm by weight; (*c*) clays with plasticity indexes of more than 12
F4	(*a*) All silts; (*b*) very fine silty sands containing more than 15% finer than 0.02 mm by weight; (*c*) clays with plasticity indexes of less than 12; (*d*) varved clays and other fine-grained banded sediments

areas. The method may be used for rigid pavements over subgrade soil groups F1 and F2 (Table 6.14) and flexible pavements on soil groups F1, F2, and F3 when subgrade conditions are sufficiently uniform to assure that objectionable differential heaving or subsidence will not occur. In certain cases nonuniform subgrade conditions are correctable by removal and replacement of pockets of more highly frost-susceptible or high-ice-content soils. For permafrost areas an estimate, based on a study of the area and local experience, should be made of the magnitude and probable unevenness that will result from future subsidence as thaw occurs in the existing frozen soil. In some areas maintenance may be more economical than providing adequate initial fill. This approach is referred to as *controlled subsidence*. For paved areas, base-course thickness may be increased as needed over the reduced-strength-design requirements to provide a surcharge load sufficient to reduce differential heave resulting from seasonal freezing of a frost-susceptible subgrade.

The design curves shown in Fig. 6.30 are used to determine the combined thickness of flexible pavement and non-frost-susceptible base. The design index represents all traffic expected to use the pavement during its service life. It is based on typical magnitudes and composition of traffic reduced to equivalents in terms of repetition of an 80-kN single-axle dual-tire load (U.S. Army, 1962). For the design index and soil group representative of the site, Fig. 6.30 gives the combined thickness of pavement and non-frost-susceptible base required by the reduced-subgrade-strength method. The combined thickness of the pavement and base should in no case be less than 230 mm where frost action is a consideration. Again the lower 100 mm of the base should be graded to provide filter action against the subgrade.

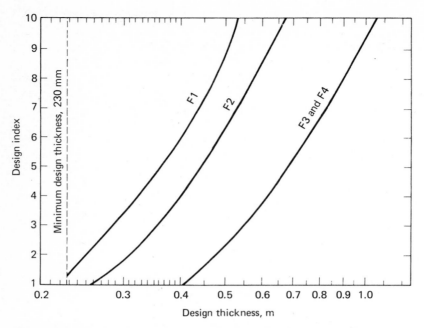

Figure 6.30 Frost-condition reduced-subgrade-strength design curves for flexible highway pavements. (*Adapted from Lobacz et al., 1973.*)

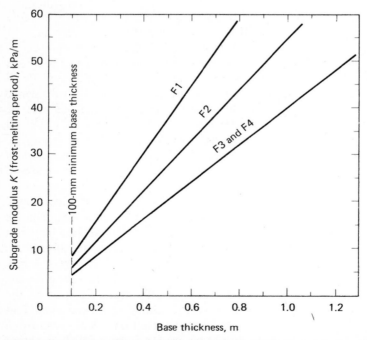

Figure 6.31 Frost-condition reduced-subgrade-strength design subgrade-modulus curves for rigid highway pavements. (*Adapted from Lobacz et al., 1973.*)

The reduction in subgrade-strength design for rigid pavements is accomplished by determining a reduced subgrade modulus, as indicated in Fig. 6.31. It is necessary to design the concrete pavement for normal conditions and then assume a base course equal to this depth. Using this thickness of base, one determines a reduced subgrade modulus from Fig. 6.31, and this value is used in the normal (nonfrost) condition design (Yoder and Witczak, 1975). Several exceptions are permitted in the reduced-strength design. When the reduced-subgrade-strength method is permitted over F3 soils, the non-frost-susceptible base course should be equal to a minimum of $1\frac{1}{2}$ times the concrete slab thickness. Over F4 soils the minimum thickness of non-frost-susceptible base course should be equal to one-half the average depth of subgrade that will be subject to annual freezing and thawing. In the application of this criterion, the lesser computed depth of freeze or thaw should be employed. The use of insulation should be considered in the design over F3 and F4 soils, and the design decision should be based on initial estimated cost of construction and future maintenance and operational requirements of the pavement.

6.8 EXCAVATION IN FROZEN GROUND

Excavation in seasonally frozen and permafrost soils becomes very difficult in winter as a result of very low temperatures which introduce difficulties in operation and equipment handling. Moreover, worker efficiency is reduced with fewer daylight hours and low temperatures. The compressive strength of frozen soils is increased at low temperatures and may be compared with those of weak concrete. Therefore, most excavation work is limited to the summer months unless soil conditions are so poor that they generate potential soil-stability or thermal-erosion problems. In general, excavations are limited to the actual area needed for construction so that the thermal regime of adjacent areas is maintained.

Excavation in Seasonally Frozen Ground

Depending on the depth of frost penetration and soil type, excavation may be carried out in both summer and winter. Excavation work is preferably carried out in the summer, when the soils are unfrozen. In winter special equipment may be required to rip open the upper frozen layer, after which methods common to unfrozen soils can be used. Excavation depth will depend on requirements for the planned structure. Limited-area vertical excavations may require stabilization in the form of lateral supports common to unfrozen soils. In areas where organic or very soft or loose soils are encountered, winter excavation and/or backfill may be planned so that the upper frozen layer will support the equipment loads during excavation. Some areas may require a working pad for the equipment in summer. Dewatering measures (Mansur and Kaufman, 1962) may be essential for stabilizing sandy soils to permit excavation to the required level. Artificial soil freezing (Sanger, 1968) can be used to stabilize the walls and bottom of excavations in fine-grained, permeable, saturated soils subject to quick conditions.

Excavation in Permafrost

Excavation in permafrost can be carried out in three ways:

1. Thawing the frozen soil before actual excavation and using standard earth-moving equipment. Prethawing of fine-grained soils to a considerable depth may not be practical since they can produce very soft or liquid conditions, in which the equipment cannot operate effectively. Heat input to the permafrost must be controlled so that only the required areas are thawed.
2. Fracturing or ripping the frozen soil into convenient sizes before excavation; this includes blasting and use of pneumatic tools and rippers mounted on or towed by tractors.
3. Using heavy machinery, including power shovels and pile drivers with special attachments.

Thawing of permafrost before excavation may be accomplished by solar radiation, steam jet, water needle, electric needle, or the valveless pulse-jet-engine methods (U.S. Navy, 1967). In some cases a combination of two or more of the methods may be effective. The solar method includes stripping the insulating vegetative cover or active layer, permitting the sun's heat to thaw the ground surface. Such a process is generally very slow and will advance up to 150 mm per day following surface exposure. Moreover, various factors, such as the climatic conditions, soil type, topography, and latitude, will dictate the use of the solar method. This method is most time-consuming as well as less efficient, and several months may be required for construction scheduling. The main advantage is that no extensive equipment is required.

The method of steam jets is generally restricted to small excavations for column footings, piles, and anchors. The rate of thaw penetration will vary depending on the soil type, spacing of points, and size and depth of excavation. The use of water needles, similar to steam jets, is applicable to large excavations. In this method the equipment needed includes use of drill rigs to prepare holes for water jetting. The method of electric needles is confined to major excavations and is generally very expensive. However, a primary advantage in using this method is the saving of time. The valveless pulse-jet method is restricted to small excavations. The engine is portable and appears to have definite advantages in digging small holes.

Explosives are the most common method for excavating in frozen ground. They are especially effective, as well as less expensive, in frozen gravelly soils. Various types and composition of explosives are available on the present market. More or less conventional drilling and explosives may be used. However, trials should be carried out at a particular site to determine the optimum values for explosives and hole spacing to achieve the best results. Mellor (1972) has found distinct advantages in use of liquid or slurried explosives for excavations in frozen materials. The use of pneumatic tools with chisel points or spades is limited to shallow frozen ground and is not very productive, as most frozen soils are too resilient to be broken by the pneumatic equipment. Rooters and rippers are effective under certain conditions. Generally, blasting is carried out first, through the frost layer, and then ripping operations follow. Back rippers are used successfully to break up ice and permafrost.

Heavy equipment can be used economically to break up frozen soils. Where the ground temperature is around -1 to $0°C$ and a large area has to be excavated, the use of heavy equipment with a sturdy ripper will be more economical than the use of explosives (U.S. Army/Air Force, 1966*b*). Tsytovich (1975) reported that a pile driver with a tubular attachment and a power shovel have been used successfully for the excavation of strip-foundation trenches and other earthwork operations.

Although summer is generally the most useful season for excavation in permafrost, considerable excavation has been carried out in the continuous permafrost zones for deep foundations as well as shallow foundations on gravel mats in the fall or early winter, just after freezing of the active layer. Where the excavation includes disturbance or removal of the insulating vegetative cover, subsoil investigations must be adequate to determine the actual extent of ground ice present. Extensive differential settlement or collapse of the ground, up to a meter or more, may take place as the thermal degradation of ground ice is caused by the stripping operation.

Handling excavated materials may be troublesome if the materials contain moisture which can freeze to any surface it touches, such as power-shovel buckets, loading hoppers, conveyor belts, and railroad-car bodies. The problem is most severe at temperatures between -9 and $-1°C$ (Woods, et al. 1963). Such problems can be eliminated by drying the materials to lower moisture content and heating the surfaces with which the materials may come in contact. No difficulties are generally encountered in handling, processing, or transporting moisture-free excavated materials, regardless of temperature conditions. The addition of calcium chloride to excavated soils for easier handling and winter storage has been discussed by Tsytovich (1975).

NOTATION

A	area
A'	effective contact area of footing
B	footing width; soil parameter in Vyalov's equation
c	cohesion
c'	reduced strength parameter
c_{ps}	cohesion for plane-strain conditions
c_r	volumetric heat capacity
D	diameter

D_e	equivalent duct diameter
D_f	footing depth
d	layer thickness; duct spacing
d'_c, d'_q, d'_γ	foundation depth factors (Ladanyi, 1975)
e	eccentricity of footing load
F	freezing index, degree-days
F_s	safety factor
f'	dimensionless friction factor for air flow
H	$c \cot \phi$; layer thickness; stack height
h_d	natural draft head
h_f	friction head
h_v	velocity head
I	thaw index, degree-days
I_r	rigidity index
k	thermal conductivity
k_u	thermal conductivity of unfrozen soils
k_f	thermal conductivity of frozen soils
L	latent heat of fusion; length
l	duct length
l_e	equivalent duct length
m	duct spacing; soil constant in Vyalov's equation; constant in Vesić's equation
m_v	coefficient of volume compressibility
N_c, N_q, N_γ	bearing-capacity factors
N'_c, N'_q, N'_γ	bearing-capacity factors
N_R	Reynolds number
N_ϕ	flow value $= (1 + \sin \phi)/(1 - \sin \phi)$
n	exponent in creep equation
P	load; period
P_a	heave force
P_b	end bearing
P_i	cavity-expansion pressure
P_{ias}	ultimate cavity-expansion pressure
P_p	adfreeze bond
P_r	downdrag force
P_{ult}	ultimate pulling capacity
P_0	average total original ground stress at footing level
Q	load; heat flow
q	applied footing pressure; surcharge load
q_a	safe or allowable soil pressure
q_{as}, q_{ult}	ultimate resistance (bearing capacity) of footing
R	thermal resistance
r	radius
s	settlement or displacement
T	temperature
T_R	temperature rise in air duct
T_S	mean surface temperature
T_0	mean annual air temperature
t, t_0	time
V	duct air velocity
W	weight
w	soil water content (percent dry weight)
X	frost penetration; thaw depth
z	depth
α	dimensionless parameter; thermal diffusivity

β	soil parameter in Vyalov's equation
γ	unit weight
γ_d	dry unit weight
Δ	increment
δ	angle of wall friction degrees; angle of friction between footing and soil
ϵ	conventional or engineering strain
ε	true or logarithmic strain
$\zeta_c, \zeta_q, \zeta_\gamma$	dimensionless foundation shape factors
$\zeta_{ci}, \zeta_{qi}, \zeta_{\gamma i}$	dimensionless inclination factors
η	degree of friction mobilization on cone below footing
θ	absolute value of negative temperature, $^\circ C = 273 - T$ K
λ	correction coefficient in Berggren's equation; soil parameter in Vyalov's equation
μ	dimensionless parameter
v	kinematic viscosity
ρ	air density; settlement
σ	normal stress
σ_f	creep failure stress
σ_c	proof stress (creep modulus) in creep equation
σ_{cu}	σ_c for creep in uniaxial compression
σ_{cu0}	σ_c at freezing temperature close to $0^\circ C$
$\sigma_{cu\theta}$	$\sigma_{cu} f(\theta) = \sigma_{cu}$ at freezing temperature θ
σ_{fu}	creep failure stress in uniaxial compression
σ_1, σ_3	major and minor principal stresses
τ	shear stress
ϕ	angle of internal friction, degrees; total heat flow
ϕ'	reduced angle of shearing resistance
ψ	angle in Fig. 6.8
ω	soil parameter in Vyalov's equation

REFERENCES

Aitken, George W. 1963. Reduction of Frost Heave by Surcharge Loading, *Proc. 1st Int. Conf. Permafrost, Lafayette. Ind., NAS-NRC Publ.* 1287, pp. 319–324.

Aldrich, H. P., and H. M. Paynter. 1953. Analytical Studies of Freezing and Thawing in Soils, *U.S. Army Corps Eng. Arct. Constr. Frost Eff. Lab., New Engl. Div., Boston, Mass., First Interim Rep.*

ASHRAE. 1963. "Guide and Data Book," American Society of Heating, Refrigerating and Air-Conditioning Engineers, New York.

Beresantsev, V. G., V. S. Kristoforov, and V. N. Golubkov. 1961. Load Bearing Capacity and Deformation of Pile Foundations, *Proc. 5th Int. Conf. Soil Mech. Found. Eng., Paris*, **2**: 11–15.

Berg, Richard L., and George W. Aitken. 1973. Some Passive Methods of Controlling Geocryological Conditions in Roadway Construction, *North Am. Contrib. 2d Int. Conf. Permafrost, Yakutsk, U.S.S.R.*, National Academy of Sciences, Washington, pp. 581–586.

Bowles, J. E. 1968. "Foundation Engineering," McGraw-Hill, New York.

Broms, B. B. 1965. Design of Laterally Loaded Piles, *J. Soil Mech. Found. Div. Am. Soc. Civ. Eng.*, **91**(SM3): 79–99.

Caquot, A., and J. Kerisel. 1953. Sur le Terme de surface dans le calcul des fondations en milieu pulverulent, *Proc. 3d Int. Conf. Soil Mech. Found. Eng. Zurich*, **1**: 336–337.

Carslaw, H. S., and J. C. Jaeger. 1959. "Conduction of Heat in Solids," 2d ed., Oxford University Press, London.

Crory, F. E. 1963. Pile Foundations in Permafrost, *Proc. 1st Int. Conf. Permafrost, Lafayette, Ind., NAS-NRC Publ.* 1287, pp. 467–476.

————. 1968. Bridge Foundations in Permafrost Areas, Goldstream Creek, Fairbanks, Alaska, *U.S. Army Cold Reg. Res. Eng. Lab. Tech. Rep.* 180, Hanover, N.H.

————. 1973. Installation of Driven Test Piles in Permafrost at Bethel Air Force Station, Alaska, *U.S. Army Cold Reg. Res. Eng. Lab. Tech. Rep.* 139, Hanover, N.H.

————, and R. E. Reed. 1965. Measurement of Frost Heaving Forces on Piles, *U.S. Army Cold Reg. Res. Eng. Lab. Tech. Rep.* 145, Hanover, N.H.

De Beer, E. E. de. 1949. "Grondmechanica," Funderingen N. V. Standard Bockhandel, Antwerp, deel II, pp. 41–51.

————. 1967. Proefondervindelijke bijdrage tot de studie van het gransdraagvermogen van zand onder funderingen op staal: bepaling von der vormfactor s_b, *Ann. Trav. Pub. Belg.*, **68**(6): 481–506; **69**(1): 41–88; **69**(4): 321–360; **69**(6): 495–522.

Fulwider, C. W., and G. W. Aitken. 1962. Effect of Surface Color on Thaw Penetration beneath an Asphalt Surface in the Arctic, *Proc. Int. Conf. Struct. Des. Asphalt Pavements, Univ. Michigan*, pp. 958–963.

Gibson, R. E. 1950. Discussion, *J. Inst. Civ. Eng.*, **34**: 382.

Hansen, J. Brinch. 1961. A General Formula for Bearing Capacity, *Dan. Geotech. Inst. Copenhagen Bull.* 11.

Hennion, F. B., and E. F. Lobacz. 1973. Corps of Engineers Technology Related to Design of Pavement in Areas of Permafrost, *North Am. Contrib. 2d Int. Conf. Permafrost, Yakutsk, U.S.S.R.*, National Academy of Sciences, Washington, pp. 658–664.

Hoekstra, Pieter. 1969. Water Movement and Freezing Pressures, *Proc. Soil Sci. Soc. Am.*, **33**(4): 512–518.

Hwang, C. T., D. W. Murray, and E. W. Brooker. 1972. A Thermal Analysis for Structures on Permafrost, *Can. Geotech. J.*, **9**: 33–46.

Johnston, G. H., and B. Ladanyi. 1972. Field Tests of Grouted Rod Anchors in Permafrost, *Can. Geotech. J.*, **9**: 176–194.

————, and ————. 1974. Field Tests of Deep Power-installed Screw Anchors in Permafrost, *Can. Geotech. J.*, **11**: 348–358.

Kezdi, Arpad. 1975. Pile Foundations, chap. 19 in H. F. Winterkorn and H. Y. Fang (eds.), "Foundation Engineering Handbook," Van Nostrand Reinhold, New York.

Ladanyi, B. 1961. Étude théorique et expérimentale du problème de l'expansion dans un sol pulvérulent d'une cavité présentant une symétrie sphérique ou cylindrique, *Ann. Trav. Publ. Belg.*, **3**: 105–138, **4**: 365–406.

————. 1963. Expansion of a Cavity in a Saturated Clay Medium, *J. Soil Mech. Found. Div. Am. Soc. Civ. Eng.*, **89**(SM4): 127–161.

————. 1967. Deep Punching of Sensitive Clay, *Proc. 3d Panam. Conf. Soil Mech. Found. Eng.*, *Caracas*, **1**: 535–546.

————. 1973. Bearing Capacity of Deep Footings in Sensitive Clays, *Proc. 8th Int. Conf. Soil Mech. Found. Eng. Moscow*, **2.1**, 159–166.

————. 1975. Bearing Capacity of Strip Footings in Frozen Soils, *Can. Geotech. J.*, **12**: 393–407.

————, and G. H. Johnston. 1974. Behavior of Circular Footings and Plate Anchors in Permafrost, *Can. Geotech. J.*, **11**: 531–553.

Lambe, T. William, and Robert V. Whitman. 1969. "Soil Mechanics." Wiley, New York.

Lee, T. M. 1962. Freezeback Time of Slurry around Piles in Permafrost, *U.S. Army Cold Reg. Res. Eng. Lab. Tech. Note*, Hanover, N.H.

Leonards, G. A. (ed.). 1962. "Foundation Engineering," McGraw-Hill, New York.

Linell, K. A., F. G. Hennion, and E. F. Lobacz. 1963. Corps of Engineers Pavement Design in Areas of Seasonal Frost, *Highw. Res. Rec.* 33, Washington.

————, and G. H. Johnston. 1973. Engineering Design and Construction in Permafrost Regions, *North Am. Contrib. 2d Int. Conf. Permafrost, Yakutsk, U.S.S.R.*, National Academy of Sciences, Washington, pp. 553–575.

Lobacz, E. F., G. D. Gilman, and F. B. Hennion. 1973. Corps of Engineers Design of Highway Pavements in Areas of Seasonal Frost, *Proc. Symp. Frost Action Roads, Oslo*, pp. 142–152.

Long, E. L. 1963. The Long Thermopile, *Proc. 1st Int. Conf. Permafrost, Lafayette, Ind.*, NAS-NRC Publ. 1287, pp. 487–491.

————. 1973. Designing Friction Piles for Increased Stability at Lower Installed Cost in Permafrost, *North Am. Contrib. 2d Int. Conf. Permafrost, Yakutsk, U.S.S.R.*, National Academy of Sciences, Washington, pp. 693–699.

Mansur, C. I., and R. I. Kaufman. 1962. Dewatering, chap. 3 in G. A. Leonards (ed.), "Foundation Engineering," McGraw-Hill, New York.

Matlock, H., and L. C. Reese. 1962. Generalized Solutions for Laterally Loaded Piles, *Trans. Am. Soc. Civ. Eng.*, vol. 127, pap. 3370.

Mellor, M. 1972. Use of Liquid Explosives for Excavation in Frozen Ground, *Symp. Mil. Appl. Commer. Explos., Valcartier, Que.*, Defense Research of Canada, Ottawa.

Meyerhof, G. G. 1951. The Ultimate Bearing Capacity of Foundations, *Geotechnique*, **1**: 301–331.

————. 1953. The Bearing Capacity of Foundations under Eccentric and Inclined Loads, *Proc. 3d Int. Conf. Soil Mech. Found. Eng., Zurich*, **1**: 440–445.

NCHRP. 1974. Roadway Design in Seasonal Frost Areas, *Natl. Coop. Highw. Res. Prog., Synth. Highw. Pract.* 26.

Newmark, N. M. 1935. Simplified Computation of Vertical Pressures in Elastic Foundations, *Univ. Ill. Eng. Exp. Stn. Circ.* 24.

Nixon, J. F., and E. C. McRoberts. 1973. A Study of Some Factors Affecting the Thawing of Frozen Soils, *Can. Geotech. J.*, **10**: 439–452.

Penner, E. 1974a. Uplift Forces on Foundations in Frost Heaving Soils, *Can. Geotech. J.*, **11**: 323–338.

————. 1974b. Frost-Heave Uplift Forces on Foundations, *2d Int. CIB/RILEM Symp. Moisture Prob. Build. Rotterdam, Sept. 10–12*; also *Natl. Res. Coun. Can. Div. Build. Res., Res. Pap.* 635.

Poulos, H. G., and E. H. Davis. 1974. "Elastic Solutions for Soil and Rock Mechanics," Wiley, New York.

Prandtl, L. 1921. Uber die Eindringungsfestigkeit (Harte) plastischer Baustoffe und die Festigkeit von Schneiden, *Z. Angew. Math. Mech.*, **1**(1): 15–20.

Reed, R. E. 1966. Refrigeration of a Pipe Pile by Air Circulation, *U.S. Army Cold Reg. Res. Eng. Lab. Tech. Rep.* 156, Hanover, N.H.

Reissner, H. 1924. Zum Erddruckproblem, *Proc. 1st Int. Congr. Appl. Mech., Delft*, pp. 295–311.

Robinsky, Eli I., and Keith E. Bespflug. 1973. Design of Insulated Foundations, *J. Soil Mech. Found. Div. Am. Soc. Civ. Eng.*, **99**(SM9): 649–667.

Rowley, R. K., G. H. Watson, and B. Ladanyi. 1975. Prediction of Pile Performance under Lateral Load, *Can. Geotech. J.*, **12**: 510–523.

Sanger, Frederick J. 1968. Ground Freezing in Construction, *J. Soil Mech. Found. Div. Am. Soc. Civ. Eng.*, **94**(SM1): 131–158.

————. 1969. Foundations of Structures in Cold Regions, *U.S. Army Cold Reg. Res. Eng. Lab. Monogr.* III-C4, Hanover, N.H.

Schultze, E. 1952. Der Widerstand des Baugrundes gegen schräge Sohlpressungen, *Bautechnik*, **29**(12): 336–342.

————, and A. Horn. 1967. The Base Friction for Horizontally Loaded Footings in Sand and Gravel, *Geotechnique*, **17**: 329–347.

Skempton, A. W., A. A. Yassin, and R. E. Gibson. 1953. Théorie de la force portante des pieux, *Ann. Inst. Tech. Batiment Trav. Pub.*, no. 63–64, pp. 285–290.

Terzaghi, Karl. 1943. "Theoretical Soil Mechanics," Wiley, New York.

Tobiasson, Wayne. 1973. Performance of the Thule Hangar Soil Cooling Systems, *North Am. Contrib. 2d Int. Permafrost Conf., Yakutsk, U.S.S.R.*, National Academy of Sciences, Washington, pp. 752–758.

Tsytovich, N. A. 1958. Bases and Foundations on Frozen Soils, *Highw. Res. Board Spec. Rep.* 58; Russian original published by the Academy of Sciences, Moscow, 1958.

————. 1975. "The Mechanics of Frozen Ground," McGraw-Hill, New York.

U.S. Army. 1962. Roads, Streets, Walks, and Open Storage Areas: Flexible Pavement Design, *Eng. Man.* EM 1110-345-291.

U.S. Army/Air Force. 1966a. Calculation Methods for Determination of Depths of Freeze and Thaw in Soils, *Tech. Man.* TM 5-852-6/AFM 88-19, chap. 6.

————. 1966b. Arctic and Subarctic Construction: General Provisions, *Tech. Man.* TM 5-852-1/AFM 88-19, chap. 1.

————. 1967. Arctic and Subarctic Construction: Structure Foundations, *Tech Man.* TM 5–852–4/ AFM 88–19, chap. 4.

————. Draft. Arctic and Subarctic Construction: Foundations for Structures, *Tech. Man.* TM 5–852–4/AFM 88–19, chap. 4.

U.S. Navy. 1967. Design Manual, *Cold Reg. Eng. Dep.* NAVFAC DM–9.

Vesić, A. S. 1970. Research on Bearing Capacity of Soils (unpublished).

————. 1973. Analysis of Ultimate Loads of Shallow Foundations, *J. Soil Mech. Found. Div. Am. Soc. Civ. Eng.*, **99**(SM1): 45–73.

————. 1975. Bearing Capacity of Shallow Foundations, chap. 3 in H. F. Winterkorn and H. Y. Fang (eds.), "Foundation Engineering Handbook," Van Nostrand Reinhold, New York.

Vyalov, S. S. 1959. Rheological Properties and Bearing Capacity of Frozen Soils, *U.S. Army Cold Reg. Res. Eng. Lab. Trans.* 74, Hanover, N.H.

————, and G. V. Porkhaev (eds.). 1969. Handbook for the Design of Bases and Foundations of Buildings and Other Structures on Permafrost, *Natl. Res. Counc. Can. Tech. Trans.* 1865, 1976.

Woods, K. B., K. A. Linell, and F. E. Crory. 1963. Alaska Canada Trip Report. *U.S. Army Cold Reg. Res. Eng. Lab.* File, Hanover, N.H.

Yoder, E. J., and M. W. Witczak. 1975. "Principles of Pavement Design," 2d ed. Wiley, New York.

SEVEN

SLOPE STABILITY IN COLD REGIONS

Edward C. McRoberts

INTRODUCTION

A *landslide* is the downward and outward movement of slope-forming materials composed of soil, natural rock, artificial fill, or combinations of these materials. The moving mass may proceed by one or more of the three principal types of movement, flowing, sliding, falling, or by their combinations. The lower limit of the rate of movement for frozen soils will include surficial creep. Movements due to freezing and thawing (solifluction) are of special interest in cold regions. Debris avalanches and rock falls illustrate the upper limit of very rapid movement rates. Slopes in thawing permafrost and in frozen soils introduce new failure processes which need to be considered in the stability analyses and design of slope-control methods.

There is extensive literature on the subject of landslides in the geological and geographical fields, which as a whole affords an excellent overview of many of the processes involved. For example, textbooks by Washburn (1973), Bird (1967), Carson and Kirkby (1972), Embleton and King (1975), and Jahn (1975) provide starting points for background studies. The classification of landslides presented in Sec. 7.1 gives a convenient framework for understanding slope processes common to cold regions and in particular permafrost.

A landslide is primarily the result of a shear failure along the boundary of the moving mass of soil or rock. Failure is generally assumed to occur when the average shear stress along the slip surface is equal to the shear strength of the soil or rock as evaluated by field or laboratory tests. The geotechnical engineer is concerned with methods of analysis and the measured shear strengths needed to quantify slope processes in order to provide a safe design or to guide remedial measures. Slopes in thawing permafrost (Sec. 7.2) and in frozen soils (Sec. 7.3) require an understanding of the ground thermal regime, thaw-consolidation theory, and the mechanical properties of frozen ground. Sections 7.2 and 7.3 draw on material presented in Chaps. 3 to 5 for the development of models needed for the analysis of slopes in thawing and frozen soils.

Some slope processes which are characteristic of cold regions but which are of lesser importance to the geotechnical engineer have been omitted for lack of space. Examples include such phenomena as talus slopes and cambering or shallow-slope movements induced by needle-ice growth. Readers interested in periglacial processes should consult Embleton and King (1975) and Jahn (1975).

7.1 CLASSIFICATION OF LANDSLIDES IN PERMAFROST

The range of slope-failure processes observed in permafrost soils is embraced in a classification of landslides presented in Fig. 7.1. The types of mass movement encountered in permafrost terrain are described in a pictorial manner and are based upon morphological evidence. The primary level of classification (flow, slide, and fall) is used in a descriptive sense with no mechanistic meanings implied. This descriptive approach was selected over a mechanistic or genetic classification as many landslides have complex origins. The primary level of classification follows the usage established in geotechnical practice by Varnes (1958).

The term *flow* has been chosen for a broad type of movement that exhibits the characteristics of a viscous fluid in its downslope motion. In many cases these movements resemble pure flow, as there is no evidence that shear displacements have occurred along localized failure planes. In other landslides, move-

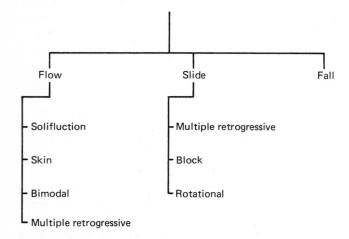

Figure 7.1 Classification of landslides in permafrost. (*After McRoberts, 1973.*)

these movements resemble pure flow, as there is no evidence that shear displacements have occurred along localized failure planes. In other landslides, movements can be seen partly along pronounced slip surfaces with the possibility that the remainder of the displacement is distributed throughout the moving mass. Mobility is substantial, and as it is distributed throughout the flow, prefailure relief is rapidly destroyed. Flow movements continue until reduced gradients or obstacles are reached. Many flows terminate in swiftly moving rivers. This definition parallels the description of a flow landslide given by Varnes (1958) who restricted the use of the term flow to a landslide form in which mobility is substantial, flow resembles that expected of a viscous fluid, and where slip surfaces are either not visible or are short lived. Conversely, landslides exhibiting more coherent displacements having a greater appearance of rigid-body motion are called *slides*. Prefailure relief remains substantially intact, and although the total magnitude of movements may be greater, they appear to have occurred over a period of time.

Falls involve direct outward and downward movement of detached blocks falling under the influence of gravity and under conditions of no resistance once movement is initiated.

Flows

Solifluction Although there is general agreement on the periglacial features which constitute solifluction, there is a wide range of terminology used in describing these features. It is apparent from a review of the literature that these difficulties in terminology arise from a mixing of descriptive classification and mass-movement mechanisms. For geotechnical purposes, solifluction is an established term for a type of mass movement common to cold regions. Excellent reviews of solifluction features are given by Washburn (1947, 1973), Bird (1967), Benedict (1970), Carson and Kirkby (1972), and Embleton and King (1975). Solifluction movements occur in all the cold regions of the world, but they are particularly favored in permafrost zones, where movements are restricted to the active layer, although in this case the term congelifluction is often used. It is generally accepted that fine-grained soils are required for solifluction movements to occur. It is often noted that solifluction is particularly active when frozen high-ice-content soils are thawed. Most downslope movements in a solifluction slope can be observed to occur during the summer thaw season, the remainder of downslope movement occurring during freezeback in early winter. Vegetation plays an important role in the appearance of solifluction slopes. If soil movements are constrained by vegetation, terrace, bulbous, or lobate features may dominate, whereas if the slope is bare, patterned ground features are common. A peculiar feature of solifluction movements, discussed in Sec. 7.2, is instability on low-angle slopes. Evidence of these low-angle movements exists in the fossil features of the Pleistocene periglacial zone, and many active features have been observed in contemporary periglacial areas.

Skin flows Skin flows involve the detachment of a thin veneer of vegetation and mineral soil and subsequent movement over a planar inclined surface. They are commonly active in long ribbonlike forms and may coalesce into broad, unstable sheets. A typical example of skin flow is shown in Fig. 7.2. This category of flow is shallow in comparison to its length and can develop on a wide range of slope inclinations. Skin flows which begin as a thin detachment of vegetation and mineral soil and then move out in a planar fashion over the permafrost table have been observed in Alaska (Capps, 1919, 1940; Sigafoos and Hopkins 1952). Hardy and Morrison (1972) noted a form of surface scouring initiated by brush fires in the Mackenzie Valley and commented that forest fires can precipitate surface movements on quite flat slopes. Hughes et al. (1973) noted the frequency of active-layer detachment failures caused by the movement of the active layer over underlying permafrost. Long ribbonlike skin flows are reported by Isaacs and Code (1972), and similar landslides, called *active-layer glides*, are reported by Mackay and Mathews (1973). Another example of a skin-flow form of landslide is the bentonite-debris flows in Northern Alaska, reported by Anderson et al. (1969). The landslide forms discussed by these various workers are all identical to the skin-flow type as classified by McRoberts and Morgenstern (1973).

From a mechanistic point of view there are many similarities between solifluction and skin-flow landslides. However, a fundamental difference between solifluction and skin flows is the marked difference in the rate at which movements develop. Solifluction usually involves the slow downslope movement of

Figure 7.2 Skin flows in colluvial slopes near Wrigley, N.W.T.

mineral soil and stretching of the overlying vegetation mat. The mat is contorted and often regrows in harmony with downslope motion. On the other hand, skin flows are characterized by a violent tearing of the vegetation mat and catastrophic movements which result in an entirely different appearance. Another more subtle difference is that solifluction might be considered to be the characteristic deformation mode of many naturally occurring active layers. By specifying naturally occurring active layers one seeks to exclude the effects of catastrophic events like forest fires, heavy rains, or high temperatures which increase the rate and depth of thaw. That is, a natural depth of active layer could be conceived of as being the mean depth under seasonally average conditions. If this average slope regime is violently disturbed, solifluction becomes more intense or other forms of landslides evolve from this base condition.

Bimodal flow The term *bimodal flow* was introduced by McRoberts and Morgenstern (1973) to describe a form of mass movement that has a distinctly biangular profile composed of a steep headscarp and a low-angled tongue. This term also indicates that two different modes of mass movement occur within the overall confines of the flow, as it is apparent on observation that the mechanisms of movement in the headscarp differ from those in the tongue. This form of landslide has been called a *retrogressive-thaw flow slide* (Hughes et al., 1973) although there is no evidence of true slide movements, mudflows, or mudslumps (Mackay, 1966; Lamothe and St. Onge, 1961). This form of natural landslide is a valuable indicator of the probable response of cuts in permafrost soils. In the most active bimodal flows, the permafrost in the headscarp is directly exposed to the atmosphere and degrades by ablation. Thin veneers of soil along these ablating headscarps continually melt and flow in pulses down to the break in slope where the lobe begins. In some instances, the permafrost soils are not sufficiently ice-rich to allow a sustained ablation process, and a thawed layer begins to form on the steeply inclined slope. This thaws to some critical depth, at which time the headscarp fails by the development of a skin flow in the thawed layer. In other headscarps, less thaw-susceptible soils can be subject to rapid desiccation and after undermining by melting ice may fail as a fall landslide. Vegetation overhangs often develop, protecting the upper portions of the scarp and inhibiting melting, while the underneath parts of the headscarp still ablate actively. This differential melting may also lead to the formation of a fall landslide. All these processes result in the formation of a steeply inclined headscarp region, variously described in plan view as an expanded spatulate bowl (Capps, 1940), as a semicircular hollow (Bird, 1967), or as a characteristic horseshoe shape (Washburn, 1947).

The tongue region of bimodal flows generally develops an angle of a few degrees. However, steeper inclinations can occur, depending upon the characteristics of the debris. In ice-rich fine-grained soils, where the headscarp fails by ablation, highly mobile tongues active on slopes as low as a few degrees are common. The water content of the tongue may approach or exceed the liquid limit of the soil, and high pore-water pressures result in little shearing resistance. In many cases the headscarp is so ice-rich it may be arguable that the process

Figure 7.3 A bimodal flow on the MacKenzie River near Fort Norman, N.W.T. The flow is seated in glaciolacustrine frozen silts and clays overlying an ice-poor till. The retrogressive movement occurs in the overlying silt and clays and is perched on the till.

Figure 7.4 A small bimodal flow near Fort Simpson, N.W.T. This flow, apparently initiated by ice-jam-induced scour on the banks of the MacKenzie River, was arrested by the development of the vegetative overhang apparent in the photograph. Cutting away this moss cover, as shown, exposed ice-rich permafrost. In turn this caused more ablation until the overhang reestablished itself.

is a thermokarst feature and not a landslide; the tongue's water content is so high that soil grains are moved more by mass transport than by mass movement. If the headscarp consists of ice-poor or coarse-grained free-drained soils, skin-flow processes can dominate in the headscarp and the tongues are much steeper. Figures 7.3 and 7.4 illustrate typical features of a bimodal flow. Excellent photographs of features that would be classified as bimodal flows are given by Jahn (1975, photographs 7, 9, 65, and 66).

Multiple retrogressive flow This form of mass movement adopts an overall flow movement, but, unlike skin or bimodal flows, these multiple retrogressive flows retain some portion of their prefailure relief. Contained within the landslide bowl are a series of arcuate, concave downslope ridges derived from the headscarp as it receded backward by a series of failures. Although the overall profile of these landslides is biangular, their form suggests that a series of retrogressive failures has occurred at the headscarp. These headscarps exhibit, in some locations, flow-dominated processes, but in others rotational slides can be found. While these features can be found in the discontinuous permafrost zone of the Mackenzie River valley, they have not been reported elsewhere.

Slides

There are few published case histories of slide movements in permafrost. Washburn (1947) reported on a slide at De Salis Bay, Victoria Island, in the Canadian arctic that occurred through frozen ground adjacent to a lake. Washburn also attributed features in the vicinity of Mount Pelly to slides in frozen soil, and although he notes that mass movement may have occurred in thawed soil which had then frozen, he discounts this possibility. Mass movements in glaciolacustrine clays have been studied by Wahrhaftig and Black (1958) along the Alaska Railroad. Large deep-seated slides with some rotational movement were described, and permafrost has been documented in areas adjacent to recent activity. Movements were seated in extensive deposits of lake clays and in a well-developed network of lattice ice made up of horizontal and vertical ice veinlets. They quoted a unique case record in which a railroad roadmaster, lowered down the headscarp crack of a large slide, reported that the crack extended through permafrost and that running water could be heard at the bottom of the crack. This suggests that failure had occurred through permafrost with the base of the slide in unfrozen soil. Deep-seated rotational failures have been reported in the Mackenzie River valley (Isaacs and Code, 1972, McRoberts and Morgenstern, 1973, 1974a) in permafrost soils composed of sands and gravels overlying glaciolacustrine silts and clays and in frozen tills. While the evidence is meager in terms of reported events from different geographical regions, the following classification of slide movements in permafrost soils has been suggested (McRoberts and Morgenstern, 1973) as a result of detailed studies in the Mackenzie River valley.

Block and multiple retrogressive slides Block slides involve the movement of a large block that has moved out and down with varying degrees of backtilting. A typical block slide is illustrated in Fig. 7.5. The moving mass remains intact, and the surface of the block supports living vegetation, which is similar to that found upslope beyond the slide. Multiple retrogressive slides (Fig. 7.6) are characterized by a series of arcuate blocks concave toward the toe that step backward higher and higher towards the headscarp. A degree of backtilting or rotational failure of the components may be found, but this is usually observed only in blocks that have fallen too near the toe. Intense gullying is also found in conjunction with both block and multiple retrogressive slides. Both types of slides are common where glaciofluvial sands and gravels overlie glaciolacustrine silts and clays. Deep-seated gullying is always observed in these soils, and it is likely that the gullies are seated in the finer-grained, less erodible clays found at the bottom of the stratigraphical sequence near river level. Isolated multiple retrogressive slides are also found in high banks in till. Detailed field observations of multiple retrogressive slides are given by McRoberts (1973) and Isaacs and Code (1972).

Rotational slide The term *rotational slide* was reserved by McRoberts and Morgenstern (1973) for landslides which occur in completely thawed soil. These landslides are similar to the classical circular type of failure common in clays in more temperate regions.

Figure 7.5 A block slide developed in glaciofluvial sand-silts overlying glaciolacustrine clay close to river level near San Sault Rapids on the MacKenzie River. The frozen nature of the block was apparent as exposures of ice wedges and lenses were visible in the undercut segments at river level.

Figure 7.6 A multiple retrogressive slide on the Mountain River, N.W.T. Drilling in the vicinity of this landslide found frozen glaciofluvial sand-silts overlying unfrozen clay.

Although there is no present evidence for deep-seated creep movements in the slopes observed along the Mackenzie River valley, the possibility exists (McRoberts, 1975a) that creep movements may occur in icy permafrost slopes. Creep movements might be initiated by a warming up but not thawing of frozen slopes. If such a process occurs, one result may be long-term creep rupture of the frozen soil, which would result in a landslide form like the block slides. Alternatively, the existing shear stress may be supported over long periods of time, the only effect being a certain amount of slope deformation. As this form of mass movement has not been observed, it is not classified in Fig. 7.1. However, mass movements due to the rheologic flow of frozen soil could be introduced into the classification as a subtype under flow-dominated movements.

Falls

The final form of failure in natural slopes in permafrost is the *fall*, which simply involves the downward movement of detached blocks falling under the influence of gravity. Falls occur commonly along the banks of rivers or large bodies of water, where thermal and physical erosion results in an undercut by the formation of a thermal-erosion niche and the subsequent breaking off of large blocks of frozen material, which in turn facilitates bank recession. This form of landslide is reviewed in detail by Embleton and King (1975) and Jahn (1975).

Figure 7.7 A fall landslide in the process of development in an alluvial bank of the Mountain River.

Falls can also occur in the headscarps of bimodal flows as the result of differential melting (McRoberts, 1973; McRoberts and Morgenstern, 1974a). A fall in the process of initiation is shown in Fig. 7.7.

7.2 SLOPES IN THAWING PERMAFROST

Slope Stability and Thaw Consolidation

Methods of analysis Solifluction slopes, skin flows, and tongues of bimodal flows can all be considered mechanistically as shallow-instability problems. Experience in temperate regions suggests that it is appropriate to consider the stability of long shallow slopes in terms of an infinite-slope analysis. The factor of safety F_s for the condition of limit equilibrium of a shallow slope using an effective-stress $c'\phi'$ analysis becomes

$$F_s = \frac{c' + z \cos^2 \theta \, (\gamma - m\gamma_w) \tan \phi'}{\gamma z \sin \theta \cos \theta} \qquad (7.1)$$

where the groundwater flow is parallel to the slope with the groundwater table at a vertical height mz above the slip surface. The total unit weight of soil is γ, and γ_w is the unit weight of water. For no cohesion and the groundwater table at the surface ($c' = 0$, $m = 1$) Eq. (7.1) reduces to (see Fig. 7.8)

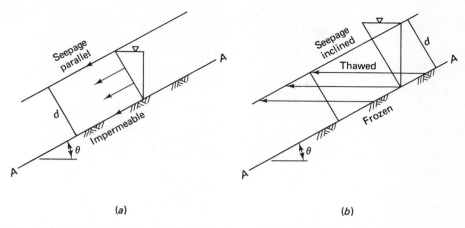

(a)   (b)

Figure 7.8 Infinite-slope analysis. (a) Case 1: seepage slope. On plane A-A, pore pressure $= \gamma_w d \cos \theta$, total stress $= \gamma d \cos \theta$, effective stress $= (\gamma - \gamma_w) d \cos \theta = \gamma' d \cos \theta$, $F_s = (\gamma' \tan \phi')/(\gamma \tan \theta)$. (b) Case 2: thaw slope. On plane A-A, pore pressure $= \gamma_w d \cos \theta + \gamma' d \cos \theta [1/(1 + 1/2R^2)]$ effective stress $= \gamma d \cos \theta - \gamma_w d \cos \theta - \gamma' d \cos \theta [1/(1 + 1/2R^2)]$,

$$F_s = \frac{\gamma'}{\gamma} \left(1 - \frac{1}{1 + 1/2R^2} \right) \frac{\tan \phi'}{\tan \theta} \qquad \text{where } R = \frac{a}{2(c_v)^{1/2}}$$

(*After McRoberts and Morgenstern, 1974a.*)

$$F_s = \frac{\gamma' \tan \phi'}{\gamma \tan \theta} \tag{7.2}$$

or

$$F_s = (\cos^2 \theta - r_u) \frac{\tan \phi'}{\sin \theta \cos \theta} \tag{7.3}$$

where $r_u = u/\gamma z$ and γ' is the submerged unit weight of the soil. For slopes that have undergone a considerable degree of movement it is appropriate to introduce the residual angle of friction ϕ'_r. Since the ratio γ'/γ is about $\frac{1}{2}$, slopes should be stable at angles less than or equal to

$$\theta = \tan^{-1} \left(\tfrac{1}{2} \tan \phi'_r \right) \tag{7.4}$$

This effective-stress method of analysis requires knowledge of the appropriate strength parameters and the pore-water pressure in the slope.

If we adopt a total-stress ($\phi = 0$) analysis, it can readily be shown that the factor of safety based on the undrained shear strength c_u is

$$F_s = \frac{c_u}{\gamma z \sin \theta \cos \theta} = \frac{2c_u}{\gamma z} \csc 2\theta \tag{7.5}$$

This total-stress method requires the specification of the value of c_u along a potential slip surface.

The singular feature of both solifluction slopes, i.e., skin flows and tongues of bimodal flows, is that instability can occur on slopes of much less inclination

Table 7.1 Comparison of failed and predicted low-angle slopes†

Site	Strength ϕ_r' ($c_r' = 0$)	Failed angle	Predicted‡ angle	r_u required for failure
Britain (fossil slopes)	12.5–23°	3–7°	6.8–12.0°	0.44–0.87
Northern Norway	29–33°	5–17°	15.5–18°	0.41–0.86
Vestspitzbergen	36°	6–12°	20°	0.68–0.85
Mackenzie Valley	23°	3–10°	12.5°	0.57–0.87

† Taken from case records discussed in McRoberts and Morgenstern (1974a)
‡ Based on $\gamma'/\gamma = 0.5$.

than can be predicted by Eq. (7.4). Evidence of this seeming paradox has been documented in the fossil features of the Pleistocene periglacial zone and in contemporary cold regions. Table 7.1 summarizes certain case records by comparing the slope inclination below which stable slopes should be obtained with the angles on which slope failures occurred. The stable angles were assessed using Eq. (7.4) and measured residual-strength parameters, as documented in Table 7.1. It can be seen that for all cases instability occurred on slope inclinations significantly below those which can be predicted using Eq. (7.4). Hutchinson (1974) has discussed the propensity for low-angle movements in terms of undrained analysis, using Eq. (7.5).

Equation (7.4) was developed using the maximum possible pore-pressure conditions for steady-state seepage parallel to the slope in conjunction with the lowest possible effective-stress parameter ϕ_r'. Consider now whether it is appropriate to use effective-stress parameters based on conventional testing of unfrozen, thawed soils to describe the effective-stress parameters mobilized at the interface between thawing and frozen soil. Thomson and Lobacz (1973) have investigated the effective-stress parameters characteristic of this interface. They modified a direct-shear apparatus such that a frozen-thawed interface could be maintained coincident with the shear plane imposed by a direct-shear test. A direct-shear test was then conducted in the usual manner and the results compared with tests on completely unfrozen samples. Identical values were obtained for the two conditions. A summary of test results for Manchester silt is shown in Table 7.2.

It can be argued, within an effective-stress framework, that the inability to predict the factor of safety correctly lies with an underestimation of the value of the pore pressure used in the analysis. The magnitude of the parameter r_u required to cause instability for the slopes considered above is shown in Table 7.1, and it can be seen that the required values can be considerably in excess of a value $r_u = 0.5$, characteristic of $m = 1.0$. The importance of pore pressure in this regard has been appreciated for some time, although, as we shall see, various mechanisms characteristic of periglacial regions have been proposed to account for such conditions.

Table 7.2 Summary of strength parameters for Manchester silt (from Thomson and Lobacz, 1973)

Test conditions	Strength	Angle of shearing Resistance	Cohesion intercept, (kPa)	Type of shear
Unfrozen	Residual	32°	0	Direct
Thaw interface	Residual	33°	8.8	Direct
Unfrozen	Peak	34°	1.0	Direct
Thaw interface	Peak	30°	24.5	Direct
Frozen-thawed	Peak	36°	10.8	Triaxial

Example 7.1 Calculate the factor of safety F_s for a saturated soil ($\gamma' = 929$ kg/m^3, $\phi' = 25°$) standing on a 7° slope assuming a parallel to the slope-seepage condition.

SOLUTION From Eq. (7.2) obtain $F_s = 1.83$.

Thaw-consolidation theory A process which is unique to thawing ground and which resolves this paradox of movement on low-angle slopes is thaw consolidation. It is contended that excess pore-water pressures can be set up on thawing and that they are consequent upon thaw consolidation. The concept of thaw-consolidation theory and its role in solifluction and skin flow can be summarized no more succinctly than was done by Taber (1943), who stated that rapid thawing and slow drainage are conducive to slope movements in originally frozen soil. He noted that when a frozen soil expanded by freezing thaws, part of the load may be carried by the water phase if drainage is impeded.

The yearly cycle of freeze and thaw plays an important role in solifluction movements. The importance and association of freeze and thaw in solifluction movements stem from the characteristic properties of the fine-grained soils common to solifluction slopes. During the freezing cycle the fine-grained soils bulk and develop ice lenses as water is attracted to the freezing front. On completion of freezeback the active layer of the zone of seasonal frost penetration has undergone a net increase in volume. Then, during the following thaw cycle, instability can result because of the characteristic mechanical properties of the low permeability and high compressibility of the fine-grained soil. An extensive treatment of thaw-consolidation theory was presented in Chap. 4. However, certain salient features are considered here.

Morgenstern and Nixon (1971) have solved a one-dimensional thaw-consolidation problem by coupling the traditional Terzaghi consolidation theory with a moving thaw boundary, defined by the Neuman solution

$$d = \alpha t^{1/2} \tag{7.6}$$

where d = depth of thaw
   t = time
   α = constant

Nixon and McRoberts (1973) gave a set of boundary conditions and soil properties. The solution was developed in Chap. 4 in terms of the thaw-consolidation ratio

$$R = \frac{\alpha}{2(c_v)^{1/2}} \tag{7.7}$$

where α is defined by Eq. (7.6) and c_v is the coefficient of consolidation. This ratio expresses the relative influence of the rate at which water is produced during thawing and the rate at which it can be squeezed out of the thawed soil overlying the moving thaw interface. For an infinite soil mass, thaw-consolidating under self-weight conditions, the excess pore pressure is

$$u = \frac{\gamma'd}{1 + 1/2R^2} \tag{7.8}$$

where $\gamma'd$ is the effective stress after complete dissipation of excess pore pressures (Morgenstern and Nixon, 1971; and Chap. 4).

Thaw-consolidation theory has been applied to the prediction of thaw slope stability by McRoberts (1972) as follows. Consider a slope (Fig. 7.8) where a thaw front has penetrated to a depth d. The effective stress on a plane AA' after the dissipation of excess pore pressures would be $\gamma'd \cos \theta$. It is therefore assumed, analogous to Eq. (7.8), that a measure of the excess pore pressure u on AA' is

$$u = \gamma'd \cos \theta \frac{1}{1 + 1/2R^2} \tag{7.9}$$

and when we apply a statical balance of forces, the factor of safety becomes

$$F_s = \frac{\gamma'}{\gamma} \frac{1}{1 + 2R^2} \frac{\tan \phi'}{\tan \theta} \tag{7.10}$$

It is apparent that if no thaw occurs or if no excess pore pressures are set up, Eq. (7.10) reduces to Eq. (7.2). Equation (7.10) can be solved in terms of R and water content for a typical set of soil properties, as shown in Fig. 7.9.

The solution to Eq. (7.10) can be extended if it is assumed that α is governed by the Stefan solution (Nixon and McRoberts, 1973) as

$$d = \left(\frac{2k_u T_s t}{L}\right)^{1/2} \tag{7.11}$$

where T_s = step temperature causing thaw
   k_u = thermal conductivity of thawed soil
   L = volumetric latent heat of frozen soil
   $\alpha = (2k_u T_s/L)^{1/2}$

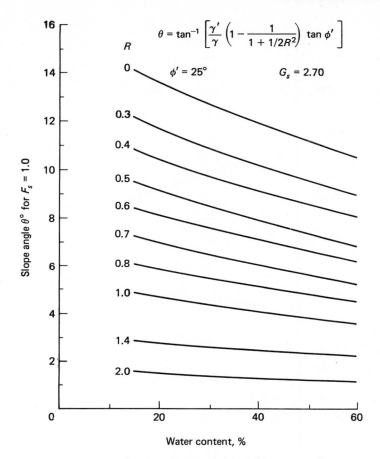

Figure 7.9 Solution in terms of R (*After McRoberts and Morgenstern, 1974a.*)

In Eq. (7.11), α is a function of k_u and L. If it is assumed that all the soil water is frozen, and if the unfrozen conductivity is defined as a function of water content, both k_u and L are uniquely defined. A solution to Eq. (7.10) is presented in Fig. 7.10 by plotting the slope angle required for limit equilibrium ($F_s = 1.0$) against water (ice) content. It is assumed that the soil is fully saturated, $S = 100\%$, and that the specific gravity of soil solids G_s is 2.70. As the solution for α is more or less independent of the frozen-ground temperature (Nixon and McRoberts, 1973), it is possible to isolate the dominant effects of temperature and coefficient of consolidation c_v in reducing the equilibrium slope angles.

The analyses introduced so far are concerned with the stability against slope failure of a single homogeneous soil layer extending downward indefinitely. In real situations, more than one distinct soil type may be present. A layer of peat would clearly modify the rate of thaw expressed by the α value, and the excess

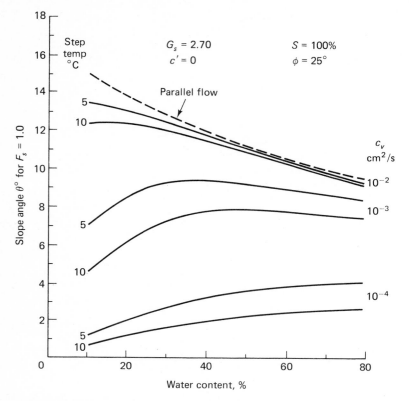

Figure 7.10 Example solution for a thawing infinite slope. (*After McRoberts and Morgenstern, 1974a.*)

pore pressures and therefore the safety factor would be altered. In certain cases a layer of gravel may be placed on the ground surface. This would not only alter the rate of thaw but also surcharge the thawing mineral soil beneath, enhancing slope stability.

Let us first consider the thermal problem introduced by two layer systems. The presence of a surface layer of different thermal properties means that the total depth of thaw X is no longer expressed by $\alpha t^{1/2}$. The time to thaw the surface layer t_0 is given by the Stefan solution as

$$t_0 = \frac{H^2 L_1}{2 k_1 T_s} \tag{7.12}$$

where H = height of surface layer consisting of free-draining highly permeable material
T_s = applied surface temperature
k_1 = thermal conductivity of surface layer
L_1 = latent heat of surface layer

The depth of thaw through the underlying layer is

$$X = \left[\left(\frac{k_2}{k_1} H \right)^2 + \frac{2k_2 T_s}{L_2} (t - t_0) \right]^{1/2} - \left(\frac{k_2}{k_1} - 1 \right) H \qquad (7.13)$$

where the thaw penetration into the underlying soil layer is denoted by $d = X - H$.

The thaw-consolidation problem can be formulated by assuming that no excess pore pressures are maintained in the surface layer consisting of peat, insulation, or gravel. If the surcharge loading exerted by a free-draining surface layer is represented by P_0, the problem can be formulated in the manner given by Morgenstern and Nixon (1971). Making the assumption that the excess-pore-pressure distribution in the thawed layer is linear with depth, McRoberts and Nixon (1977) showed that an approximate solution can be obtained as

$$u = \frac{P_0 + \gamma' d}{1 + 1/2R^2(1 + k_2 H/k_1 d)} \qquad (7.14)$$

where R is the thaw-consolidation ratio without a surface layer.

The validity of this solution can be checked by comparison with a more rigorous finite-difference solution given by Nixon (1973). Figure 7.11 presents a comparison for a nonsurcharge case where thaw caused by $T_s = 10°C$ occurs in a 30.5-cm peat layer overlying mineral soil. Figure 7.11a illustrates the thaw history predicted by Eq. (7.13), and Fig. 7.11b compares the normalized excess pore pressure $u/\gamma' d$ predicted by Eq. (7.14) with a computer solution for R values of 0.6 and 1.2. Figure 7.12 presents an identical solution for the case of surcharge only overlying mineral soil, and it can be seen that the agreement for both cases is reasonable. Substituting the pore pressures given by Eq. (7.14) into the infinite-slope-stability formulation in a manner similar to that undertaken in Eq. (7.10), we obtain

$$F = \frac{P_0 + \gamma' d}{P_0 + \gamma d} \left[\frac{1 + k_2 H/k_1 d}{2R^2 + 1 + k_2 H/k_1 d} \right] \frac{\tan \phi'}{\tan \theta} \qquad (7.15)$$

If $P_0 = 0$ and $H = 0$ we note that Eq. (7.15) becomes Eq. (7.10). Equation (7.15) gives a good approximate solution for the factor of safety in layered-soil systems, and it can be used to design remedial measures for thawing slopes. A multilayer system overlying mineral soil can be converted into one layer by weighting individual materials by the ratio of their conductivities.

Example 7.2 For the slope used in Example 7.1, which consists of bare mineral soil, calculate F_s assuming that the slope is initially in a frozen condition with an active layer forming under conditions such that $T_s = 10°C$; assume $c_v = 0.128$ mm^2/s and use the geothermal properties from Fig. 7.11.

SOLUTION From Eq. (7.11) obtain $\alpha = 0.43$ mm/s$^{1/2}$; Eq. (7.7) gives $R = 0.60$, and Eq. (7.10) gives $F_s = 1.06$.

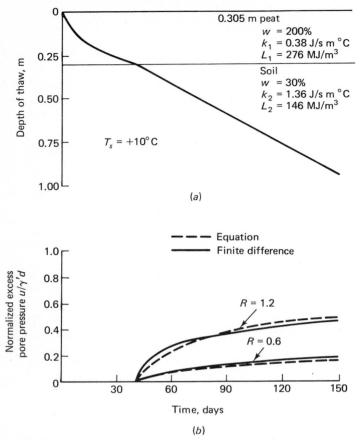

Figure 7.11 Excess pore pressures in a peat over mineral soil. (*Adapted from McRoberts and Nixon, 1977.*)

Example 7.3 Calculate F_s at the end of a 150-day thaw season if a 0.61-m layer of gravel surcharge ($P_0 = 11.5$ kPa, thermal properties given in Fig. 7.11) is placed on the mineral-soil slope in Example 7.2.

SOLUTION From Eq. (7.13) at 150 days obtain $d = 1.29$ m and $k_2 H/k_1 d = 0.464$; $R = 0.6$ as before. From Eq. (7.15) obtain $F_s = 1.55$ (note that R is calculated assuming the gravel layer is not present).

Application of thaw-consolidation theory The application of thaw-consolidation theory in design requires solutions to both a geothermal problem and the specification of the pore-water pressure. For many geothermal problems simple analytical solutions are available, and they have been reviewed by Nixon and McRoberts (1973). For more complex problems, numerical techniques like those discussed in Chap. 3 are required. If recourse must be had to numerical

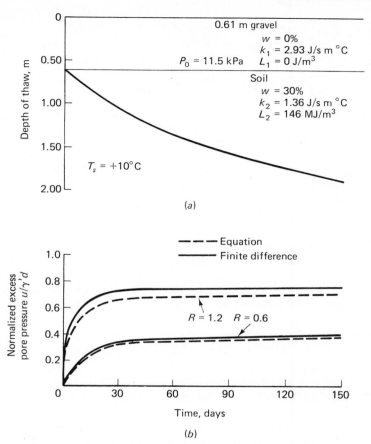

Figure 7.12 Excess pore pressures in a gravel over mineral soil. (*Adapted from McRoberts and Nixon, 1977.*)

techniques for the solution of the geothermal problem, it will also be necessary to consider numerical techniques for the solution of the thaw-consolidation problem as a whole; the available approaches have been discussed in Chap. 4. McRoberts (1975b) has discussed in general terms the variation in α and suggests that the entire range of likely values for thaw-slope calculations lies between 0.1 and 1.0 mm/s$^{1/2}$.

On the other hand, the value of c_v may range over a wide spectrum, and while c_v enters the R value under the square root, its potential variation and the factors affecting it make it a critical variable in thaw-slope-stability calculations. The coefficient of consolidation can be obtained by the direct interpretation of consolidation tests, or it can be computed as

$$c_v = \frac{k}{m_v \, \gamma_w} \tag{7.16}$$

where k = coefficient of permeability
m_v = coefficient of volume compressibility
γ_w = unit weight of water

The coefficient of volume compressibility is defined as

$$m_v = \frac{\Delta V/V}{\Delta \sigma'} \tag{7.17}$$

where $\Delta \sigma'$ is the change in effective stress, or

$$\Delta \sigma' = \sigma'_f - \sigma'_0 \tag{7.18}$$

For complete consolidation σ'_f is the effective stress and σ'_0 is the initial effective stress (see Chap. 4). The volumetric strain equals

$$\frac{\Delta V}{V} = \frac{e_0 - e_f}{1 + e_0} \tag{7.19}$$

where e_0 is the initial void ratio and e_f is the final void ratio at the end of consolidation.

The value of c_v depends on both the permeability and the compressibility of a given soil. The value of m_v can be calculated by substituting Eqs. (7.18) and (7.19) into Eq. (7.17). If it is assumed that the initial effective stress is zero, which is clearly appropriate for ice-rich soils and conservative for ice-poor soils, m_v can be obtained for a given soil type if the initial void ratio, the void-ratio–effective-stress relationship, and the final effective stresses are known. The value of k must be obtained by direct measurement either in situ or in the laboratory.

The soil structure can have a dominant influence on the in situ permeability of the soil and therefore on the coefficient of consolidation. The presence of fissures and cracks in a soil mass results in an increased overall permeability compared with the permeability of intact masses bounded by cracks. Unless a representative, i.e., large enough, volume of soil is considered, laboratory testing may yield k or c_v values that are considerably lower than will be found in situ. This macrostructure effect will be especially marked in thawed permafrost soils, as these soils inherit a well-developed crack structure as a result of the thawed cryogenic structure; i.e., the network of ice lenses that is always found in fine-grained ice-rich soils will impart a network of fissures and cracks to a thawed soil. These cracks will markedly increase both the in situ permeability and the coefficient of consolidation over that which would be otherwise expected for fine-grained soils.

The designer can choose from two methods for arriving at a c_v value which accounts for macrostructure. One may adopt a testing procedure whereby different sized samples are tested in order to assess the effects of structure on c_v directly. Alternatively, it is possible to measure k in situ and, using the method outlined above, determine c_v by calculation. This method assumes that m_v is not affected as much by structure, which is a reasonable assumption.

The application of the thaw-consolidation mechanism in terms of Eq. (7.10) also requires the specification of the effective-stress parameters. We have seen in a preceding section that it is appropriate to acquire the necessary c' and ϕ' values based on testing of completely thawed samples. In view of the very low effective stresses obtained in situ in a shallow thawing slope it is necessary to be aware of the possible influence of effects of curvature of the Mohr-Coulomb strength envelopes for both peak and residual values of c' and ϕ'. If direct-shear-strength tests are conducted at effective normal stresses significantly in excess of the actual values operative in situ and extrapolated back to the stress range of interest, the c' and ϕ' values may be incorrectly estimated.

An alternative method for accounting for the potential loss of shear strength due to thaw consolidation is to obtain the in situ undrained shear strength. Once a representative value for c_u is obtained, it can be introduced into an undrained analysis [Eqs. (7.5) and (7.22)]. The drawback of such an approach is that there is no direct means of extrapolating the strength data to situations in which the rate of thaw is different from that operative at the time of the strength measurement. Hutchinson (1974) has discussed the application of the total-stress approach in regard to the stability of periglacial slopes. The value of the undrained analysis is that it permits some check to be made against the effective-stress approach, discussed earlier.

Many aspects of thaw-consolidation theory which have been confirmed by laboratory tests on remolded samples and positive excess pore pressures have been measured in the laboratory in thaw tests on natural soil samples. A detailed discussion of these tests has been given in Chap. 4 with reference to a case where excess pore pressures were recorded in the field under an instrumented hot-oil-pipeline test at Inuvik, N.W.T. In all cases it was shown that thaw-consolidation theory predicted measured pore pressures reasonably accurately.

Excess pore-water pressures have also been measured in the field at certain slope sites in the Mackenzie River valley by McRoberts and Morgenstern (1973, 1974a). While these case records cannot be considered complete, as no direct measurements were made of c_v or k either in field or in laboratory tests on natural undisturbed samples, the high pore pressures measured are consistent with thaw-consolidation theory.

Excess pore-water pressures have also been measured by Chandler (1972) during the study of a thawing slope in Vestspitsbergen. Chandler measured pore pressures significantly in excess of hydrostatic conditions, and his data suggest that thaw-consolidation processes may explain the measured pore pressures. It should be noted, however, that the thaw-consolidation mechanism was not considered by Chandler, who suggested that the observed pore pressures were due to a blocked drainage mechanism.

Other Causes of Instability

While thaw-consolidation theory resolves certain mechanistic paradoxes, thaw consolidation is certainly not the only factor that contributes to the instability of shallow slopes in permafrost. In this section a range of factors is reviewed which, to a lesser or greater extent, may influence slope stability. The control exerted by periods of heavy rainfall in initiating skin flows and in contributing to solifluction movements, especially on slopes steeper than that predicted by Eq. (7.4), is considerable. Rainfall increases the total shear stress due to saturation of the soil and organic cover, and accompanying this increase in shear stress is a concomitant decrease in shear strength due to reduced effective stresses. The presence of an active layer at shallow depths contributes to the maintenance of saturated conditions, and while the presence of frozen soil may aid other instability mechanisms, skin flows can be initiated under conditions in most respects similar to those for shallow landslides in temperate regions. Mackay and Mathews (1973) have emphasized the importance of heavy rainfall in initiating skin flows in the Mackenzie River valley, and Savel'yev (1972) noted that the stability of the active layer on slopes formed of silty sands and sandy loams is usually disrupted during prolonged rains.

Mass wasting at the headscarp of bimodal flows may create excess pore pressures in the tongues of these flows by undrained loading. This process, whereby low-angle movements can be induced in flow landslides by the loading of debris discharged from steeper slopes onto the tongues of flows, is not peculiar to periglacial areas.

A mechanism called *ice-blocked drainage* has been proposed by various authors (Siple 1952; Weeks 1969; Chandler 1970, 1972) to account for instability in solifluction slopes. It is reasoned that when a freezing front advances into a slope, it forms a blanket of impermeable frozen soil overlying the talik in the still unfrozen active layer. This blanket can then block or back up the water flow and thus set up excess pore pressures. While this mechanism is entirely possible, there are certain factors to be considered. We have seen that solifluction slopes usually consist of fine-grained silty or clayey soils. For the usual depths of active layers, say up to 2.0 m, the stress levels in the slope are such that water will always be attracted to an advancing freezing front. Therefore, during freezeback pore-water subpressure may be expected. That this is the case is witnessed by the frequent observations made of ice lenses in solifluction slopes. The condition of ice-blocked drainage may tend to nourish the growth of ice lenses and in this manner contribute to solifluction during the following thaw season. It is noted that the formation of ice lenses and the bulking of solifluction slopes during the freezing cycle are vital elements in the cycle of events that leads to instability due to the thaw-consolidation processes.

Aquiferlike conditions within a thawing active layer may also allow for conditions under which excess pore pressures can be sustained if the water table can be backed up the slope. Chandler (1972) discussed the likelihood of this mechanism for slopes in the Vestspitsbergen, where excess pore pressures were measured. He suggested that internal erosion had formed subsurface channels of higher permeability. It might be argued, on the other hand, that this process would tend to contribute to reduced pressures due to improved drainage conditions. However, it is entirely possible that such conditions might develop on a slope blanketed by colluvial sediments; e.g., a fine-grained soil moving over a coarse-grained soil and underlain by permafrost could provide for a blocked drainage mechanism.

The process of frost creep has been the subject of considerable investigation as it is amenable to direct field measurement. The theoretical or potential downslope movement due to frost creep C results when soil freezes and heaves perpendicular to the slope a distance H and then thaws. The downslope movement is then

$$C = H \tan \theta \qquad (7.20)$$

where θ is the slope angle. The actual frost creep equals the potential if, on thaw, the soils settle vertically. However, as pointed out by Carson and Kirkby (1972), the heaved soil seldom settles vertically, and retrograde components of movement occur (Washburn, 1967, Benedict, 1970) that considerably lessen the total movement attributable to frost creep.

Field measurements of frost creep also suggest that its importance may be overstated. Williams (1966) found that the frost heave H required to account for the measured displacement using Eq. (7.20) was unrealistically high when compared with the observed ice stratigraphy and rejected the likelihood of frost creep in accounting for observed winter movements. Washburn (1967) reported an average winter movement of 12 mm occurring on a slope of 2.5°. Equation (7.20) predicts a required heave of 0.28 m, but vertical deformations of this order of magnitude are not reported. Jahn (1975), considering frost heave on a 4° slope in Spitsbergen, found that the measured heave of 0.15 m predicted a movement of 10 mm, which is considerably less than the total downslope movement of 30 mm measured during spring thaw. A comparison of frost heave, potential frost creep calculated by Eq. (7.20), and recorded movements for solifluction slopes in northern Norway was given by Harris (1972), who found that the total measured downslope movements were greater than movements that can be attributed to frost creep. Benedict (1970) measured both frost heave and downslope winter movement on a solifluction lobe of known angle and found that actual movements are at least double winter movements.

Low-angle movements present few conceptual problems to those investigators who emphasize the flow aspects of thawing permafrost slopes. Mass movements are based on a concept of viscous flow initiated by a loss of cohesive strength caused by high water contents. For example, Washburn (1967) noted that the Atterberg limits are an important parameter in solifluction and that significant solifluction probably occurs only at moisture-content values exceeding the liquid limit. It is appropriate to observe that if the water content of a soil approaches the liquid limit, mobility will be enhanced. A geotechnical viewpoint favors the application of the principle of effective stresses. The observed loss of shear strength near the liquid limit is due to low effective stresses which must necessarily coexist with the high in situ void ratios of a high-ice-content thawing soil. Low effective stresses in turn lead to the loss of shear strength, defined in terms of the effective stresses, and such a response is predicted by thaw-consolidation theory. Thaw-consolidation theory predicts that if a soil is thawed under conditions of a high thaw-consolidation ratio R, zero effective-stress conditions can be approached. An example of this process can be found in the scarps of bimodal flows. However, if the same soil is thawed more slowly, substantial effective stresses are realized and viscous conditions are not created.

It is clear that a soil mass, especially at low effective-stress conditions and in a state of limiting equilibrium, will exhibit some form of rate-dependent or viscous shear-strength response. However, while it is a relatively straightforward matter to discuss qualitatively conditions under which flow landslides continue to deform and to even formulate realistic mass-movement models (Morgenstern, 1967; Savel'yev, 1972), any consideration of the problem is handicapped by a lack of appropriate constitutive relationships for a "frictional-viscous" soil. From a geotechnical point of view the thaw-consolidation model presented earlier is entirely adequate, as we are generally more interested in predicting the onset of unstable conditions in thawing slopes than we are in predicting the gross movements involved in slope failures. The processes by which a viscous liquid of soil slurry can be created and sustained at zero effective-stress conditions has been considered by McRoberts (1973). If excess ice was abundant in a thawing soil, the mineral grains would tend to be highly dispersed. In this condition, the movement of the particles is most conveniently viewed in terms of settling velocities. McRoberts (1973) developed a theory of soil sedimentation (McRoberts and Nixon, 1977) and applied it to a consideration of thawing soil. It was found that if thaw proceeds at a sufficient rate, zero effective stresses can be sustained by thaw-sedimentation processes which result if the velocity of the advancing thaw front exceeds the velocity of fall of soil particles. The conditions favoring such a process are unlikely to be met in terms of geotechnical design considerations; i.e., the ice contents would have to be so high to sustain thaw sedimentation that thaw would be prohibited in any event if safe designs are to be realized.

Shallow-Slope Movements

Extensive reviews of the rates of movement characteristic of shallow thawing slopes (Washburn, 1973; Jahn, 1975; Embleton and King, 1975) are available. Typical movement rates of 20 to 60 mm/year are common in solifluction slopes, while movements of up to tens of meters per year may be encountered in skin flows. Velocity profiles have been measured at a variety of sites, and characteristically they have a concave downslope profile (Carson and Kirkby, 1972) so that velocities are high near the surface and decrease rapidly with depth. Studies by Washburn (1967) and Benedict (1970) have attempted to separate the components of downslope movement due to frost creep and solifluction.

Some authors tend to seek a relationship between rates of movement and some function of the slope angle. Washburn (1967) reported a linear relation between annual movement and the size of the slope angle. Although the relationship is presented as being a good fit between average measurements, the apparent standard deviation is high. Higashi and Corté (1971) conducted model experiments on solifluction and reported a linear relation between movement and the tangent squared of the slope angle.

Even though a slope may be designed to have a more than adequate factor of safety, downslope movements can still occur. Any thaw settlement occurring on a long, essentially infinite slope will have a downward component of motion, as predicted by Eq. (7.20). For example, assume that thermal degradation is initiated on a slope due to some form of surface disturbance and a thaw settlement of 500 mm is predicted. Applying Eq. (7.20) shows that a downslope component of movement of 88 mm is possible on a 10° slope. Any structure which is buried or founded on this slope which cannot deform to accommodate these movements can have significant loadings imposed by this thaw-settlement downdrag.

Thaw-Plug Stability

An assessment of thaw-plug stability may be necessary if permafrost begins to degrade deeply over a limited width. For example, thermal disturbance due to road construction, the clearance of right-of-way in warm permafrost regions, or the operation of a buried hot pipeline may all cause the formation of a thaw plug. While much has been said about the possible consequences of thaw-plug instability (Lachenbruch, 1970; Kachadoorian and Ferrians, 1973), a rigorous method for the calculation of thaw-plug stability is not available. While this might seem a serious deficiency at first glance, a consideration of the problem suggests that in most cases the use of some form of infinite-slope analysis will suffice.

In the early stages of most thaw bulbs, the width of thaw is much greater than the depth. Since the near-surface permafrost soils are usually the most ice-rich and therefore the most prone to failure, the most critical stage occurs during the development of a thaw bulb. The infinite-slope-analysis methods considered in the preceding section are applicable because thaw is shallow in relation to the width of thaw. As thaw develops with time, denser soils with lower ice contents and measurable residual stresses (see Chap. 4) may be encountered, an effect which enhances stability. Moreover, the rate of thaw will decrease with depth, as two-dimensional effects begin to exert influence on the overall geothermal solution. All else being equal, this decreased rate of thaw will also lead to greater stability.

It is possible to account for the increased stability offered by two-dimensional effects by considering a simple model. Assume that the thaw bulb is represented by a rectangular channel section of width S and depth Z inclined on an infinite slope of angle θ to the horizontal (Fig. 7.13). Assuming that vertical effective stresses are related to horizontal effective stresses by the parameter k_0, we can show (Fig. 7.13) that the factor of safety F_s becomes

$$F_s = \frac{\tan \phi'}{\cos \theta \sin \theta} (\cos^2 \theta - r_u) + \frac{K_0 Z \cos \theta}{S} (1 - r_u) \qquad (7.21)$$

Note that if the ratio Z/S is small, Eq. (7.21) reduces to Eq. (7.3). In this equation r_u is defined in terms of the sum of the hydrostatic and excess-

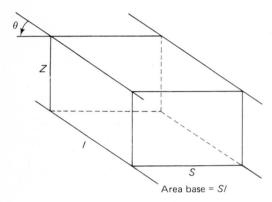

Figure 7.13 Solution for two-dimensional infinite-slope analysis. Weight of block $= \gamma ZSl \cos \theta$, weight normal to base $= \gamma ZSl \cos^2 \theta$, area of base $= Sl$, normal stress on base $= \gamma Z \cos^2 \theta$, effective normal stress on base $= \gamma Z \cos^2 \theta - r_u \gamma Z$, total base resistance $= (\gamma Z \cos^2 \theta - r_u \gamma Z)Sl \tan \phi'$, total side resistance $= 2$ (average lateral stress)$(Zl \cos \theta)$, lateral stress $= K_0 \times$ vertical stress, vertical stress $= \gamma Z - r_u \gamma Z$, average lateral stress $= 0.5K_0(\gamma Z - r_u \gamma Z)$, total side resistance $= K_0(\gamma Z - r_u \gamma Z)Zl \cos \theta \tan \phi'$, net unbalanced downslope force $= \gamma ZSl \cos \theta \sin \theta$

Factor of safety $=$
$$\frac{\text{sum of resisting forces}}{\text{net unbalanced downslope force}}$$

Area base $= Sl$

$$F_s = \frac{\tan \phi'}{\cos \theta \sin \theta}$$
$$\left[(\cos^2 \theta - r_u) + \frac{K_0 Z \cos \theta}{S}(1 - r_u) \right]$$

pore-water pressures, where the excess-pore-water pressures must be obtained from a two-dimensional solution. This problem was discussed in Chap. 4; however, for most purposes it will be sufficient, and conservative, to estimate pore pressures using one-dimensional theory. In terms of total stresses

$$F_s = \frac{c_u}{\gamma Z \cos \theta \sin \theta} + \frac{Z c_u}{\gamma S \sin \theta} \tag{7.22}$$

which in turn reduces to Eq. (7.5) as S becomes large.

Cuts and Bimodal Flows

The feature complicating the design of cuts in permafrost soils is the instability that may occur when exposed frozen soils are allowed to thaw. The behavior range of cuts in frozen ground parallels the range of landslide forms that have been described as bimodal flows. The response of cuts in frozen ground is directly related to the nature of the soil and the distribution of ground ice. If the soil is fine-grained and ice-rich, ablation processes can generate substantial rates of mass wasting. Table 7.3 contains a summary of observations of the rates of movements in natural bimodal flows taken from data in McRoberts and Morgenstern (1974a). The magnitude of the movements produced by actively retreating cuts is substantial. For example, a flow initiated in a 10-m-high bank and thawing at a rate of 7.0 m per thaw season would, if it produced a 3° tongue, retrogress some 190 m over a 27-year period.

Table 7.3 Rates of headscarp movement in bimodal flows†

Flow	Movement, m		Rate of movement, mm/day
Hume River, N.W.T.	20 in 6 years		36‡
	76 in 6 years		127‡
	152 in 28 years		54‡
Fort Simpson landslide, mile 226	3 in 6 weeks		73
Fort Norman landslide, mile 517	37 in 11 years		33‡
Arctic Red River, gravel pit	12 spring thaw to Aug. 2, 1972		200
Isachsen	7–10 per summer		70–100‡
Kendall Island, Mackenzie Delta	2 in 41 days (av)		48
	Average	Maximum	
Garry Island, Mackenzie Delta:			
Site A, 1964	1.7	3.2	17–32‡
1965	1.6	2.9	16–29‡
Site B, 1964, July 10–Aug. 15	...	...	78, 75
Aug. 16–Sept. 5	...	...	53, 53
Site C, 1964	1	1.6	10–16‡
1965	1.5	2.1	15–21‡
Banks Island, Western Arctic, 1972			
Site 1, June 30–July 10	...	...	140
July 10–23	...	...	130
July 23–Aug. 3	...	...	90
Aug. 3–13	...	...	60
Site 2, July 15–28	...	...	140
July 28–Aug. 12	...	...	110

† Taken from case records discussed in McRoberts and Morgenstern (1974a).
‡ Based on 100-day thaw season.

Bimodal flows are initiated by some process or combination of processes that removes insulating vegetation cover and thawed soil, exposing ice-rich material so that retrogression can be started and sustained. Skin flows are a common agent in initiating bimodal flows, as they expose ice-rich permafrost to direct melting. Small rotational slides in the recently thawed and unfrozen deposits along the toes of banks may also expose ice-rich permafrost. These rotational slides may occur due to rapid drawdown conditions in the wake of flood crests. This process would be favored at locations where the erosive attack of a river was high so that the initial and subsequent colluvial debris could be removed. Fall landslides may also be initiated by intense erosive attack either by river or wave action. This erosive attack results in the formation of a thermal-erosion niche and the undermining of a block of frozen soil, which fails in tension, exposing ice-rich soil. If the collapsed block is rapidly removed by water action, conditions favorable for bimodal-flow activity are then created. The designer must keep in mind that bimodal flows may begin at some distance from the facility under consideration, but because of the rates of movement involved they could begin to impinge if left unchecked.

The performance of actual cuts in permafrost soils has been studied by several workers. Lotspeich (1971) has observed highway cuts in interior Alaska and concluded that cuts should be made vertically. Where this has been done ensuing melting is more readily self-stabilizing. While this will be true for small cuts irrespective of terrain type, this particular method may not be appropriate in larger cuts where the ground ice is horizontally continuous. For example, McPhail et al. (1976) reported on the experience at a road cut in the far northern continuous permafrost zone of Alaska where an essentially vertical cut in an ice-rich zone did not self-stabilize as expected, apparently because of the distribution of ground ice. The interaction of ground ice in the performance of highway cuts in Alaska has been discussed by Smith and Berg (1973), who reviewed various aspects of the problem and concluded that the construction techniques that have been evolved in high-ice-content cuts appear to have been successful. Highway cuts in Alaska and the Yukon and Northwest Territories have been studied by Pufahl et al. (1974), who found that cut-slope stability conditions varied widely, depending primarily on the soil type and ground-ice conditions. In many cases cut slopes performed adequately with little visible distress or had retrogressed to some extent and then had stabilized. In some cuts conditions were such that it was necessary to undertake stabilization measures, and the authors commented that the use of a thick layer of select fill placed along the headscarp is the only reliable stabilization technique. An extensive study of the behavior of cuts in permafrost and the energy budget at the headscarp of an actively ablating scarp has been presented by Pufahl (1975).

Experience in permafrost terrain, to date, suggests that the following designs and cut configurations are appropriate.

Type I These are small cuts about 1 to 3 m high which, irrespective of terrain, are capable of self-stabilization as long as there is a reasonably well-developed (minimum 0.2 to 0.3 m thick) organic cover overlying the mineral soil. If the cut is made vertically, and if all large-diameter trees are removed by hand from the upslope part of the cut to a distance on the order of 1.5 times the depth of the cut, the organic mat will fall down over the melting scarp. In doing so, the mat will retard melting and allow vegetation to be quickly reestablished. If trees are not removed, they tend to cause tearing of the organic mat as it begins to drape over the exposed thawing permafrost.

For cuts greater than 1.5 m, a reinforcing mesh over the organic cover may be needed in order to develop sufficient tensile strength in the mat. Cuts where the organic mat is less than 0.2 m thick can be treated in one of two ways. If the soil is ice-rich, it should be treated as an ice-rich cut (see type IV). If any other conditions are encountered, the cut can be made vertical and allowed to slough. If cuts are made in the high arctic tundra, the vegetation mat may be too brittle to develop a drape on any size of cut. However, in the forested area the strength imparted to the organic mat by root structure is considerable (see Fig. 7.3).

Type II: cuts in frozen ice-poor soil, bedrock Cuts in soil or bedrock which are stable upon thaw can be designed so that the slope angle is compatible with the unfrozen properties. In the continuous-permafrost zone, cut slopes will tend to freeze each winter, while in the discontinuous zone there may be a long-term degradation of permafrost. The use of several forms of surface treatments such as revegetation of erosion-control mats may be considered in order to prevent surface erosion.

Type III: cuts in ice-wedge terrain If a cut is made in terrain in which the ground-ice condition exists as a matrix of ice-wedge ice in ice-poor mineral soil, the most suitable design response depends on local conditions. By and large, steep cuts are desirable because fewer ice wedges are encountered. If the ice-wedge distribution is low and a good organic mat is present, the cut may self-heal. However, as it is likely that some excess water will be produced during the self-healing process, environmental constraints may require preventing this discharge from entering water courses. In this case, one design approach is to place revetments along the toe of the slope to retain the soil but to allow water to drain. For highway cuts, reasonably wide ditches are required to provide space for accumulated debris and the placement of revetments. However, this increases the amount of excavation required. Alternatively, it may be desirable to excavate out the large exposed ice wedges to some reasonable distance depending upon geothermal considerations and backfill to cut grade with select material. The cut slope can then be considered as type II. It should be noted that, depending upon the volume of ice and climatic considerations, it may be more expedient to treat the cut as a type IV cut.

Type IV: cuts in ice-rich permafrost Cuts in which the ground-ice conditions are horizontally continuous and such that they will sustain a continuous backsapping of the headscarp require positive thermal-protective measures to inhibit thawing. Various design configurations can be considered, depending upon geographical location. For example, in the continuous permafrost zone, insulation configuration can be designed which will prevent thaw into the underlying ice-rich headscarp soils. In the southern fringe of the discontinuous zone the insulation required to prevent thaw completely would probably be prohibitive. Because it can be exceedingly difficult to prevent degradation, the design of ice-rich cuts in warm permafrost must necessarily allow for some thaw into the ice-rich soil under the protective covering. This protective covering must be reasonably free-draining and have sufficient flexibility and strength to accommodate whatever thaw settlement is considered acceptable. A suitable stabilization technique is to consider some combination of sand, gravel, or crushed rock and insulation.

The development of suitable criteria for the recognition of terrain conditions requiring differing design techniques must be developed by experience. Self-healing conditions may be anticipated in permafrost soils found in many tills, alluvial or colluvial silts and sands, and bedrock where ground-ice forms are essentially wedges or lenses of limited areal extent. Nonhealing conditions may be expected in glaciolacustrine sediments, certain ice-rich tills, and in the ice-cored topography found in segments of the continuous permafrost zones of Alaska and Canada. It is difficult to determine the conditions favorable for either condition from a site-investigation program alone, and a clear picture of the anticipated response may not emerge until actual ground-ice conditions are exposed during construction. A detailed inspection of the performance of natural slopes is the best guide to the expected performance of cut slopes in a given geographical location.

7.3 SLOPES IN FROZEN SOIL

Load-deformation characteristics of frozen soil depend on the magnitude of the applied stress, time, and temperature, as described in Chap. 5. At high stress levels frozen soils in a slope may fail, resulting in creep rupture. The mobilized shear strength is time-dependent, lower strengths being developed for increasing times to failure. It is also observed that for a range of frozen soils there exists an ultimate or long-term strength. Above this stress, creep deformations will occur which, with the passage of sufficient time, will terminate in creep rupture or tertiary creep. Below this ultimate stress, creep movements exhibit either a zero or continuously decreasing strain rate with time or primary creep. This concept of long-term strength is generally accepted as being inappropriate for ice as ice can creep under extremely small shear stresses. Moreover, it appears that ice will not exhibit a damped, or primary-creep mode, but that load deformation either terminates in tertiary creep or continues at a more or less constant rate, called secondary creep. From a geotechnical point of view this range of frozen-soil behavior must be approached by consideration of limit equilibrium, in terms of mobilized strength of the frozen ground and of tolerable deformation in terms of creep behavior.

Deep-seated Landslides

Evidence for the existence of creep rupture or shear failure of frozen soil is documented by the occurrence of deep-seated slides in permafrost in the Mackenzie River valley. While a considerable amount of information can be collated for these block and multiple retrogressive slides, such information may be of lesser value for other permafrost regions. However, a study of these slides is instructive, as conditions favoring their development may be found in other areas. Certainly the designer must be aware of the possibility of such landslides; whether or not they are likely can best be decided by a detailed study of slope processes in the design area.

A detailed description of the conditions favoring block and multiple retrogressive slides (McRoberts and Morgenstern, 1973, 1974b) can be summarized as follows. First, field inspection of this type of landslide indicates that active toe erosion is a necessary element of this landslide activity. Block and multiple retrogressive slides can be found throughout the Mackenzie River valley in reaches of both the Mackenzie River and its tributaries, where intense toe

Table 7.4 Block-slide profiles (from McRoberts and Morgenstern, 1974b)

Name	Mile number†	Bank height, m	Angle overall
Camsell Bend	275	37	15°
Fort Norman	513–515	40	13.5°
	641–653	38–53	
		(some to 60 m)	

† Mileages are approximate distances from the head of the Mackenzie River.

erosion is occurring. However, the same terrain types which are prolific producers of slide activity become stable on the cessation of active toe erosion. It is possible that creep movements may still occur. The occurrence of block and multiple retrogressive slides in the Mackenzie valley is essentially restricted to glaciolacustrine soils although they can be found in certain till units. However, an apparently necessary condition for their development is that soil extend to low river level. No block or multiple retrogressive slides have been observed in drift above bedrock where bedrock occurs at river level or higher, although sections have been observed where the stratigraphy is otherwise favorable.

Another necessary condition for block- and multiple-retrogressive-slide development is related to the morphology of the slides. The bank heights and failed slope angles observed along the Mackenzie valley (McRoberts and Morgenstern, 1974b) are listed in Tables 7.4 and 7.5. The minimum bank height that failed in this mode ranges from 30 to 60 m. Furthermore the overall slope angle at failure ranged from 9.5 to 20°, with the banks at steeper angles before failure. From morphologic evidence it appears that block- or multiple-retro-

Table 7.5 Multiple-retrogressive-slide profiles (from McRoberts and Morgenstern, 1974b)

Location, mile number,† or name	Bank height, m	Angle overall
293	37	13.6°
300	52	13.6°
350	79	
475	69	10.0°
484	73	14.0°
621, Axel Island	56–72	9.5–14°
Mountain River	100	12–20°
Hume River	30–38	

† Mileages are approximate distances from the head of the Mackenzie River.

gressive-slide movements in the Mackenzie valley are unlikely in frozen or partly frozen slopes less than 30 m high and less than 9° in slope.

A final condition is that permafrost bottoms out at near river level. Geomorphological evidence supports this observation, as does experience during drilling at a site at Mountain River N.W.T. (McRoberts and Morgenstern, 1974*b*). Drilling at this site recorded some 45 m of permafrost overlying unfrozen silty sand in a slope about 67 m high. High pore-water pressures were inferred.

These landslide types are readily apparent on aerial photographs. Recognition of the conditions necessary for their development and appropriate site selection will help minimize the likelihood of such features. However, in some cases it may be desirable to assess the overall stability of a given slope. The stability analysis for this type of landslide has been considered in detail by McRoberts and Morgenstern (1974*b*), who applied the same type of limit-equilibrium analysis as used in unfrozen soils to frozen slopes and have considered the use of noncircular-analysis and circular-arc methods. They found that the conventional methodology could readily be adapted to analysis of frozen slopes.

The analysis of deep-seated slides in permafrost requires the specification of the in situ shear strength of frozen ground. McRoberts and Morgenstern (1974*b*) found that the strength of frozen soil can be approximated realistically using two long-term strength models. It was argued that the analysis of any potential block or multiple retrogressive slide should be considered using a long-term strength because this type of slope is loaded over long periods due to natural processes. Because the strength of permafrost soils decreases with the duration of load, long-term estimates of strength are clearly appropriate.

The classical method by which the time dependence of the strength of frozen soil can be empirically correlated is credited to Vyalov and involves plotting the reciprocal of the creep stress against the log of the time to failure (see Chap. 5). This relationship has been shown to be linear for test durations on the order of 0.1 to 100 h and when extrapolated gives a measure of the long-term or ultimate strength taken at, say, 50 to 100 years. The long-term shear strength can then be established. It should be noted that there is little difference between the strength predicted between 100 and 200 years. This method assumes that the frozen soil has an essentially cohesive response.

The second method, proposed by McRoberts and Morgenstern (1974*b*), centers around the fact that the long-term strength of ice-poor, or structured soil, is frictional. The authors summarized evidence that suggests that the long-term frictional strength of structured soil can be deduced from triaxial testing in unfrozen soils. Both these long-term-strength models have been used by McRoberts and Morgenstern (1974*b*) to investigate the stability of a landslide at the Mountain River, N.W.T. It was concluded that stability analysis which used a frictional response for the frozen soil gave reasonable agreement. Clearly, if unfrozen soil is found at river level, knowledge of the pore-water pressures and the effective-stress parameters of unfrozen soil will also be required for a complete analysis.

Creep Movements

Downslope movement of permafrost slopes can be caused by creep deformation of permafrost soils. The possibility that creep movement, due to the rheologic nature of frozen ground, may occur in solifluction slopes has been discussed by Washburn (1967), who noted that downslope winter movements cannot be completely explained in terms of frost creep. While there is no documented evidence at this time of deep-seated creep movement in slopes, experiments on the creep of ice and ice-rich soils suggest that significant creep deformation may accumulate in permafrost slopes under sustained stresses. Certainly, creep movements can be encountered in rock glaciers, where the flow of frozen rubble and interstitial ice is akin to glacier flow. Like glaciers, rock glaciers have their beginnings in source areas which, by virtue of the constant supply of material, may add to the overall tendency for movement. This supply, or continual additional loading, may not be present in permafrost slopes. Rock glaciers may pose geotechnical problems, and a review of their salient features is provided by Embleton and King (1975).

McRoberts (1975a) has presented a simple secondary-creep model for deformation in permafrost slopes by assuming a secondary-creep relationship of the form

$$\dot{\varepsilon}_0 = A\tau_0^m + B\tau_0^n \tag{7.23}$$

where $\dot{\varepsilon}_0$ is the octahedral shear strain rate, τ_0 is the octahedral shear stress, and A, B, m, and n are parameters which must be derived experimentally and which are a function of temperature.

Applying this equation to an infinite-slope model where the deformation occurs as simple shear over a no-slip surface at depth H measured in the Z direction taken normal to the slope surface, we can show (McRoberts, 1975a) that the downslope velocity profile with depth can be obtained as

$$V(Z) = \frac{6A(\frac{2}{3}\gamma \sin \theta)^m (H^{m+1} - Z^{m+1})}{m+1} + \frac{6B(\frac{2}{3}\gamma \sin \theta)^n (H^{n+1} - Z^{n+1})}{n+1} \tag{7.24}$$

where θ is the slope inclination and γ is the total unit weight.

This approach can be extended to a consideration of primary creep in an approximate manner by subdividing a time-dependent relationship between strain and stress into a series of constant-strain-rate increments. For more complex slope geometries (in turn complicated by stratigraphical layering and spatial variations in temperature) numerical techniques are required. While it is possible to formulate a range of methods that can be used to simulate slope-deformation processes, there is a lack of both experimental data on undisturbed-soil samples from which relevant constitutive relationships can be derived and of field observations to confirm or modify mass-movement models. Since ice forms a significant part of many permafrost soils, a study of the creep behavior of ice serves as a reasonable guide to the creep behavior of frozen soils.

Table 7.6 Creep constants for ice (from Nixon and McRoberts, 1976)

Temperature, °C	A (year $\cdot$ kPa^m)$^{-1}$	m	B (year $\cdot$ kPa^n)$^{-1}$	n
0	7.5×10^{-4}	1.34	3.6×10^{-10}	4
-2	1.8×10^{-5}	1.72	5.5×10^{-11}	4
-5	2.9×10^{-6}	1.92	1.5×10^{-11}	4
-11	3.3×10^{-7}	2.12	1.8×10^{-12}	4

McRoberts (1975a) and Nixon and McRoberts (1976) have reviewed published creep data from a variety of sources and have suggested values for A, B, n, and m for ice. A range of these values for several temperatures is given in Table 7.6.

Falls

This form of mass movement found along the banks of rivers or large bodies of water is caused by the undermining action of warm water aided by the physical erosion and removal of thawed soil by river or wave action. This waterline erosion results in the formation of a large niche, or undercut, and the subsequent breaking off by large blocks of frozen material. This process of bank recession caused by thermal and fluvial erosion of permafrost at the waterline was reviewed by Gill (1972), who noted the importance of wave action in increasing erosion rates in the Mackenzie River delta. He found that the greatest period of undercutting occurred in mid-July, when water temperatures reached as high as 19°C. At this time of year high winds in conjunction with high water temperatures may cause niche penetration of up to 3 to 5 m in less than 48 h. Movements of approximately 180 m in 19 years were observed along one shifting channel and are attributed to thermal-erosional processes. Similar rates of 10 m/year were also reported in the Colville River area by Walker and Arnborg (1963). Observations by McRoberts (1973) along the Mountain River, a highly braided gravel-bed tributary to the Mackenzie River, suggested lateral shifts of up to 100 m over four summer seasons, due to fall landslides, a typical example of which is shown in Fig. 7.7.

7.4 FACTORS CONTRIBUTING TO SLOPE INSTABILITY

River Erosion

The influence of oversteepening, erosive action of rivers is a major causative agent in slope instability for a wide range of landslide forms. The importance of river action in promoting landslide activity along the Mackenzie Valley has been commented on by Hughes et al. (1973) and McRoberts and Morgenstern

(1973). Block and multiple retrogressive slides can be found in parts of the valley in reaches where intense toe erosion is occurring. However, the same terrain types which are prolific producers of slide activity become stable on the cessation of active toe erosion. Along many reaches of the Mackenzie River well-developed boulder pavements protect the banks up to the trim line. These boulder pavements apparently result from an ice-shove mechanism (Kindle, 1918) and have a riprap, or stabilizing, effect on the banks. Kindle (1918) commented that the boulder pavements are effective in protecting clay islands from erosion, and McRoberts and Morgenstern (1973) noted that few landslides occur in boulder-paved reaches. Field evidence certainly indicates that erosion prevention and toe loading are viable methods for slope stabilization in permafrost terrain.

Unlike landslide activity associated with river action in temperate regions, the importance of river action is as much one of thermal influence as physical erosion. For example, slopes abandoned from direct erosive attack by natural processes may be stabilized not only by the halting of continued toe erosion but also by the cessation of thermal degradation. In more northerly regions, further stability may also be realized if permafrost becomes reestablished in the now more thermally stable portion of a landslide toe.

The prevention or stabilization of landslides in permafrost influenced by river action, whether they are falls, bimodal flows, or deep-seated landslides, revolves around the development of adequate bank protection. For the larger landslide types, toe-loading berms may be required to restore an overall balance of forces. In general the design requirements for such designs are identical with conventional practice in more temperate regions.

A parallel and common technique used in landslide stabilization in temperate regions which may not find application in these cases is the reduction of shear stress in the potential landslide mass by benching or flattening. Slopes which may develop slope instability in cold regions tend to have ice-rich permafrost conditions. Benching or cutting back such slopes may introduce significant surficial instability problems in the exposed permafrost soils requiring further stabilization.

Vegetation Cover

Surface vegetation in the form of living canopy and the underlying moss or peat cover exerts a tremendous influence on the stability of thawing slopes. This control is experienced by both the energy and mass budgets at the interface between permafrost soils and the atmosphere. In passing we have already considered some of these influences, but it is useful to restate them by considering the following examples.

The most obvious control established by vegetation is the insulating effect gained from the combination of tree cover and an organic or peat layer, commonly found in the forested section of permafrost regions. If this cover is destroyed either artificially or naturally, thermal degradation can result. The consequent thickening of the active layer or the long-term loss of permafrost may lead to significant slope-stability problems. For example, Linell (1973) reviewed a 26-year permafrost degradation experiment at Fairbanks, Alas., where permafrost degraded at two sites. One site was cleared of all living vegetation except the moss and peat cover, and then the vegetation was allowed to reestablish. The second site was cleared of all vegetation down to the bare mineral-soil surface and then kept clear for the ensuing 26 years. The permafrost began and continued to degrade at both sites, while at a third and identical undisturbed control site permafrost was maintained. The original data presented by Linell (1973) are replotted in Fig. 7.14 showing depth of degradation against the square root of time in years$^{1/2}$. It is of interest to note that permafrost is degrading at rates of 0.85 and 1.29 m/year$^{1/2}$ for the two sites. It can therefore be expected that even for surface clearing using the most careful techniques in which all upright vegetation is removed but the organic mat remains intact, a deepening of the active layer or degradation in warmer permafrost may result. The mass balance is also affected by artificial vegetation removal or destruction as a result of forest fires. The loss of green canopy results in the removal of an effective natural process which by evapotranspiration tends to maintain un-saturated conditions or depressed pore-water pressures in the soil contained within the active layer. During periods of exceedingly heavy rainfall in conjunction with humid cloudy weather, evapotranspiration stops, and pore-water pressures increase as the active layer becomes saturated and a steady-state flow condition is reached. This tends to reduce the mobilized shear strengths, and as shear stresses have also increased as a result of complete saturation, failures may occur. This situation may occur only once in many years, in part as a result of extreme meteorological events, and accounts for the observations made by such workers as Hughes et al. (1973), Mackay and Mathews (1973), and Savel'yev

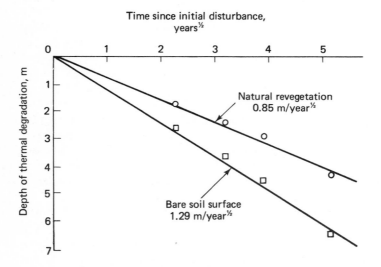

Figure 7.14 Permafrost degradation at a site in Alaska. (*Data from Linell, 1973.*)

(1972) on the destructive effects of periods of intense rainfall on the stability of sloping active layers.

However, when the canopy is removed, the sequence of events which promotes instability during the undisturbed phase can be encountered during much less extreme meteorological conditions. This may also account for the frequent observation on the importance of forest fires in promoting instability. Therefore, with regard to shallow-slope stability, vegetation removal has two effects: (1) the depth and rate of thaw increases, and the possibility exists that instability can be produced; (2) the mass balance is affected so that it is possible for stable slopes to become potentially unstable due to changes in the evapotranspiration rate alone. The implications with respect to potential stabilization schemes is that retardation of the rate and depth of thaw and the removal of surface runoff by drainage-control measures will be effective in realizing stable slope conditions.

Vegetation covers also play an important role in the development of bimodal flows or in the stability of cut slopes. In unburnt areas, it has been observed (Lotspeich, 1971; McRoberts 1973) that organic vegetation covers are frequently found draped over the head and side scarps of bimodal flows. The curtains never develop over about 2 to 3 m in height, as their height is limited by the tensile strength that can develop. In small flows, where the headscarp is of the order of 0.6 to 0.9 m in height, the draped vegetation cover significantly retards the melting of the headscarp. When a fire occurs and the mat is desiccated, the natural resilience of the mat is lost and the vegetation curtain cannot develop. Small flows which begin as a result of the fire or from other natural processes can then develop at a rapid rate once this natural stabilizing effect is lost. Thus while there are no natural processes available which can stabilize the flow, it is evident that well-devised artificial insulation of the headscarp region would have the same effect.

Given the consequences of vegetation removal, it follows that the revegetation of disturbed permafrost slopes may constitute an important design tool in slope-stabilization schemes in that it may allow for a rapid return to original conditions. However, the application of revegetation on slope designs may be overstated if careful attention is not paid to the design problems in the interim between initial disturbance and the establishment of sufficient vegetation either in the form of green canopy to retard thaw or root establishment to prevent surficial erosion. The Fairbanks case record shown in Fig. 7.14 also makes it clear that revegetation will not necessarily prevent thermal degradation although it does have a significant and beneficial effect in reducing the rate of degradation. The revegetation of northern slopes as a design factor should be encouraged, as it offers a long-term enhancement of slope stability.

Drainage Control

The control of internal slope drainage may offer beneficial effects in certain permafrost slopes by reducing pore pressures and thereby increasing effective stresses. The slope-failure modes most amenable to internal drainage control are skin flows or solifluction slopes. While counterfort or trench drains are a useful technique in the stabilization of shallow slopes in temperate regions, they may not be completely suitable for thawing active layers, as the surficial disturbance associated with their presence may aggravate slope stability. This may be of more concern if trench drains are contemplated for use as a preventative measure. However, if failures have already occurred, the incremental effects associated with the geothermal influence of trench drains of themselves will be far outweighed by the drainage effects. The use of closely spaced sand drains or wicks may be considered, especially as preventative measures. The theory for the use of sand drains has been investigated by Nixon (1973) and can readily be modified for use in slope-stabilization schemes.

The regulation of surficial drainage is an indispensable component of the overall design of permafrost slopes, especially for fine-grained ice-rich soils, which are vulnerable to the combined thermal and mechanical erosion of running water. For example, concentration of surface runoff in a disturbed permafrost slope can rapidly result in the formation of a deep gully. Ice-rich soils which are now exposed on either side of the gully walls will in turn rapidly lead to the formation of a bimodal flow. This landslide form or the gully itself may threaten any engineering works located on or above the slope segment, and the resultant siltation may be of environmental concern.

While erosion-control guidelines are well established in more southerly regions, the presence of permafrost complicates the implementation of many traditional methods. For example, drainage ditches will find little application in permafrost slopes. However, in some instances thermokarst ponds may develop on shallow-slope segments, and it may be necessary to drain them. In such cases a wide shallow ditch can be formed by a few passes of a tracked vehicle in the early spring; this induces sufficient surficial disturbance to promote some slight thermal degradation, causing thaw settlement, and in turn a ditch. Ditches formed in this fashion retain their vegetative cover, an essential element in protecting the underlying permafrost. The diversion of water using such flow obstructions as diversion dikes and dispension barriers consisting of mounds of placed trees or shrubs may find application. The identification of significant drainways, especially on cross-slope segments, is another aspect of drainage control. In many permafrost terrains drainage patterns are defined and frequently obscured by vegetation, and remote sensing or a vegetation analysis may be required to delineate such features. In any event, once they are detected, design measures must be devised to conduct any potentially erosive flows safely across or away from the slope. Dingman (1975) has presented a literature review and synthesis of hydrologic effects of frozen ground.

Slope-revegetation programs may be an essential ingredient of erosion-control designs in permafrost slopes. If construction activities result in the exposing of bare soil, any overall erosion-control program will generally be less costly if revegetation can be quickly established. Revegetation will certainly augment long-term integrity.

Construction Disturbance

In no other area of slope-stability design do construction activities offer such an important influence as in permafrost terrain, especially in regard to the design of shallow thawing slopes. From the initial site-clearing operation to actual construction and through to final cleanup, inappropriate construction activities may disrupt slope stability. For example, for any tree- or brush-covered slopes, site clearance is required. If this operation is done by hand and debris removed from the site, vegetation disturbance is kept to a minimum. However, if mechanical equipment is used for site clearance, the integrity of the vegetation mat can be severely disrupted, possibly leading to erosion problems or slope instability. Vegetation disturbance may also be caused by vehicular movement on access roads located on slope segments. Current planning in the Canadian arctic calls for the use of compacted snow roads to prevent direct traffic on the tundra surface. Experience in the Mackenzie valley suggests that if snow roads are not used, vehicular traffic directly on the exposed vegetation surface can result in slope failures, especially in fine-grained ice-rich soils. Because the control of construction activities may be some distance removed from the designer, either the implications of disturbance effects must be accounted for in the design or a mechanism for control must be available to ensure that design assumptions are realized.

Seismic Effects

The possible implications of seismic events may require consideration in the design of thawing permafrost slopes depending upon the tectonic activity of the design location and the implications of failure. One method by which seismic influence can be accounted for is the pseudostatic method, where the effects of ground motion are allowed for by applying a horizontal ground acceleration N, defined as some percentage of gravity. Newmark (1965) discussed the application of this method in detail. For this case, the factor of safety for a thawing infinite slope becomes

$$F_s = \frac{\gamma'}{\gamma} \frac{[1/(1 + 2R^2) - N \tan \theta] \tan \phi'}{\tan \theta + N} \tag{7.25}$$

The major factor in the seismic stability of frozen slopes is the gain of strength of frozen soils as a function of rate of loading. Unlike slopes in unfrozen or thawed soils, where seismic influence may result in a loss of shear strength, the mobilized shear strength in frozen slopes may be considered to be increased during a seismic event; i.e., if an analysis is undertaken using a frozen-soil strength consistent with an imposed time to failure of the duration of an earthquake, higher shear strengths will be mobilized than those obtained in situ during long-term slope stability.

The second consideration in thawing permafrost slopes is whether or not the thawed permafrost is seismically liquefiable. Depending upon soil type and relative density, position of the groundwater table, and the intensity and duration of ground shaking, thawed permafrost may be considered to be liquefiable. Methods of dealing with this problem are available (Seed and Idriss, 1971).

While there are many documented slope failures due to seismic liquefaction in unfrozen soils, the author is not aware of any documented case records in thawing permafrost. Any consideration of the liquefaction potential of permafrost soils should take into account the possible influence of the cryogenic structure. The macrostructure imparted to a thawed soil by ice-lens formation and the formation of peds, or nuggetlike chunks of overconsolidated soil, may significantly alter the response of a thawed soil compared with that expected for similar soils which have never experienced a freeze-thaw cycle.

We have seen in Sec. 7.2 that liquefaction or zero effective-stress conditions may develop in fine-grained clayey soils due to thaw consolidation. Thaw consolidation is of concern in soils which have low values of the coefficient of consolidation, while soils which have a seismic liquefaction potential have a high c_v. Therefore, it is unlikely that a soil susceptible to seismic liquefaction will be of concern with regard to thaw-consolidation effects or that a soil capable of sustaining excess pore pressures during thaw could be further liquefied during a period of ground shaking.

REFERENCES

Anderson, D. M., R. C. Reynolds, and J. Brown. 1969. Bentonite Debris Flows in Northern Alaska, *Science*, **164**: 173–174.

Benedict, J. B. 1970. Downslope Soil Movement in a Colorado Alpine Region, *J. Arct. Alp. Res.*, **2**(3): 165–226.

Bird, J. B. 1967. The Physiography of Arctic Canada, John Hopkins, Baltimore.

Capps, S. R. 1919. The Kantishna Region, Alaska, *U.S. Geol. Surv. Bull.* 687, pp. 7–112.

———. 1940. Geology of the Alaska Railroad, *U.S. Geol. Surv. Bull.* 907, pp. 1–197.

Carson, M. A., and M. J. Kirkby. 1972. "Hillslope Form and Process," Cambridge University Press, London.

Chandler, R. J. 1970. Solifluction on Low Angle Slopes in Northamptonshire, *Q.J. Eng. Geol.*, **3**(1): 65–69.

———. 1972. Periglacial Mudslides in Vestspitsbergen, *Q.J. Eng. Geol.*, **5**(3): 223–242.

Dingman, S. L. 1975. Hydrologic Effects of Frozen Ground, *U.S. Army Cold Reg. Res. Eng. Lab. Spec. Rep.* 218, Hanover, N.H.

Embleton, L., and L. King. 1975. "Periglacial Geomorphology," Arnold, London.

Gill, D. 1972. Modification of Levee Morphology by Erosion in the Mackenzie River Delta, N.W.T., in R. G. Price and A. Sugden (eds.), Polar Geomorphology, *Inst. Br. Geog. Spec. Publ.* 4, pp. 123–138.

Hardy, R. M., and H. A. Morrison. 1972. Slope Stability and Drainage Considerations for Arctic Pipelines, *Natl. Res. Counc. Tech. Mem.* 104, pp. 249–267.

Harris, C. 1972. Processes of Soil Movement in Turf-banked Solifluction Lobes, Okstindan, Norway, in R. G. Price and A. Sugden (eds.), Polar Geomorphology, *Inst. Br. Geog. Spec. Publ.* 4, pp. 155–173.

Higashi, A., and A. E. Corté. 1971. Solifluction: A Model Experiment, *Science*, **171**: 480–482.

Hughes, O. L., J. J. Veillette, J. Pilion, P. T. Henley, and R. O. Everdingen. 1973. Terrain Evaluation with Respect to Pipeline Construction, Mackenzie Transportation Corridor, [*Gov. Can.*] *Environ. Soc. Comm. North. Pipeline, Task Force North. Oil Dev. Rep.* 73–37.

Hutchinson, J. N. 1974. Periglacial Solifluction: An Approximate Mechanism for Clayey Soils, *Geotechnique*, **24**: 438–443.

Isaacs, R. M., and J. A. Code. 1972. Problems in Engineering Geology Related to Pipeline Construction, *Natl. Res. Counc. Tech. Mem.* 104, pp. 147–179.

Jahn, A. 1975. Problems of the Periglacial Zone, *USNTIS* TT 72–54011.

Kachadoorian, R., and O. J. Ferrians. 1973. Permafrost Related Engineering Geology Problems Posed by the Trans-Alaska Pipeline, *North Am. Contrib. 2d Int. Conf. Permafrost, Yakutsk, U.S.S.R.*, National Academy of Sciences, Washington, pp. 684–688.

Kindle, E. M. 1918. Notes on Sedimentation in the Mackenzie River Basin, *J. Geol.*, **76**: 341–360.

Lamothe, L., and D. St. Onge. 1961. A Note on Periglacial Erosional Processes in the Isachsen Area, N.W.T., *Geogr. Bull. Can.* 16, pp. 104–113.

Lachenbruch, A. H. 1970. Some Estimates of the Thermal Effects of a Heated Pipeline in Permafrost, *U.S. Geol. Surv. Circ.* 632.

Linell, K. A. 1973. Long-Term Effects of Vegetative Cover on Permafrost Stability in an Area of Discontinuous Permafrost, *North Am. Contrib. 2d Int. Conf. Permafrost, Yakutsk, U.S.S.R.*, National Academy of Sciences, Washington, pp. 688–693.

Lotspeich, F. B. 1971. Environment Guidelines for Road Construction in Alaska, Environmental Protection Agency, College, Alas.

Mackay, J. R. 1966. Segregated Epigenetic Ice and Slumps in Permafrost, Mackenzie Delta Area, N.W.T., *Geogr. Bull. Can.* 8, pp. 59–80.

———, and W. H. Mathews. 1973. Geomorphology and Quaternary History of the Mackenzie River Valley near Fort Good Hope, N.W.T., *Can. J. Earth Sci.*, **10**(1): 26–41.

McPhail, J. F., W. B. McMullen, and A. W. Murfitt. 1976. Yukon River to Prudhoe Bay: Lessons in Arctic Design and Construction, *Civ. Eng. (N.Y.)*, **46**(2): 78–82.

McRoberts, E. C. 1972. Discussion, *Proc. Can. North. Pipeline Res. Conf. Ottawa, Natl. Res. Counc. Can. Tech. Mem.* 104, pp. 291–295.

———. 1973. The Stability of Slopes in Permafrost, unpublished Ph.D. thesis, University of Alberta, Edmonton.

———. 1975a. Some Aspects of a Simple Secondary Creep Model for Deformations in Permafrost Slopes, *Can. Geotech. J.*, **12**: 98–105.

———. 1975b. A Note on Field Observations of Thawing in Soils, *Can. Geotech. J.*, **12**: 126–130.

———, and N. R. Morgenstern. 1973. A Study of Landslides in the Vicinity of the Mackenzie River, Mile 205 to 660, [*Can. Gov.*] *Environ. Soc. Comm. North. Pipelines, Task Force North. Oil Dev.*

——— and ———. 1974a. The Stability of Thawing Slopes, *Can. Geotech. J.*, **11**: 447–469.

——— and ———. 1974b. The Stability of Slopes in Frozen Soil, Mackenzie Valley, N.W.T., *Can. Geotech. J.*, **11**: 554–573.

———, and J. F. Nixon. 1977. Extensions to Thawing Slope Stability Theory, *2d Int. Symp. Cold Reg. Eng., Univ. Alaska*, pp. 262–276.

Morgenstern, N. R. 1967. Submarine Slumping and the Initiation of Turbidity Currents, in A. F. Richards (ed.), "Marine Geotechnique," University of Illinois Press, Urbana. pp. 189–220.

———, and J. F. Nixon. 1971. One-dimensional Consolidation of Thawing Soils, *Can. Geotech. J.*, **8**: 558–565.

Newmark, N. M. 1965. Effects of Earthquakes on Dams and Embankments, *Can. Geotech. J.*, **15**: 139–159.

Nixon, J. F. 1973. The consolidation of thawing soils, unpublished Ph.D. Thesis, University of Alberta, Edmonton.

———, and E. C. McRoberts. 1973. A Study of Some Factors Affecting the Thawing of Frozen Soils, *Can. Geotech. J.*, **10**: 439–452.

——— and ———. 1976. A Design Approach for Pile Foundations in Permafrost, *Can. Geotech. J.*, **13**: 40–57.

Pufahl, D. E. 1975. The Stability of Thawing Slopes, unpublished Ph.D. thesis, University of Alberta, Edmonton.

———, N. R. Morgenstern, and W. D. Roggensack. 1974. Observations on Recent Highway Cuts in Permafrost, *Rep. Dep. Civ. Eng. Univ. Alta. Terrain Sci. Div. Geol. Surv. Can.*

Savel'yev, V. S. 1972. Effects of Groundwater on Stability of Slopes and Structures Erected on Them on Thawing of Frozen Soils, *U.S. Cold Reg. Res. Eng. Lab. Draft Trans.* 369, Hanover, N.H.

Seed, H. B., and I. M. Idriss. 1971. Simplified Procedure for Evaluating Soil Liquefaction Potential, *J. Soil Mech. Found. Div. Am. Soc. Civ. Eng.,* **97**(SM9): 1249–1274.

Sigafoos, R. S., and D. M. Hopkins. 1952. Soil Unstability on Slopes in Regions of Perennially Frozen Ground, in Frost Action in Soils, *Highw. Res. Board Spec. Rep.* 2, pp. 176–192.

Siple, P. A. 1952. Ice Blocked Drainage as a Principal Factor in Frost Heave, Slump and Solifluction, in Frost Action in Soils, *Highw. Res. Board Spec. Rep.* 2, pp. 172–175.

Smith, N., and R. Berg. 1973. Encountering Massive Ground Ice during Road Construction in Central Alaska, *North Am. Contrib. 2d Int. Conf. Permafrost, Yakutsk, U.S.S.R.,* National Academy of Sciences, Washington, pp. 730–735.

Taber, S. 1943. Perennially Frozen Ground in Alaska, *Geol. Soc. Am. Bull.* 54, pp. 1433–1548.

Thomson, S., and E. F. Lobacz. 1973. Shear Strength at a Thaw Interface, *North Am. Contrib. 2d Int. Conf. Permafrost, Yakutsk, U.S.S.R.,* National Academy of Sciences, Washington, pp. 419–426.

Varnes, D. J. 1958. Landslide Types and Processes, in E. B. Eckert (ed.), Landslides and Engineering Practice, *Highw. Res. Board Spec. Rep.* 29, pp. 20–45.

Wahrhaftig, C., and R. F. Black. 1958. Engineering Geology along Part of the Alaska Railroad, *U.S. Geol. Surv. Prof. Pap.* 293, pp. 69–118.

Walker, H. J., and L. Arnborg. 1963. Permafrost and Ice Wedge Effect on River Bank Erosion, *Proc. 1st Int. Permafrost, Conf., NAS-NRC Publ.* 1287, pp. 164–171.

Washburn, A. L. 1947. Reconnaissance Geology of Portions of Victoria Island and Adjacent Regions, *Geol. Soc. Am. Mem.* 22.

———. 1967. Instrumental Observations of Mass-Wasting in the Mesters Vig District, Greenland, *Medd. Groenl.,* **166**(4): 1–297.

———. 1973. Periglacial Processes and Environments, Arnold, London.

Weeks, A. G. 1969. The Stability of Natural Slopes in South-east England as Affected by Periglacial Activity, *Q.J. Eng. Geol.,* **2**: 49–63.

Williams, P. J. 1966. Downslope Soil Movements at a Sub-arctic Location with Regard to Variations with Depth, *Can. Geotech. J.,* **4**: 191–203.

RESPONSE OF FROZEN GROUND TO DYNAMIC LOADING

Ted S. Vinson

INTRODUCTION

Problems requiring a knowledge of the dynamic response of frozen ground can arise in connection with (1) vibrating machinery, e.g., turbines, compressors, or radar installations being placed on or in frozen ground deposits, (2) geophysical exploration for mineral or energy reserves in frozen ground deposits, (3) excavation of frozen ground deposits by blasting, and (4) earthquake loadings of frozen ground deposits. The ground motions associated with these problems are significantly different and are shown in Fig. 8.1. Three components of motion are important to solving dynamic problems: (1) frequency (or frequency content), (2) amplitude, and (3) duration. These terms are identified in Fig. 8.1a. Frequency relates to the rate at which the load is applied, the greater the frequency the higher the rate. Amplitude is associated with the magnitude of the applied load. It is usually expressed in terms of the strain (or stress) level caused by the loading. Duration is associated with the length of time over which the loading acts.

Vibratory machinery causes periodic loading which may be either harmonic or nonharmonic, as shown in Fig. 8.1a and b. The loading is of a relatively high frequency and subjects the ground to relatively low strain amplitudes. The duration is equal to the time interval over which the machinery is operating. Geophysical-exploration surveying techniques (Chap. 9) and blasting cause transient loading, as shown in Fig. 8.1c. The motion is characterized by its high-frequency content and short duration. In geophysical surveying the ground is subjected to low

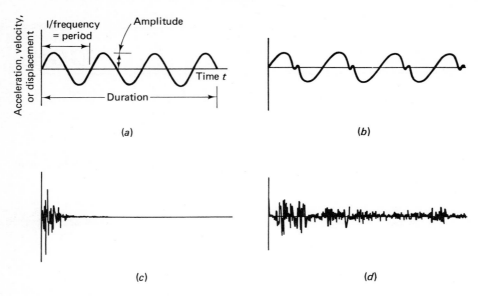

Figure 8.1 Dynamic-loading motion characteristics: (*a*) Harmonic, periodic, vibrating machinery; (*b*) nonharmonic, periodic, vibrating machinery; (*c*) transient, blasting, geophysical exploration; (*d*) irregular, earthquake.

strain amplitudes whereas close to a high-energy blast, e.g., a nuclear explosion, the ground is subject to high strain amplitudes. Transient motion usually attenuates rapidly with distance from the source. Earthquakes subject the ground to irregular loadings of relatively low frequency. During strong-motion earth-quakes the ground is subjected to high strain amplitudes, whereas during weak-motion earthquakes it is subjected to relatively low strain amplitudes of loading. The duration of loading is related to the magnitude of the earthquake. Strong-motion earthquake loadings can last for several minutes whereas weak-motion earthquakes generally last for only a few seconds.

Many different terms have been used to characterize the properties of frozen ground which are of significance to the analysis of dynamic-loading problems. These fall into two major groups. The first group, *dynamic stress-strain properties*, includes such terms as compression, dilatational, longitudinal, irrotational, primary, bulk, or P wave; shear, transverse, secondary, rotational, or S wave velocity; sound velocity; complex Young's and shear (rigidity) moduli; and dynamic Young's and shear (rigidity) moduli. The second group, *energy-absorbing properties*, includes such terms as angle of phase lag, attenuation coefficient, damping coefficient, loss factor, quality factor, log decrement, and damping ratio. Several of these terms are identified in Table 8.1, and conversion equations between them are given. The conversions between several of the dynamic stress-strain properties require representative values of Poisson's ratio, which are given for several soil types in Table 8.4.

This chapter is divided into three sections. Section 8.1 reviews field and laboratory techniques used to measure the dynamic properties of frozen ground. Section 8.2 presents a summary of dynamic properties of frozen ground measured in both the field and the laboratory. Emphasis is on the influence of several material and field and/or test-condition parameters on dynamic properties. Section 8.3 reviews the analytic techniques presently available for predicting the response of frozen ground to dynamic loadings and presents a guide to appropriate material properties for use in the analytic techniques.

Example 8.1 The complex Young's and shear modulus and loss factor have been determined for a frozen silt with a density of 1430 kg/m³ at a temperature of $-9°C$ under a dynamic load at a frequency of 1000 Hz. The values obtained are

$$E^* = 12.11 \text{ GN/m}^2 \qquad G^* = 4.28 \text{ GN/m}^2 \qquad \tan \delta = 0.031$$

Calculate values of the longitudinal-, shear-, and compression-wave velocities, quality factor, phase lag, damping ratio, and attenuation coefficient.

SOLUTION The shear- and longitudinal-wave velocities are given by

$$V_L = \left(\frac{E^*}{\rho}\right)^{1/2} = \left(\frac{12.11 \text{ GN/m}^2}{1430 \text{ kg/m}^3}\right)^{1/2} = 2910 \text{ m/s}$$

$$V_S = \left(\frac{G^*}{\rho}\right)^{1/2} = \left(\frac{4.28 \text{ GN/m}^2}{1430 \text{ kg/m}^3}\right)^{1/2} = 1730 \text{ m/s}$$

The compression-wave velocity can be calculated after Poisson's ratio is determined

$$\mu = \frac{E^*}{2G^*} - 1 = \frac{12.11 \text{ GN/m}^2}{2 \times 4.28 \text{ GN/m}^2} - 1 = 0.41$$

Then

$$V_p = \left[\frac{E^*}{\rho} \frac{1-\mu}{(1+\mu)(1-2\mu)}\right]^{1/2} = \left[\frac{12.11}{1430} \frac{1-0.41}{(1+0.41)(1-2 \times 0.41)}\right]^{1/2}$$

$$= 4437 \text{ m/s}$$

The quality factor, phase lag, and damping ratio are given by

$$Q = \frac{1}{\tan \delta} = \frac{1}{.031} = 32.3$$

$$\delta = \tan^{-1} \delta = \tan^{-1} 0.031 = 1.78°$$

$$D = \sin \frac{\delta}{2} = \sin \frac{1.78°}{2} = 0.015$$

Table 8.1 Conversion equations between terms to characterize dynamic properties

Given	Dynamic stress-strain properties			To calculate		
	Dynamic or complex Young's modulus E or E^*†	Dynamic or complex shear modulus G or G^*†	Poisson's ratio μ or μ^*†	Compression-wave velocity V_p	Shear-wave velocity V_s	Longitudinal-wave velocity V_L
E, ρ, μ	E	$\dfrac{E}{2(1+\mu)}$	μ	$\left[\dfrac{E}{\rho}\dfrac{1-\mu}{(1+\mu)(1-2\mu)}\right]^{1/2}$	$\ldots$	$\left(\dfrac{E}{\rho}\right)^{1/2}$
G, μ, ρ	$2(1+\mu)G$	G	μ	$\left[\dfrac{(1-\mu)2G}{(1-2\mu)\rho}\right]^{1/2}$	$\left(\dfrac{G}{\rho}\right)^{1/2}$	
E, G	E	G	$\dfrac{E}{2G}-1$	$\ldots$	$\left(\dfrac{G}{\rho}\right)^{1/2}$	$\left(\dfrac{E}{\rho}\right)^{1/2}$
ρ, μ, V_p	$\dfrac{V_p^2\rho(1-2\mu)(1+\mu)}{1-\mu}$	$\dfrac{(1-2\mu)\rho V_p^2}{2(1-\mu)}$	μ	V_p	$V_p\left[\dfrac{1-2\mu}{2(1-\mu)}\right]^{1/2}$	$V_p\left[\dfrac{(1+\mu)(1-2\mu)}{1-\mu}\right]^{1/2}$
ρ, μ, V_s	$2\rho(1+\mu)V_s^2$	ρV_s^2	μ	$V_s\left[\dfrac{2(1-\mu)}{1-2\mu}\right]^{1/2}$	V_s	$V_s[2(1+\mu)]^{1/2}$
ρ, V_p, V_s	$\dfrac{V_s^2(3V_p^2-4V_s^2)\rho}{V_p^2-V_s^2}$	ρV_s^2	$\dfrac{1}{2}\dfrac{V_p^2-2V_s^2}{V_p^2-V_s^2}$	V_p	V_s	

Energy-absorbing properties[‡]

Given	To calculate		
	Damping ratio D	Loss factor $\tan \delta$	Quality factor Q
Phase lag δ	$\sin \dfrac{\delta}{2}$	$\tan \delta$	$\dfrac{1}{\tan \delta}$
Attenuation coefficient a and wavelength λ	$\sin \dfrac{\tan^{-1}(a\lambda/2\pi)}{2}$	$a\,\dfrac{\lambda}{2\pi}$	$\dfrac{2\pi}{a\lambda}$
Damping coefficient β and angular frequency ω	$\sin \dfrac{\tan^{-1}(2\beta/\omega)}{2}$	$\dfrac{2\beta}{\omega}$	$\dfrac{\omega}{2\beta}$
Log decrement Δ	$\left(\dfrac{\Delta^2}{4\pi^2+\Delta^2}\right)^{1/2}$	$\tan 2\left[\sin^{-1}\left(\dfrac{\Delta^2}{4\pi^2+\Delta^2}\right)^{1/2}\right]$	$\dfrac{\pi}{\Delta}$

† Complex moduli are not significantly different from elastic moduli for materials with low damping.
‡ Conversion equations for materials with low damping.

The attenuation coefficient can be calculated after the wavelength has been determined

$$\lambda = \frac{V_L}{f} = \frac{2910 \text{ m/s}}{1000 \text{ Hz}} = 2.91 \text{ m}$$

$$\alpha = \frac{2\pi \tan \delta}{\lambda} = \frac{2\pi \times 0.031}{2.91 \text{ m}} = 0.067 \text{ m}^{-1}$$

8.1 MEASUREMENT OF DYNAMIC PROPERTIES OF FROZEN GROUND

The dynamic properties of frozen ground have been evaluated in the field with seismic methods (associated with geophysical exploration surveys) and cylindrical in situ tests and in the laboratory from ultrasonic, resonant-frequency, and cyclic triaxial tests. Seismic, ultrasonic, and resonant-frequency methods are associated with relatively high frequencies and low strain amplitudes of loading. The cylindrical in situ test and cyclic triaxial method are associated with high and low frequencies, respectively, and high strain amplitudes of loading.

Seismic Method

Dynamic properties of frozen ground are determined by the seismic method as a by-product of geophysical-exploration sounding, i.e., reflection or refraction surveys. In the seismic method elastic waves are produced at the ground surface or at a shallow depth within a hole either by an explosive charge or the impact of a hammer. From a knowledge of the travel time for the waves to reach a point at a known distance from the source the wave velocities can be determined. The waves are detected with vibration-sensitive instruments called seismographs. The waves produced are of two different types, boundary waves and body waves. In most seismic work the boundary (surface) waves are not used directly, but they may interfere with the signals of the body waves, which are used. The body waves are of a compressional-dilatational or shear nature and can be further classified as direct, reflected, or refracted. The names direct-arrival, reflection, or refraction survey indicate the measurement of the associated waves. A significant number of velocity measurements of glacial ice have been made with reflection surveys. Velocity measurements of frozen soil and rock have generally been made with refraction surveys. Velocity measurements in ice sheets have been made with reflection and refraction surveys.

The basic elements of a reflection survey at a site with horizontally layered strata are shown in Fig. 8.2a. There are two possible paths for waves to travel from the source to the detector: (1) directly from the source to the detector, and (2) from the source to the interface of layer 1 and 2 and back up to the detector. The reflection survey is performed by recording the arrival times t for the direct and reflected waves with detectors placed at several distances x from

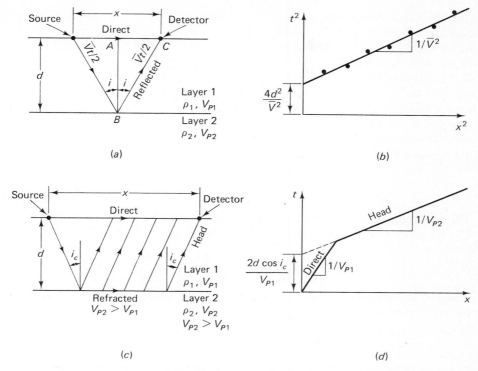

Figure 8.2 Seismic methods of determining wave velocities: (a) reflection survey; (b) t^2 vs. x^2; (c) refraction survey; (d) travel time vs. distance.

the source. The average velocity $\overline{V}$ of layer 1 can be determined from a consideration of the geometry of triangle ABC in Fig. 8.2a. The hypotenuse of triangle ABC is $\overline{V}t/2$. Then by the pythagorean theorem

$$\frac{\overline{V}^2 t^2}{4} = \frac{x^2}{4} + d^2 \tag{8.1}$$

If the depth d to the interface of layer 1 and 2 is known, $\overline{V}$ can be solved for directly with Eq. (8.1). Alternatively, if the depth is not known, $\overline{V}$ can be determined by rearranging Eq. (8.1) as follows

$$t^2 = \frac{x^2}{\overline{V}^2} + \frac{4d^2}{\overline{V}^2} \tag{8.2}$$

This is the equation of a straight line for t^2 vs. x^2. Therefore, if t^2 is plotted against x^2, as shown in Fig. 8.2b, the slope of the best-fit straight line through the data set is $1/\overline{V}^2$.

The basic elements of a refraction survey at a site with horizontally layered strata are shown in Fig. 8.2c. Again, there are two possible paths for the waves to travel: (1) directly from the source to the detector and (2) from the source to the interface of layer 1 and 2, along the interface, and up to the detector. If the distance x is small, the direct wave will reach the detector before any other. If the distance x is large, however, the refracted wave traveling along the top of the faster-velocity layer 2 will reach the detector first. If one plots the travel time for the first wave arrivals at the detector as a function of distance, as shown in Fig. 8.2d, the velocity of layer 1 and 2, V_{p1} and V_{p2}, can be determined. The travel time for the direct wave t_d is given by

$$t_d = \frac{x}{V_{p1}} \tag{8.3}$$

This is the equation of a straight line through the origin, as shown in Fig. 8.2d. The travel time for the refracted wave t_r is given by

$$t_r = \frac{d}{V_{p1} \cos i_c} + \frac{x - 2d \tan i_c}{V_{p2}} + \frac{d}{V_{p1} \cos i_c} \tag{8.4}$$

where i_c is the critical angle of incidence of the refracted wave. Substituting the relationships

$$\sin i_c = \frac{V_{p1}}{V_{p2}} \quad \text{and} \quad \cos i_c = \left[1 - \left(\frac{V_{p1}^2}{V_{p2}^2}\right)\right]^{1/2}$$

into Eq. (8.4) and rearranging terms, one arrives at

$$t_r = \frac{x}{V_{p2}} + \frac{2d \cos i_c}{V_{p1}} \tag{8.5}$$

Equation (8.5) represents a straight line with a slope of $1/V_{p2}$, as shown in Fig. 8.2d.

There are limitations on both the reflection and refraction method to determine wave velocities of frozen ground. The refraction method is only applicable to field situations where a lower-velocity layer overlies a higher-velocity layer. In the reflection method the reflected waves arrive at the recording station after the detector has already been excited by direct waves. It is difficult to distinguish clearly the exact time of arrival of the reflected wave unless one has a relatively thick upper layer so that the time of arrival of the direct and reflected wave is significantly different. (Seasonally frozen ground and thin permafrost are far too shallow to be investigated by the reflection method.) In theory, energy-absorbing properties in terms of the attenuation coefficient α can be determined by seismic methods. In practice, however, they are extremely difficult to determine.

The horizontal layered system chosen to illustrate the principles of the reflection and refraction method is obviously quite elementary. More advanced treatments of the subject which relate to complex geometry are given in many textbooks, e.g., Dobrin (1960) and Grant and West (1965). An excellent treatment of the applicability of the reflection and refraction methods in cold regions including a theoretical treatment of complex field problems and equipment requirements is given by Roethlisberger (1972). Chapter 9 also contains information on field investigations using geophysical techniques.

Cylindrical in Situ Test

In the cylindrical in situ test an explosive is detonated along the entire length of a borehole, and the time for the waves generated to travel to instrument stations at various distances from the borehole is recorded. The compression-wave velocity is the slope of the best-fit straight line through the data points on a plot of station distance vs. travel time. The attenuation coefficient as a function of frequency can be determined from a comparison of the amplitudes of the motion recorded at increasing distances from the borehole.

The field configuration for a cylindrical in situ test conducted near Eielson Air Force Base, Alas. (Blouin, 1976) is shown in Fig. 8.3. A 0.6-m-diameter borehole was drilled to a depth of 10 m. The hole was filled with a racked explosive, and detonators were placed at 1.5-m intervals. With this spacing there is a negligible delay in the detonation of the explosive along the length of the

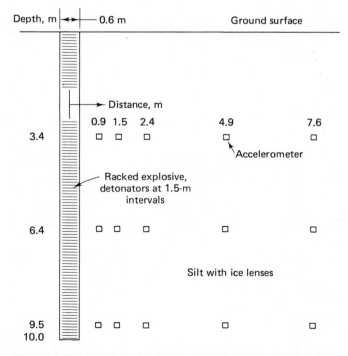

Figure 8.3 Field configuration for cylindrical in situ test, Eielson Air Force Base, Alas.

borehole. Accelerometers were located in 0.2-m boreholes at ranges of 0.9, 1.5, 2.4, 4.9, and 7.6 m from the borehole and at depths of 3.4, 6.4, and 9.5 m from the ground surface. The depths at which the accelerometers were installed varied according to major changes in the strata at the site. The accelerometers were encapsulated in an epoxy resin canister, which was fixed securely in the instrumentation hole. The instrumentation holes were placed on different azimuths to eliminate errors associated with diffraction of the stress waves around a hole in the same path as another hole.

Ultrasonic Methods

Both the pulse-transmission (pulse first arrival) and critical-angle method have been used to evaluate ultrasonic wave velocities and damping properties of frozen materials. In most of the investigations the pulse-transmission technique has been employed because of its simplicity.

In the pulse-transmission technique a sample is impulsed at one end, and the travel time required for the wave produced to reach the other end of the sample is measured. The wave velocity V is then computed from

$$V = \frac{L}{t_L} \tag{8.6}$$

where L is the length of the sample (distance traversed by the pulse) and t_L is the pulse transit time over L. The main advantage of the pulse-transmission technique over other laboratory test techniques is that an arbitrarily shaped sample can be tested. In general, however, cylindrical samples are used.

A schematic diagram of a typical pulse-transmission test system is shown in Fig. 8.4a. The pulse generator supplies a short-duration electric pulse to the piezoelectric crystal in contact with one end of the sample. The piezoelectric crystal converts the electric pulse into a mechanical wave, which is transmitted to the sample, travels through it, and is received by the piezoelectric crystal at the other end of the sample. The receiving crystal converts this to an electric output signal, which is generally filtered and amplified before being input to an oscilloscope. At the same time that the pulse generator excites the piezoelectric crystal it sends a signal to a device (several types are available) which allows the travel time of the wave to be determined. Measured transit times must be corrected for instrumentation delays. The error of the velocity measurement is typically less than 1 percent.

To obtain the longitudinal body wave V_p from a pulse-transmission test the sample dimension D normal to the direction of wave propagation must be large compared with the length λ of the transmitted wave. In general D/λ should be greater than 2. To avoid excessive attenuation of the transmitted wave, the wavelength should be long compared with the grain size of the sample (Thill et al, 1974).

The critical-angle method is based upon the variation in intensity of transmitted-wave energy with the angle of incidence α between a wave train

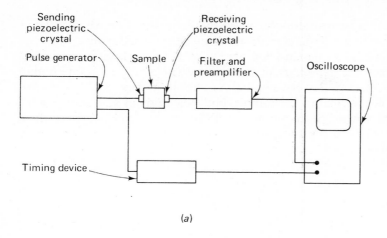

(a)

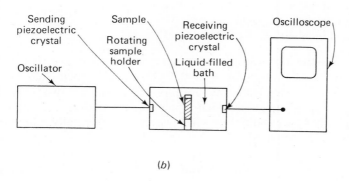

(b)

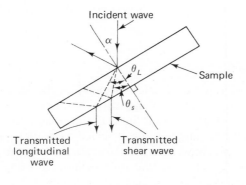

(c)

Figure 8.4 Schematic diagram of ultrasonic test equipment: (a) pulse-transmission method; (b) critical-angle method; (c) wave transmission through parallel plate.

and sample face. In a typical test system, as shown in Fig. 8.4b, the oscillator excites the sending piezoelectric crystal, which produces a mechanical wave in the fluid at one end of the liquid-filled bath. The wave impinges on one side of the disk sample. The sample is in a holder which is free to rotate about an axis perpendicular to the wave train. As shown in Fig. 8.4c, when the incident wave is not normal to the sample, both longitudinal and shear waves are induced in the sample. Since the wave velocity in the solid is greater than in the liquid, the waves in the solid are refracted away from the normal. From Snell's law the following relations hold:

$$\frac{\sin \alpha}{\sin \theta_L} = \frac{V_{Lq}}{V_L} \tag{8.7a}$$

$$\frac{\sin \alpha}{\sin \theta_s} = \frac{V_{Lq}}{V_s} \tag{8.7b}$$

where θ_L = angle of refraction for longitudinal waves
θ_s = angle of refraction for shear waves
V_{Lq} = velocity of incident wave in bath liquid

It is apparent from these relationships that the two types of waves are refracted at different angles in the sample because of the difference in their velocities. As the sample is rotated away from the normal, there will be two critical angles of incidence, $\alpha_{1,\,cr}$ and $\alpha_{2,\,cr}$, at which θ_L and θ_s, respectively, equal 90°. At these critical angles the longitudinal or shear waves will be totally reflected, and only the shear waves or longitudinal waves, respectively, will be transmitted. The determination of wave velocities in the sample involves monitoring the wave transmitted through the sample with the receiving piezoelectric crystal and noting when it is at a minimum amplitude. The first minimum allows V_L to be calculated from Eq. (8.7a) upon substitution of 90° for θ_L and $\alpha_{1,\,cr}$ for α. The second minimum allows V_s to be calculated from Eq. (8.7b) upon substitution of 90° for θ_s and $\alpha_{2,\,cr}$ for α.

Resonant-Frequency Method

In the resonant-frequency technique a sample is excited in the longitudinal or torsional mode and the longitudinal or shear wave velocity, respectively, is determined from the frequency at resonance†. Since the resonant frequencies are usually in the audible range, the technique is also referred to as the *sonic method*. Both beam and cylindrical samples have been used to evaluate dynamic properties of frozen soils. It appears likely, however, that only cylindrical samples will be used in the future owing to the comparative ease of sample preparation.

---

† It is also possible to determine the wave velocity in a cylindrical sample in the nonresonant condition (Stevens, 1975).

The resonant-frequency method employing cylindrical samples is commonly termed the *resonant-column test*. A schematic diagram of typical resonant-column-test equipment is shown in Fig. 8.5a. The vertical cylindrical sample is subjected to harmonic vibrations in the longitudinal or torsional mode with the drive motor(s). Piezoelectric accelerometers attached to the sample base are used to monitor the input motion. The other end of the sample is free except for a light, rigid cap with accelerometers attached to monitor the wave output through the sample. The accelerometer signals from the cap and base are output to various readout devices to determine when the sample is at resonance. It has been shown that the sample is at resonance when the ratio of the displacement (or equivalently, the acceleration) of the two ends, the sample ratio R, is a maximum (Lee, 1963; Brown and Selway, 1964). To conduct a test the operator vibrates the sample in either the longitudinal or torsional mode with the frequency at a low level. The frequency is increased, and the amplitude ratio is monitored. The first maximum of the amplitude ratio is the fundamental resonance. Successive maximums indicate the harmonics.

A mathematical model of the resonant-column-test system for a vertical cylindrical sample subjected to longitudinal harmonic vibrations has been

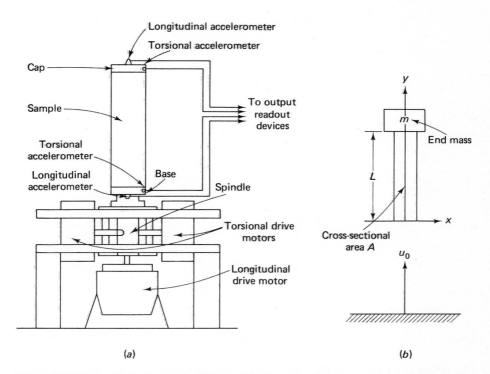

(a)   (b)

Figure 8.5 Resonant-frequency test equipment: (a) schematic of resonant-column-test equipment; (b) mathematical representation of resonant-column test.

provided by Norris and Young (1970) and Stevens (1975). If we start with the assumption that the frozen soil behaves like a linear viscoelastic material and that the stress wave propagated through the sample is one-dimensional, the equation of motion for the system represented in Fig. 8.5b can be written

$$\frac{\partial \sigma}{\partial y} = \frac{\rho \partial^2 (u + u_0)}{\partial t^2} \tag{8.8}$$

where σ = uniaxial stress
ρ = mass density of sample
u = axial (longitudinal) displacement of point in sample measured relative to the xy coordinate system fixed at driven end, $y = 0$, of the bar
u_0 = sinusoidal displacement equal to $U_0 e^{i\omega t}$

The stress σ and strain ε at any point in the bar can be written

$$\sigma = \bar{\sigma} e^{i\omega t} \tag{8.9}$$

$$\varepsilon = \bar{\varepsilon} e^{i(\omega t - \delta)} \tag{8.10}$$

where $\bar{\sigma}$ and $\bar{\varepsilon}$ are the amplitude of stress and strain during sinusoidal excitation and δ is the lag angle between the stress and strain vectors. The constitutive law between stress and strain can be obtained by dividing Eq. (8.9) by Eq. (8.10):

$$\frac{\sigma}{\varepsilon} = \frac{\bar{\sigma}}{\bar{\varepsilon}} e^{i\delta} = E^* \, e^{i\delta} = E \, i\omega \tag{8.11}$$

where E^* and E are the complex modulus and the magnitude of the complex modulus, respectively. Rewriting Eq. (8.11) in terms of the axial displacement gives

$$\sigma = Ei\omega \frac{\partial u}{\partial y} \tag{8.12}$$

If the axial displacement is written

$$u = \bar{u} e^{i\omega t} \tag{8.13}$$

where $\bar{u}$ is the amplitude of displacement during sinusoidal excitation, and Eq. (8.12) is substituted into Eq. (8.8), the following ordinary differential equation results:

$$\frac{d^2 u}{d^2 y} + p^2 \bar{u} = -p^2 U_0 \tag{8.14}$$

where

$$p^2 = \frac{\rho \omega^2}{E(i\omega)}$$

The solution to Eq. (8.14) is

$$\bar{u} + U_0 = C_1 \cos py + C_2 \sin py \tag{8.15}$$

where C_1 and C_2 can be evaluated from the boundary conditions

$$u(0, t) = 0 \quad \text{and} \quad A\sigma(L, t) = \frac{-m\, \partial^2(u + u_0)_{y=L}}{\partial t^2} \tag{8.16}$$

where the terms are defined in Fig. 8.5b. Applying these boundary conditions gives the solution for the displacements

$$\frac{\bar{u}(y, \omega)}{U_0} = \cos py + \frac{\tan pL + \gamma}{1 - \gamma \tan pL} \sin py - 1 \tag{8.17}$$

where

$$\gamma = \frac{m\omega^2}{pAE(i\omega)}$$

If we rewrite Eq. (8.17) for $y = L$, the ratio R of the bar end displacements (or equivalently, the acceleration) may be written

$$R = \left| \frac{\bar{u}(L, w) + U_0}{U_0} \right| = \left| \frac{\sec pL}{1 - \gamma \tan pL} \right| \tag{8.18}$$

At this point it is convenient to introduce the frequency ratio ξ

$$\xi = \frac{\omega L}{V_L} \tag{8.19}$$

and phase velocity V_L

$$V_L = \left(\frac{E^*}{\rho} \right)^{1/2} \sec \frac{\delta_l}{2} \tag{8.20}$$

Substituting (8.19) and (8.20) into (8.18) and rearranging terms gives

$$\frac{1}{R^2} = \tfrac{1}{2}[Q^2(\xi^2 + \psi^2)(\cosh 2\psi - \cos 2\xi)$$

$$+ 2Q(\psi \sinh 2\psi - \xi \sin 2\xi) + (\cosh 2\psi + \cos 2\xi)] \tag{8.21}$$

where $\psi = \xi \tan(\delta_l/2)$ and $Q = m/\rho AL$ is the ratio of end mass to specimen mass.

The desired dynamic properties can be determined when the specimen is in the resonant condition. For this condition R will be a maximum and $1/R^2$ will be a minimum. Differentiating Eq. (8.21) with respect to ξ and setting it equal to zero gives

$$Q^2\xi\left(1 + \frac{\psi^2}{\xi^2}\right)(\cosh 2\psi - \cos 2\xi + \xi \sin 2\xi + \psi \sinh 2\psi)$$

$$+ \frac{1 + Q}{\xi}(\psi \sinh 2\psi - \xi \sin 2\xi) + \frac{2Q}{\xi}(\psi^2 \cosh 2\psi - \xi^2 \cos 2\xi) = 0 \tag{8.22}$$

Equations (8.21) and (8.22) can be solved simultaneously for ξ and ψ. V_L and $\tan(\delta_l/2)$ can be calculated from these quantities.

With values of V_L and $\tan(\delta_l/2)$ the complex Young's modulus can be computed as follows:

$$E^* = \frac{V_L^2 \rho}{1 + \tan^2(\delta_l/2)} \tag{8.23}$$

The torsional case can be developed in an analogous fashion and yields

$$G^* = \frac{V_s \rho}{1 + \tan^2 \delta_t/2} \tag{8.24}$$

where E^* = complex Young's modulus
δ_l = lag angle in longitudinal mode
G^* = complex shear modulus
δ_t = lag angle in torsional mode

Cyclic Triaxial Method

The stress states to which a sample is subjected during a cyclic triaxial test are shown in Fig. 8.6a. A cylindrical sample is placed in a cell and confined to an initial isotropic stress state. The axial load on the sample is then cycled causing a reversal of shear stresses in the sample, which are a maximum on 45° planes. The principal stress directions rotate through 90° every half cycle of loading.

During the test the cyclic axial load and sample deformation are recorded. The axial stress and strain in the sample are determined with a knowledge of the cross-sectional area and length of the sample. The axial stress when the sample is confined is the deviator stress, i.e., major principal stress minus the minor principal stress, $\sigma_1 - \sigma_3$. Typical test results expressed in these terms for one cycle of loading are shown in Fig. 8.5b. From this record the dynamic Young's modulus E_d and damping ratio D are determined as follows:

$$E_d = \frac{\sigma_{\text{max deviator}}}{\varepsilon_{\text{max axial}}} \tag{8.25}$$

and

$$D = \frac{A_L}{4\pi A_T} \tag{8.26}$$

with the terms as defined in Fig. 8.6b. A_L represents the total dissipated energy per cycle, and A_T represents the work capacity per cycle.

A typical cyclic triaxial test system is shown schematically in Fig. 8.7. It consists of three basic components: (1) an electrohydraulic closed-loop test system, which applies a cyclic axial load to the sample (hydraulic power supply, servo controller, hydraulic controller, servovalve, actuator), (2) a triaxial cell which contains the sample, and (3) the output recording and readout devices to monitor the axial load, sample deformation, and sample temperature, i.e., load cell, thermistors, linear variable differential transformer (LVDT), strip-chart recorder, and storage oscilloscope.

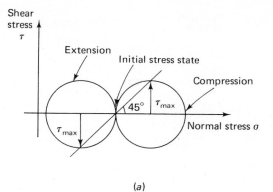

(a)

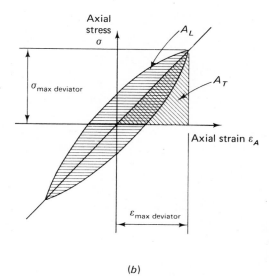

(b)

Figure 8.6 Stress state and stress vs. strain for cyclic triaxial test: (a) Mohr's-circle representation of cyclic stress states; (b) stress vs. strain for one load cycle.

Example 8.2 A refraction-survey record at a site with discontinuous permafrost is shown in Fig. 8.8. Determine the compression-wave velocities in the unfrozen and frozen silt.

SOLUTION The seismograph records shown in Fig. 8.8 are plotted to scale along the horizontal axis and therefore represent a plot of travel time vs. distance. On this plot two lines are constructed through the first wave-arrival times on the seismograph record. These lines are shown in Fig. 8.8 and intersect at point A. The compression-wave velocity in the unfrozen layer is the slope of the line from the "shot instant" to point A

$$V_{p1} = \frac{24 \text{ m}}{0.045 \text{ s}} = 533 \text{ m/s}$$

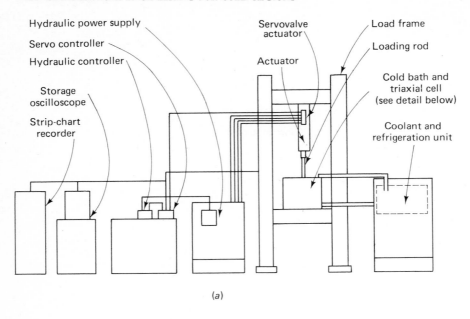

(a)

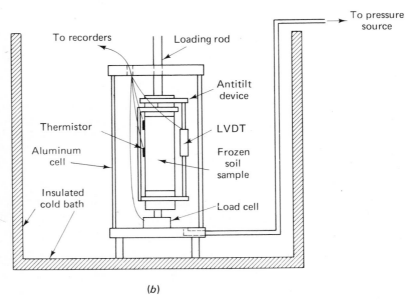

(b)

Figure 8.7 Cyclic triaxial test equipment: (a) schematic of cyclic triaxial test system; (b) triaxial cell inside cold bath.

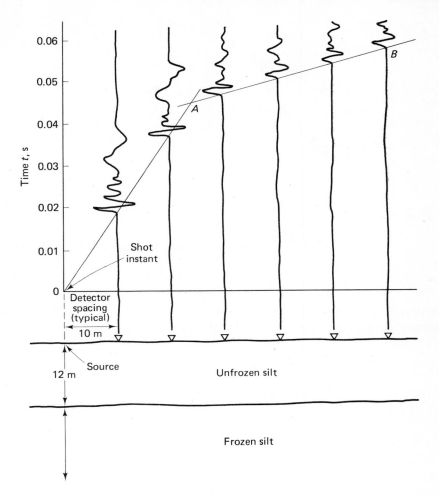

Figure 8.8 Refraction record at a site with discontinuous permafrost.

The compression-wave velocity in the frozen layer is the slope of the line through points A and B

$$V_{p2} = \frac{36 \text{ m}}{0.0125 \text{ s}} = 2880 \text{ m/s}$$

Example 8.3 The results from a cyclic triaxial test for one cycle of loading on a cylindrical sample of Hanover silt at a temperature of $-1°C$ and a confining pressure of 350 kN/m^2 are shown in Fig. 8.9. The sample had a diameter of 70 mm and a height of 150 mm. Calculate the dynamic Young's modulus and the damping ratio.

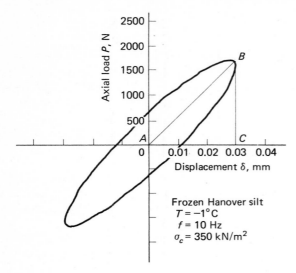

Figure 8.9 Load vs. deformation for one load cycle.

SOLUTION The dynamic Young's modulus can be calculated after the maximum deviator stress and strain amplitude have been determined.

$$\sigma_{\text{max deviator}} = \frac{P_{\text{max}}}{A} = \frac{1700 \text{ N}}{(\pi \times 70^2 \text{ mm})/4} = 442 \text{ kN/m}^2$$

$$\varepsilon_{\text{max axial}} = \frac{0.03 \text{ mm}}{150 \text{ mm}} = 2 \times 10^{-4} \text{ mm/mm}$$

Then, from Eq. (8.25),

$$E_d = \frac{442 \text{ kN/m}^2}{2 \times 10^{-4} \text{ mm/mm}} = 2.21 \text{ GN/m}^2$$

To calculate the damping ratio the area of the hysteresis loop and triangle *ABC* must be determined. The area of the hysteresis loop can be determined with a planimeter and is

$$A_L = 0.060 \text{ J}$$

The area of triangle *ABC* is

$$A_T = \frac{1700 \text{ N} \times 0.03 \text{ mm}}{2} = 0.026 \text{ J}$$

Then
$$D = \frac{0.060 \text{ J}}{4\pi \times 0.026 \text{ J}} = 0.184$$

8.2 DYNAMIC PROPERTIES OF FROZEN GROUND

Frozen ground is a multiphase system of mineral particles, ice, unfrozen pore water, and entrapped air. Its behavior is strongly dependent on the duration, amplitude and rate of loading, and temperature. When this is recognized, it is apparent that many parameters will influence the response of frozen ground to dynamic loading. These parameters may be divided into two groups: (1) field- and/or test-condition parameters and (2) material parameters. Table 8.2 lists specific parameters in these groups. It is possible to combine several of these parameters. For example, the combined influence of the ice content and void ratio of the soil can be expressed by the ratio of the volume of ice to the volume of soil. To date, however, all these parameters have generally been considered separately. Undoubtedly there are many combinations of the parameters which would result in equivalent dynamic properties.

In this section frozen ground is divided into two groups, ice and soil. The dynamic properties of ice have been studied extensively in both the laboratory and the field, and a reasonable amount of data exist to assess the influence on dynamic properties of the parameters listed in Table 8.2. A considerable amount of data on the dynamic properties of frozen soils is available from laboratory investigations which would allow an assessment to be made of the influence on dynamic properties of the parameters listed in Table 8.2. However, relatively little field data exist on the dynamic properties of frozen soils. The dynamic properties of frozen rock are not reviewed in this chapter. The reader is referred

Table 8.2 Parameters influencing the response of frozen ground to dynamic loading

A. Field and/or test condition

1. Temperature
2. Strain (or stress) amplitude of loading
3. Frequency of loading
4. Confining pressure
5. Duration of loading

B. Material

1. Material type and composition
2. Material density or void ratio
3. Ice content or degree of ice saturation
4. Unfrozen water content
5. Anisotropy

to Barnes (1963), Frolov (1961), Frolov and Zykov (1971), King and Bamford (1971), Kurfurst and King (1972), Roethlisberger (1972), King et al. (1974), and Timur (1968) for a discussion of this topic.

Dynamic Properties of Ice

Frozen ground deposits frequently contain ice ranging in quantity from an amount not discernible to the eye but still effective as a cementing or bonding agent for soil grains to "massive" ice: thick, tabular, or irregular bodies with vertical sections up to 30 m thick and greater than 1 km^2 in area (Mackay and Black, 1973). Consequently, any discussion of the dynamic response of frozen ground must include a discussion of the dynamic properties of ice.

From the literature three types of ice structure can be identified: (1) single crystal, (2) nonporous polycrystalline, and (3) bubbly. Single-crystal ice is one large ice crystal. It can be grown artificially in the laboratory or found in nature as old glacier ice. Nonporous polycrystalline ice is an aggregate of randomly oriented crystals. It can be regarded as homogeneous and isotropic. It is found in nature in dry polar ice sheets at depths where there is sufficient pressure to cause the porosity to be negligible. Ice which contains air voids is termed bubbly ice. The distinction between snow and bubbly ice is that snow is permeable to air whereas bubbly ice is not. Glacier ice is usually bubbly. A genetic classification of ice relative to ice covers is given in Chap. 10.

The dynamic properties reported in this section are associated with field work done on the antarctic and Greenland ice sheets and a few glaciers, laboratory tests conducted on ice cores taken from the Greenland ice sheet, and ice samples prepared in the laboratory. While there are differences in the structure of these various types of ice which would cause the dynamic properties to be different, they are not discussed here. Instead the reader is referred to the discussions by Roethlisberger (1972), Bennett (1972), and Bentley (1972, 1975).

In recent years considerable progress has been made in determining the dynamic properties of ice in both the field and the laboratory. From this work several parameters influencing the dynamic properties have been identified and investigated. The most important field and/or test-condition parameters appear to be temperature, frequency, and confining pressure. The most important material parameter appears to be density.

Temperature The influence of temperature on dynamic stress-strain properties of ice is shown in Fig. 8.10. The results from the three different methods employed indicate that the compression- or longitudinal-wave velocity is not significantly affected by temperature. Robin (1958) determined the velocity-temperature relationship with ultrasonic equipment and established a *temperature coefficient* of -2.3 m/s °C. This value of the temperature coefficient has been confirmed by Kohnen (1974) using field velocity measurements from the Greenland and antarctic ice sheets. Both these investigations further substantiate the minor influence of temperature on the dynamic stress-strain properties.

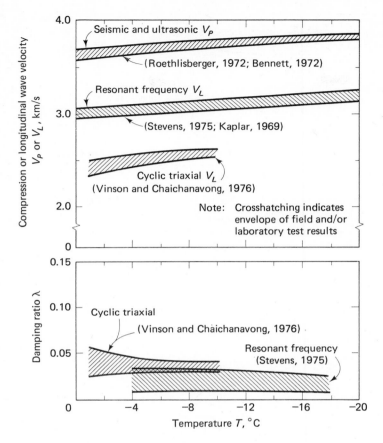

Figure 8.10 Wave velocity and damping ratio of ice vs. temperature.

The influence of temperature on energy-absorbing properties is also shown in Fig. 8.10. It appears that the influence of temperature on damping ratio is relatively small.

Frequency The influence of frequency on dynamic stress-strain properties is shown in Fig. 8.11. The results from both resonant-column and cyclic triaxial tests indicate that the compression-wave velocity increases as the frequency increases. The increase appears to be greater in the lower range of frequencies, 0.05 to 5 Hz, than in the higher range of frequencies, 1 to 10 kHz. The increase is not too significant, however, in either range. Smith (1969) reports similar results.

The influence of frequency on energy-absorbing properties is also shown in Fig. 8.11. It appears that at higher frequencies the damping ratio decreases with increasing frequency. At lower frequencies there is an initial decrease and then

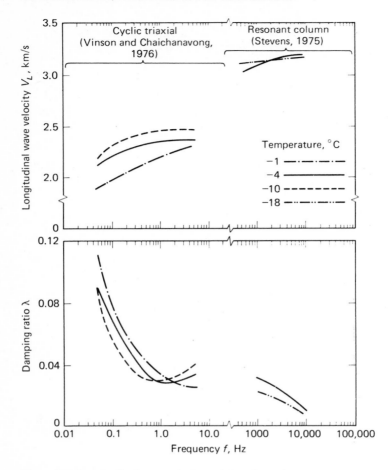

Figure 8.11 Longitudinal-wave velocity and damping ratio of ice vs. frequency.

an apparent increase in damping with increasing frequency. The degree to which damping follows these trends appears to be independent of temperature. The decrease in damping ratio with an increase in frequency is contrary to the behavior of other materials, such as rock.

Confining pressure Information on the effect of confining pressure on dynamic elastic properties is very limited. Bennett (1972) conducted ultrasonic tests on unconfined ice cores, and seismic surveys were performed in the field at locations where the cores were taken. The results from the ultrasonic tests on the unconfined core samples were not significantly different from the results of the seismic survey in which the ice was subjected to in situ confining pressure. This possibly indicates that confining pressure had a negligible influence. Roethlisberger (1972) reported that the effect of pressure was to reduce porosity and hence

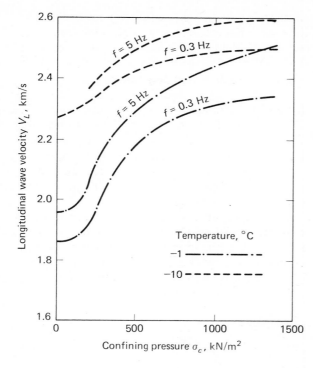

Figure 8.12 Longitudinal-wave velocity of ice vs. confining pressure.

increase the density of bubbly ice. With increasing density an increase in velocity should be expected.

The results from cyclic triaxial tests conducted on ice samples subjected to a range of confining pressures are shown in Fig. 8.12. It is apparent that there is a substantial increase in compression-wave velocity with increasing confining pressure. The increase appears to be greatest in the range from 200 to 700 kN/m² and steeper for warmer temperatures than for colder. For the test samples at a density of 904 kg/m³, it appeared that there were no substantial changes in density with confining pressure; hence this would not explain the increase in wave velocity. Changes in the microstructure of the ice under the confining pressure may have been responsible for the increase in velocity. Microfissures could close when a sample is subjected to a high confining pressure, and this could cause a sample to have a higher dynamic modulus.

The influence of confining pressure on energy-absorbing properties is not well understood. Vinson and Chaichanavong (1976) concluded that no identifiable relationship existed between damping ratio and confining pressure for the majority of samples they tested. Several samples were tested, however, which showed a decrease in damping ratio with increasing confining pressure.

Strain amplitude The strain amplitude of loading apparently does not have an important effect on the dynamic properties of ice. Vinson and Chaichanavong (1976) found that the dynamic Young's modulus decreased only slightly, on the order of 10 percent, for an increase in axial-strain amplitude from 10^{-3} to 2×10^{-2} percent. Damping was found to increase approximately 20 percent over this range. Stevens (1975) found that there was no significant change in longitudinal-wave velocity over an axial strain range from 8×10^{-6} to 4×10^{-4} percent. Damping was found to decrease slightly over this range.

Density The influence of density on dynamic-stress-strain properties has been studied by many investigators. The results from several of these studies are shown in Fig. 8.13. The compression- or longitudinal-wave velocity decreases with decreasing density. According to seismic field results, the rate of decrease is slightly greater for densities below 600 kg/m³ than for densities above this value. The results from seismic and ultrasonic tests are in good agreement, particularly for values of density greater than 600 kg/m³.

The influence of density on energy-absorbing properties has not been extensively investigated. Data obtained by Smith (1969) from resonant-column tests on ice and snow cores indicated a decrease in energy-absorbing properties with increasing density over the range 400 to 900 kg/m³. Data from Vinson and Chaichanavong (1976) suggests that there is no well-defined relationship between damping ratio and density over the range 700 to 900 kg/m³.

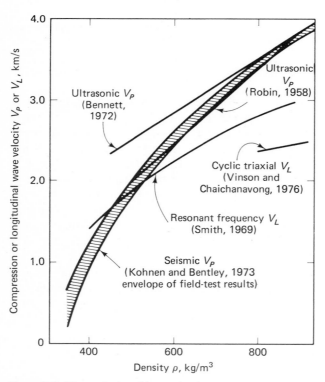

Figure 8.13 Wave velocity of ice vs. density.

Dynamic Properties of Frozen Soil

When discussing the static or dynamic properties of frozen soil it should be recognized that the structure of a sample reconstituted and frozen in the laboratory (artificially frozen soil) can differ markedly from the structure of a sample of comparable soil type taken in situ from a frozen ground deposit (naturally frozen soil). It follows that the measured properties of the two samples may differ significantly. To date, nearly all dynamic properties measured in the laboratory are associated with artificially frozen soil. Only dynamic properties measured in the field are associated with naturally frozen soil.

Field-test results A summary of compression-wave velocities from seismic methods is given in Table 8.3. Most of the measurements were a by-product of investigations whose primary aim was to determine geologic structure. The ground temperatures given are based, in general, on climatic data or are from temperature instrumentation at locations close to the areas where the seismic velocities were measured.

The conclusions that can be drawn from the data presented are (1) that the coarse-grained soils (gravels and glacial till) generally have higher compression-wave velocities than the fine-grained soils (silts and clays) and (2) that the compression-wave velocities of material in the frozen state are much greater than in the unfrozen state. Further conclusions cannot be drawn because the soil descriptions are too general and the temperature data too unreliable.

Gagne and Hunter (1975) have correlated measured ground temperatures and ice content with the results obtained from a shallow hammer-refraction survey. At a site underlain by frozen sands, silts, and ice they found an approximate linear decrease in the compression-wave velocity with increasing temperature. At $-15°C$ the velocity was 3.3 km/s, and at $-1°C$ the velocity was 1.1 km/s. From 30 observations for ice contents in the range of 7 to 34 percent it was concluded that the velocity increases as the ice content increases. From this analysis Gagne and Hunter (1975) suggested that the ice content is probably a major factor controlling the compression-wave velocity of surficial materials at low permafrost temperatures.

Laboratory test results The results from ultrasonic, resonant-frequency, and cyclic triaxial tests provide the only comprehensive body of information for assessing the influence of the various parameters listed in Table 8.2 on the dynamic properties of frozen soils (with the exception of the influence of duration and anisotropy). Further, as discussed in Sec. 8.3, this body of information provides a basis for the selection of representative dynamic properties for use in analytic techniques to predict frozen-ground response to dynamic loading.

The following discussion is based primarily on the dynamic properties obtained in four laboratory test programs: Kaplar (1963, 1969) tested frozen-soil beams with resonant-frequency equipment; Stevens (1973, 1975) tested frozen-soil cylinders with resonant-frequency equipment; Nakano et al. (1972),

Table 8.3 Compression-wave velocities of frozen soil from seismic surveys

Soil type	Locality	Compression-wave velocity, km/s		Estimated ground temperature, °C	Ref.
		Frozen	Unfrozen		
Coarse-grained:					
Floodplain alluvium	Fairbanks area, Alas.	2.4–4.3	1.9–2.1	−1	Barnes (1963)
Gravel	Fairbanks area, Alas.	4.0–4.6	1.8–2.3	−1	Barnes (1963)
Glacier moraine	Delta Junction, Alas.	2.3–4.0	...	−2	Barnes (1963)
Aeolian sand	Tetlin Junction, Alas.	2.4	...	−3	Barnes (1963)
Outwash gravel	Tanacross, Alas.	2.3–3.0	...	−3	Barnes (1963)
Glacier outwash	Thule, Greenland	4.5–4.7	...	−11	Roethlisberger (1961)
Glacier till	Thule, Greenland	4.7–4.8	...	−11	Roethlisberger (1961)
	McMurdo Sound, Antarctica	3.0–4.3	0.5–1.5	−20	Bell (1966)
Till	Norman Wells, N.W.T.	2.2–3.6	...	...	King et al. (1974)
Frozen ground	Lake Fryxell, Lake Vanda, Lake Bonney, Antartica	3.8–4.5	...	...	McGinnis et al. (1973)
Sand and clay	Norman Wells, N.W.T.	3.1–3.4	...	...	King et al. (1974)
Saturated sand	...	3.2–4.0	...	...	Hunter (1973)
Water-saturated gravel	...	3.6–4.0	...	...	Hunter (1973)
Gravel	Klondike area, Yukon	5.5	...	...	Hobson (1966)
Outwash with relatively thick ice lenses	Lake Vida, Antartica	5.7–5.9	...	...	McGinnis et al. (1973)
Outwash	Meirs Valley, Antarctica	3.6–4.0	...	...	Bell (1966)

Fine-grained:

Silt and gravel	Fairbanks area, Alas.	2.3–3.0	...	−1	Barnes (1963)
Silt and organic matter	Fairbanks area, Alas.	1.5–3.0	0.6–1.2	−1	Barnes (1963)
Silt with ice lenses	Eielson Airforce Base, Alas.	2.0–2.8	...	−1.5	Blouin (1976)†
Alluvial clay	Northway, Alas.	2.4	...	−2	Barnes (1963)
Silt	Glen Creek valley, Alas.	2.7–3.3	...	−4.2	Hunter (1974)
Tundra silts, sands, and peats:					
Gubik Formation, probably saline	Barrow area NPR-4,‡ Alas.	2.4–2.7	...	−9	Woolson (1963)
	Skull Cliff area, NPR-4,‡ Alas.	2.3–2.7	...	−9	Woolson (1963)
Gubik Formation, less saline	Topagoruk area, NPR-4,‡ Alas.	2.4–3.7	...	−9	Woolson (1963)
Unclassified sediments	Isachsen, N.W.T.	2.7	...	−10	Hobson (1962)
Silt and clay	Norman Wells, N.W.T.	3.1	...	...	King et al. (1974)
	...	1.5–2.1	...	...	Hunter (1973)
Clay	Norman Wells, N.W.T.	2.5–2.8	...	...	King et al. (1974)
Ice-saturated silts	...	1.8–3.1	...	...	Hunter (1973)

† Cylindrical in situ test result.
‡ Northern Petroleum Reserve.

Table 8.4 Index and classification properties of frozen soil samples tested in the laboratory

Soil name	Unified Soil Classification group symbol	Coefficient of uniformity C_u	Coefficient of curvature C_c	Atterberg limits w_L w_p I_p	Sp. gr.	Soil legend[f]
Coarse-grained:						
Peabody gravelly sand	SP	10.7	0.7	Nonplastic	2.72	PGS
McNamara concrete sand	SP	5.4	0.8	Nonplastic	2.72	MCS
East Boston till	SC	220	5.9	21 14 7	2.76	EBT
Mixture McNamara concrete sand and East Boston till	SM	220	5.9	Nonplastic	2.72	CEB
Mixture Manchester fine sand and East Boston till	SM	57	9.6	Nonplastic	2.72	MEB
20/30 Ottawa sand	SP	1.1	1.1	Nonplastic	2.65	OS
						OSL
Thetford till	SW	25.8	1.0	Nonplastic	2.64	TT
Fine-grained:						
Alaska silt	ML	c	c	Nonplastic	2.70	AS
New Hampshire silt	CL-ML	c	c	26 21 5	2.70	NHS
Yukon silt	CL-ML	c	c	28 19 9	2.73	YS
Boston blue clay	CL	c	c	47 20 27	2.81	BBC
Fargo clay	CH	c	c	68 22 46	2.76	FC
Fairbanks silt	ML-OL	c	c	28 24 4	2.69	FS
Hanover silt	ML	c	c	Nonplastic	2.74	HS
Goodrich clay	CL	c	c	41 23 18	2.82	GC
Manchester silt	ML	c	c	Nonplastic	2.73	MS
Suffield clay	CL	c	c	45 24 21	2.69	SC
Ontonagon clay	CH	c	c	61 24 37	2.74	OC
Mixture Ontonagon and sodium montmorillonite clay	CH	c	c	98 37 61	2.74	OMC

[a] 1 = Kaplar (1969); 2 = Nakano, Martin, and Smith, (1972); 3 = Stevens (1975); 4 = Vinson, Czajkowski, and Li, (1977); 5 = Czajkowski (1977); 6 = Chaichanavong (1976).

[b] Average value.

[c] Not applicable.

Degree of ice saturation S_i %	Void ratio e	Test frequency, Hz	Strain amplitude ε_A, %	Poisson's ratio μ	Density, kg/m³	Confining pressure, kN/m²	Source[a]
83[b]	0.48[b]	7100	...	0.28	2100	0	1
85[b]	0.48[b]	6300	...	0.23	2110	0	1
80[b]	0.34[b]	5700	...	0.28	2260	0	1
99[b]	0.37[b]	6200[b]	...	0.36	2250	0	1
87[b]	0.45[b]	6500[b]	...	0.31	2140	0	1
100	0.38	10^6	...	0.25	2190	0	2
99[b]	0.54[b]	5000	$2^b \times 10^{-5}$	0.30[b]	2070	0	3
100	0.49	0.3	10^{-2}	...	2000	345	4
100	3.73	0.3	10^{-2}	...	1290	345	4
93	0.80[b]	5000	4×10^{-5}	...	1880	0	
100	0.59	0.3	10^{-2}	...	2090	345	5
93[b]	1.05[b]	5400[b]	...	0.28	1790	0	1
99[b]	0.60[b]	5100	...	0.39	2080	0	1
96[b]	1.87[b]	4800[b]	...	0.44	1600	0	1
92[b]	1.13[b]	2700[b]	...	0.38	1780	0	1
99[b]	0.68[b]	5500[b]	...	0.28 0.18[d]	2000	0	1
100	1.10	10^6	...	0.28[e]	1830	0	2
100	0.60	0.3	10^{-2}	... 0.15[d]	2030	345	5
100	1.28	10^6	...	0.28[e]	1810	0	2
97	0.83	5000	$1^b \times 10^{-4}$	0.39	1980	0	3
96	0.73	5000	$3^b \times 10^{-5}$	0.27	1980	0	3
100	0.51	5000	$1^b \times 10^{-4}$	...	2120	0	3
100	1.50	0.3	10^{-2}	...	1620	345	6
100	1.56	0.3	10^{-2}	...	1660	345	6

[d] At − 2°C.

[e] At − 4 to − 14°C.

[f] Letter appended to soil legend in Figs. 8.15 to 8.19 and 8.22 indicates source (K = source 1, N = source 2, S = source 3, V = sources 4–6).

Nakano and Arnold (1973), and Nakano and Froula (1973) tested frozen-soil cylinders and disks with ultrasonic equipment; and Vinson and Chaichanavong (1976) and Vinson et al. (1977) tested frozen-soil cylinders with cyclic triaxial equipment. A summary of the index properties and grain-size distribution for all the soil types associated with these investigations is given in Table 8.4 and Fig. 8.14, respectively. A soil and source (Table 8.4) legend has been established to facilitate reference to a specific soil type and test program. For example, PGS-K indicates the Peabody gravelly sand tested by Kaplar. This legend is used in Figs. 8.14 to 8.20 and 8.22.

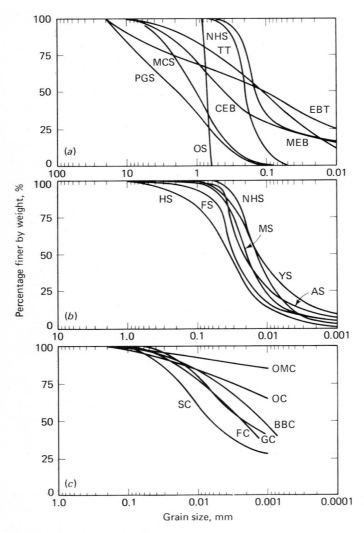

Figure 8.14 Grain-size distribution of frozen-soil samples tested in the laboratory. Symbols identified by soil legend in Table 8.4: (a) coarse-grained silts; (b) fine-grained silts; (c) fine-grained clays.

The test results from several laboratory studies using ultrasonic equipment have not been included in this section because in general detailed soil descriptions for the materials tested were not easily obtainable. These include Müller (1961), Frolov (1961), Frolov and Zykov (1971), Dzhurik and Leshchikov (1973), Zykov and Baulin (1973), Zykov et al. (1973), Khazin and Goncharov (1974), Inoue and Kinosita (1975), and Kurfurst (1976).

Temperature All investigators have found that dynamic stress-strain properties of frozen soil increase with descending temperature. This relationship is summarized in Fig. 8.15 for all the test and material conditions indicated in Table 8.4. No particular significance should be given to the relative order of the relationships as they are associated with different test conditions, as noted in Table 8.4. It appears that the increase in longitudinal-wave velocity with descending temperature is greatest for the fine-grained soils, particularly in the range 0 to $-5°C$. However, there are exceptions to this statement, e.g., CEB-K, OS-N, and OS-V. There is a severe lack of data between 0 and $-1°C$, a range that is particularly important to field problems. Stevens (1975) reported that dynamic moduli in the frozen state are generally more than two orders of magnitude greater than moduli in the unfrozen state. This corresponds to longitudinal-wave velocities in the frozen state more than one order of magnitude greater than velocities in the unfrozen state.

The influence of temperature on the damping ratio is shown in Fig. 8.16 for the test and material conditions indicated in Table 8.4. The damping ratio decreases with descending temperature in the range of -1 to $-10°C$. Between -10 and $-20°C$ the damping ratio is not significantly influenced by temperature. Stevens (1975) stated that the energy-absorbing properties of frozen soils are not significantly different from those of unfrozen soils. This is surprising considering the fact that the modulus in the frozen state is significantly higher than the modulus in the unfrozen state and damping properties generally decrease when the modulus increases.

Strain amplitude of loading The influence of the strain amplitude of loading on dynamic properties is shown in Fig. 8.17 for the test and material conditions indicated in Table 8.4. It would appear that the longitudinal-wave velocity and the damping ratio of frozen soils change very little up to a strain amplitude of 10^{-3} percent. For strain amplitudes between 10^{-3} and 10^{-1} percent the longitudinal-wave velocity decreases and the damping ratio increases. This type of behavior is also found in unfrozen soils. It is believed that this relationship is independent of temperature and frequency (Stevens, 1975; Chaichanavong, 1976; Vinson et al., 1977).

Frequency of loading The influence of the frequency of loading on dynamic properties is shown in Fig. 8.18 for the test and material conditions indicated in Table 8.3. Data are available only for the low frequencies 0.1 to 10 Hz and the high frequencies 10^3 to 10^4 Hz. It would appear that the longitudinal-wave velocity of frozen soils increases gradually with increasing frequency. The rate

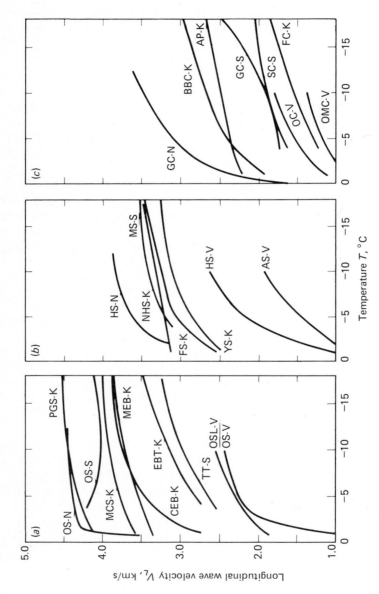

Figure 8.15 Longitudinal-wave velocity of frozen soil *vs.* temperature. Symbols identified by soil legend in Table 8.4: (*a*) coarse-grained soils; (*b*) fine-grained soils/silts; (*c*) fine-grained soils/clays.

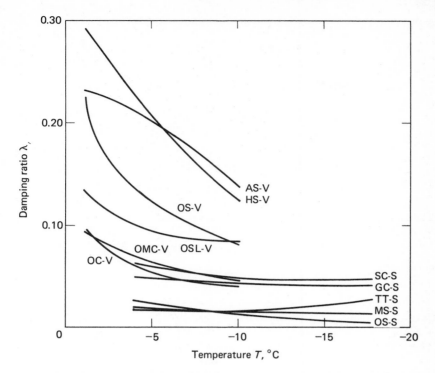

Figure 8.16 Damping ratio of frozen soil vs. temperature. Symbols identified by soil legend in Table 8.4.

of increase is apparently independent of soil type. The damping ratio of frozen soils apparently decreases with increasing frequency. The results from Vinson and Chaichanavong (1976) and Vinson et al. (1977) indicate a sharp decrease of damping ratio with frequency over the range of 0.1 to 10 Hz whereas Stevens' results indicate a gradual decrease over the range 10^3 to 10^4 Hz.

Confining pressure Most of the laboratory investigations are associated with unconfined samples. Only the samples tested with cyclic triaxial equipment were confined. The influence of confining pressure on dynamic properties of five soil types is shown in Fig. 8.19 for the test and material conditions indicated in Table 8.4. It is obvious that for the four fine-grained soils shown there is no significant change in either the dynamic Young's modulus or the damping ratio over the range of confining pressure from 0 to 1400 kN/m². The dynamic properties of unfrozen fine-grained soils (specifically clays) are also independent of confining pressure. There is a significant increase in modulus with increasing confining pressure for the coarse-grained sand-ice mixture. The damping ratio is apparently not affected by confining pressure. This behavior should perhaps be expected. The dynamic stress-strain properties of unfrozen coarse-grained soils are strongly dependent on the confining pressure, and the results from

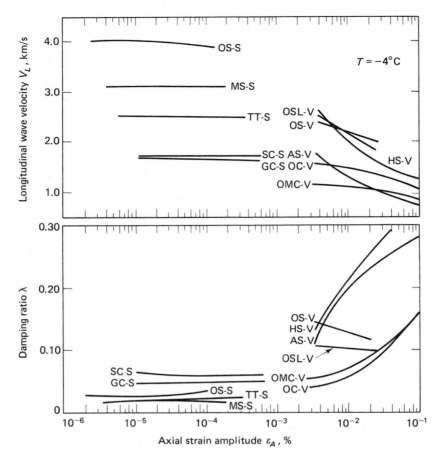

Figure 8.17 Longitudinal-wave velocity and damping ratio of frozen soil vs. axial-strain amplitude. Symbols identified by soil legend in Table 8.4.

cyclic triaxial tests on ice indicate a dependence of dynamic stress-strain properties on confining pressure. Research reported by Chaichanavong (1976) and Vinson et al. (1977) suggests that the relationships shown in Fig. 8.19 are independent of the strain amplitude and frequency of loading and the test temperature.

Void ratio The influence of void ratio on dynamic stress-strain properties of ice-saturated samples is shown in Fig. 8.20. The complex shear modulus decreases as the void ratio increases. The results from Stevens' work on cohesionless soils and ice are shown in Fig. 8.21a. It is clear that the complex Young's modulus approaches the value for ice as the void ratio increases. This appears to be quite logical since the stiffness of most frozen cohesionless soils is greater than that of ice alone. The increase in dynamic modulus with void ratio appears

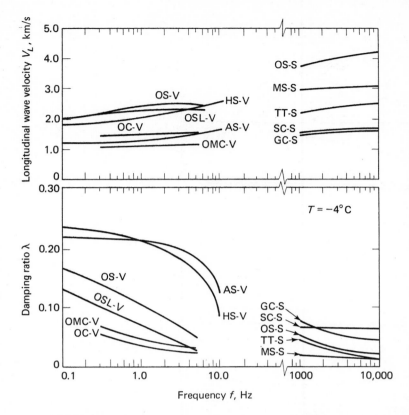

Figure 8.18 Longitudinal-wave velocity and damping ratio of frozen soil vs. frequency. Symbols identified by soil legend in Table 8.4.

to be greatest in the range from 1.0 to 0.5, presumably because the soil grains come in contact. This observation is supported by the fact that the maximum void ratio for cohesionless soils just at contact is approximately 0.91.

The effect of void ratio on energy-absorbing properties of cohesionless soils is shown in Fig. 8.21*b*. On the average there is a slight decrease in tan δ with increasing void ratio. Stevens (1975) interpreted this as evidence that the energy-absorbing properties of ice govern those of the frozen soil. More specifically, however, Stevens' results indicate that with increasing void ratio there may be an increase in tan δ for coarse-grained soils and a decrease for fine-grained soils.

Effect of degree of ice saturation and unfrozen water content The unfrozen water content and degree of ice saturation are related by

$$S_{ice} = \frac{(w - w_u)G_s \gamma_w}{e \gamma_{ice}} \tag{8.27}$$

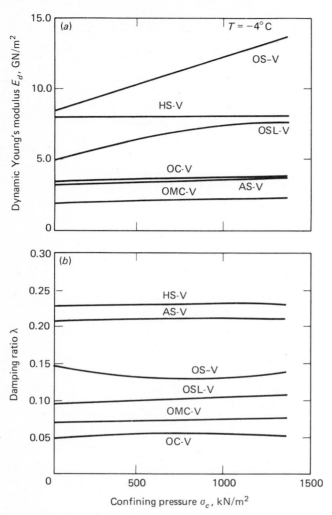

Figure 8.19 Dynamic Young's modulus (*a*) and damping ratio (*b*) of frozen soil vs. confining pressure. Symbols identified by soil legend in Table 8.4.

where S_{ice} = degree of ice saturation
     w = total water content
    w_u = unfrozen water content
    γ_w = unit weight of water
    G_s = specific gravity of solids
    e = void ratio
    γ_{ice} = unit weight of ice

For a soil at a constant void ratio and total water content, as the degree of ice saturation increases, the unfrozen water content must decrease. In cohesive soils

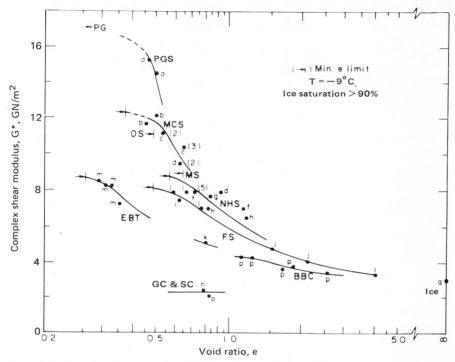

Figure 8.20 Complex shear modulus of frozen soil vs. void ratio. (*After Stevens, 1975.*)

there can be significant amounts of unfrozen water which would substantially reduce the degree of ice saturation calculated with the assumption that all the water in the voids is frozen. For cohesionless soils the unfrozen water in the voids is negligible.

The effect of the degree of ice saturation on shear-wave velocity is shown in Fig. 8.22. As the degree of ice saturation increases, the shear-wave velocity increases. The increase is an order of magnitude over the range of ice saturation 0 to 100 percent. The value of shear-wave velocity at 0 percent ice saturation corresponds to the dry state. The rate of increase appears to be somewhat dependent on soil type. The coarse-grained Ottawa sand shows an increase in shear-wave velocity up to 40 percent ice saturation. The fine-grained soils Suffield clay and Manchester silt increase in shear-wave velocity steadily with ice saturation over the entire range. The increase in dynamic stress-strain properties with ice saturation is undoubtedly due to the increase in adhesive bond between the soil grains provided by the ice.

Nakano and Froula (1973) developed an experimental technique to measure wave velocity and unfrozen water content simultaneously. The results from this work are shown in Fig. 8.23. It is obvious that the dilatational-wave velocity is directly related to unfrozen water content. Note that the unfrozen water

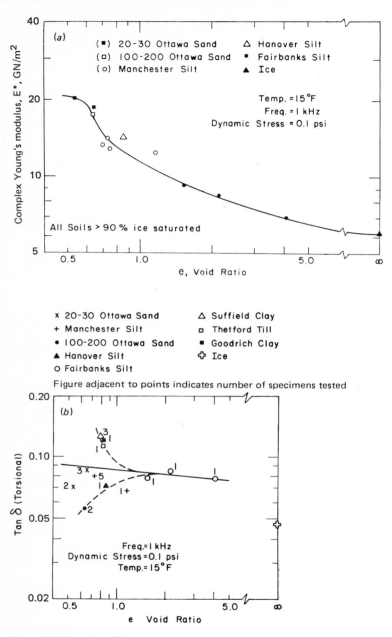

Figure 8.21 Complex Young's modulus and tan δ of frozen soil vs. void ratio. (*After Stevens, 1975.*)

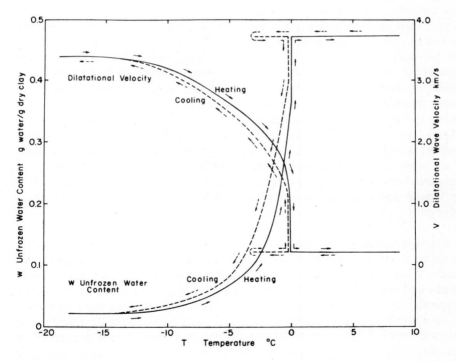

Curve	Frozen soils	f kHz	Temp °F
A	Suffield clay	1	15
B	Manchester silt	1	25
C	20–30 Ottawa sand	1000	14

Point	Non-frozen soils σ_0 = 5 psi	Water content	e
A'	Suffield clay	12.7	0.94
B'	Manchester silt	18.3	0.80
C'	20–30 Ottawa sand	Dry	0.50

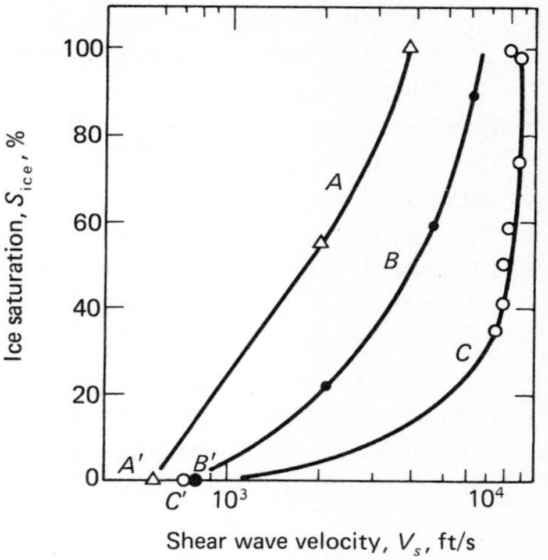

Figure 8.22 Shear-wave velocity of frozen soil vs. ice saturation. Original units (feet, seconds, and degrees Fahrenheit) retained. (After Stevens, 1975).

Figure 8.23 Dilatational-wave velocity and unfrozen water content of kaolinite vs. temperature. (*After Nakano and Froula, 1973.*)

contents on the cooling and heating cycle are not equal at a given temperature. The longitudinal-wave velocities also follow this trend.

Nakano et al. (1972) have provided an explanation of the relationship between wave velocity and unfrozen water content by considering soil to be a three-phase material with the solid particles acting as a framework whose interstitial spaces are filled with water and ice. A longitudinal-wave passing through the sample travels part of the time through the framework and part of the time through the ice and water. Since the longitudinal-wave velocity in water is approximately one-half that of ice, the more water there is in the soil the lower the wave velocity of the solid-particle–ice–water system.

Nakano and Arnold (1973) have found that the energy-absorbing characteristics of Ottawa sand expressed in terms of the quality factor Q are strongly dependent on the degree of ice saturation. The quality factor at a degree of ice saturation of 100 percent is 4 times greater than the value at 40 percent. Stevens' (1975) results are opposite this for fine-grained soils. For Manchester silt and Suffield clay tan δ decreases for increasing degrees of ice saturation.

Soil type The influence of soil type on dynamic properties is shown in Figs. 8.15 to 8.20. All investigators have found that coarse-grained soils have higher dynamic stress-strain properties than fine-grained soils. Silts have been found to have higher dynamic stress-strain properties than clays. The wave velocities of gravelly sand were found by Kaplar (1969) to be approximately 3 times the velocities of a plastic clay. This appears to be the maximum ratio of properties. An interesting correlation between particle size and dynamic modulus is shown in Fig. 8.24a. There appears to be a linear increase in dynamic modulus with an increase in the D_{50} particle size. A similar correlation is shown in Fig. 8.22b using Stevens' results.

Data available from Stevens (1975) would suggest that energy-absorbing properties are higher for frozen clay than for frozen sand or silt and that sand and silt have similar energy-absorbing properties. Stevens' results show no correlation between energy-absorbing properties and D_{50} particle size. Data from Vinson and Chaichanavong (1976) and Vinson et al. (1977) suggest that the damping ratio of cohesionless soils is greater than that of cohesive soils.

Unconfined compressive strength The combined influence of several of the material parameters listed in Table 8.2 may be reflected by the unconfined compressive strength. Stevens (1975) has developed a correlation between complex Young's modulus and unconfined compressive strength, as shown in Fig. 8.25. As might be expected, the modulus increases when the compressive strength increases. The relationship suggests that the unconfined compressive strength might serve as a good index property to approximate dynamic stress-strain properties of frozen soil. This procedure has already been suggested to approximate dynamic properties of unfrozen cohesive soils (Seed and Idriss, 1970). Stevens' results show no correlation between energy-absorbing properties and the unconfined compressive strength.

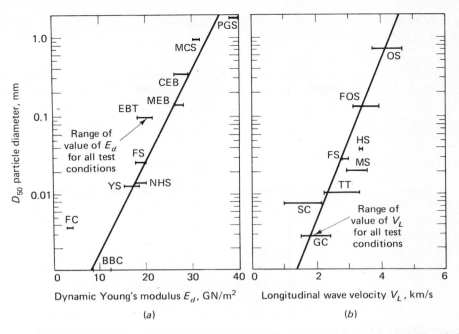

Figure 8.24 Dynamic stress-strain properties of frozen soil vs. D_{50} particle size. Symbols identified by soil legend in Table 8.4: (*a*) data from Kaplar (1969); (*b*) data from Stevens (1975).

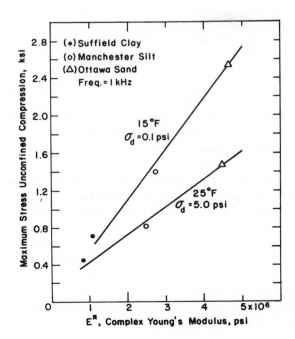

Figure 8.25 Complex Young's modulus vs. unconfined compressive strength. (*After Stevens, 1975.*)

8.3 ANALYSIS OF RESPONSE OF FROZEN GROUND TO DYNAMIC LOADINGS

Analysis of the response of frozen ground to dynamic loadings requires (1) selecting a suitable analytic technique to predict ground response to the loading condition under consideration, e.g., vibrating machinery, blasting, or earthquake, and (2) determining appropriate material properties.

Analytic Techniques for Predicting Ground Response

At the present time no analytic techniques have been developed specifically for predicting the response of frozen ground to dynamic loadings, except for those associated with geophysical exploration in cold regions. However, a considerable number of analytic techniques have been developed for predicting the response of unfrozen ground to dynamic loadings. The only alternative to the geotechnical engineer who must predict frozen-ground response is to use these techniques. When this alternative is exercised, considerable care should be taken to ensure that the assumptions on which the techniques are based are not violated. For example, a few of the analytic techniques for unfrozen ground assume that dynamic stress-strain properties are constant or increase with increasing depth from the ground surface. For frozen-ground deposits dynamic stress-strain properties can decrease with increasing depth from the ground surface owing to the increase in temperature with depth.

A comprehensive review of the theory behind the analytic techniques for predicting ground response to dynamic loadings is beyond the scope of this chapter. As mentioned in Sec. 8.1, detailed treatments of the analytic techniques for solving geophysical exploration problems can be found in Dobrin (1960), Grant and West (1965), and Roethlisberger (1972). Analytic techniques for solving foundation vibration problems can be found in several textbooks, including Richart et al. (1970), Richart (1975), and Wu (1971). Analytic techniques for determining ground response to earthquake loadings are presented by Schnabel et al. (1972), Idriss et al. (1973), Lysmer et al. (1974, 1975), and Streeter et al. (1974). These techniques require relatively sophisticated computer codes.[†] They generally have subroutines which provide dynamic properties of unfrozen soils based on average relationships, e.g., Seed and Idriss (1970), Hardin and Drnevich (1972). These subroutines must be rewritten to reflect the dynamic properties assumed to be representative of the frozen soils being analyzed (see, for example, Singh and Donovan, 1977).

There are several cases cited in the literature where the unfrozen-ground response predicted with presently available analytic techniques has been compared

---

[†] These codes are available from National Information Service: Earthquake Engineering Computer Applications, University of California, Berkeley, Calif. 94720.

with observed ground response to dynamic loading in the field. The comparisons are quite favorable, which would tend to support both the use of the analytic techniques and the assumed soil properties. Unfortunately, no similar comparisons have been made to support response predictions of frozen ground to dynamic loadings.

Determination of Dynamic Properties of Frozen Soils

Ideally, to obtain material properties appropriate for use in analytic techniques for predicting ground response to various loading conditions engineers (1) obtain "undisturbed" samples from a project site and (2) transport the samples to the laboratory for testing under conditions which approximate those anticipated in the field. The execution of these steps is not a simple task for unfrozen ground in temperate climates; it is extremely difficult for frozen ground when the samples are obtained under subfreezing conditions and there is the possibility of both mechanical and thermal disturbance. Further, the laboratory test systems presently used to measure dynamic properties of frozen soils are costly, and the test equipment and procedures are relatively complicated. Therefore, this approach can only be justified for major projects.

Two alternatives to the approach outlined above to obtain dynamic properties are possible. First, one can evaluate dynamic properties in situ using seismic methods or the cylindrical in situ test. As mentioned in Sec. 8.2 seismic methods are associated with low strain amplitudes and high frequencies of loading and therefore yield material properties which would not be useful in dynamic problems involving high strain amplitudes and low frequencies of loading. Also, seismic methods, in general, yield only average wave velocities and no information on energy-absorbing properties. This would not be satisfactory for most dynamic problems. Only one cylindrical in situ test has been conducted in permafrost. While its potential use for evaluating dynamic properties appears to be high, the instrumentation and cost of the test would probably be prohibitive for most projects. The second alternative is to relate index, classification, and other material characteristics of a soil whose properties are to be determined to those of soils whose properties have previously been determined. Presumably, if the dynamic properties of a soil of a similar type and structure have been determined, they should be close to those of the soil in question. This is a common approach to establishing the dynamic properties of unfrozen soils, at least in cases where only a "good" estimate of dynamic response is required.

If this second approach is adopted, one must rely on existing information on the dynamic properties of frozen ground. As presented in Sec. 8.2 this consists of seismic data obtained in the field and laboratory tests conducted on ice cores and artificially frozen soil samples. The soil descriptions associated with the seismic-wave velocities obtained in the field may be adequate for geophysical surveys to interpret geologic structure, but they are too general to allow translation to other sites for other dynamic-loading problems. Also, the temperature data are very approximate. Consequently, this body of information may not be useful for most problems. The laboratory data are associated with a significant range of artificially frozen soil types and composition and other material and test condition parameters. It would appear that this represents the only reasonable alternative in obtaining dynamic properties of frozen soils.

A methodology for determining the dynamic properties of frozen soils based on previous laboratory test results can be developed from a knowledge of (1) the relationship between test conditions associated with laboratory equipment used to measure dynamic properties and field dynamic-loading conditions, (2) the relative importance of material and field- and/or test-condition parameters on dynamic properties, and (3) values of dynamic properties for representative types of frozen soil tested in the laboratory, a complete description of the soil, and the test conditions with which the properties are associated. Figure 8.26 shows the relationship between field and laboratory strain amplitudes of loading. Machine foundation vibration and geophysical exploration strain amplitudes of loading are associated with ultrasonic and resonant-frequency test methods. Strong-motion-earthquake strain amplitudes of loadings are associated with the cyclic triaxial test method. Further, the loading frequencies for foundation vibration and geophysical exploration problems are compatible with those associated with ultrasonic and resonant-frequency test methods while the loading frequencies for strong-motion earthquakes are compatible with those associated with the cyclic triaxial test method. An assessment of the relative importance of material and field and/or test-condition parameters on dynamic properties is given in Table 8.5. This assessment is based on the data presented in Figs. 8.15 to 8.24. Obviously different interpretations of the data are possible. Values of dynamic properties for representative types of frozen soil, a description of the soil, and the test conditions with which the properties are associated are given in Figs. 8.14 to 8.16 and Table 8.4.

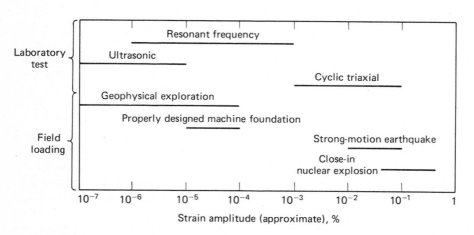

Figure 8.26 Relationship between laboratory and field strain amplitudes of loading for frozen ground.

A methodology for determining the dynamic properties of frozen soils follows: (1) Determine the laboratory test technique(s) associated with the field loading condition (refer to Fig. 8.26). In general, ultrasonic and resonant-frequency test results will be suitable for foundation-vibration and geophysical-exploration problems, and cyclic triaxial results will be suitable for earthquake-response analyses. (2) Determine the soil type which has previously been tested with the technique from step 1 which most closely approximates the soil type in the field (refer to Table 8.4 and Fig. 8.14). Primary consideration should be given to the soil classification, grain-size distribution, and Atterberg limits or the coefficient of uniformity and curvature to establish the "best match." (3) Determine values of longitudinal-wave velocity and damping ratio from Figs. 8.15 and 8.16 at the field temperatures. (4) Modify the values to reflect differences in void ratio, degree of ice saturation, strain amplitude and frequency of loading, and confining pressure in accordance with the relative importance of these parameters (Table 8.5). (5) Convert the longitudinal-wave velocity and damping ratio into other dynamic properties as required. Representative values of density ρ and Poisson's ratio are given in Table 8.4. Obviously this procedure requires *considerable judgment*. Its validity and usefulness will be improved as additional data on the dynamic properties of frozen soils, particularly naturally frozen soils, are obtained in laboratory investigations. Undoubtedly many problems will occur in practice for which there is insufficient information to use this approximate approach.

Example 8.4 A ground-response analysis to a strong-motion earthquake is to be made at the site shown in Fig. 8.27. It is assumed that the ground-surface motion will be the result of the upward propagation of shear waves through the frozen clay from the bedrock level to the ground surface. Estimate relationships between shear-wave velocity and damping ratio and shear-strain amplitude ε_s for the frozen clay which would be suitable for a ground-response analysis to a strong-motion earthquake with a predominant frequency of motion of 1.0 Hz.

SOLUTION Relationships between longitudinal-wave velocity and damping ratio and axial (longitudinal) strain amplitude will first be developed. They are easily converted into the required relationships with a knowledge of Poisson's ratio.

From Fig. 8.26 it is apparent that the results from cyclic triaxial tests should be used for the ground-response analysis to a strong-motion earthquake. From Table 8.4 it is apparent that two types of frozen clays have previously been tested: Ontonagon (OC) and a mixture of Ontonagon plus Montmorillonite (OMC). The frozen brown clay has Atterberg limits which are intermediate to those for the clays that have been tested. Consequently it will be assumed to have dynamic properties which are intermediate to the two clays which have been tested.

Table 8.5 Relative importance of material and field- and/or test-condition parameters on dynamic properties of frozen soils

	Dynamic stress-strain properties	Energy-absorbing properties	Fig.
Material parameters:			
Material type and composition	Very important; dynamic stress-strain properties for coarse-grained soils can be nearly an order of magnitude greater than for fine-grained soils	Very important; energy-absorbing properties can differ by an order of magnitude or greater for different soil types	8.15, 8.16, 8.24
Material density or void ratio (for fully saturated soils)	Important; over a range of void ratios from 0.3 to ice, dynamic stress-strain properties can decrease by a factor of 5; over the range of void ratios associated with a given soil type the influence of dynamic stress-strain properties will not be as great; dynamic stress-strain properties of ice decrease substantially with decreasing density	Probably unimportant; there may be a slight decrease in damping ratio with decreasing density over the range associated with the given soil type	8.20, 8.21
Ice content or degree of ice saturation per unfrozen water content	Very important; however, occurrence of coarse-grained soils with 90% ice saturation is rare in nature; degree of ice saturation for fine-grained soils is related to unfrozen water content and the influence in this case is reflected by temperature	Important; see comments under Dynamic stress-strain properties	8.22

452

Field- and/or test-condition parameters:		
Temperature	Very important for frozen soils, particularly in the range 0 to $-5°C$	Very important for frozen soils in the range 0 to $-5°C$; relatively unimportant in the range -5 to $-20°C$	8.15, 8.16
Strain (or stress) amplitude of loading	Unimportant for axial strain amplitudes less than $10^{-3}\%$ for frozen soils and ice; important for axial strain amplitudes between 10^{-3} and $10^{-1}\%$ for frozen soils	Unimportant for axial strain amplitudes less than $10^{-3}\%$; important for axial strain amplitudes between 10^{-3} and $10^{-1}\%$ for most frozen soils	8.17
Frequency of loading	Relatively unimportant	Probably important	8.18
Confining pressure	Important for coarse-grained soils and ice; unimportant for fine-grained soils	Unimportant	8.19

453

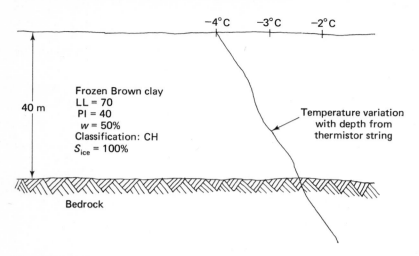

Figure 8.27 Soil characteristics and temperature variation with depth at site underlain by frozen clay.

The temperature variation with depth is given in Fig. 8.27. From this the average temperature in the layer is determined as $-3.2°$C. The properties at this temperature will be assumed to be representative of the entire layer (note that the deposit can be divided into additional layers if conditions warrant). From Figs. 8.15 and 8.16 values of compression-wave velocity and damping ratio are interpolated as follows: $V_L = 1.13$ km/s and $D = 0.07$. As noted in Table 8.4, these properties were determined at ε_A equal to 10^{-2} percent and f equal to 0.3 Hz. Since S_{ice} and w for the frozen brown clay are close to the values for the OC and OMC tested, it is not necessary to modify the properties obtained above to reflect differences in these parameters. The frequency of loading, 0.3 Hz, is lower than that required in the analysis, 1.0 Hz. From Fig. 8.18 it would appear that V_L should be increased by approximately 10 percent and D should be reduced by approximately 25 percent to reflect the difference in frequencies. At $T = -3.2°$C and $\varepsilon_A = 10^{-2}$ percent this results in the following dynamic properties: $V_L = 1.24$ km/s and $D = 0.05$. The relationship between V_L, D, and ε_A is obtained by interpolation from similar relationships for OC and OMC shown in Fig. 8.17. These interpolated relationships are shown in Fig. 8.28. The relationships are drawn through the coordinates representing the dynamic properties established above. The relationships between V_S and ε_S and V_L and ε_A are

$$V_S = \frac{V_L}{[2(1 + \mu)]^{1/2}} \qquad \text{Table 8.1}$$

$$\varepsilon_S = \varepsilon_A(1 + \mu) \qquad (8.28)$$

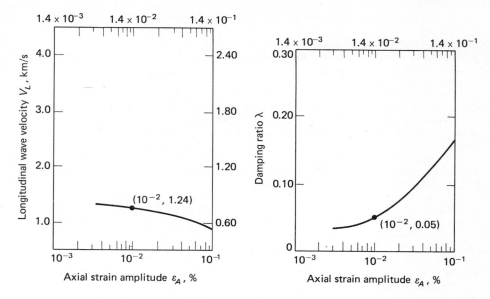

Figure 8.28 Longitudinal-wave velocity and damping ratio vs. axial-strain amplitude for frozen brown clay.

Representative values for μ are not available for OC and OMC. From Table 8.4, however, values of μ are available for Suffield, Fargo, and Boston blue clay. Considering these values, a representative value for the frozen brown clay is

$$\mu \approx 0.40$$

Then $\qquad V_S = \dfrac{V_L}{[2(1 + 0.4)]^{1/2}} = 0.60 V_L \qquad \varepsilon_S = 1.4\varepsilon_A$

The scales indicated in Fig. 8.28 for V_L and ε_A should be multiplied by 0.60 and 1.4 to obtain the desired relationships.

REFERENCES

Barnes, D. F. 1963. Geophysical Methods for Delineating Permafrost, *Proc. 1st Int. Conf. Permafrost, Lafayette, Ind., NAS-NRC Publ.* 1287, pp. 349–355.

Bell, R. A. I. 1966. A Seismic Reconnaissance of the McMurdo Sound Region, Antarctica, *J. Glaciol.,* 6(44): 209–221.

Bennett, H. F. 1972. Measurements of Ultrasonic Wave Velocities in Ice Cores from Greenland and Antarctica, *U.S. Army Cold Reg. Res. Eng. Lab. Res. Rep.* 237, Hanover, N.H., June.

Bentley, C. R. 1972. Seismic Wave Velocities in Anisotropic Ice: A Comparison of Measured and Calculated Values in and around the Deep Drill Hole at Byrd Station, Antarctica, *J. Geophys. Res.* 77(23): 4406–4420.

————. 1975. Advances in Geophysical Exploration of Ice Sheets and Glaciers, *J, Glaciol.*, **15**(73): 113–135.

Blouin, S. 1976. Personal communication.

Brown, G. W., and D. R. Selway. 1964. Frequency Response of Photoviscoelastic Material, *Exp. Mech.* **4**(3): 57–63.

Chaichanavong, T. 1976. Dynamic Properties of Ice and Frozen Clay under Cyclic Triaxial Loading Conditions, unpublished Ph.D thesis, Michigan State University, East Lansing.

Czajkowski, R. L. 1977. The Dynamic Properties of Frozen Soils under Cyclic Triaxial Loading Conditions, unpublished M.S. thesis, Michigan State University, East Lansing.

Dobrin, M. B. 1960. "Introduction to Geophysical Prospecting," McGraw-Hill, New York.

Dzhurik, V. I., and F. H. Leshchikov. 1973. Experimental Investigations of the Seismic Properties of Frozen Soils, *Proc. 2d Int. Conf. Permafrost, Yakutsk, U.S.S.R*, pp. 387–404.

Frolov, A. D. 1961. The Propagation of Ultrasonic Waves in Sandy-Clayey Rocks, *Izv. Geophys. Ser.* pp. 732–736.

————, and Y. D. Zykov. 1971. Peculiarities of the Propagation of Elastic Waves in Frozen Rocks, *Izv. Vyssh. Uchebn. Zaved. Geol. Razved.* no. 10, pp. 89–97.

Gagne, R. M., and J. A. M. Hunter. 1975. Hammer Seismic Studies of Surficial Materials, Banks Island, Ellesmere Island, and Boothia Peninsula, *Geol. Surv. Can. Pap.* 75-1B, pp. 13–18.

Grant, F. S., and G. F. West. 1965. "Interpretation Theory in Applied Geophysics," McGraw-Hill, New York.

Hardin, B. O., and V. P. Drnevich. 1972. Shear Modulus and Damping in Soils: Design Equations and Curves, *J. Soil Mech. Found. Am. Soc. Civ. Eng.*, **98**(SM7): 667–692.

Hobson, G. D. 1962. Seismic Exploration in the Canadian Arctic Islands, *Geophysics*, **27**(2): 253–273.

————. 1966. A Shallow Seismic Experiment in Permafrost, Klondike Area, Yukon Territory, *Geol. Surv. Can. Rep. Act. Nov. 1965 Apr. 1966, Pap 66-2*, Ottawa, pp. 10–14.

Hunter, J. A. M. 1973. The Application of Shallow Seismic Methods to Mapping of Frozen Surficial Materials, *North Am. Contrib. 2d Int. Conf. Permafrost, Yakutsk, U.S.S.R.*, National Academy of Science, Washington, pp. 527–535.

————. 1974. Seismic Velocity Measurements in Permafrost, Fox Tunnel, Fairbanks, Alaska, *Geol. Surv. Can. Pap.* 74–1, pt. B, pp. 89–90.

Idriss, I. M., J. Lysmer, R. Hwang, and H. B. Seed. 1973. QUAD-4-A Computer Program for Evaluating the Seismic Response of Soil Structures by Variable Damping Finite Element Procedures, *Univ. Calif. Berkeley, Earthquake Eng. Res. Cent. Rep.* EERC 73–16.

Inoue, M., and S. Kinosita. 1975. Mechanical Properties of Frozen Soil, *Low Temp. Sci., ser. A, Phys. Sci.*, **33**: 243–253.

Kaplar, C. W. 1963. Laboratory Determination of the Dynamic Moduli of Frozen Soils and of Ice, *Proc. 1st Int. Conf. Permafrost, Lafayette, Ind.*, *NAS-NRC Publ.* 1287, pp. 293–301.

————. 1969. Laboratory Determination of Dynamic Moduli of Frozen Soils and of Ice, *U.S. Army Cold Reg. Res. Eng. Lab. Res. Rep.* 163, Hanover, N.H.

Khazin, B. G., and B. V. Goncharov. 1974. The Use of Ultrasound to Estimate the Strength of Frozen Soils during Working, *Soil Mech. Found. Eng.*, **11**(2): 122–125.

King, M. S., and T. S. Bamford. 1971. Static and Dynamic Elastic Properties of Sandstone at Permafrost Temperature, *Proc. 5th Conf. Drill. Rock Mech.* pp. 83–92.

————, ————, and P. J. Kurfurst. 1974. Ultrasonic Velocity Measurements on Frozen Rocks and Soils, *Proc. Symp. Permafrost Geophys., Calgary*, pp. 35–42.

Kohnen, H. 1974. The Temperature Dependence of Seismic Waves in Ice, *J. Glaciol.*, **13**(67): 144–147.

————, and C. R. Bentley. 1973. Seismic Refraction and Reflection Measurements at Byrd Station, Antarctica. *J. Glaciol.*, **12**(64): 101–111.

Kurfurst, P. J. 1976. Ultrasonic Wave Measurement on Frozen Soils at Permafrost Temperatures, *Can. J. Earth Sci.*, **13**: 1571–1576.

————, and M. S. King. 1972. Static and Dynamic Elastic Properties of Two Sandstones at Permafrost Temperatures, *J. Pet. Technol.*, **24**: 495–504.

Lee, T. M. 1963. Method of Determining Dynamic Properties of Viscoelastic Solids Employing Forced Vibration, *U.S. Army Snow Ice Permafrost Res. Establ. Res. Rep.* 122., Hanover, N.H.

Lysmer, J., T. Udaka, H. B. Seed, and R. Hwang. 1974. LUSH: A Computer Program for Complex Response Analysis of Soil-Structure Systems, *Univ. Calif., Berkeley, Earthquake Eng. Res. Cent. Rep.* EERC 74–4.

———, ———, C. Tsai, and H. B. Seed. 1975. FLUSH: A Computer Program for Approximate 3-D Analysis of Soil-Structure Interaction Problems, *Univ. Calif., Berkeley, Earthquake Eng. Res. Cent. Rep.* EERC 75–30.

Mackay, J. R., and R. F. Black, 1973. Origin, Composition, and Structure of Perennially Frozen Ground and Ground Ice: A Review, *North Am. Contrib. 2d Int. Conf. Permafrost, Yakutsk, U.S.S.R.,* National Academy of Science, Washington, pp. 185–192.

McGinnis, L. D., K. Nakao, and C. C. Clark. 1973. Geophysical Identification of Frozen and Unfrozen Ground, *North Am. Contrib. 2d Int. Conf. Permafrost, Yakutsk, U.S.S.R.,* National Academy of Science, Washington, pp. 136–146.

Müller, G. 1961. Geschwindigkeitbestimmungen elastischer Wellen in gefrorenen Gesteinen und die Anwendung auf Undersuchungen des Frostmantels an Gefreirshachten, *Geophys. Prospec.,* **9**(2): 276–295.

Nakano, Y., and R. Arnold. 1973. Acoustic Properties of Frozen Ottawa Sand, *J. Water Resour. Res.,* **9**(1): 178–184.

———, and N. H. Froula. 1973. Sound and Shock Transmission in Frozen Soils, *North Am. Contrib. 2d Int. Conf. Permafrost, Yakutsk, U.S.S.R.,* National Academy of Science, Washington, pp. 359–369.

———, R. J. Martin, and M. Smith. 1972. Ultrasonic Velocities of the Dilational and Shear Waves in Frozen Soils, *J. Water Resour. Res.,* **8**(4): 1024–1030.

Norris, D. M., Jr., and W. Young. 1970. Longitudinal Forced Vibration of Viscoelastic Bars with End Mass, *U.S. Army Cold Reg. Res. Eng. Lab. Spec. Rep.* 135, Hanover, N.H.

Richart, F. E., Jr. 1975. Foundation Vibrations, chap. 24 in H. F. Winterkorn and H. Y. Fang (eds.), "Foundation Engineering Handbook," Van Nostrand Reinhold, New York.

———, J. R. Hall, and R. D. Woods. 1970. "Vibrations of Soils and Foundations," Prentice-Hall, Englewood Cliffs, N.J.

Robin, G. de Q. 1958. Seismic Shooting and Related Investigations, Glaciology III, *Norw.-Br. Swed. Antarct. Exped. 1949–52, Sci. Res.,* **5**(3): 48–80.

Roethlisberger, H. 1961. Applicability of Seismic Refraction Soundings in Permafrost near Thule, Greenland, *U.S. Army Cold Reg. Res. Eng. Lab. Tech. Rep.* 81, Hanover, N.H.

———. 1972. Seismic Exploration in Cold Regions, *U.S. Army Cold Reg. Res. Eng. Lab. Techn. Monogr.* II-A2a, Hanover, N.H.

Schnabel, P. B., J. Lysmer, and H. B. Seed. 1972. SHAKE: A Computer Program for Earthquake Response Analysis of Horizontally Layered Sites. *Univ. Calif., Berkeley, Earthquake Eng. Res. Cent. Res. Rep.* EERC 72–12.

Seed, H. B., and I. M. Idriss. 1970. Soil Moduli and Damping Factors for Dynamic Response Analyses, *Univ. Calif., Berkeley, Earthquake Eng. Res. Cent. Res. Rep.* EERC 70–10.

Singh, S., and N. C. Donovan. 1977. Seismic Response of Frozen-Thawed Soil Systems, 6th *World Conf. Earthquake Eng., New Delhi,* January.

Smith, N. 1969. Determining the Dynamic Properties of Snow and Ice by Forced Vibration, *U.S. Army Cold Reg. Res. Eng. Lab. Tech. Rep.* 216, Hanover, N.H.

Stevens, H. W. 1973. Viscoelastic Properties of Frozen Soil under Vibratory Loads, *North Am. Conf. Permafrost, Yakutsk, U.S.S.R.,* National Academy of Sciences, Washington, pp. 400–409.

———. 1975. The Response of Frozen Soils to Vibratory Loads, *U.S. Army Cold Reg. Res. Eng. Lab. Techn. Rep.* 265, Hanover, N.H.

Streeter, V. L., E. B. Wylie, and F. E. Richart. 1974. Soil Motion Computations by Characteristics Methods, *J. Geotech. Eng. Div. Am. Soc. Civ. Eng.,* **100**(GT3): 247–263.

Thill, R. E., T. R. Bur, and K. E. Hjelmsted. 1974. Elastic Response to Ultrasonic Pulse, in Bureau of Mines Test Procedures for Rocks, *U.S. Bur Mines Inf. Circ.* 8628, pp. 132–139.

Timur, A. 1968. Velocity of Compressional Waves in Porous Media at Permafrost Temperatures, *Geophysics*, pp. 584–595.

Vinson, T. S., and T. Chaichanavong. 1976. Dynamic Properties of Ice and Frozen Clay under Cyclic Triaxial Loading Conditions, *Mich. State Univ. Div. Eng. Res. Rep.* MSU-CE-76-4.

————, R. Czajkowski, and J. Li. 1977. Dynamic Properties of Frozen Cohesionless Soils under Cyclic Triaxial Loading Conditions, *Mich. State Univ. Div. Eng. Res. Rep.* MSU-CE-77-1.

Woolson, J. R. 1963. Seismic and Gravity Surveys of Naval Petroleum Reserve no. 4 and Adjoining Areas, Alaska, *U.S. Geol. Surv. Prof. Pap.* 304-A.

Wu, T. H. 1971. "Soil Dynamics." Allyn and Bacon, Boston, Mass.

Zykov, Y. D., and I. Baulin. 1973. Potential Use of Seismic-Acoustic Techniques in Engineering: Geologic Investigations of Construction on Permafrost, *Proc. 2d Int. Conf. Permafrost, Yakutsk, U.S.S.R.*, vol. 6.

————, A. D. Frolov, Y. P. Shuerina. 1973. Application of Ultrasound for Evaluating the Phase Composition of Water and Strength Characteristics of Permafrost, *Proc. 2d Int. Conf. Permafrost, Yakutsk, U.S.S.R.*, vol. 4, *U.S. Army Cold Reg. Res. Eng. Lab. Trans.* 439, pp. 257–261.

FIELD INVESTIGATIONS OF FROZEN GROUND

B. Ladanyi and G. H. Johnston

INTRODUCTION

For most engineering projects in seasonal frost and permafrost areas, detailed information on subsurface conditions is required for design and construction purposes if structures and facilities are to perform satisfactorily (Johnston 1963c; Linell and Johnston, 1973). Determination of the type, distribution, properties, and behavior of frozen foundation materials is essential. Sampling of the materials (soil or rock) for examination and testing in the field and the laboratory will be an important part of field investigation programs. Valuable information can also be obtained at the site using in situ test methods and geophysical techniques.

In all cases, information that will permit identification and classification of the materials, their moisture (ice) content, and frost-susceptibility characteristics will be required. In most cases, the mechanical properties and deformation behavior of frozen, thawing, and thawed soils must be determined. In some cases, data on the thermal, chemical, and electrical properties may be required. Temperature greatly influences the properties and behavior of frozen materials, particularly those containing ice and unfrozen water. Measurement of ground temperatures is most important and should be included in any field investigation.

Soil, rock, and permafrost conditions can be quite variable and will significantly influence the location of a structure and foundation design. Irregular massive ice deposits and ice-rich fine-grained materials may underlie relatively ice-free granular materials. Bedrock is often badly fractured by frost action and the seams and fissures filled with ice to depths exceeding 4 m. The maximum depth of frost penetration in seasonal frost areas, the distribution of frozen ground in marginal permafrost areas (and adjacent to water bodies), and the thickness of the active layer are important considerations.

As a rule, subsurface exploration should be carried out to a depth equal to at least the width of a structure unless a competent bearing stratum is encountered at a shallower depth. All foundation materials that might thaw during the operating life of a structure should be investigated. Normally, exploration is carried to a depth of at least 6 m, and in many cases information may be required to a depth of 30 m or more.

The scope and nature of a site investigation and the methods used will depend on many factors, including the type, size, and importance of the structure or facility, previous experience in the area, whether it is for foundation design or evaluation of construction materials, and location, i.e., seasonal frost area and discontinuous or continuous permafrost zones. Major structures, such as bridges, dams, buildings with heavy structural and/or thermal loads, and airfields, usually require very detailed site investigations, whereas only limited information that can be obtained by relatively simple methods may be needed for small or temporary structures. Extensive exploration may be required for linear structures such as roads, railways, pipelines, and power-transmission lines (towers) that traverse highly variable terrain.

9.1 SAMPLING FROZEN GROUND

The type and number of samples to be taken from a vertical profile will depend primarily on the variability of the materials encountered and the ultimate use of the samples, i.e., what information is required and what tests are to be performed. These factors will also determine the methods that should be employed to obtain the samples. In some cases, representative grab samples (disturbed) may be adequate. On the other hand, samples that have not been subjected to undue physical, mechanical, or thermal disturbance or contamination may be required for special laboratory tests, e.g., thaw consolidation, strength, and creep.

Samples of unfrozen ground (in seasonal frost areas or in the active layer) can be obtained using conventional techniques and will not be discussed in this chapter. This work is best carried out during the summer but because of difficult access conditions or environmental restrictions it may have to be conducted during the winter. In this case undisturbed samples will have to be protected against freezing.

Techniques used for sampling frozen ground (seasonal or permafrost) are similar to those used for unfrozen materials, but much greater attention must be paid to avoiding thermal disturbance. At present, there are no set standards or guidelines for sampling frozen materials. The selection of appropriate methods and equipment will depend greatly upon the experience and judgment of the field engineer and on the needs of the project. Procedures that have proved successful for procuring, handling, and transporting samples are described in the following sections.

Sampling Methods

Samples can be obtained from natural exposures, test pits, or boreholes (Cass, 1959; Johnston, 1963a). Soil and rock profiles can be examined on the banks of rivers and lakes, in gullies, and the scarps of landslides. Colluvial or thawed material can be removed and representative samples taken from the relatively undisturbed face by cutting out blocks or using coring tools.

Test pits, which can be excavated to depths of 2 to 10 m by several methods, permit the complete profile to be examined, logged, and sampled in situ; disturbed and excellent undisturbed block or core samples can be taken from the walls or bottom. Natural and artificial thawing and hand tools have been used to dig pits to shallow depths (2 to 3 m), but they are time-consuming and labor intensive. Pits have been dug by hand using power tools to depths of 8 to 10 m in 2 to 3 days. Explosives are not widely used for exploration, usually because of the cost of drilling and blasting and very irregular "break" and scattering of the frozen ground. Better results have been obtained, but at greater cost, with a shaft-sinking type of operation. Trenches have been excavated to depths of 8 to 10 m in a few hours using bulldozers and rippers or power shovels (Fig. 9.1). Progress is highly variable, depending on the type of material and its temperature; warm-temperature frozen materials are usually more easily excavated than hard frozen or granular materials. Although the use of test pits may have certain disadvantages (mainly associated with rate of advance and cost), it is an excellent exploration method that should not be overlooked. It may be the only way to obtain reliable information in frozen granular materials and at remote sites when heavy equipment is not available; hand methods can then be used.

Most subsurface information is obtained from boreholes—sometimes drilled by hand but usually by rotary power equipment. Hand borings are only practicable in warm-temperature frozen fine-grained materials. Holes have been advanced to depths of from 2 to 10 m by chopping bits (the cuttings are removed by posthole augers) or by driving heavy-walled steel pipe or Shelby tubes. Relatively undisturbed cores can be obtained using the latter method.

Various types of rotary drilling equipment are used to obtain information to depths of more than 30 m. Churn drills and power augers are often used to drill holes 75 to 300 mm in diameter or larger. Cuttings are collected for identification of the materials and in some cases may be suitable for classification and water-content tests. Fairly good results have been obtained by driving heavy-walled tubes into fine-grained frozen soils whose temperature is $-4°C$ or warmer (Kitze, 1956; Davis and Kitze, 1967). Drive or auger sampling is not effective, however, in hard frozen soils at very low temperatures or in stony frozen soils.

Excellent samples of all types of frozen soil and rock can be obtained from any depth using special core-drilling equipment and techniques (Hvorslev and Goode, 1963; Lange, 1963, 1973a, 1973b; Lange and Smith, 1972; Sellman and Brown, 1965). Drills may range in size from those that can be transported by helicopter (Fig. 9.2) (Pihlainen and Johnston, 1953; Veillette, 1975b) to larger

Figure 9.1 Test pit (0.8 m wide by 5 m deep) excavated in ice-rich fine-grained frozen material by backhoe.

Figure 9.2 Lightweight hand-feed power drill taking 75-mm-diameter core samples to depth of 15 m in fine-grained frozen soils.

ones mounted on trucks or tracked vehicles. Various types of core barrels and bits can be used, depending on the nature of the investigation, type of frozen material and depth, and size of hole required (Hvorslev and Goode, 1963; Veillette, 1975a). Water, air, and diesel fuel are the circulating fluids most widely used although brine, alcohol, and other types of antifreeze solutions have also been tried. The fluids may contaminate or partially thaw the surface of the core, but providing the diameter is greater than, say, 70 or 80 mm, a good undisturbed sample can be obtained by carefully removing the affected layer. Although the fluids can be cooled to ground temperature relatively easily during the winter, special refrigeration and circulation equipment may be required for summer drilling and sampling operations.

An accurate and detailed log of the soil profile should be kept using the unified frozen soil description and classification system (Linell and Kaplar, 1963) given in Chap. 1. Particular attention should be paid to describing the ice inclusions. Frozen cores are examined and logged as they are extruded from the sample tube (usually at the drill site). In some cases, all frozen cores are retained for subsequent, more detailed examination and selection of samples for testing; in other cases, only select pieces of core may be retained. A typical

Table 9.1 Typical exploration log in permafrost area

Depth, m		Soil	Ice
0			
		Living moss cover	Nil
0.2			
	Pt	Dark brown peat, top 300 mm contains partly decomposed small roots; very wet	Nil
1.0		—Top of permafrost	
1.2			
	Pt	Dark-brown peat, very fibrous	Irregularly oriented lenses from 1–25 mm thick (av. 10 mm) spaced at ~ 5–10 mm
2.0	Vr	Frozen	Excess ice ~ 50% by volume
2.2			
	Ice	Ice	Ice, hard colorless, few air bubbles (?) and random peat and silt inclusions
2.8			
3.0		Organic silt, black to gray, changing to brown	Stratified ice lenses 1–5 mm thick, spacing increases with depth from 5 to 20 mm
	OL	Organic content decreases with depth	
4.0	Vs	Frozen	Excess ice ~ 10% by volume
4.2			
		Brown sandy silt	Predominantly horizontal ice lenses, 1–5 mm thick spaced at 30 mm increasing to 50 mm with depth
5.0	ML	Frozen	
6.0	Vs		Excess ice ~ 10% by volume
6.4			
	SW	Brown, well-graded fine to coarse sand with random pebble	Random horizontal lenses 2 mm thick, spaced at 50 to 100 mm
	Nbe		
7.0		Frozen, well bonded	Excess ice ~ 5% by volume
7.3			
	GW	Brown, well-graded sandy gravel	No visible ice
8.0		Frozen, well bonded	
	Nbn		
8.5			
	Rock	Granite bedrock, no fractures, sound	Frozen (?) No ice
9.0			
		Bottom of hole at 10 m	
10.0			

Possible Ice wedge (margin note at 2.8 m)

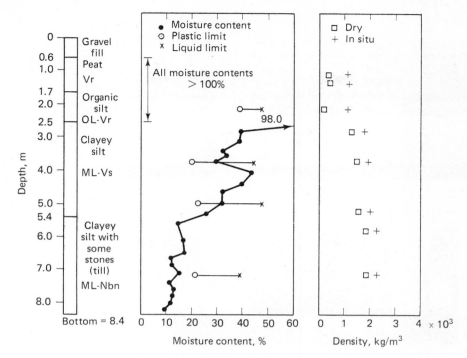

Borehole no. 3 drilled 30/10/76, permafrost table at 1.0 m

Figure 9.3 Test results from permafrost borehole.

exploration log and test results are given in Table 9.1 and Fig. 9.3. Photographs of core samples and the walls of test pits are invaluable as a permanent record (Fig. 9.4).

Sample Protection

Facilities are frequently available at or near the field site so that some of the simpler soil tests, e.g., moisture content, field unit weights, and some classification tests, can be carried out shortly after samples are obtained. For the more sophisticated tests the samples must be stored and shipped some distance to a properly equipped laboratory.

Undisturbed frozen samples must be carefully prepared and handled to prevent disturbance to their thermal and moisture regimes. The soil structure, ice distribution, and unfrozen water content may change if precautions are not taken and may radically affect the properties and behavior of the materials. Smith et al. (1973) have described the effects of sample disturbance on test results of cores obtained from depths exceeding 300 m.

All core and block samples of frozen ground must be protected from loss of moisture and (depending on the tests to be performed) from thawing or

Sample 2

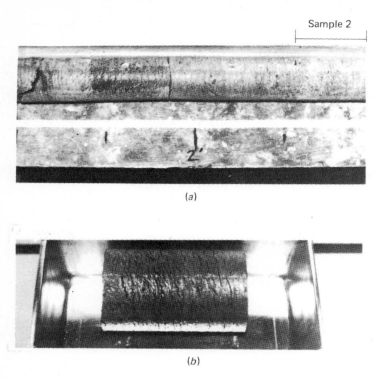

(a)

(b)

Figure 9.4 Photographs of permafrost core: (a) immediately after extrusion from the core barrel; (b) partially thawed in the field laboratory (note ice lenses; sample 2, depth 0.79 to 0.91 m.)

even change in temperature from the time they are taken from the ground until they are tested. Baker (1976) has described methods of handling and transporting frozen samples. Usually the samples are wrapped in cellophane and placed in well-sealed, polyethylene bags, from which the air has been evacuated to prevent sublimation. This procedure has been used successfully to keep moisture loss within acceptable limits for periods of 8 months or more.

If it is critical that the samples be kept from thawing, or if they must be maintained at the in situ ground temperature, additional precautions must be taken. Unfrozen samples obtained for frost-heaving experiments should not be allowed to freeze. Samples in sealed tubes or plastic bags are normally kept in insulated boxes which are stored in warm enclosures. Frozen samples taken, say, for strength, creep, and thaw-consolidation tests should be kept at their original in situ temperature. Ground temperatures vary with depth during the year and therefore should be determined when the sample is taken.

To provide positive protection against temperature changes, samples must be placed in portable refrigerators powered by portable electric generators for storage and shipment to the laboratory. A less expensive procedure but one usually quite adequate to prevent thawing is to place the bagged samples in well-insulated boxes packed with ice, snow, or dry ice. Sample temperatures can be maintained within acceptable limits (1 or 2°C) for many test purposes for more than a day, depending on the temperature of the ambient air.

If the samples are to remain frozen but adequate storage facilities are not available at the field site, they must be transported immediately to a temperature- and humidity-controlled storage area. They must be shipped in refrigerated containers or insulated boxes.

The preparation and transportation of undisturbed frozen samples from the field to the laboratory is a difficult and costly operation requiring careful planning. In most cases and for most purposes, insulated boxes have been used successfully (Baker, 1976).

9.2 GROUND-TEMPERATURE MEASUREMENT

Information on the ground thermal regime at construction sites in frozen ground areas should always be collected. In some cases, only the position of the 0°C isotherm, which can be obtained by relatively simple methods, may be required. For most projects detailed information on ground temperatures and their fluctuation at various depths will be required for thermal design and for assessing the performance of structures during their service life. Temperature data will also assist in delineating unfrozen zones, particularly at sites in marginal permafrost areas, and in determining temperatures to be used for laboratory testing of samples.

Various techniques and equipment are used for obtaining information on the ground thermal regime. The selection of appropriate instrumentation will depend on a number of factors, including the depths at which temperatures are required, the frequency of observations, measurement accuracy, long-term or short-term study, location (remote area vs. site with easy access), cost of equipment, installation, and making observations.

Active Layer and Seasonal Frost Zone

Steel rods, 10 to 20 mm in diameter, are often used as probes to determine the rate and depth of thaw in the active layer. Care must be taken when probing fine-grained materials to make certain that the rod does not penetrate the plastic frozen layers (containing thin ice lenses) just below the permafrost table. If this should happen, the actual depth of thaw may be more than 0.3 m less than that indicated by the probe. Hand coring tools, that will take a sample from 10 to 50 mm in diameter and 0.15 to 0.3 m long (Fig. 9.5a), give much more reliable results (Day et al., 1961) and have been used to sample frozen peat and fine-grained soils to depths of 4 or 5 m. These tools cannot be used in stony materials.

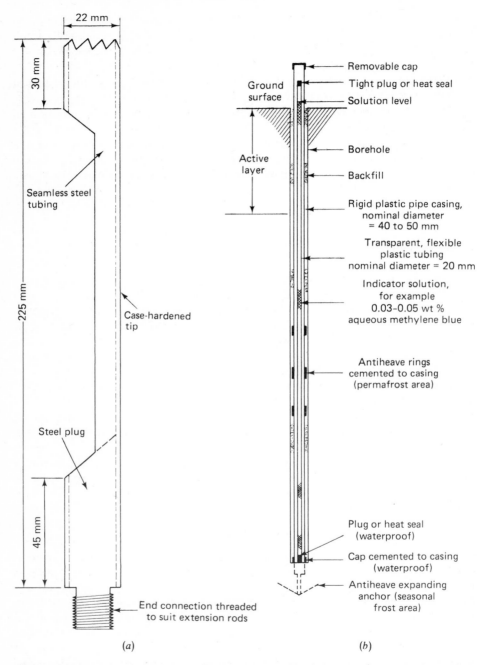

Figure 9.5 (*a*) Small core tube for probing depth of thaw in permafrost areas (all dimensions approximate). (*b*) Simple frost tube for measurement of rate and depth of thaw or seasonal frost penetration (not to scale).

The *frost tube* is widely used to determine the depth and rate of thaw and frost penetration in the active layer and seasonal frost zone (Gandahl, 1963; Rickard and Brown, 1972; Mackay, 1973). It consists of an outer casing containing a removable, transparent inner tube filled with an indicator solution, e.g., methylene blue, that changes color upon freezing (Fig. 9.5*b*). This device is readily fabricated, inexpensive, easy to read, and accurate to about ±50 mm. It is usually installed in a carefully backfilled drill hole to ensure good contact between the casing and the adjacent soil. The frost tube has also been installed well below the original permafrost table to monitor degradation of permafrost beneath engineering structures over a period of years (Johnston, 1969).

Although the probes and frost tube indicate the position of the 0°C isotherm, no information on the soil temperature profile is obtained. Mackay (1974*a*) designed a self-positioning thermistor probe that fits inside a frost tube to measure the upward freezing of the active layer. Good results were obtained with this device, which can also be used to monitor the aggradation of permafrost under thick fills or the degradation of permafrost in disturbed areas.

Temperature Sensors and Measuring Equipment

Various types of temperature sensors, including mercury thermometers, thermocouples, thermistors, and diodes, are available for the measurement of ground temperatures. Each has its place, depending on the particular conditions and accuracy required. Thermocouples and thermistors are the most widely used sensors for engineering field investigations. Their use and the advantages and disadvantages of each have been described by Hansen (1963), Johnston (1963*b*, 1972), and Judge (1972). A comparison of thermocouples and thermistors is beyond the scope of this discussion, but the papers just cited contain information and additional references that will assist the reader in selecting an appropriate sensor.

For most engineering purposes, an accuracy of ±0.2°C is desirable and can be obtained either with thermocouples or with thermistors provided that great care is taken in planning the installation, fabricating the probes, connectors, switches, and circuitry, in the installation of the probes, and in selecting and using the readout instruments. Thermocouples of copper and constantan (20-gauge wire) or interchangeable (±0.1°C) precision thermistors are commonly used for ground-temperature work and will give the required accuracy. Although thermocouples are ideal for measurement of temperature gradients, if very precise measurements, e.g., absolute accuracy of ±0.1°C, and temperature-difference resolution to several millidegrees are required, individually calibrated precision thermistors should be used.

Since temperatures usually are to be measured at several depths at one location, multiconductor cables containing sensors at the desired intervals are inserted in a borehole. The sensors will be closely spaced (say 0.25 to 0.5 m) to a depth of 3 to 6 m and at intervals of 1 or 2.5 m from there to the bottom of the hole (Fig. 9.6). For most installations the cable can be placed directly in

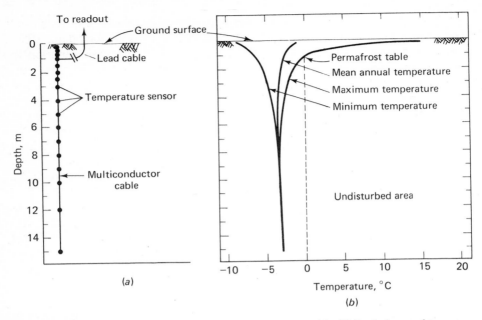

Figure 9.6 (*a*) Typical spacing of sensors in ground-temperature cable. (*b*) Typical ground-temperature envelope in permafrost; results from data obtained at 2-h intervals in 1-year period.

the hole (it is essential that all connections be moistureproof) so that the sensors are in intimate contact with the surrounding material. The hole should be carefully backfilled, particularly near the ground surface, to prevent percolation of surface water down the hole. The ground surface should be marked on the cable at the time of installation so that any movements due to frost action or thaw settlement and the subsequent position of the sensors can be determined. Cables placed in deep holes or those which are to measure temperatures precisely and/or over long periods of time may have to be cased to protect them from damage or moisture and to make it possible to retrieve the thermistors for recalibration.

Depending on the amount of disturbance caused by the drilling operation, it may take several days or weeks before thermal equilibrium is reestablished in most drill holes. Mackay (1974*b*) and Veillette (1975*c*) found that temperatures measured in plugged, air-filled drill holes 6 to 30 m deep stabilized within 1 day.

Ground temperatures at shallow depths, e.g., within the top 1 to 2 m, change continually (hourly, daily) in response to air (or other) temperatures imposed on the ground surface. Measurements must be made at frequent intervals, e.g. hourly, if useful data are desired. In addition, heat conduction along the lead wires can seriously affect the temperatures in the ground. In such cases, the sensors should be installed in the side of a test pit or the lead wires buried well below the ground surface to reduce or eliminate these effects.

The type of readout equipment required will depend largely on project requirements. A wide variety of instruments and circuitry is available, ranging from simple hand-operated potentiometers and resistance bridges to very sophisticated data-acquisition systems. Portable instruments used under ambient conditions in the field must be selected with care because many of them contain temperature-sensitive components which seriously affect their operation at temperatures below 10°C. Most of the more sophisticated (and expensive) instruments and systems must be installed in shelters where the temperature is maintained between 20 and 30°C.

9.3 FIELD TESTING OF FROZEN-SOIL PROPERTIES

A frozen soil is generally much less susceptible to mechanical disturbance than the same soil when unfrozen. As a result, when appropriate equipment is available, and when proper measures are taken to minimize the thermal disturbance of the soil during drilling and sampling (Sec. 9.1), good-quality samples can be obtained for almost any kind of frozen soil except those containing coarse gravel and rock debris. This fact would normally favor the use of laboratory over field investigations for the determination of strength and deformation parameters of frozen soils. There are two principal reasons why this is not always so: (1) the preservation of frozen samples and their transport to specialized laboratories, which are still rather scarce, often are difficult and expensive; (2) most ice-rich permafrost soils have a complex large-scale structure of ice lenses and inclusions that can much better be investigated by large-scale field tests than by testing samples in the laboratory.

For these reasons, several attempts have recently been made to find appropriate field methods for testing frozen soils, either by adapting known soil-mechanics methods or by developing new ones to furnish certain basic frozen-soil parameters needed in design.

The field methods used up to now in permafrost soils have essentially been designed to furnish information either on the strength and deformation properties of the soil in its natural frozen state or on its compression and consolidation characteristics when thawed under controlled conditions. While various methods of the first kind have been used frequently in the past in all northern areas of the world, there have been some new developments in this field which warrant more detailed coverage in this section. The methods of the second kind, devised for testing thaw-consolidation characteristics of permafrost soils, have been reported mainly in Russian permafrost literature. To date they have been used very little in the North American permafrost practice.

Field-testing Methods Used in Frozen Soils

Most field methods developed for testing unfrozen soils can also be used on frozen soils, provided the equipment is sufficiently strong to deform and fail the more resistant frozen soil. Although the equipment may be of the same type as in unfrozen soils, different test procedures and data processing are usually needed to obtain the frozen-soil parameters. For example, in field tests of unfrozen soils, only short-term strength and deformation properties, including compressibility, may be required. In frozen soils, attention is concentrated on long-term creep behavior and sensitivity to temperature changes.

The field methods used in frozen soils also include some of the geophysical exploration methods described in Sec. 9.4. These methods measure the dynamic elastic constants of the frozen soil. This section will describe two quasistatic field tests which have recently been adapted and examined for possible use in testing mechanical properties of frozen ground. The two tests include the pressuremeter test and the deep-static-cone-penetration test, both of which are well known in conventional soil-mechanics practice.

The Pressuremeter Test

The Ménard pressuremeter (Ménard, 1957) (Fig. 9.7) is a special borehole dilatometer that has been used quite extensively during the last 25 years for in situ measurement of stress-strain and strength properties of soils and rocks. It consists of an inflatable probe composed of two coaxial cells and a pressure-

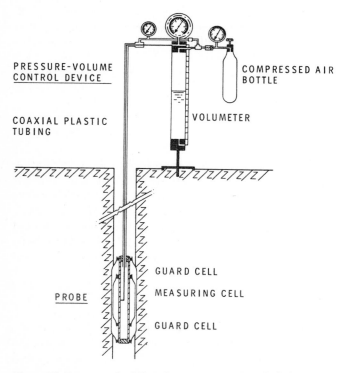

Figure 9.7 Test setup for Ménard pressuremeter type G. (*After Ladanyi and Johnston, 1973.*)

volume control device that permits a given pressure to be applied to the wall of the borehole and the volume increase of the hole to be measured.

Ladanyi and Johnston (1973) performed pressuremeter tests in permafrost soils of northern Manitoba with a standard 10-MPa-capacity pressuremeter together with a standard probe (70 mm in diameter and 0.7 m long) which fitted into an NX-sized borehole. The probe had an inflating capacity of 700 cm^3, and its outer rubber membrane was protected by an extensible jacket made of overlapping metal strips.

This field study showed that good-quality results in frozen soils, especially in long-term tests, can be obtained using a pressuremeter system with an accurate and reliable pressure control which can maintain a constant applied pressure for long periods of time. Since some temperature disturbance of the soil around the borehole was inevitable, it was necessary to check the temperature of the soil in contact with the probe continuously, using thermocouples attached to the outside of the probe. An antifreeze mixture of equal parts of ethylene glycol and water should be used for inflating the probe when testing permafrost soils. In summer, the liquid to be injected into the probe should be cooled to the permafrost temperature.

Experience with unfrozen soils shows that the quality of pressuremeter test results depends greatly on the uniformity and size accuracy of the drilled borehole. This is even more true in frozen soils, where not only a mechanical but also a thermal disturbance may occur during drilling. A method which can be used for minimizing these disturbances includes augering the hole to about 0.75 m above the required test level. Next a special sampling tube with an inward-tapered cutting edge is pushed into the frozen soil. Removal of this tube leaves a tight hole for the probe. Sometimes, during high air temperatures and when working in relatively warm permafrost soils, some thermal disturbance of the soil cannot be avoided. In this case, the probe should be lowered into the borehole and the temperature at the contact with the probe should be checked. The test is run when the probe temperature equals the permafrost temperature. A waiting period at at least 1 h was normally used before starting each test, but longer periods, up to 24 h, may be necessary for good-quality results in warm permafrost soils.

Test procedure Conventional pressuremeter tests in unfrozen soils are performed as short-term loading tests, their main purpose being the determination of short-term strength and deformation parameters of the soil. In frozen soils, the knowledge of the short-term strength parameters is necessary in many design problems involving rapid stress changes and failure of the soil, e.g., under moving loads and during excavation and drilling. In addition, the short-term parameters represent the starting point in planning any long-term testing program.

The loading procedure adopted by Ladanyi and Johnston (1973) for a standard short-term test consisted of increasing the pressure in the probe in about 10 to 20 equal increments until the limit volume capacity, that is, 700 cm^3 of injected liquid, was reached. After each increment the pressure was kept constant for 2 min with volume readings after 30 s, 1 min, and 2 min.

Ladanyi and Johnston (1973) have shown that two different kinds of tests are required to obtain a reasonably clear picture of the long-term behavior of the frozen soil:

1. In the one-stage creep test the pressure is brought rapidly to a given level and is left at that level as long as possible. The deformation of the borehole is limited by the inflation capacity of the probe, which is 700 cm^3 and corresponds to about 40 percent increase of the hole diameter. The total creep time is inversely proportional to the load level and can vary from about 20 min to a maximum of about 24 h.
2. In the multistage or incremental creep test the pressure is brought rapidly up to an initial level and is then increased to the limit probe capacity in several equal stress increments, each kept constant for at least 15 min.

Data processing for short-term tests Since a detailed description of the standard pressuremeter testing procedure, including all corrections and calibrations, is usually furnished with the apparatus, only a few basic principles for interpretation of short-term tests with some typical results will be given here. The results of a short-term pressuremeter test are usually plotted as a corrected pressuremeter curve (Fig. 9.8a) defined as

$$V_m = f(p_c) \tag{9.1}$$

where V_m is the total volume of fluid injected into the measuring cell from the start of pressure application and p_c is the applied pressure that has been corrected for the piezometric head and the extension resistance of the unloaded probe.

The test interpretation is based on a "true pressuremeter curve," such as would be obtained in an ideal test starting from the original lateral ground pressure p_0. The true pressuremeter curve represents a relationship of the form $\Delta V = f(p)$, where

$$p = p_c - p_0 \tag{9.2}$$

and

$$\Delta V = V_m - V_{m0} \tag{9.3}$$

in which V_{m0} denotes the volume of the liquid injected into the probe up to $p_c = p_0$. The true pressuremeter curve is obtained from the corrected curve by shifting the origin from O to O', as shown in Fig. 9.8a. The new origin O' of the true pressuremeter curve can be found approximately by extending the linear portion of the corrected pressuremeter curve back to the ordinate corresponding to the calculated value of the total original horizontal pressure p_0 at the level of the test.

From a soil-mechanics point of view, an ice-saturated frozen soil approximates a $c\phi$ material having a relatively high time- and temperature-dependent cohesion c and an angle of internal friction ϕ which is relatively independent of time and temperature. Since little is known about the true intergranular

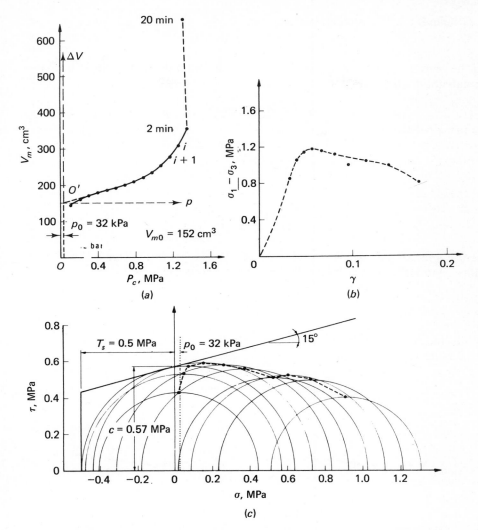

Figure 9.8 Results of a short-term pressuremeter test in a frozen varved clay: (*a*) pressuremeter curve, (*b*) stress-strain curve; (*c*) vector curve. (*After Ladanyi and Johnston, 1973.*)

stresses in frozen soils, c and ϕ are assumed to be total-stress parameters. Moreover, if the soil is fine-grained and ice-saturated, the volumetric component of the deformation will be very small and therefore can be neglected. With these assumptions, a pressuremeter curve for frozen soil can be interpreted using the method proposed by Ladanyi (1972).

Stress-strain curve Ladanyi (1972) has shown that for any two points i and $i + 1$ of the true pressuremeter curve (Fig. 9.8*a*), the corresponding mobilized strength

$q_{i, i+1}$ defines the principal stress difference

$$q_{i, i+1} = (\sigma_1 - \sigma_3)_{i, i+1} \tag{9.4}$$

and the corresponding average engineering shear strain defined as the principal-normal-strain difference:

$$\gamma_{i, i+1} = (\varepsilon_1 - \varepsilon_3)_{i, i+1} \tag{9.5}$$

The principal-stress difference is

$$q_{i, i+1} = \frac{p_i - p_{i+1}}{\frac{1}{2}[\ln (\Delta V/V)_i - \ln (\Delta V/V)_{i+1}]} \tag{9.6}$$

and the shear strain is

$$\gamma_{i, i+1} = \frac{1}{2}\left[\left(\frac{\Delta V}{V}\right)_i + \left(\frac{\Delta V}{V}\right)_{i+1}\right] \tag{9.7}$$

where p and ΔV denote the coordinates of the true pressuremeter curve at the points i and $i + 1$. The current volume V of the borehole is

$$V = V_0 + \Delta V \tag{9.8}$$

where

$$V_0 = V_{\text{empty}} + V_{m0} \tag{9.9}$$

denotes the volume of the measuring section of the probe at the moment when the pressure in the probe has attained the original ground pressure p_0.

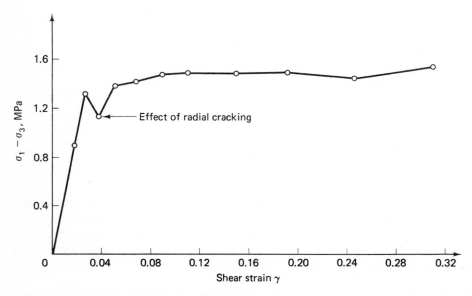

Figure 9.9 Stress-strain curve from a pressuremeter test in frozen silt, showing the effect of radial cracking.

Note that the stress-strain relationship obtained by this procedure (Fig. 9.8b) is valid for a constant-volume plane-strain condition. It can be transformed into the more usual axial symmetrical case by the von Mises yield criterion (Ladanyi, 1972). Some caution is necessary when this stress-strain curve is compared with those obtained in a triaxial test. For some frozen soils it has been found that a pressuremeter test produces radial cracking of the soil early in the test, leading to an irregular shape of the stress-strain curve. The first peak appears to be due to tensile failure (Fig. 9.9).

Vector curve in the Mohr plot Since both the major principal stress (σ_1 equal to the applied radial stress) and the principal-stress difference ($\sigma_1 - \sigma_3$ equal to $q_{i, i+1}$) are known at any moment of the test, the data can be used for plotting a series of Mohr circles and a vector curve in the Mohr plot. For the plane-strain deformation condition represented by the test, the values of the total principal stresses σ_1 and σ_3 for an interval i, $i + 1$ of the pressuremeter curve are given by

$$\sigma_1 = \tfrac{1}{2}(p_{c, i} + p_{c, i+1}) \tag{9.10}$$

and
$$\sigma_3 = \sigma_1 - q_{i, i+1} \tag{9.11}$$

where p_c is the applied radial stress and $q_{i, i+1}$ is the stress difference defined by Eq. (9.6). Figure 9.8c shows one such plot obtained for a frozen varved silt. To make it easier to follow the sequence of Mohr circles they have been connected by a vector curve. Note that the pseudoelastic behavior of the soil is reflected by the first two or three circles, which increase in diameter but remain concentric. This is predicted by the theory of expansion of a cylindrical hole in an infinite elastic medium.

The following two or three circles are failure circles and correspond to the peak strength of the soil. The remaining circles are all in the plastic domain and correspond to increasing plastic deformations. The diameters of these remaining circles depend simultaneously on the strength characteristics of the soil and on its postfailure stress-strain behavior. It follows that the three kinds of Mohr circles cannot be expected to have one common failure envelope. In fact, one is justified in drawing one failure envelope over all failure and postfailure circles only if the postfailure behavior of the soil is very close to the ideal plastic assumption. If the postfailure behavior of the soil is either strain-hardening or strain-softening, which is most often the case, the circles will not have a common failure envelope and the determination of failure parameters c and ϕ from a single pressuremeter curve will be very difficult or impossible.

Nevertheless, the Mohr-circle plots can be used for estimating probable lower limits of the short-term tensile strength T_s and the cohesion c. To estimate the two parameters, the Mohr circles are enclosed by a bilinear envelope, composed of a Coulomb straight-line and a vertical tension-cutoff. For the Coulomb line, a most probable value of the short-term friction angle should be assumed for the frozen soil, for example, 25 to 35° for sands, 15 to 25° for silts, and 0 to 10° for clays. In addition, the values of the pressuremeter modulus E_p can be calculated from the initial straight-line portion of the pressuremeter curve by using the formula valid for incompressible soil:

$$E_p = \frac{3\Delta p}{\Delta(\Delta V/V)} \tag{9.12}$$

Processing pressuremeter creep-test results Two different methods for processing frozen-soil creep data have been described in Chap. 5, one valid for long-term creep tests, in which the steady-state creep is dominant, and another valid for relatively short-term creep tests, in which the creep is essentially of a primary or hardening type. As the creep time that can be realized in a pressuremeter test usually does not exceed several hours, the test should be considered as a short-term creep test to which the second method is applicable.

According to the second method, the creep data obtained in a pressure-meter test can be generalized using the solution to the problem of stationary creep under internal pressure of a cylindrical cavity of infinite length located in an infinite medium. The solution is based on a creep equation of the form

$$\varepsilon_e^{(c)} = \left(\frac{\dot{\varepsilon}_c}{b}\right)^b \left(\frac{\sigma_e}{\sigma_c}\right)^n t^b \tag{9.13}$$

which is a more general form of Eq. (5.24), used for generalizing primary-creep data.

In order to process the pressuremeter creep data, the only relationship needed from the solution is the one relating the creep cavity-expansion rate with the applied internal pressure, which, according to Odqvist (1966), is

$$\frac{dr}{d\tau} = \left[\frac{(3)^{1/2}}{2}\right]^{n+1} Ar \left(\frac{2(p_i - p_0)}{n\sigma_c}\right)^n \tag{9.14}$$

where r = current radius of cavity
p_i = constant applied internal pressure
p_0 = radial pressure acting at infinity

The symbol τ denotes the transformed time unit, related to the real time t by

$$\tau = t^b \tag{9.15}$$

A is defined by

$$A = \left(\frac{\dot{\varepsilon}_c}{b}\right)^b \tag{9.16}$$

with the same notation as in Chap. 5. The purpose of pressuremeter creep tests is to determine the values of the creep modulus σ_c (for a given value of $\dot{\varepsilon}_c$) and the two creep exponents b and n so that the creep behavior of the soil can be defined by Eq. (9.13). This can be done in a manner similar to the determination of the same parameters from laboratory creep tests described in Chap. 5.

If p_i is replaced by p_c, using the notation adopted for the corrected pressure in the borehole, Eq. (9.14) can be written as

$$\frac{dr}{r} = G(p)\, d\tau \tag{9.17}$$

where $G(p)$ is a function of pressure p, defined by

$$G(p) = \left[\frac{(3)^{1/2}}{2} \right]^{n+1} A\left(\frac{2p}{n\sigma_c} \right)^n \tag{9.18}$$

For a finite interval of time at a constant stress, Eq. (9.17) can be integrated to give

$$\ln r = G(p)\tau + C \tag{9.19}$$

Taking $r = r_{i-1}$ at $\tau = 0$, that is, at the beginning of the considered ith creep stage, the integration constant C can be eliminated and Eq. (9.19) becomes

$$\ln \frac{r}{r_{i-1}} = G(p)\tau \tag{9.20}$$

Since for a cylindrical cavity

$$\left(\frac{r}{r_{i-1}} \right)^2 = \frac{V}{V_{i-1}} \tag{9.21}$$

Eq. (9.20) becomes finally

$$\frac{V}{V_{i-1}} = \exp 2G(p)t^b \tag{9.22}$$

where (Fig. 9.10) V_{i-1} denotes the cavity volume at $t = 0$, that is, at the start of a given constant-pressure creep stage, and $V = V_{i-1} + \Delta V_c$ denotes the volume of the cavity at any time t after the step increase of pressure p in the stage i.

In order to determine the creep parameters b, n, and σ_c, the semigraphical procedure described in Chap. 5 for the primary-creep case can be followed. Taking first a natural and then an ordinary logarithm of Eq. (9.22), one obtains

$$\log \left(\ln \frac{V}{V_{i-1}} \right) = \log 2G(p) + b \log t \tag{9.23}$$

showing that pressuremeter creep curves should linearize if $\ln (V/V_{i-1})$ is plotted against time in a log-log plot. According to Eq. (9.23), the slope of the creep straight lines is equal to b, or, from Fig. 9.11,

$$b = \frac{D}{C} \tag{9.24}$$

The intercept at the unit time ($t = 1$ min in Fig. 9.11) of any creep line, each intercept corresponding to a different value of pressure p, is then equal to $2G(p)$.

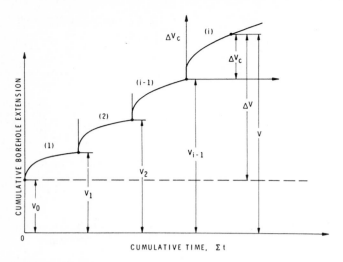

Figure 9.10 Notation for interpretation of stage-loaded pressuremeter tests. (*After Ladanyi and Johnston, 1973.*)

To determine the parameters n and σ_c, Eq. (9.18) can be written

$$\log 2G(p) = \log M - n \log \sigma_c + n \log p \tag{9.25}$$

where

$$M = 2\left[\frac{(3)^{1/2}}{2}\right]^{n+1} A\left(\frac{2}{n}\right)^n \tag{9.26}$$

Equation (9.25) shows that plotting $2G(p)$ against p in a log-log plot will give a straight line with the slope equal to n. In Fig. 9.11 such a plot is shown superimposed on a plot of $\ln (V/V_{i-1})$ vs. time. The new straight line has a slope

$$n = \frac{F}{E} \tag{9.27}$$

and its intercept N, read at an arbitrary value of $p = p_N$, according to Eq. (9.25) is equal to

$$N = M\left(\frac{p_N}{\sigma_c}\right)^n \tag{9.28}$$

Since, for an arbitrary value of $\dot{\varepsilon}_c$, and with known b and n, the value of M can be calculated from Eq. (9.26), the value of σ_c is

$$\sigma_c = p_N\left(\frac{M}{N}\right)^{1/n} \tag{9.29}$$

In Fig. 9.11, $b = 0.85$, $n = 3.00$ and $N = 6.5 \times 10^{-4}$ min^{-b} (for $p_N = 1$ MPa). Now, taking $\dot{\varepsilon}_c = 10^{-5}$ min^{-1}, one obtains $A = 6.456 \times 10^{-5}$ min^{-b} and $M = 2.152 \times 10^{-5}$ min^{-b}, from which [Eq. (9.29)] $\sigma_c = 0.321$ MPa.

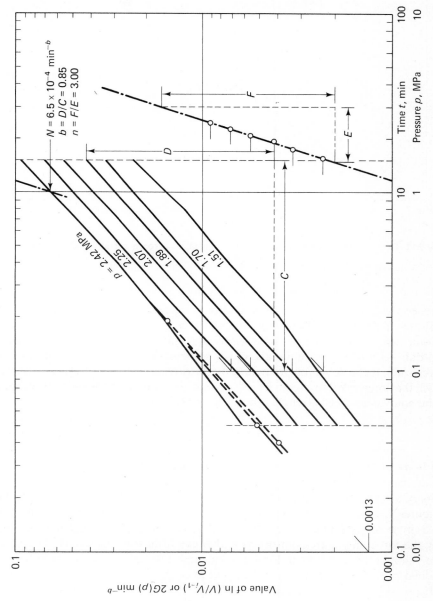

Figure 9.11 Determination of creep parameters from the results of a stage-loaded pressuremeter test.

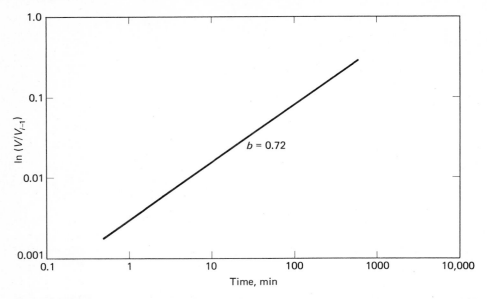

Figure 9.12 The 10-h pressuremeter creep curve obtained in a frozen silt at $-1.6°C$ and $p = 1.27$ MPa.

Once the creep parameters b, n, and σ_c have been determined, they can be substituted into Eq. (9.13), giving a general creep equation of the soil. The equation can subsequently be used either for extrapolating the pressuremeter creep data to longer time intervals, or, in association with an estimated creep-failure strain, it can serve for predicting the long-term strength of frozen soil. To predict the long-term strength, let ε_{ef} denote the equivalent failure strain and σ_{ef} the equivalent creep strength; then Eq. (9.13) yields

$$\sigma_{ef} = \sigma_c \varepsilon_{ef}^{1/n} \left(\frac{\dot{\varepsilon}_c t}{b} \right)^{-b/n} \tag{9.30}$$

Figure 9.11 shows typical creep information obtained in a multistage pressuremeter creep test with 15 min per stage. Figure 9.12, in turn, shows the results of a one-stage creep test kept at a constant stress for more than 5 h. In the figures, the logarithmic creep-strain measure, $\ln (V/V_{i-1})$, was plotted against time t in a log-log plot, as required for creep-parameter determination. To apply the foregoing analysis in practice, two conditions are necessary: (1) creep curves should linearize in a log-log plot, and (2) creep curves for different sustained pressures should be parallel to each other.

From the experience available with this test procedure in permafrost, it appears that the two conditions are best satisfied in a colder permafrost soil. In warmer permafrost the high unfrozen water content introduces some consolidation effects not taken into account in the theory.

Note that the theory as described neglects the instantaneous strains; i.e., all such strains must be added to the creep strains in processing experimental data. In some cases better results are obtained if the instantaneous strains are separated from the total strains. The instantaneous strains can be obtained approximately by extending each of the total strain lines in Fig. 9.11 back to a selected time, say 0.1 min, and by reading the strain at that time. The true creep line is then obtained by shifting the total-strain line down by the value of the instantaneous strain and to the left by 0.1 min, as shown in Figure 9.11. The instantaneous strains can then be treated separately and added later to the creep strains to get the total strain response.

The Deep Static-Cone Penetration Test

The deep static- (or Dutch-) cone penetration test was developed in Holland in the thirties and has been used since that time with much success for a quick evaluation of strength properties of unfrozen soils (Sanglerat, 1972). The original Dutch penetrometer of the mechanical type, in which the point and the rods are pushed into the soil intermittently, is still in use in many places but is being replaced by electrical penetrometers, in which the penetration is continuous and can be continuously recorded (De Ruiter, 1971). This latter type of penetrometer is also better suited for testing frozen soils because it permits much better control of the rate of penetration during the test. The static-cone penetrometer usually has a 60° conical point with a diameter equal to 35.7 mm, giving a projected end-bearing area of 10 cm^2.

For testing frozen soils, a penetrometer of at least 100 kN capacity is required. To permit a clear interpretation of the test, the penetrometer should have a straight cylindrical shaft above the tip with the same diameter as the tip. The thrust for pushing the penetrometer into the ground is usually provided by jacking it either against a system of anchors or against a dead weight supplied by a heavy drill rig. Sometimes with all the reaction-system capacity available at the site it is difficult to push the penetrometer continuously into the frozen soil for more than about $\frac{1}{2}$ m. In this case, the tests can be carried out at various levels, either by starting from the bottom of a predrilled hole (Ladanyi, 1976), or by using the rods of a slightly smaller diameter from about 20 cone diameters above the penetrometer tip.

Testing procedure In unfrozen soils the main purpose of the test is to evaluate the short-term strength properties of the soil; hence the penetration rate used is very high, usually on the order of 20 mm/s. In frozen soils, where one is interested not only in the short-term strength but also in the dependence of strength on the rate of strain, the conventional procedure is not sufficient, and some modifications are necessary. Ladanyi (1976) has shown that valuable information on the in situ behavior of a frozen soil can be obtained by performing the following two types of deep penetration tests: (1) quasistatic penetration test, carried out at a well-controlled constant rate of penetration, and (2) static or incremental-loading penetration test, carried out by increasing the load in steps and keeping the load constant in each step for a given interval of time.

The first type of test is similar to the standard test but with an improved control of the penetration rate. The second type of test is similar to an ordinary incremental-plate-loading test carried out at the end of a borehole. For unfrozen soil one is mainly interested in determining the complete load-settlement curve. In a frozen soil the relationship between the load and the rate of penetration may be of more interest. For this reason, the total penetration in such a test should not necessarily be kept small and can in fact exceed several diameters of the cone, provided the soil remains homogeneous within the depth of penetration.

In principle, the rate dependence of strength of a given permafrost soil can be evaluated by performing several closely spaced quasistatic penetration tests, each at a different rate. Figure 9.13 shows the results of two of such tests at different rates carried out in a frozen varved silt-clay at Thompson, Man. (Ladanyi, 1976).

In practice this procedure is difficult to realize, because at very low rates of penetration it takes a long time to penetrate the required depth interval. It is assumed when low penetration rates are needed for extrapolation to requirements for foundation design that the incremental penetration test will give much better information on the soil behavior.

Figure 9.14 shows the results of two incremental penetration tests carried out in frozen varved clay (Ladanyi, 1976). The load was kept constant for 15 min

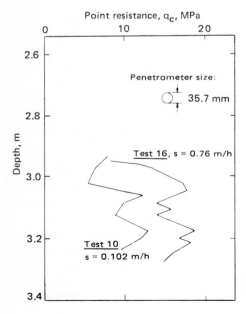

Figure 9.13 Results of two closely spaced rate-controlled penetration tests in frozen varved clay. (*From Ladanyi, 1976.*)

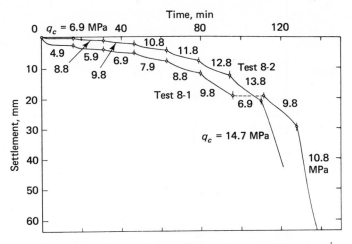

Figure 9.14 Results of two stage-loaded penetration tests in frozen varved clay. (*From Ladanyi, 1976.*)

after each increment. It is clear that however slowly such loading tests are performed, the terminal strain rates attained still correspond to very short time intervals compared with those involved in the foundation design. For this reason, to permit the results of a static penetration test to be used in the foundation design, they should be represented in a graphical or analytical form that will enable a realistic extrapolation to be made to rates much smaller than those used in the tests.

Interpretation of test results If it is possible to determine the terminal penetration rates at each load increment, and if these rates seem to be close to a steady-state behavior, a convenient way of expressing the rate dependence involves plotting the penetration resistance q_c against the terminal penetration rate $\dot{s}$ in a log-log plot, as shown in Fig. 9.15 (Ladanyi, 1976). Most often some portions of this plot or the whole relationship linearizes, which enables one to express the relationship by a power law of the form

$$q_c = q_{c0}\left(\frac{\dot{s}}{\dot{s}_0}\right)^{1/n} \tag{9.31}$$

The exponent $1/n$ is equal to the slope of a straight-line portion in the plot, while q_{c0} and $\dot{s}_0$ represent the coordinates of any reference point on the same straight line.

Because the results are based on rates measured at relatively short time intervals, this extrapolation is usually on the safe side but may sometimes overpredict the long-term penetration rates. A more accurate method would be first to plot all the time-settlement curves in a log-log coordinate system and to deduce from that plot, in the same manner as shown for the pressuremeter

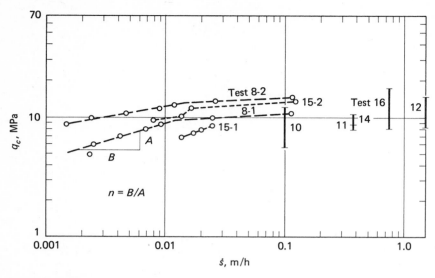

Figure 9.15 Point resistance q_c vs. penetration rate $\dot{s}$ obtained in a series of static and quasistatic penetration tests in a frozen varved clay. (*From Ladanyi, 1976.*)

creep tests, the relationship

$$S_{\text{creep}} = S_c \left(\frac{q_c}{q_{c0}}\right)^n \left(\frac{\Delta t}{t_c}\right)^b \tag{9.32}$$

Rowley et al. (1975) used the same procedure for laterally loaded pile tests. Equation (9.32) defines the creep portion of settlement S_{creep} for any loading stage under a constant applied stress q_c, where Δt is the time interval within that stage, s_c is a unit settlement, (for example, 1 cm), and t_c is a unit time (for example, 1 h). The experimental parameters to be determined from such a stage-loaded penetration test are the reference stress q_{c0} and the two exponents $0 < b \leq 1$ and $n \geq 1$.

The size effect should be taken into account when the results of deep penetration tests are used for estimating the point resistance of a full-scale pile. This can be done by replacing all settlements and settlement rates in Eqs. (9.31) and (9.32) by their ratios with respect to the diameter of the pile or the penetrometer (Ladanyi, 1976).

A strength–vs.–strain-rate relationship, comparable to that obtained in a triaxial test performed on a cylindrical specimen, can be obtained from the results of a static penetration test. This transformation can be made approximately as follows (Ladanyi, 1976):

1. Note that the penetration rate for a penetrometer of diameter B is related with the time to failure t_f in a triaxial test by the approximate relationship

$$t_f \approx 0.5(\eta^{-1/3} - 1)\gamma_{af}^{-1/3} \frac{B}{\dot{s}} \tag{9.33}$$

where γ_{af} is the shear strain at failure in a triaxial test, equal to 1.5 times the corresponding axial strain if the volume change is neglected, and η is a small fraction of the failure strain. For example, assuming that $\eta = 2$ percent gives

$$t_f = 1.34\gamma_{af}^{-1/3}\frac{B}{\dot{s}} \qquad (9.34)$$

which corresponds to the time necessary for the strain in a soil element located below the advancing point of the penetrometer to increase from a negligible value to the failure strain.

2. The relationship between the penetration resistance, q_c and the cohesion c for an ice-saturated soil with a total friction angle ϕ can be deduced from the conventional bearing-capacity formula valid for a deep circular foundation:

$$q_c = p_0 N_q^0 + cN_c^0 \qquad (9.35)$$

where p_0 denotes the total mean normal ground pressure at the level of the test and N_q^0 and N_c^0 are the bearing-capacity factors for the deep circular foundation given in Fig. 9.16.

For example, if the penetration resistance recorded in a frozen silt at a depth of 3 m and at a penetration rate of 100 mm/h is $q_c = 10$ MPa, the equivalent cohesion and the time to failure can be calculated as follows. Consider the frozen silt with $\phi \approx 15°$, the failure strain $\gamma_{af} = 0.05$, and a bulk density of about 2000 kg/m³. From Fig. 9.16 read $N_q^0 = 6.7$, $N_c^0 = 21.1$, and

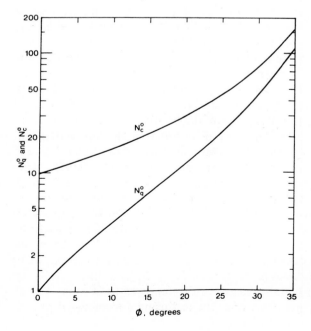

Figure 9.16 Bearing-capacity factors N_q^0 and N_c^0 for a deep circular load. (*After Hansen, 1961, from Ladanyi, 1976.*)

compute $p_0 = 2000(3.0)(9.81) = 59$ kPa. Using Eq. (9.35), compute

$$c = \frac{q_c - p_0 N_q^0}{N_c^0} = \frac{10,000 - 59(6.7)}{21.1} = 455 \text{ kPa}$$

The equivalent time to failure is obtained using Eq. (9.34):

$$t_f \approx 1.34 \times 0.05^{-1/3} \frac{3.57}{10} = 1.30 \text{ h} = 78 \text{ min}$$

Other Types of Field Tests

Other types of tests used in unfrozen soils, in addition to the pressuremeter test and the deep-cone-penetration test, can also be used for the determination of certain mechanical properties of frozen soils. For example, there is a great amount of information available on both plate-bearing tests and pile-loading tests in permafrost (Vyalov, 1965). In most of these tests a stage-loading method was applied, with the load duration in each stage going from several days to several months. The tests furnish valuable information on long-term behavior of full-scale footings and piles in permafrost.

In addition to serving as a model of the behavior of similar full-scale foundation elements, certain field loading tests have also been used for determining some basic frozen-soil properties. As examples, one should mention the pile-loading tests that have been used for the determination of adfreeze strength between the piles and the frozen soil, reported by Crory (1966), as well as the grouted-rod-anchor tests conducted by Johnston and Ladanyi (1972). In the grouted-rod-anchor tests the strength and the creep properties of the frozen soil in contact with the piles were determined. Another example includes the lateral pile-loading tests reported by Rowley et al. (1975), which permitted the evaluation of time-dependent lateral subgrade reaction moduli of frozen soil. The Russian literature also includes the field determination of thaw-settlement characteristics of frozen ground. Tsytovich (1975), for example, described how the two basic parameters in his thaw-settlement equation can be determined by performing a plate-loading test using a steam-heated plate of 0.5 by 0.5 m.

Another promising field method for the determination of thaw-settlement properties of frozen ground is the heated-pressuremeter test, described by Shvets et al. (1973) and theoretically analyzed by Guryanov and Valyshev (1975). The pressuremeter used by Shvets was a 127-mm-diameter pneumatic-electric type and included a heating element using hot exhaust gases. In the tests, an initial pressure of 10 kPa was applied to the ground, after which the temperature of the pressuremeter was increased to 70 or 90°C and held constant for 6 to 10 h. This resulted in the formation of a cylindrical thawed zone 0.3 to 0.5 m in diameter. After thawing, the consolidation properties of the thawed soil were determined by increasing the pressure in steps of 20 to 50 kPa. Each load was held constant until settlement had decreased to 0.1 mm in 15 to 30 min. Actual size of the thawed zone was determined after the test using a mechanical probe.

9.4 GEOPHYSICAL SURVEY

Adequate knowledge of permafrost distribution and character is needed during the planning stages of resource development in the North, including exploration and mining, design of mine shafts, and the construction of roads, pipelines, and foundations. The three-dimensional distribution of frozen ground is clearly more complex and more difficult to determine in the discontinuous zone than in the continuous permafrost zone.

The basic tool for quantitative delineation of permafrost has been the measurement of ground temperatures, described in Sec. 9.2. Temperature measurements provide information at one point only and are expensive, especially if the cost of drilling is included. Geophysical methods provide a useful alternative not only for delineating permafrost areas but also for measuring some of the physical properties of permafrost.

Success of several geophysical prospecting methods tried in permafrost depends on freezing the interstitial water in soils and rocks, which causes changes in their physical properties. Since the physical properties that change most when interstitial water freezes are the elastic moduli and the electrical conductivity, seismic and electrical methods are the most useful geophysical methods for permafrost studies. On the other hand, freezing of pore water has little or no effect on density, magnetism, or radioactivity of soils and rocks, so that the other standard geophysical prospecting techniques are generally not suitable for permafrost detection; a probable exception is gravity surveys used for detecting large ice cores in pingos (Mackay, 1962).

It should be noted that seismic and electrical methods are primarily sensitive to the presence of ice in the soil or rock pores and do not give information on the thermal regime that defines permafrost. For that reason their results may be misleading in dry or salt-water areas (Barnes, 1963). The velocity of elastic waves and the electrical resistivity increase as the water component is transformed into ice. The greatest change in these parameters takes place between 0 and $-10°C$, and they do not change linearly with the amount of ice.

Seismic Velocities in Frozen Ground

The parameters known to influence the velocities of compressional and shear waves in soils and rocks include lithology and grain size, total moisture content and the nature of interstitial fluid, temperature and degree of freezing of interstitial water, porosity and pore structure, confining pressure, and degree of cementation (Garg, 1973). Values of compressional-wave velocities for a number of frozen and unfrozen earth materials have been compiled by Barnes (1963). As may be expected, the largest increase in the compressional-wave velocity from unfrozen to frozen state occurs in the unconsolidated sediments.

The compressional-wave velocities of three typical soil types—Ottawa sand, Hanover silt, and Goodrich clay (fully water-saturated)—are shown as a function of temperature in Fig. 9.17. They represent the results of measurements made

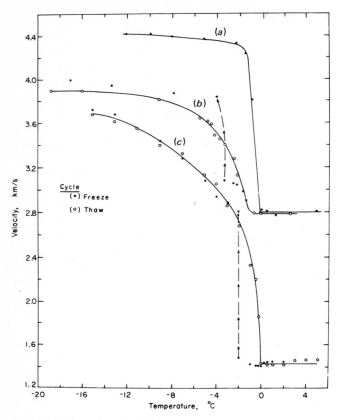

Figure 9.17 The compressional-wave velocity vs. temperature for (*a*) 20/30 Ottawa sand, wet density 2200 kg/m³; (*b*) Hanover silt, 1830 kg/m³, and (*c*) Goodrich clay, 1800 kg/m³, under fully saturated conditions. (*From Nakano and Froula, 1973.*)

by Nakano and Froula (1973) on cylindrical specimens using a pulse-transmission method. The same investigation also found a strong correlation between compressional-wave velocity and unfrozen water content. The observed hysteresis in the velocity of both Hanover silt and Goodrich clay in Fig. 9.17 during a freeze-thaw cycle is considered to be caused by the hysteresis of unfrozen water content. For comparison, the velocity of compressional waves in most soil-forming minerals (with the exception of clay minerals) varies from 4.0 to 6.5 km/s; pure ice has a velocity of about 4.0 km/s, water about 1.45 to 1.58 km/s (depending on temperature and salinity), and air at 0°C about 0.36 km/s (Barnes, 1963).

Since the shear waves propagate mainly through the mineral skeleton and ice rather than through the pore fluid, which cannot accommodate shear stress, they are much less affected by the unfrozen water content than the compressional waves. The shear velocities of crystalline rock and polycrystalline ice are about 3.0 and 1.6 km/s, respectively. The measured velocities of frozen soils fall between these two bounds (Nakano and Froula, 1973).

Electrical Properties of Frozen Ground

The dc electrical resistivities of frozen ground are affected by temperature to a greater extent than the seismic velocities in the temperature range from 0 to $-10°C$. Figure 9.18 shows the variation of resistivity of several soils and one rock type as a function of temperature. As seen in the figure and also from the data compiled by Barnes (1963), the resistivities of frozen soils and rocks may

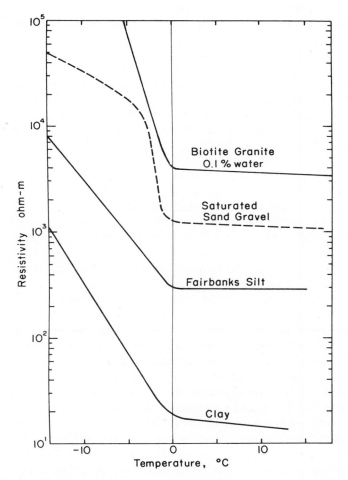

Figure 9.18 Resistivity for several soils and one rock type as a function of temperature. (*From Hoekstra and McNeill, 1973.*)

be 10 to more than 100 times larger than the resistivities of the same materials when unfrozen. However, differentiating between frozen and unfrozen ground solely on the basis of resistivity is not always possible because the resistivity of frozen clay can be less than the resistivity of unfrozen silt, sand, or rock. In addition, the resistivity is especially sensitive to the amount of ionic conduction in the interstitial fluids, so that an increasing salinity of pore water results in a corresponding reduction in resistivity. Therefore, resistivity surveys alone are not sufficient for mapping the permafrost; they must be supplemented by other geological information.

Geophysical Techniques Used in Permafrost

The use of geophysics in permafrost has a long history. In the U.S.S.R., geophysical surveys are performed on a routine basis to map the distribution of permafrost (Dement'ev, 1959). Of the available geophysical methods, seismic-refraction surveys and galvanic-resistivity soundings have been used most frequently in the past for delineating permafrost and for determining the thickness of the active layer. In addition, ground and airborne resistivity surveys based on electromagnetic geophysical techniques are faster and do not require galvanic electrode contact with the ground. Use of permafrost mapping has increased in the recent years. A brief description of these methods and an outline of their use in permafrost investigations follows.

Hammer seismic-refraction survey This method allows subsurface exploration to a depth of about 30 m. It is well suited if loose, soft, or fractured rock strata lying on top of hard rock are to be delineated and if the area is generally flat. It has also been used with success for delineating permafrost in the discontinuous permafrost zone, where frozen-ground occurrences are scattered (Garg, 1973; Hunter, 1973).

The hammer seismic-refraction method is based on the travel of vibrations through the ground. These vibrations or shock waves are produced by hitting a steel plate on the ground with a suitable weight, for example, a 2.5-kg sledge-hammer with shock switch. Basically, the ground shock develops a variety of waves, such as the fast longitudinal (or compressional) waves, followed by slower transverse waves and the even slower transverse surface waves. In seismic exploration one works only with longitudinal waves, which can be directly transmitted, refracted, and reflected. The speed of the longitudinal waves depends on the elastic properties of the material encountered.

The longitudinal wave will penetrate to a higher-velocity layer, travel along this layer, and send a longitudinal refracted wave continuously back to the surface (Fig. 9.19a). This wave is easily recognized as the first arrival when ground vibrations are monitored by a shock detector or geophone placed on the ground surface. The striker plate is placed at increasing distances from the geophone, and the arrival time is measured with an accuracy of at least ± 0.25 ms. The timing device is activated by a shock switch built into the impact

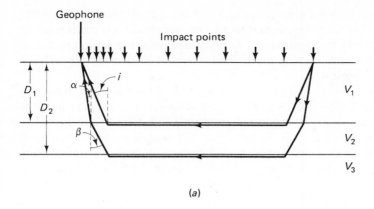

(a)

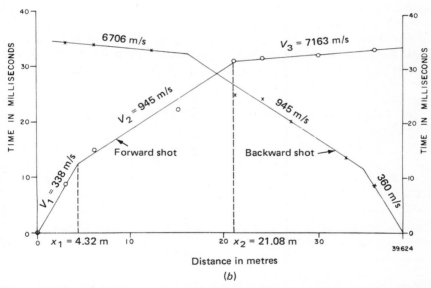

Distance in metres

(b)

Figure 9.19 Hammer seismic-refraction survey: (a) wave paths, two-layer case; (b) a typical distance-time plot obtained in iron ore. (*After Garg, 1973.*)

weight. From the distance between geophone and the striker plate, the velocity can be calculated. Usually the distances to the geophone are increased in increments of 1.5 to 6 m up to about 45 to 60 m and then the same procedure is used by returning to the starting point. This reverse course provides a check on the data (Fig. 9.19b).

For calculation of depth, the assumption is made that a series of flat-lying layers exists, each succeeding deeper layer being characterized by a higher longitudinal-wave velocity. As the distance between geophone and striker plate increases, the transit path of the first arrival at the geophone will include increasingly deeper structural layers (Fig. 9.19a). In plotting transit time vs. distance of striker plate to geophone, a segmented curve of the type shown in Fig. 9.19b is obtained. The reverse slope of each section of the curve is the velocity of the first, second, third, etc., layers. The separation distances, where the line segments intersect, combined with the velocity of the layers are used for calculating the depths to the interfaces. The first two interface depths can be determined using the formulas (Heiland, 1968)

$$D_1 = \frac{x_1}{2} \left(\frac{V_2 - V_1}{V_2 + V_1} \right)^{1/2} \tag{9.36}$$

$$D_2 = D_1 \left[1 + \frac{\cos i - \cos \alpha}{\sin i \cos \beta} \right] + \frac{x_2}{2} \left(\frac{V_3 - V_2}{V_3 + V_2} \right)^{1/2} \tag{9.37}$$

where $\sin i = V_1/V_2$, $\sin \alpha = V_1/V_3$, and $\sin \beta = V_2/V_3$. For the example given in Fig. 9.19b, involving an unfrozen and two different frozen layers of iron ore (middle iron formation) at Schefferville, Que. (Garg, 1973), the calculated depths are $D_1 = 1.5$ m and $D_2 = 10.5$ m.

When both compressional- and shear-wave velocities are recorded in such a survey, the values of dynamic elastic constants of the frozen ground can be calculated using the relationships

$$E_{dyn} = \rho V_p^2 \frac{3 - 4/n^2}{n^2 - 1} \tag{9.38}$$

$$v_{dyn} = \frac{n^2/2 - 1}{n^2 - 1} \tag{9.39}$$

$$n = \frac{V_p}{V_s} \tag{9.40}$$

where V_p = compressional-wave velocity
V_s = shear-wave velocity
ρ = density of material
E_{dyn} = dynamic Young's modulus
v = Poisson's ratio

For example, for a frozen iron ore in which $V_p = 4878$ m/s, $V_s = 2438$ m/s, and $\rho = 3600$ kg/m^3 (Garg, 1973) gives $E_{dyn} = 57,107$ MPa and $v = 0.33$.

Galvanic electrical-resistivity surveys The objective of electrical-resistivity surveys is to investigate the subsurface by means of surface measurements. They complement the seismic-refraction surveys in detection of depth of soil cover and determination of water and permafrost tables. A standard technique consists in producing an electric current in the ground between two electrodes, the current electrodes, and simultaneously measuring the electric field between two different electrodes, the potential electrodes. Two electrode configurations are commonly used, both linear and symmetrical with respect to the center (Fig. 9.20). In the Schlumberger configuration, the separation l of the potential (inner) electrodes is small compared with the distance L between the current (outer) electrodes ($l < L/5$) (Fig. 9.20a). In the Wenner configuration, the total length of the line determined by the outer electrodes is divided into three equal sections of length a by the two inner electrodes ($l = a$, $L = 3a$), as in Fig. 9.20b.

When the values of current I between the outer electrodes have been obtained with the ammeter and the voltage ΔV between the inner electrodes and the spacings L and l or a are known, the apparent resistivity ρ_a of the material below the electrodes is calculated using one of the following two formulas. The Schlumberger configuration gives

$$\rho_a = \frac{\pi(L^2 - l^2)\,\Delta V}{4Il} \tag{9.41}$$

and the Wenner configuration gives

$$\rho_a = \frac{2\pi a\,\Delta V}{I} \tag{9.42}$$

While the Schlumberger configuration gives a very sharp definition of vertical boundaries between materials of different resistance, the Wenner configuration is more appropriate for detecting horizontal-layer interfaces. In the Wenner

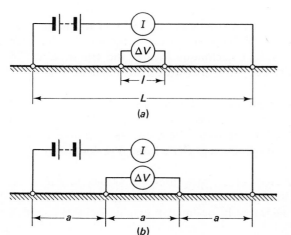

Figure 9.20 Common electrode configurations in surface-resistivity surveys: (*a*) Schlumberger configuration; (*b*) Wenner configuration.

configuration, the depth to which the strata affect the resistivity established with Eq. (9.42) is approximately a. Thus, by varying spacing a, various depths can be sounded.

Where at most two or three layer structures are involved, the following rules may assist interpretation:

1. The depth probed is equal to the probe-separation distance a.
2. As each horizontal layer with sufficient resistivity contrast is intersected, a change in the slope of the curve will occur.
3. Lower apparent resistivity values should be approached asymptotically.

The accuracy of detection of the depth of an interface depth between two zones will depend on the resistivity ratio of the two materials.

The interpretation of more complex curves related to complex structures requires experience. Typical theoretically determined curves for a great number of structural conditions are available to assist in interpretation (e.g., Mooney and Wetzel, 1966; van Dam and Meulenkamp, 1969). Examples illustrating use of the method in permafrost can be found in Barnes (1963), Garg (1973), and Mackay (1975).

It should be noted that frozen ground poses several specific problems for the use of galvanic methods. In order to have current flow into the ground the contact resistance of the probes with the ground must be kept below certain limits. In winter, when the ground is frozen, special measures are required to lower the resistance of the probes to the ground (Hessler and Franzke, 1958). In summer, especially when the thawed active layer consists of low-resistivity organic matter, it is sometimes difficult to measure the resistivity of underlying frozen ground accurately.

Electromagnetic methods Two electromagnetic methods for mapping electrical resistivity of the ground, the radiohm method (Collett and Becker, 1968, Hoekstra, et al. 1975) and the inductive-coupling method are discussed in this section. The main difference between these two methods is that the first technique uses propagating plane radio waves with the receiver located in the far field from an existing transmitter whereas the second technique locates the transmitter and receiver dipoles in close proximity and emits its own electromagnetic field.

Radiohm method Radio waves propagating over the earth's surface are influenced by the nature of the subsurface, and from measurements the ratio of ground wave to the resistivity of ground can be derived. The radio-wave sources used in field work include existing very low-frequency (VLF) and low-frequency (LF) transmitters.

The electromagnetic field vectors of a transmitter are shown in Fig. 9.21. At the ground surface there are three field vectors: a horizontal radially oriented electric field E_r, a horizontal azimuthally oriented magnetic field H_ϕ, and a

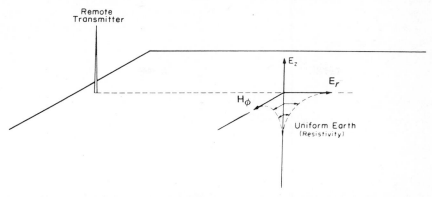

Figure 9.21 Electromagnetic field components of a vertically polarized radio surface wave. (*After Hoekstra et al., 1974.*)

vertical electric field E_z. All three field vectors decay in amplitude with increasing distance from the transmitter and are affected by daily changes in the ionosphere and the nature of the path between the transmitter and measurement station. Changes in local subsurface conditions cause only perturbations in amplitude and phase of E_r, while local changes do not affect E_z and H_ϕ. Therefore, measuring the ratio E_z/H_ϕ, called *surface impedance*, gives a measurement of the local resistivity of the ground. The factors of propagation path, topography, and daily variation equally influence E_z, H_ϕ, and E_r and are eliminated in a ratio measurement.

Figure 9.21 shows how the field vectors E_r and H_ϕ penetrate vertically into the ground and attenuate with depth. The exploration depth of this method is related to the attenuation of the wave in the ground and is approximately 0.5 to 0.8 times the skin depth. The skin depth of the radiation is defined as the depth of ground at which the electromagnetic field decays to e^{-1} (37 percent) of its value at the surface. The skin depth depends on frequency and resistivity, and the dependence is shown in Fig. 9.22. The skin depth decreases with increasing frequency and decreasing resistivity. Over homogeneous ground the resistivity measured with radiohm equipment is equal to ground resistivity, but over layered ground an apparent resistivity is measured and computer modeling is required to resolve the layering in the ground.

Surveying with radiohm methods has three main advantages over galvanic-probe methods: (1) The determination of E_r is a voltage measurement; virtually no current needs to flow between the probes and the ground. Probes can therefore be inserted in the snow cover, and surveys can be made when the ground is frozen. (2) Figure 9.22 shows that the depth of penetration of VLF surveys is often 50 m or more. To obtain a depth of penetration of 50 m with the galvanic method, spreads are required over a distance of 150 m. Over such distances permafrost conditions frequently are variable. The radiohm method,

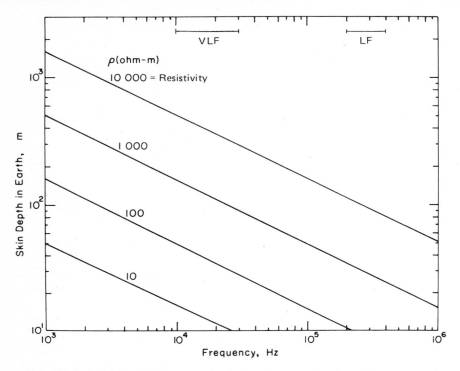

Figure 9.22 Skin depth of electromagnetic plane waves as a function of frequency and ground resistivity. VLF—very low frequency, LF—low frequency. (*After Hoekstra et al., 1974.*)

on the other hand, appears to map ground conditions on a much more local scale (25 m²); therefore a local resolution is maintained with deep exploration. (3) The measurement productivity of the radiohm method is much greater than that of the galvanic method.

The disadvantage of the radiohm method is that the depth of exploration depends on frequency and ground resistivity (see Fig. 9.22) and the choice of frequency is usually limited to one VLF and one LF transmitter. In the galvanic-probe method the depth of exploration is chosen by changing the electrode spacing.

Inductive-coupling methods (ICM) In inductive coupling (Keller and Frischknecht, 1966; Hoekstra and McNeill, 1973), as in the radiohm method, a time-varying electric field is used for geophysical exploration. The radiohm method is a passive method; the instrument is a receiver of the electromagnetic field of distant existing transmitters. In two-loop inductive coupling, one loop is a transmitter and the other loop is a receiver of the transmitted signal. The method does not rely on signals from distant transmitters but emits its own electromagnetic field.

ICM has been used for many years as a geophysical prospecting tool in mineral exploration. The objective in mineral exploration often is to detect a conductive anomaly in the surrounding rock. Very large contrasts ($> 10^3$) between resistivities of ore bodies and host rock are common. In engineering geology it is necessary to map resistivity contrasts of at least a factor 1.2. Conventional ICM equipment is too crude for permafrost geophysics, and much more sensitive instruments are presently being developed.

The two-loop ICM system appears to be one of the most convenient and productive ways of ground-resistivity mapping. The advantages are as follows: (1) no contact with the ground is required, (2) the instrument is self-contained and does not require the field from a distant transmitter, (3) a continuous record of ground resistivity along a traverse can be obtained if desired, and (4) the depth of exploration is dominantly a function of separation distance of transmitter and receiver. Better control of depth of exploration can be obtained than in the radiohm method.

The theoretical aspects of radiowave methods, as well as their applications in ground and airborne resistivity surveys of permafrost, have been reviewed and discussed by Hoekstra and McNeill (1973) and by Hoekstra et al (1974, 1975).

Borehole Logging in Permafrost

Commercial companies have solved many of the problems associated with obtaining high-quality quantitative data from drill holes in permafrost zones. However, the cost and size of such equipment usually precludes its use in the shallow small-diameter drill holes commonly used in permafrost investigations for construction purposes.

Of many available borehole geophysical tools and methods that could be used for this purpose, quite a number have already been tried in permafrost with variable success. A brief description will be given of four methods which have shown promising results either for delineating permafrost formations or for determining the ice content of frozen ground. These are (1) acoustic or sonic log, (2) electrical-resistivity log, (3) induction log, and (4) gamma-gamma log.

Acoustic or sonic log The acoustic or sonic log provides a measure of the time of travel of compressional waves over a certain interval of the formation immediately adjacent to the borehole. From the travel time the velocity of propagation of compressional waves in the formation can be calculated. Under certain conditions the velocity of propagation of shear waves can also be measured. Variations in the velocity of compressional waves can be correlated with changes in lithology and porosity of formations adjacent to the borehole. Knowledge of compressional- and shear-wave velocities, together with the density of the formation, enables the dynamic elastic properties of the formation to be calculated.

The apparatus consists of a logging tool, a winch and multiconductor armored cable, and surface electronics for conditioning and displaying the signal from the acoustic receiver. The logging tool has a transmitter of acoustic waves mounted at one end and one or two receivers at the other end, where they are acoustically insulated from the transmitter.

The borehole must be filled with a liquid, usually water or drilling mud, before the sonic log is run. However, a new acoustic borehole logging sonde developed by King et al. (1974) can operate in either water-filled or empty AX-sized boreholes. The sonde consists of hydraulically activated transmitting and receiving shoes, spaced 30 cm apart, which are forced into contact with the borehole wall when measurements are made. This system shows great promise in permafrost delineation and in field testing of its dynamic properties. More information about the acoustic logging can be found in Schlumberger (1972), King et al. (1974) and in Commission on Standardization of Laboratory and Field Tests (1976).

Electrical-resistivity log The normal resistivity log is the record of the apparent resistivity of the formations along the uncased and conductive-mud-filled borehole made by sending a current into the formation through two electrodes (A, B) and measuring the potential difference in the other two (M, N). Electrodes A, M, and N are placed in the borehole, and electrode B may be placed at the ground surface or at a distance greater than AN. This method can be used in lithological determinations and to mark bed boundaries. A successful application of this method to permafrost delineation in an iron mine was described by Seguin and Garg (1974). More information about this and similar resistivity logging methods can be found in Keller and Frischknecht (1966) and in Commission on Standardization of Laboratory and Field Tests (1976).

Induction log The induction log is a recording of the signal received by a coil and induced by eddy currents in the conductive formations, which in turn are electromagnetically induced by a transmitter coil through which a high-frequency (20 to 60 kHz) alternating current is sent. The signal is proportional to the conductivities of the formations affected by the transmitter coil. Because this method does not require galvanic contact between the logging system and the borehole wall, it can be used not only in water- or drilling-mud-filled holes but also in uncased empty holes, which is of special interest in permafrost investigations. The method can be used to mark bed boundaries, to make lithological determinations, and to measure the true formation resistivity.

Recently a small-diameter (64-mm) induction sonde for potential use in micrologging of permafrost formations was developed and tested by Yu and Ladanyi (1975). More details about the method can be found in Keller and Frischknecht (1966) and in Commission on Standardization of Laboratory and Field Tests (1976).

Gamma-gamma log (or density log) The gamma-gamma log measures the back-scattered gamma rays emitted by a source. Since the scattering depends on the electron density, the bulk density can be evaluated. The method uses a sonde which contains a shielded gamma-ray source and one or two detectors of scattered gamma rays (scintillation counter) together with preamplifiers. The sonde should be applied against the wall of the borehole or should have a diameter very close to hole diameter. The gamma-gamma log is strongly affected by hole, mud, and casing characteristics. Quantitative evaluation is performed using calibration curves determined by considering the diameters of the hole, mud, and casing characteristics which will be employed in the field. In ice-saturated permafrost formations, where the ice content is proportional to the bulk density, the gamma-gamma log can be used indirectly for ice-content determination, from which the amount of potential thaw settlement can be estimated (McKay and O'Connell, 1976). More details about the method can be found in Pirson (1963) and in Commission for Standardization of Laboratory and Field Tests (1976).

REFERENCES

Baker, T. H. W. 1976. Transportation, Preparation and Storage of Frozen Soil Samples for Laboratory Testing, *ASTM Spec. Tech. Publ.* 599, pp. 88–112.

Barnes, D. F. 1963. Geophysical Methods for Delineating Permafrost, *Proc. 1st Int. Conf. Permafrost, Lafayette, Ind., NAS-NRC Publ.* 1287, pp. 349–355.

Cass, J. R. 1959. Subsurface Exploration in Permafrost Areas, *Div. Soil Mech. Found. Eng., J. Am. Soc. Civ. Eng.* **85**(SM5): 31–41; also discussion in vol. 86, no. SM3, 1960.

Collett, L. S., and A. Becker. 1968. Radiohm Method for Earth Resistivity Surveying, Canadian patent 795.919.

Commission on Standardization of Laboratory and Field Tests. 1976. Suggested Methods for Geophysical Logging of Boreholes, International Society for Rock Mechanics, Lisbon.

Crory, F. E. 1966. Pile Foundations in Permafrost, *Proc. 1st Int. Conf. Permafrost, Lafayette, Ind., NAS-NRC Publ.* 1287, pp. 467–472.

Davis, R. M., and F. F. Kitze. 1967. Soil Sampling and Drilling near Fairbanks, Alaska: Equipment and Procedures, *U.S. Army Cold Reg. Res. Eng. Lab. Tech. Rep.* 191, Hanover, N.H.

Day, J. H., F. S. Nowosad, and D. J. Cooper. 1961. Note on Improved Soil Borer for Sampling in Permafrost, *Can. J. Soil Sci.*, **41**(1): 138–139.

Dement'ev, A. I. 1959. In "Principles of Geocryology," pt. II, *Natl. Res. Counc. Can. Tech. Trans.* 1287, Ottawa.

De Ruiter, J. 1971. Electric Penetrometer for Site Investigations, *J. Soil Mech. Found. Div. Am. Soc. Civ. Eng.*, **97**(SM2): 457–472.

Gandahl, R. 1963. Determination of the Ground Frost Line by Means of a Simple Type of Frost Depth Indicator, trans. rev. by P. T. Hodgins, *Natl. Swed. Road Res. Inst.*, Rep. 30A, Stockholm.

Garg, O. P. 1973. In situ Physicomechanical Properties of Permafrost Using Geophysical Technique, *North Am. Contrib. Proc. 2d Int. Conf. Permafrost, Yakutsk, U.S.S.R.*, National Academy of Sciences, Washington, pp. 508–517.

Guryanov, I. E., and M. V. Valyshev. 1975. "Investigation of the Compressibility of Thawing Soils by Means of a Pressuremeter," trans. from *Osn. Fundam. Mekh. Gruntov*, no. 4, Plenum, New York, pp. 249–256.

Hansen, B. L. 1963. Instruments for Temperature Measurements in Permafrost, *Proc. 1st Int. Conf. Permafrost, Lafayette, Ind., NAS-NRC Publ.* 1287, pp. 356–358.

Hansen, J. Brinch. 1961. A General Formula for Bearing Capacity. *Dan. Geotech. Inst. Bull.* 11, Copenhagen.

Heiland, C. A. 1968. "Geophysical Exploration," Hafner, New York.

Hessler, V. P., and A. R. Franzke. 1958. Earthpotential Electrodes in Permafrost and Tundra, *Arctic,* **11:** 211–217.

Hoekstra, P., and D. McNeill. 1973. Electromagnetic Probing of Permafrost, *North Am. Contrib. Proc. 2d Int. Conf. Permafrost, Yakutsk, U.S.S.R.,* National Academy of Sciences, Washington, pp. 517–526.

———, P. V. Sellman, and A. Delaney. 1974. Airborne Resistivity Mapping of Permafrost near Fairbanks, Alaska, *U.S. Army Cold Reg. Res. Eng. Lab. Res. Rep.* 324, Hanover, N.H.

———, ———, and ———. 1975. Ground and Airborne Resistivity Surveys of Permafrost near Fairbanks, Alaska, *Geophysics,* **40:** 641–656.

Hunter, J. A. M. 1973. The Application of Shallow Seismic Methods to Mapping of Frozen Surficial Materials, *North Am. Contrib. Proc. 2d Int. Conf. Permafrost, Yakutsk, U.S.S.R.,* National Academy of Sciences, Washington, pp. 527–535.

Hvorslev, M. J., and T. B. Goode. 1963. Core Drilling in Frozen Soils, *Proc. 1st Int. Conf. Permafrost, Lafayette, Ind., NAS-NRC Publ.* 1287, pp. 364–371.

Johnston, G. H. 1963a. Soil Sampling in Permafrost Areas, *Natl. Res. Counc. Can. Div. Build. Res. Tech. Pap.* 155.

———. 1963b. Instructions for the Fabrication of Thermocouple Cables for Measuring Ground Temperatures, *Natl. Res. Counc. Can. Div. Build. Res. Tech. Pap.* 157.

———. 1963c. Engineering Site Investigations in Permafrost Areas, *Proc. 1st Int. Conf. Permafrost, Lafayette, Ind., NAS-NRC Publ.* 1287, pp. 371–374.

———. 1969. Dykes on Permafrost, Kelsey Generating Station, Manitoba, *Can. Geotech. J.,* **6:** 139–157.

———. 1972. Ground Temperature Measurements using Thermocouples, *Proc. Sem. Therm. Regime Meas. Permafrost, Natl. Res. Counc. Can. Ass. Comm. Geotech. Res. Tech. Memo.* 108, pp. 1–12.

——— and B. Ladanyi. 1972. Field Tests of Grouted Rod Anchors in Permafrost, *Can. Geotech. J.,* **9**(2): 176–194.

Judge, A. S. 1972. Ground Temperature Measurements Using Thermistors, *Proc. Sem. Therm. Regime Meas. Permafrost, Natl. Res. Counc. Can. Ass. Comm. Geotech. Res. Tech. Mem.* 108, pp. 13–22.

Keller, G., and F. C. Frischknecht. 1966. "Electrical Methods in Geophysical Prospecting," Pergamon, Oxford.

King, M. S., V. S. Pobran, and B. V. McConnell. 1974. Acoustic Borehole Logging System, *Proc. 9th Can. Rock Mech. Symp., Montreal,* pp. 21–51.

Kitze, F. F. 1956. Some Experiments in Drive Sampling of Frozen Ground. U.S. Army Arctic Constr. Frost Effects Lab. Misc. Pap. 16.

Ladanyi, B. 1972. In situ Determination of Undrained Stress-Strain Behavior of Sensitive Clays with the Pressuremeter, *Can. Geotech. J.,* **9**(3): 313–319.

———. 1976. Use of the Static Penetration Test in Frozen Soils, *Can. Geotech. J.,* **13**(2): 95–110.

——— and G. H. Johnston. 1973. Evaluation of in situ Creep Properties of Frozen Soils with the Pressuremeter, *North Am. Contrib. Proc. 2d Int. Conf. Permafrost, Yakutsk, U.S.S.R.,* National Academy of Sciences, Washington, pp. 310–318.

Lange, G. R. 1963. Refrigerated Fluids for Drilling and Coring in Permafrost, *Proc. 1st Int. Conf. Permafrost, Lafayette, Ind., NAS-NRC Publ.* 1287, pp. 375–380.

———. 1973a. An Investigation of Core Drilling in Perennially Frozen Gravels and Rock, *U.S. Army Cold Region Res. Eng. Lab. Tech. Rep.* 245, Hanover, N.H.

———. 1973b. Investigation of Sampling Perennially Frozen Alluvial Gravel by Core Drilling, *North Am. Contrib. 2d Int. Conf. Permafrost, Yakutsk, U.S.S.R.,* National Academy of Sciences, Washington, pp. 535–541.

——— and T. K. Smith. 1972. Rotary Drilling and Coring in Permafrost, Deep Core Drilling, Core Analysis and Borehole Thermometry at Cape Thompson, Alaska. *U.S. Army Cold Reg. Res. Eng. Lab. Tech. Rep.* 95, pt. III, Hanover, N.H.

Linell, K. A., and G. H. Johnston. 1973. Engineering Design and Construction in Permafrost Regions, *North Am. Contrib. 2d Int. Conf. Permafrost, Yakutsk, U.S.S.R.*, National Academy of Sciences, Washington, pp. 553–575.

———, and C. W. Kaplar. 1963. Description and Classification of Frozen Soils, *Proc. 1st Int. Conf. Permafrost, Lafayette, Ind., NAS-NRC Publ.* 1287, pp. 371–374.

Mackay, J. R. 1962. Pingos of the Pleistocene Mackenzie River Delta Area, *Geogr. Bull. (Can.)* 18, pp. 21–63.

———. 1973. A Frost Tube for the Determination of Freezing in the Active Layer above Permafrost, *Can. Geotech. J.*, **10**(3): 392–396.

———. 1974*a*. Measurement of Upward Freezing above Permafrost with a Self-positioning Thermistor Probe, *Geol. Surv. Can. Pap.* 74–1, pt. B, pp. 250–251.

———. 1974*b*. Seismic Shot Holes and Ground Temperatures, Mackenzie Delta Area, Northwest Territories, *Geol. Surv. Can. Pap.* 74–1, pt. A, pp. 389–390.

———. 1975. Some Resistivity Surveys of Permafrost Thickness, Tuktoyaktuk Peninsula, N.W.T., *Geol. Surv. Can. Pap.* 75–1, pt. B, pp. 177–180.

Mckay, A. S., and L. P. O'Connell. 1976. The Permafrost Density Logger. *J. Can. Pet. Technol.*, pp. 69–74.

Ménard, L. 1957. Mesures in situ des propriétés physiques des sols, *Ann. Ponts Chaussées*, **127**: 357–377.

Mooney, H. M., and W. W. Wetzel. 1966. "The Potentials about a Point Electrode and Apparent Resistivity Curves for a Two-, Three-, and Four-Layer Earth," University of Minnesota Press, Minneapolis.

Nakano, Y., and N. H. Froula. 1973. Sound and Shock Transmission in Frozen Soils, *North Am. Contrib. 2d Int. Conf. Permafrost, Yakutsk, U.S.S.R.*, National Academy of Sciences, Washington, pp. 359–369.

Odqvist, F. K. G. 1966. "Mathematical Theory of Creep and Creep Rupture," Oxford Mathematical Monographs, Clarendon Press, Oxford.

Pihlainen, J. A., and G. H. Johnston. 1953. Permafrost Investigations at Aklavik (Drilling and Sampling), *Natl. Res. Counc. Can. Pap.* 3393.

Pirson, S. J. 1963. Handbook of Well Log Analysis, Prentice-Hall, Englewood Cliffs, N.J.

Rickard, W., and J. Brown. 1972. The Performance of a Frost Tube for the Determination of Soil Freezing and Thawing Depths, *Soil Sci.*, **113**(2): 149–154.

Rowley, R. G., G. H. Watson, and B. Ladanyi. 1975. Prediction of Pile Performance under Lateral Load, *Can. Geotech. J.*, **12**(4): 510–523.

Sanglerat, G. 1972. The Penetrometer and Soil Exploration, Elsevier, Amsterdam.

Schlumberger Company, 1972. "Log interpretation," vol. 1, "Principles." Schlumberger Ltd, New York.

Seguin, M. K., and O. P. Garg. 1974. Delineation of Frozen Rocks from the Labrador-Ungava Peninsula Using Borehole Geophysical Logging, *Proc. 9th Can. Rock Mech. Symp. Montreal*, Information Canada, pp. 52–75.

Sellman, P. V., and J. Brown. 1965. Coring of Frozen Ground, Barrow, Alaska, *U.S. Army Cold Reg. Res. Eng. Lab. Spec. Rep.* 81, Hanover, N.H.

Shvets, V. B., V. V. Lushnikov, I. A. Mareninov, and B. I. Sukhanov. 1973. Pressure-metric Investigations of Deformation and Strength Properties of Frozen Soils during Thawing, *Proc. 2d Int. Conf. Permafrost, Yakutsk, U.S.S.R.*, vol. 4 (in Russian) pp. 104–107.

Smith, W. S., K. Nair, and R. E. Smith. 1973. Sample Disturbance and Thaw Consolidation of a Deep Sand Permafrost, *North Am. Contrib. 2d Int. Conf. Permafrost, Yakutsk, U.S.S.R.*, National Academy of Sciences, Washington, pp. 392–400.

Tsytovich, N. A. 1975. "The Mechanics of Frozen Ground," McGraw Hill, New York.

Van Dam, J. O., and J. J. Meulenkamp. 1969. "Standard Graphs for Resistivity Prospecting." European Association of Exploration Geophysicists, The Hague, Netherlands.

Veillette, J. 1975*a*. Modified CRREL Ice Coring Augers, *Geol. Surv. Can. Pap.* 75–1, pt. A, pp. 425–426.

———. 1975*b*. Helicopter Portable Drill for High Arctic Programs, *Geol. Surv. Can. Pap.* 75–1, pt. A, pp. 427–429.

————. 1975c. Stabilization of Ground Temperatures in a Shallow Borehole, *Geol. Surv. Can. Pap.* 75–1, pt. A, pp. 371–372.

Vyalov, S. S. 1965. Rheological Properties and Bearing Capacity of Frozen Soils, transl. from Russian ed., 1959, *U.S. Army Cold Reg. Res. Eng. Lab. Trans.* 74, Hanover, N.H.

Yu, T. R., and B. Ladanyi. 1975. Application of Induction Logging for Delineating Permafrost Formations, *Symp. Permafrost Geophys., Univ. Waterloo, Waterloo, Ont.*

ICE PRESSURES AND BEARING CAPACITY

L. W. Gold

INTRODUCTION

Ice pressures on dams and bridge piers, vertical forces on pile structures, caissons, and wharf walls, and bearing capacity of ice bridges all require an understanding of the deformation behavior of ice. These problems are of particular interest to the geotechnical engineer concerned with the analysis and design of foundations for these structures or the ice bridges as part of a larger project in a cold region. Ice covers on water basins are usually a seasonal phenomenon. The initiation, growth, maturity, and decay of an ice cover in a closed body of water must be considered in engineering design. Ice covers in rivers break up in the spring, often forming ice jams and causing floods, which can be destructive to bridge piers and shore installations.

Ice covers are subject to large variations in their properties because of the dependence of their growth on weather and water conditions. This chapter describes the formation of ice covers and provides a genetic classification of ice. The deformation behavior of ice is described in terms of both an elastic behavior and a viscoplastic behavior. Separate sections provide information on static ice pressures, forces due to change in water level, and dynamic pressures from moving ice floes. The final section describes the bearing capacity of ice covers used as natural bridges and platforms for both moving and static loads.

10.1 NATURE OF ICE PROBLEMS

Ice is one of the few solids whose density is less than that of its melt. As a result, it forms on the surface of lakes, rivers, and oceans in cold regions. This is a great asset since it allows the survival of aquatic plants and fish during winter and provides a natural bridge for crossing water bodies. Ice covers, however, are not static. They move due to the effects of wind, water current, change in water level, or change in temperature. Structures in contact with them must therefore be designed to resist the forces caused by this movement.

Ice covers pose a unique challenge to the engineer. They usually exist at a temperature within 60°C of that at which they melt. In this thermal state they are viscoplastic, and their strength and deformation behavior is time- and temperature-dependent. Even though our ability to predict the behavior of materials in this condition is not well developed, the engineer is often asked to make such a prediction for a variety of ice-cover problems, such as calculation of the maximum force that ice will exert on a structure and the load that can be supported safely by a cover under given conditions. These problems are associated with a wide range of temperatures, strain rates, ice types, grain sizes, densities, and ice purity.

The ice-pressure problem is one that must be resolved at the design stage. A designer must establish with acceptable certainty the maximum load to which a structure will be subjected. This requires knowledge of the cover, e.g., its thickness, temperature, and structure; the nature of the interaction that will occur between the ice and the structure; and the probable maximum effective strength of the ice for the governing mode of failure. The characteristics of an ice cover are obtained from appropriate field investigations; the effective strengths must be known a priori, and the nature of the interaction between the ice and structure is predicted from the characteristics of the cover and the structure and the strength and deformation properties of ice.

The nature of the bearing-capacity problem is completely different. In principle, the characteristics of the ice cover and the properties of the ice are known when a load is to be applied, and the bearing capacity is determined from this knowledge. It is important, in dealing with this problem, to have information about the characteristics of the ice cover, the strength and deformation behavior of ice, and their dependence on all factors that affect them.

Ice covers are subject to large variations in their properties, both spatially and with time, because of the dependence of their growth on weather and water conditions. This need not pose a serious problem concerning bearing capacity, as the current state of the ice cover can be determined through measurement and steps taken if necessary to increase the ice thickness. For the ice-pressure problem it does pose the difficulty of establishing extreme values for design calculations, often with seriously inadequate or nonexistent information.

Good progress is being made in establishing information on the strength and deformation behavior of ice through measurements on relatively small samples. There is still a gap, however, between this information and the knowledge necessary to predict behavior in the field. For many areas of engineering such a gap has been bridged on a semiempirical or fully empirical basis through observation of field performance and correlation with measured properties. Because of the nature of ice and the great variability in the properties of ice covers, this approach will probably have to be applied in establishing and confirming solutions to ice-engineering problems. Good progress is being made in its application to the bearing-capacity problem. There are still not sufficient field observations, however, on the interaction between ice and structures to establish unequivocally the correct design methods for calculating ice pressures under given conditions and the basis for extrapolation to the extreme conditions associated with ice covers in the arctic.

10.2 THE FORMATION OF ICE COVERS AND THEIR CLASSIFICATION

Both freshwater- and sea-ice covers are composed of grains of relatively pure ice. The individual grains, which are essentially single crystals of ice, vary in shape from granular to tabular to columnar, with typical dimensions of from less than 1 mm to several meters. Each grain has hexagonal crystallographic symmetry, the axis of symmetry, or c axis, being perpendicular to an important plane of deformation called the *basal plane*.

The resistance of the basal plane to viscous shear is small, being less than 7×10^4 N/m^2 at $-10°$C. The resistance of nonbasal planes to viscous deformation is from 10 to 100 times larger. As a result, each grain tends to deform like a pack of cards when subjected to a shear stress.

Pure water has a maximum density at a temperature of 3.9°C. Still bodies of water, such as lakes, cool in the fall by convective mixing until the total depth of water has attained this temperature. Thereafter, the water becomes quite stable, and further cooling occurs by conduction to the surface unless mixing is induced by wind action. Once this condition of stability is established, the surface can cool rapidly to the freezing point in cold weather.

In general, the period of freeze-up (and breakup) is fairly well defined in a given location, but the actual date will vary from year to year due to variations in the weather (Michel, 1971; Williams, 1965, 1971). Deep lakes usually store more heat in summer than shallow lakes, and so they can be expected to freeze over later. If a lake is reasonably deep, it will have a reserve of heat throughout the winter. This heat can be used at times for ice-control purpose, e.g., by bringing it to the surface with an air-bubbling system (Williams, 1961). Usually there is sufficient turbulence in rivers and streams to ensure that the water is well mixed and the full depth of water is cooled to 0°C before freezing begins. In oceans, the salinity is so high that the density of the water continuously increases with decreasing temperature down to the freezing point. The condition of thermally induced stability of the water under an ice cover does not occur as it does in a lake, and a reserve of heat exists only under special circumstances.

Several types of ice can form in ice covers. Their occurrence is determined by site conditions, such as weather and rate of flow of water, and by the characteristics of the first ice to form. It is important to be able to recognize them, as their strength and deformation properties can be significantly different.

Michel and Ramseier (1971) have developed a practical classification system for ice which is summarized in Table 10.1. They consider that an ice cover can usually be subdivided into primary, secondary, and superimposed layers. Primary ice is that which forms first. Secondary ice develops from it and often has

Table 10.1 Genetic classification of ice (from Michel and Ramseier, 1971)

Primary ice (first to form):

P1	Calm surface; low rate of cooling; c axis preferred vertical; crystal size large to extra large; crystal boundaries of irregular shape
P2	Calm surface; high rate of cooling; c-axis orientation random to preferred vertical superimposed on random; crystal size medium to extra large; crystal shape tabular to needlelike
P3	Agitated surface, ice cover initiated from frazil; c-axis orientation random; crystal size small to medium; crystal shape equiaxed and tabular
P4	Ice cover initiated by snow; c-axis orientation random; crystal size small to medium; crystal shape equiaxed

Secondary ice (develops from primary ice):

S1	Columnar-grained; c-axis orientation preferred vertical; crystal size usually large to extra large, increases with depth; grain cross section of irregular shape
S2	Columnar-grained; c-axis orientation tends to be preferred horizontal, grain size small to extra large, increases with depth; grain cross section of regular shape
S3	Columnar-grained; c-axis orientation preferred horizontal and aligned
S4	Congealed frazil slush; c-axis orientation random; grain size small to medium, shape equiaxed and tabular; formed from frazil deposited beneath ice cover
S5	Drained frazil slush; grain size small to medium, shape angular; density low, formed from frazil that has drained and subsequently frozen

Superimposed ice:

T1	Snow ice; c-axis orientation random; grain size small to medium; grains equiaxed; density usually 830 to 900 kg/m^3
T2	Drained snow ice; c-axis orientation random; grain size small to medium; grains equiaxed; density about 600 kg/m^3
T3	Surface ice; layers of columnar ice that have formed on top of primary ice

Agglomerate ice:

R	Inclusion of ice of various types due to mechanical processes; c-axis orientation random to preferred orientation; grain size small to extra large; grain shape columnar to equiaxed to tabular; can be associated with rafting or ridging

Grain size	Grain diameter, mm
Small	< 1
Medium	1–5
Large	5–20
Extra large	> 20

characteristics that are determined directly from those of the primary layer. Superimposed layers are composed of ice that has formed not by the normal downward freezing process but by secondary processes, e.g., the flooding and subsequent freezing of snow on the surface of the ice cover.

If conditions are calm when still bodies of water freeze, the first crystals to form usually are needlelike. They extend outward and grow laterally until they join with adjacent grains. As the ice grows downward from this primary layer, the boundaries between grains tend to remain vertical, and a columnar-grained structure results. In the plane perpendicular to the axis of the columns, the grains usually have a very irregular shape and dimensions that range from about 10 mm to more than a meter. If the rate of freezing is not too fast, the grains can extend through the full thickness of the cover. Their average size perpendicular to the axis of the columns tends to increase with growth. The unique characteristic of this type of ice, designated as SI, is that the axis of hexagonal symmetry of each grain tends to be perpendicular to the surface of the cover; i.e., their basal planes, the plane of easy shear deformation, tend to be parallel to the surface of the ice.

If the surface of the water is agitated when ice begins to form, due to wind for example, or if freezing is initiated by snow, the first grains that form the primary layer tend to have a random crystallographic orientation. Ice, however, tends to grow more readily in the direction perpendicular to the axis of crystallographic symmetry than parallel to it. Those grains which are favorably oriented grow at the expense of those which are not. A columnar-grained secondary layer again results but within about 100 mm of the surface there is a marked tendency for the axis of crystallographic symmetry of each grain to be horizontal and to have a random orientation in that plane. The unique feature of this type of ice, designated as S2, is that the basal plane of each grain tends to be perpendicular to the surface of the cover. In the direction perpendicular to the axis of the columns, the grains have a regular shape and range in size from about 5 mm to more than 20 mm. Their average size tends to increase with distance from the ice surface.

If snow falls on the surface of an ice cover and is flooded with water which subsequently freezes, granular ice is formed (type T1). This is an example of superimposed ice. Grains usually have a regular shape, range in size from less than 1 mm to about 5 mm, and have random crystallographic orientation.

Another type of ice structure common in rivers is formed from frazil. Frazil are plate-shaped particles of ice kept in suspension in turbulent water. They come to the surface in calm water, where they may initiate an ice cover or form a superimposed layer in one already present.

The formation of a cover is often a dynamic process. Ice formed on the surface is worked by the action of wind or current, into balls, pans, or floes. These adhere to each other, and the cover grows by their juxtaposition (Michel, 1971). Ice covers on rivers may grow upstream by this process at a rate of more than 40 km/day. If the rate of flow is sufficiently fast, or if the cover is subject to compressive forces, floes, or blocks of ice, can be forced beneath the surface of the cover and incorporated into it. Such dynamic activity can result in covers with highly variable characteristics horizontally and little or no evidence of a layered structure, e.g., the formation of ice jams, and rafted or ridged ice.

The most usual impurity in freshwater ice is air. It is an integral part of granular ice formed from snow and gives that ice a whitish appearance. Since air molecules are not easily incorporated into the ice-crystal lattice, they are rejected at the ice-water interface as an ice cover grows downward. When the concentration of air in the water is sufficiently great, air bubbles are nucleated and incorporated into the cover. The characteristics of this process and of the bubbles themselves depend largely on the rate of freezing.

The principal impurities in sea ice are salts. Like air, these salts are rejected during freezing and their concentration in the water immediately in front of the ice-water interface increases. When the concentration is sufficiently high, the interface becomes unstable, and the salt is incorporated into the ice as brine pockets (Weeks and Assur, 1967). Sea-ice grains also tend to be columnar, the basal planes of each grain tending to lie in the direction of growth (perpendicular to the ice surface). The grains are composed of platelets of the order of a millimeter thick. The basal plane of each platelet tends to be perpendicular to its short dimension. Brine is incorporated both in the boundaries between platelets and in the grain boundaries. An example of the structure of sea ice is shown in Fig. 10.1.

The freezing point of the brine in the pockets depends on the salt content, decreasing with increasing concentration. As the temperature of sea ice decreases, some of the water in the brine pockets freezes, thus maintaining the appropriate equilibrium salt content. This process continues until the temperature drops to that of the eutectic point. At this temperature, which is different for each salt, the salt comes out of solution and is incorporated into the cover as crystals. The strength and deformation behavior of sea ice are very dependent on brine content. The dependence of brine content on temperature greatly enhances the effect of temperature on the behavior of sea ice under load (Weeks and Assur, 1967).

The anisotropy in the deformation behavior of individual grains of ice has important implications for the way ice covers respond to stress. If the principal stresses are parallel or perpendicular to the basal plane of a grain, there will be no resolved shear stress on it and the grain will have its maximum resistance to deformation; i.e., it will act as a hard site in the cover. On the other hand, if there is a resolved shear stress on the basal plane, the grain will tend initially to deform relatively easily but its deformation may be severely constrained by its neighbors. The degree of restraint will depend on the direction of the stress, type of ice, and the relative crystallographic orientation of adjacent grains. These restraints are of some importance, as they are directly associated with the internal stresses responsible for the yield and failure of ice (Gold, 1972).

It can now be appreciated that ice covers are not simple structures. Not only are the grains from which they are formed anisotropic with respect to their resistance to deformation, but their shape also has a marked effect on how the cover responds to a load. Granular ice, particularly if it is fine-grained, tends

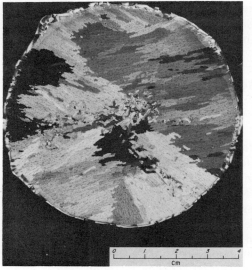

(a)

(b)

Figure 10.1 Thin section of sea ice (a) perpendicular to the direction of growth, photographed with polarized light (note the platelet structure within grains) and (b) parallel to the direction of growth. These sections were cut from a cylindrical sample obtained in June 1976 from the ice cover in Strathcona Sound. Baffin Island. They are representative of ice at the site about 2 m below the surface. The granular "pipe" in the center of (b) appeared to run the full length of the sample and was probably a drainage channel. (*Photographs by N. K. Sinha, Division of Building Research, National Research Council of Canada.*)

to be isotropic in its deformation behavior. Columnar-grained ices are markedly anisotropic, deformation properties in the long direction of the grains being different from the corresponding ones in the plane perpendicular to that direction.

10.3 DEFORMATION BEHAVIOR OF ICE

Elastic Behavior

If the period of loading for polycrystalline ice is 1 s or less, it can be assumed to respond elastically to failure. For lower loads, the period of elastic behavior is longer and increases with decreasing temperature. At temperatures of $-5°C$ and lower and stresses less than 0.5 MN/m^2, response is essentially elastic for periods of up to 100 s. This means that elastic theory can be applied to practically all bearing-capacity problems involving moving loads and ice-force problems for which the imposed strain rate is greater than 10^{-3} s^{-1}. The second group includes the impact of ice on structures.

The elastic response of polycrystalline ice depends on temperature, strain rate (or frequency of a repetitive load), density, purity, and type of ice. It can be assumed to be isotropic for granular ice but is anisotropic for columnar-grained ice. Information concerning the elastic behavior of ice and its dependence on the factors that influence it is still incomplete.

For most ice-engineering problems, the principal stresses are parallel to the surface of the ice cover. Figure 10.2 gives information on the strain-rate dependence of the initial value of Young's modulus of columnar-grained type S2 ice for this condition of stress, i.e., perpendicular to the long direction of the grains, as well as for granular ice. It can be seen that Young's modulus is strongly dependent on strain rate over the range 10^{-7} to 10^{-3} s^{-1}, tending to a constant value for strain rate greater than 10^{-2} s^{-1}. For strain rate greater than about 10^{-3} s^{-1}, ice is usually brittle and essentially "elastic" to failure. Measurement of Young's modulus for frequency of stressing greater than 10^2 Hz shows that the maximum value for both the columnar-grained S2 ice and granular ice is about 9 GN/m^2. Sonic values of Young's modulus, shear modulus and Poisson's ratio are given in Table 10.2.

The sonic values of the elastic moduli of freshwater ice can be assumed independent of temperature for engineering calculations. Sonic values of the Young's modulus of sea ice are found to be dependent on the relative brine volume, defined as the volume of brine in unit volume of air-free sea ice.

Values of Young's modulus and Poisson's ratio measured at low rates of strain (period of loading more than 1 s), are presented in Table 10.3. Young's modulus is quite temperature-dependent, tending to the sonic value at temperatures below $-40°C$. Reported values of Young's modulus of sea ice are a factor of 10 or more smaller than the sonic values.

Poisson's ratio has been observed to increase with temperature. This behavior appears to be related to the factors responsible for the marked temperature

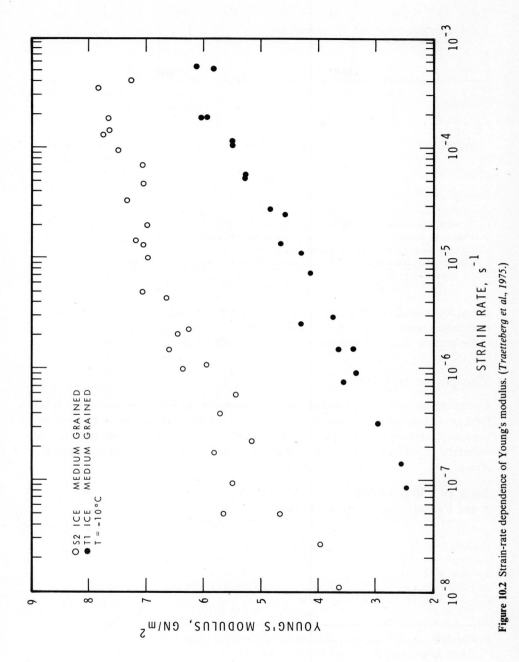

Figure 10.2 Strain-rate dependence of Young's modulus. (*Traetteberg et al., 1975.*)

Table 10.2 Sonic values of Young's modulus E, rigidity modulus G, and Poisson's ratio v for polycrystalline ice

E, GN/m²	G, GN/m²	v	Temp., °C	Ice type	Ref.
9.17	3.36[a]	0.365	−5	Freshwater[b]	Ewing et al. (1934)
9.80	3.68[a]	0.33	−5	Freshwater[c]	Northwood (1947)
9.94	3.80[a]	0.31[a]	−5	S2[d]	Gold (1958)
$10-0.0351v_b$	$\cdots$	0.295	0 to −40	Sea[e]	Pounder (1965)
$9.88-0.02v_b$	$\cdots$	$\cdots$	−2.5 to −23.9	Sea[f]	Frankenstein and Garner (1970)
$11.8-0.002v_b$	$\cdots$	$\cdots$	0.8 to −20.8	Sea[g]	Frankenstein and Garner (1970)

[a] Calculated from relationship between E, G, and v for isotropic materials.
[b] Average of samples cut parallel and perpendicular to ice surface.
[c] No great variation in velocities measured in samples cut at various orientation.
[d] Measured perpendicular to long direction of grains of type S2 ice.
[e] Determined from velocity of sonic pulse; v_b, brine volume in parts per thousand.
[f] Cut parallel to ice surface.
[g] Cut vertical, determined from velocity of sonic pulse; v_b, brine volume in parts per thousand.

dependence of the elastic moduli for strain rate less than 10^{-3} s^{-1}, but there is little information concerning it. For columnar-grained type S2 ice it can have a value greater than 0.5 because of anisotropic deformation behavior.

Viscoplastic Behavior

For many ice-engineering problems, the conditions which are experienced in the field or which must be assumed for design are no longer elastic but involve time-dependent (viscous) and plastic behavior. These aspects of the deformation behavior of ice are illustrated in Figs. 10.3 and 10.4 for uniaxial compressive stress.

Table 10.3 Representative values of static Young's modulus E and Poisson's ratio v for polycrystalline ice

E, GN/m²	v	Ice type	Ref.
$5.69-6.48 \times 10^{-2}T$	0.31–0.55	S2[†]	Gold (1958)
$5.14-6.61 \times 10^{-2}T$	$\cdots$	T1[‡]	Ramseier (1976)
$6.13-3.87 \times 10^{-2}T$	$\cdots$	S4[§]	Ramseier (1976)
0.2–2.0	$\cdots$	Sea ice[¶]	Weeks and Assur (1967)

[†] Medium-grained, stress perpendicular to long direction of grains.
[‡] Average grain size 9 mm; density 890 kg/m³.
[§] Tabular (1.8 by 5.2 mm); density 900 kg/m³.
[¶] Taken from work of Tabata, determined from beam-deflection tests; values dependent on rate of strain; $T = -1.5°C$.

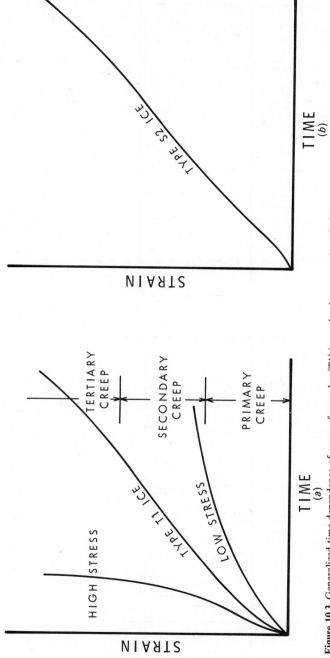

Figure 10.3 Generalized time dependence of creep of granular (T1) ice and columnar-grained (S2) ice.

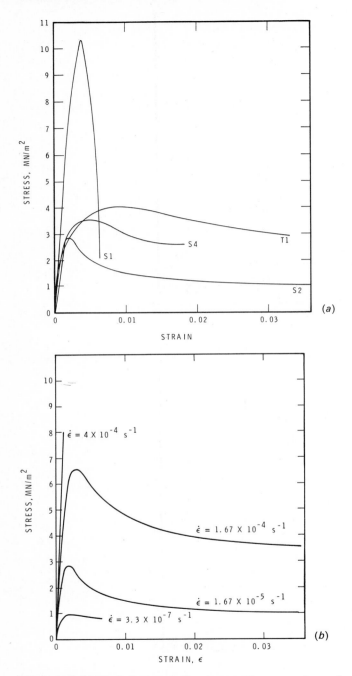

Figure 10.4 (*a*) Typical compressive stress-strain curves for various ice types, $T = -9.5°C$, $\dot{\varepsilon} = 1.67 \times 10^{-5}$ s^{-1}. (*b*) Strain-rate dependence of compressive stress-strain curves for type S2 ice, $T = -9.5°C$.

Figure 10.3 shows the time-dependent strain for a constant load. For the columnar-grained type S2 ice, the load is applied perpendicular to the long direction of the grains. The important features of this behavior are that for stress below about 1 MN/m^2 and up to a strain of about 1 percent, the strain rate varies; between about 1 and 2.5 percent strain, it is relatively constant; and above about 2.5 percent strain, it tends to increase with time. The first range of deformation behavior is called the primary stage of creep, the second the secondary stage, and the third the tertiary stage. For stress greater than about 1 MN/m^2, for example, 1.2 MN/m^2 for type S2 ice at $-10°$C, the secondary stage begins to disappear; the primary stage transforms directly to the tertiary stage, as shown in Fig. 10.3 for T1 ice. The tertiary stage is often considered to indicate failure, and it is usual for deformation to occur primarily in well-developed shear zones at this strain in uniaxial tests when the stress is greater than about 1 MN/m^2. It must be emphasized, however, that the boundaries between the three ranges of behavior vary, depending on such factors as temperature, stress, type of ice, grain size, and impurity content.

For uniaxial creep tests, attention has been directed primarily to the temperature and stress dependence of the secondary-creep rate (Glen, 1975; Weertman, 1973). Over the compressive-stress range of about 0.1 to 1.0 MN/m^2, it is described reasonably well by

$$\dot{\varepsilon}_s = A_1 \sigma^n \exp\left(-\frac{Q}{kT}\right) \tag{10.1}$$

where $\dot{\varepsilon}_s$ = secondary-creep rate
$\quad \sigma$ = applied compressive (or tensile) stress
$\quad Q$ = activation energy
$\quad T$ = temperature,
$\quad k$ = Boltzmann's constant = 1.38×10^{-23} J/K
$\quad A, n$ = constants

A second equation which is sometimes used and which appears to fit observations over a wider range of strain than Eq. (10.1) (to about 2 MN/m^2) is

$$\dot{\varepsilon} = A_2(\sinh \sigma)^n \exp\left(-\frac{Q}{kT}\right) \tag{10.2}$$

where A_2 is a constant.

The activation energy Q decreases with temperature. For temperatures higher than $-20°$C, it has a value of about 1eV; at $-50°$C a value of about 0.60 eV. Information on the temperature-compensated strain rate $\dot{\varepsilon}_s \exp\left(-Q/kT\right)$ is plotted against the stress in Fig. 10.5. A line of slope $n = 3$ is drawn through the plotted points. The results in Fig. 10.5 show that A in Eq. (10.1) has a value of about 5×10^{-5} for $\dot{\varepsilon}$ in s^{-1} and uniaxial compressive stress in newtons per square meter.

Most ice-engineering problems involve either the biaxial or triaxial states of stress, rather than the uniaxial state. There is relatively little information on the creep of ice for these multiaxial stress conditions (see Byers, 1973).

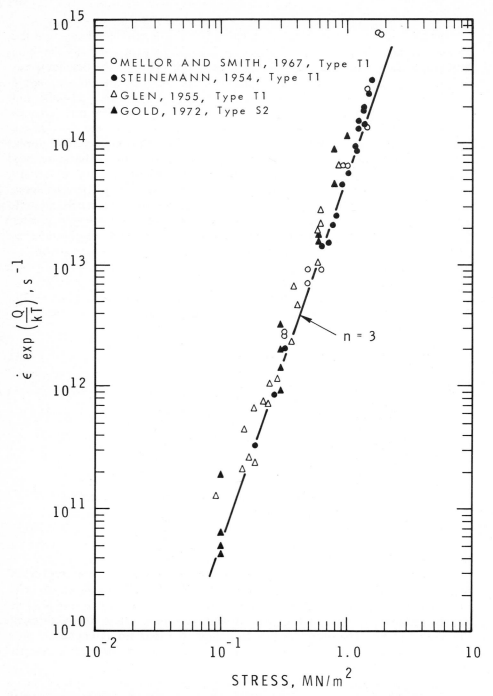

Figure 10.5 Stress dependence of the temperature-compensated strain rate, $Q = 1.08$ eV. Observations in temperature range -1 to $-25°C$.

Most uniaxial creep tests for ice have been carried out at stresses less than 2.0 MN/m². Information for stresses greater than that value is not relevant from the engineering point of view and is difficult to obtain experimentally (the tertiary stage, which is usually associated with nonuniform deformation, sets in at a strain of less than 25×10^{-4} at this stress level). It is of greater relevance to consider the deformation under conditions of constant rate of strain.

Figure 10.4a illustrates the dependence of stress on strain for four types of ice being strained at the same rate at $-10°C$. The general behavior is that the stress goes to a maximum then reduces to a relatively constant value. For granular ice, the maximum occurs over the same range of strain as the secondary-creep stage, i.e., between about 1 and 2 percent. The columnar-grained ices have their maximum at a strain of about 0.5 percent. This is in the range of primary creep and appears to be associated with an inflection in the creep curve that can be seen in Fig. 10.3, which is not observed for granular ice. The inflection is typical for columnar-grained structures that have not undergone previous deformation and is apparently associated with nonreversible structural changes. The deformation behavior of type S2 ice approaches that of granular ice if it is subject to cycles of load. Evidence has also been obtained for type S2 ice subject to low strain rates of a second maximum corresponding to that for granular ice.

Figure 10.4a also illustrates the marked dependence of the deformation behavior on ice type. Granular ice is relatively ductile at the strain rate shown. Type S2 is not so ductile, and its maximum stress is lower, which reflects its columnar structure and preferred crystallographic orientation. Columnar-grained type S1 ice has a much higher maximum stress and is generally more brittle in its behavior. This is due to the fact that when the applied stress is perpendicular to the long direction of the columnar grains, there is no resolved shear stress on the basal planes, the planes of easy slip. The deformation behavior of type S4 ice, formed from frazil and having irregular tabular-shaped grains, lies between that of granular and type S2 ice.

Figure 10.4b shows the general dependence of the maximum stress on the rate of strain for type S2 ice at $-10°C$. It illustrates the increase in the yield strength of ice with strain rate and the transition from ductile to brittle behavior that is found over the strain rate range of about 10^{-4} to 10^{-3} s^{-1}. Information (Gold and Krausz, 1971; Hawkes and Mellor, 1972; Carter and Michel, 1971), on the strain-rate dependence of the yield, compressive, and tensile strength of ice is presented in Fig. 10.6, which shows that the strain-rate dependence of the uniaxial yield and brittle compressive strengths of types S2, S4, and granular ice are essentially the same. The more brittle behavior of type S1 ice is clearly evident.

For uniaxial tension, the strain rate at which the transition of ductile to brittle occurs depends on temperature and is between 10^{-7} and 10^{-6} s^{-1} at $-10°C$. The change is relatively abrupt and is due to the formation of an internal or surface crack large enough to propagate to failure. There is a slight increase in tensile strength with strain rate, rising to a maximum at a strain rate

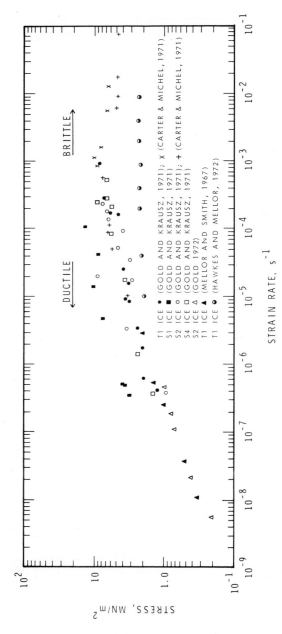

Figure 10.6 Strain-rate dependence of the yield and brittle strength (constant strain rate, compression ●, ○, ■, □, +, ×; tension ○); stress dependence of secondary-creep rate (▲, △); $T = -7$ to $-10°C$.

Table 10.4 Typical values of tensile strength of polycrystalline ice

Ice type	$\dot{\varepsilon}$, s^{-1}	Temp., °C	Tensile strength, MN/m²	Ref.
S2[a]	$>2 \times 10^{-5}$	-10	1.2	Carter and Michel (1971)
T1[b]	$>2 \times 10^{-5}$	-10	1.85	Carter and Michel (1971)
S4[c]	$>2 \times 10^{-5}$	-10	2.0	Carter and Michel (1971)
T1[d]	$>10^{-5}$	-7	2.0	Hawkes and Mellor (1972)
Sea ice[e]	...	-4 to -27	0.5	Weeks and Assur (1967)
Sea ice[f]	...	...	$0.75[1 - (5 \times 10^{-3} v_b)^{1/2}]$	Weeks and Assur (1967)
Sea ice[f]	...	...	0.2	Weeks and Assur (1967)

[a] Average grain size about 3 mm; stress perpendicular to long direction of columns.

[b] Average grain size 1 mm.

[c] Average grain size 0.9 mm.

[d] Average grain size 0.7 mm; density 899 kg/m².

[e] Direct tensile tests, quoted from investigations of Dykins; brine volume 10 to 70 parts per thousand; stress applied perpendicular to direction of growth.

[f] Flexural strength using cantilever beams, quoted from investigations of Weeks and Anderson; v_b in parts per thousand; strength constant for $v_b > 100$ parts per thousand.

of about $10^{-3} \ s^{-1}$. The maximum is probably associated with the transition from a viscoplastic condition associated with the formation of the failure surface to a fully elastic condition at high rates of strain. Typical values of the tensile strength of ice in the brittle region are given in Table 10.4. The strength does depend on type of ice and grain size but appears to be not greatly dependent on temperature.

Below strain rates of about $10^{-6} \ s^{-1}$, the strain-rate dependence of the yield strength appears to be the same for uniaxial tension and compression and also coincides with the stress dependence of the secondary-creep rate in constant-load tests. Above strain rates of $10^{-6} \ s^{-1}$, the compressive-yield stress continues to increase, rising to a maximum at about $10^{-3} \ s^{-1}$. The maximum is also associated with the transition of ductile to brittle. For strain rates greater than about $10^{-3} \ s^{-1}$, failure is fully brittle. There is evidence that the brittle strength decreases with increasing strain rate, tending to a constant value. This is a very difficult region for strength measurements, however, and the true behavior has not yet been clearly established.

Unlike tensile strength, compressive strength is strongly dependent on temperature. This appears to result from the temperature dependence of the way the ice structure breaks down by the formation of cracks before attaining the maximum value. Information on the temperature dependence of the compressive and tensile strengths for T1 and S2 ice is presented in Fig. 10.7.

Both tensile and compressive strengths are dependent on the state of stress and its relationship to the grain structure of the ice. A second principal stress has relatively little influence on the compressive strength of granular ice if it is

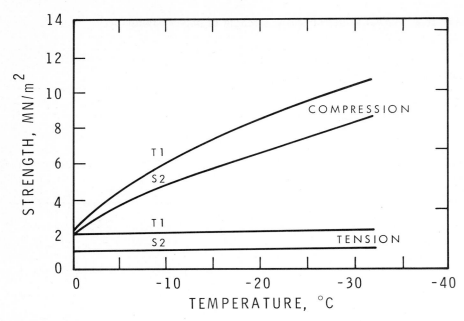

Figure 10.7 Temperature dependence of the brittle compressive and tensile strength of type T1 (fine-grained) and S2 (medium-grained) ($\varepsilon > 10^{-3}$ s^{-1}). (*Carter and Michel, 1971.*)

not subject to a stress in the third orthogonal direction. The compressive strength of columnar-grained S2 ice is about double its uniaxial strength if it is prevented from straining perpendicular to the long direction of the grains and to the applied stress.

The deformation behavior and strength of sea ice have the same general dependence on stress and rate of strain as freshwater ice; however, the dependence of the behavior of sea ice on these variables has not been investigated as extensively as it has for freshwater ice. Greatest attention has been paid to the effects of brine volume. In general, it is found that the strength of sea ice varies linearly with the square root of the relative brine volume for brine volume less than about 100 parts per thousand.

10.4 STATIC ICE PRESSURES

Ice covers exert a force on a structure only if they move relative to it. These forces may be associated with a cover that is essentially fixed or moving very slowly, such as land-fast ice in coastal regions and the covers of many lakes and rivers in midwinter, or with floes of all sizes undergoing impact with a structure. For some situations, e.g., arctic pack ice, it may be difficult to differentiate between essentially stationary ice and moving ice. For this discussion, ice pressures will be considered static if the inertial term can be neglected; if it cannot be neglected, they will be considered dynamic.

There are a number of ways by which forces may be induced in or imposed on a stationary ice cover. The extent to which these forces are exerted on a structure depends on several factors, including the size of the cover, the degree to which it is restrained at its edges, the size and shape of the structure, and the amount of movement required to cause the forces to be reduced to a negligible value. For some situations, e.g., at the head of a long narrow channel or in similar protected situations, forces imposed by an ice cover may always be insignificant due to the restraining influence of the shores or simply because the forces cannot develop to any significant degree. For others, the structure may be exposed to the full force of which the cover is capable, e.g., at an extended shoreline of an ocean or a large lake. It should be possible, in theory, to establish from appropriate site investigations the extent to which a structure will be subject to ice action. This capability is still not adequately developed, however, because of lack of knowledge concerning forces in ice covers, the factors upon which they depend, and the interaction between the cover and its surroundings.

Wind and Water Stress

Both wind and moving water exert a shear stress on an ice cover by the transfer of momentum to the surface. This wind or water stress can be estimated using the equation

$$\zeta = \rho C_d U_d^2 \tag{10.3}$$

where ζ = shear stress imposed by wind or water on ice cover
$\quad U_d$ = wind speed or water current measured at distance d from respective surface
$\quad C_d$ = drag coefficient associated with height at which U_d is measured
$\quad \rho$ = density of air or water

It is usually assumed that the wind speed or current velocity varies logarithmically with distance from the surface. The speed at distance d can be determined from measurements at distance x using the equation

$$U_d = \frac{U_x(\ln d - \ln Z_0)}{\ln x - \ln Z_0} \tag{10.4}$$

where Z_0 is a measure of the roughness of the surface. The drag coefficient depends on the roughness of the surface and is related to Z_0 by

$$C_d = k^2\left(\ln \frac{d + Z_0}{Z_0}\right)^{-2} \tag{10.5}$$

where k is von Karman's constant (equal to 0.4). Measured values of C_d and associated values for Z_0 are given in Table 10.5, along with a qualitative description of the roughness of the surface.

Table 10.5 Measured drag coefficients C_d for ice surfaces

Height or depth of measurement, m	C_d $\times 10^3$	Z_0, mm	Nature of surface	Ref.
10 (air)	0.95	0.023	Smooth snow-covered surface[†]	Banke and Smith (1973)
	2.61	3.98	Gently rolling, hummocked[†]	Banke and Smith (1973)
	3.3	9	Rafted[‡]	Langleben (1972)
0.5 (water)	9	7	Smooth[§]	Johannessen (1970)
	20	30	Rough[§]	Johannessen (1970)
	47	94	Very rough[§]	Johannessen (1970)

[†] Measured in Beaufort Sea, Arctic Ocean, Robeson Channel.
[‡] Measured in Beaufort Sea.
[§] Measured in Gulf of St. Lawrence and Arctic Ocean.

The values given for the drag coefficients are for a surface of uniform roughness. Ridges are usually a nonuniform feature that must be considered separately. There is little information on the drag coefficient for ridges. One calculation for an assumed ridge density of 7 km^{-1} and ridge height greater than 0.6 m gave a value for the drag coefficient for wind of the same order as that for uniformly rough surfaces, that is, 0.0015 (Banke and Smith, 1973).

To estimate the wind and water drag on an ice cover for design purposes, it is necessary to assume probable extreme values for both the drag coefficients and the wind speed or water current. If it is assumed that the drag coefficient for wind speed measured at the 10-m height is 0.003 and the wind speed 15 m/s, the resulting shear force on the ice is 0.875 N/m². It would require a fetch of about 10^3 km for this drag force to develop a total thrust of 1 MN. Similarly, it would require a distance of 20 km for water flowing at 1 m/s at the 0.5-m depth beneath a cover with a drag coefficient of 0.05 for the undersurface to develop the same thrust. These calculations indicate the magnitude of the drag force imposed on ice covers by wind and flowing water and the distances over which it must act to induce forces that are in the range of concern for engineering structures.

Example 10.1 The undersurface of an ice cover is found to have a roughness coefficient Z_0 of 25×10^{-3} m. What is the drag coefficient C_d for water current measured 0.5 m below the ice-water interface?

SOLUTION Using Eq. (10.5) with $k = 0.4$, $d = 0.5$, and $Z_0 = 25 \times 10^{-3}$ gives

$$C_d = 0.16 \ln \left(\frac{0.5 + 25 \times 10^{-3}}{25 \times 10^{-3}} \right)^{-2} = 1.73 \times 10^{-2}$$

Example 10.2 The drag coefficient C_d for a rafted ice surface is 3.0×10^{-3} for a wind speed measured at a height of 10 m. What is the maximum thrust imposed on an ice cover with a fetch of 500 km by a wind of 10 m/s measured 2 m above the ice surface? (Assume the density of air to be 1.29 kg/m^3.)

SOLUTION Using Eq. (10.5) with $C_d = 3.0 \times 10^{-3}$, $k = 0.4$, and $d = 10$ m gives

$$3.0 \times 10^{-3} = 0.16 \ln \left(\frac{10 + Z_0}{Z_0}\right)^{-2} \quad \text{and} \quad Z_0 = 6.74 \times 10^{-3} \text{ m}$$

Using Eq. (10.4) to obtain the wind speed U_d at the height of 10 m with $d = 10$ m, $x = 2$ m, $U_x = 10$ m/s, and $Z_0 = 6.74 \times 10^{-3}$ m gives

$$U_a = \frac{10[\ln 10 - \ln (6.74 \times 10^{-3})]}{\ln 2 - \ln (6.74 \times 10^{-3})} = 12.83 \text{ m/s}$$

Using Eq. (10.3) with $\rho = 1.29$ kg/m^3, $C_d = 3.0 \times 10^{-3}$, and $U_d = 12.83$ m/s gives $\zeta = 1.29(3 \times 10^{-3})(12.83)^2 = 0.64$ N/m^2. For a fetch of 500 km, the maximum thrust equals $0.64(500 \times 10^3) = 3.20 \times 10^5$ N $= 0.32$ MN.

Thermal Stress

Temperature changes are a source of stress in ice covers. If the response of ice to temperature-induced strains were perfectly elastic, the tensile stress due to a temperature drop of about 7°C would be sufficient to cause the formation of cracks. Ice covers are sufficiently elastic and temperature-induced strains are sufficiently large for thermal cracks to be a common feature of ice covers. These cracks can be more than a centimeter wide at the surface and extend into the cover for a depth of more than 0.2 m.

If the cracks that form on cooling were to remain perfectly "clean," the ice cover, in principle, should return to its original dimension on warming to 0°C, with no development of compressive stress. Cracks, however, may extend completely through the cover, allowing water to enter into them and subsequently freeze. They can also be completely or partially filled from above by snow. A rise in temperature can then cause a compressive stress to develop in the ice cover.

Because of the variability in the processes, in the temperature changes imposed on a cover, and in the response of ice to stress, the maximum thermal stress that could develop at a given site is indeterminate. An estimate, however, can be made. To do so, it is usual to assume that initially the ice cover is continuous and free of cracks and stress and that the temperature of the cover decreases linearly from the freezing point at the ice-water interface to the minimum value at the upper surface. The surface temperature depends on the location and conditions at the site and is established from measurements or estimates of the probable minimum air temperature. In the calculation, the temperature of the surface is normally assumed to increase linearly or sinusoidally to a given value, usually 0°C, and in a given time. The thermal stress is determined from the thermal response of the cover to the imposed temperature change and an assumed rheological behavior for the ice.

The strains induced by a temperature change are relatively small. They can be calculated from

$$\dot{\varepsilon} = \alpha \dot{T} \tag{10.6}$$

where $\dot{\varepsilon}$ = time rate of change of thermal strain, s^{-1}
$\dot{T}$ = rate of change of the temperature, °C/s
α = coefficient of linear thermal expansion

For ice, the coefficient of expansion decreases with decreasing temperature and, according to Drouin and Michel (1971), can be described by

$$\alpha = (54 + 0.18T) \times 10^{-6} \; °C^{-1} \tag{10.7}$$

where T is in degrees Celsius. Substituting Eq. (10.7) into Eq. (10.6) and integrating for a temperature change from -40 to 0°C in unit time gives thermal strain of $\varepsilon = 0.25$ percent, which is in the range of primary creep.

If the ice is completely constrained, a compressive stress is induced such that the net strain is zero. For elastic behavior, this stress would be about 25 MN/m² for the above case, appreciably larger than the uniaxial compressive strength of all ice types. Observations show that it is considerably smaller than this value because of the viscoplastic behavior of ice.

As shown by Eq. (10.6), the strain rate imposed on the ice cover is determined by the rate of temperature rise. A reasonable, practical range of rate of change of temperature to be considered for engineering calculations would be 1 to 10°C/h. This would correspond to a strain rate range of about 10^{-8} to $1.5 \times 10^{-7} \, s^{-1}$.

Since an ice cover is usually constrained in all directions, the problem is one of biaxial strain or stress rather than uniaxial. For an isotropic ice cover, therefore, the minimum and maximum principal strains would be about 50 percent greater, that is, 1.5×10^{-8} to $2.25 \times 10^{-7} \, s^{-1}$. Drouin and Michel (1971) found that for this range in strain rate, the maximum stress occurred within the first 0.25 percent strain for granular ice and columnar-grained type S1 ice. Figure 10.6 shows that the range of uniaxial stress corresponding to the above strain rates at -10°C is about 0.5 to 2.0 MN/m².

If the temperature at the surface varied sinusoidally about a mean value equal to one-half the assumed minimum value, the resulting temperature behavior in a semi-infinite solid would be given by

$$T(Z, t) = \frac{T_m}{2} \left\{ 1 + \exp\left[-Z\left(\frac{\omega}{2a}\right)^{1/2} \right] \cos\left[\omega t - Z\left(\frac{\omega}{2a}\right)^{1/2} \right] \right\} \tag{10.8}$$

where $T(Z, t)$ = temperature at depth Z and time t

$\qquad T_m$ = assumed minimum surface temperature

$\qquad \omega$ = angular frequency of temperature variation = $2\pi/t_0$

$\qquad a$ = thermal diffusivity of ice, assumed equal to 1.16 mm²/s

$\qquad t_0$ = time for one complete cycle of temperature change

Equation (10.8) shows that for the semi-infinite solid, the amplitude of the temperature disturbance decreases exponentially and its phase is retarded linearly with depth beneath the surface.

Differentiating Eq. (10.8) with respect to time gives

$$\frac{\partial T}{\partial t} = \dot{T}(Z, t) = -\frac{T_m \pi}{t_0} \exp\left[-Z\left(\frac{\omega}{2a}\right)^{1/2} \right] \sin\left[\omega t - Z\left(\frac{\omega}{2a}\right)^{1/2} \right] \qquad (10.9)$$

If T_m is $-40°C$ and t_0 is 1 day, the maximum rate of change of temperature will be about 5°C/h. For this frequency of temperature change, the amplitude will be less than 10 percent of its surface value at a depth of 0.5 m, and the maximum rate will occur 10 h later than at the surface. If the ice cover is only 0.5 m thick, the depth and time dependence of the temperature change induced in it by a daily cyclical variation at the surface begins to differ significantly from the semi-infinite case only at depths greater than about 0.3 m. For temperature calculations an ice cover of thickness greater than 0.5 m can therefore be considered as semi-infinite.

Nonsinusoidal surface-temperature changes, including linear ones, can be treated using Fourier analysis. The additional work involved in the calculations is probably not justified considering the indeterminate nature of thermal stress. Drouin and Michel (1971) have shown that the thrust due to a sinusoidal temperature rise in a given period is greater than that due to a linear rise of the same amount in the same time.

For the simplest calculation of thermal stress, it is assumed that the thermal strain rate at depth Z and time t is given by substituting Eq. (10.9) into Eq. (10.6). If the ice cover is completely constrained biaxially, the induced compressive stress must be such as to cause a strain rate that is at least 50 percent greater. The stress is calculated from this strain rate and the assumed rheological model.

Drouin and Michel (1971) have determined such a model from uniaxial tests for granular and columnar-grained S1 ice. Their calculated stress-strain curves for granular ice deformed at a rate of $7.25 \times 10^{-8} \text{ s}^{-1}$ in the temperature range of 0 to $-40°C$ are shown as dashed lines in Fig. 10.8. The stress and temperature dependence of the maximum uniaxial compressive stress for granular ice was found to satisfy the equation

$$\sigma_m = C \dot{\varepsilon}^{1/m} \exp \frac{Q_c}{mkT} \qquad (10.10)$$

where $m = 4$
$Q_c = 0.87\text{eV}$
$k = $ Boltzmann's constant
$T = $ temperature, K

The form of the stress-strain curves for granular ice and other strain rates was the same as that shown in Fig. 10.8, the maximum stress being attained at a strain of about 0.15 percent, i.e., in the primary-creep range. For the columnar-

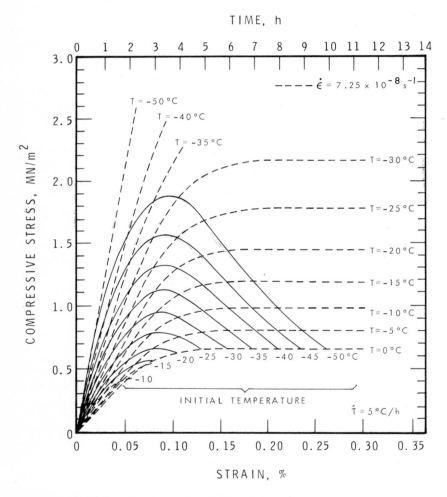

Figure 10.8 Example of the time dependence of the thermal stress developed in a uniaxially constrained thin ice plate. The solid lines give the thermal stress for a linear rise of temperature of the ice of 5°C/h starting from the given initial temperatures; the dashed lines are uniaxial stress-strain curves for a constant rate of strain of 72.5 ns⁻¹ at the given temperature, calculated using a rheological model based on laboratory measurements. (*Drouin and Michel, 1971.*)

grained S1 ice, the maximum stress occurred at about the same strain but was about twice as large and dropped off more rapidly after yield.

Drouin and Michel used their rheological model to calculate the thermal stress developed in a thin ice plate uniaxially constrained and subject to various rates of increase of temperature. Figure 10.8 shows the curves they obtained for a constant rate of increase of temperature of 5°C/h starting at the given initial temperatures (5°C/h is equivalent to a strain rate of about 7.25×10^{-8} s^{-1}). The maximum stress for each condition was attained at a strain smaller than that associated with yield in the constant-strain-rate–constant-temperature tests. This is due to the decrease in the resistance of ice to shear with increase in temperature, indicated by Eq. (10.10).

Figure 10.9 presents the dependence of the calculated maximum thermal stress (as shown in Fig. 10.8) on the rate of increase in temperature and the initial temperature. The calculations show that the maximum values for a given initial temperature are relatively insensitive to rate of temperature increase when it exceeds about 3°C/h. Laboratory measurements made by Drouin and Michel of the thermal stress induced for complete biaxial constraint indicated that the ratio $\sigma_{\text{biax}}/\sigma_{\text{uniax}}$ has a maximum value of about 1.85.

Curves of the type shown in Figs. 10.8 and 10.9 can be used to estimate the thermal thrust induced by an ice cover whose surface is subject to a given rate of increase in temperature. The rate of change of temperature at a given depth

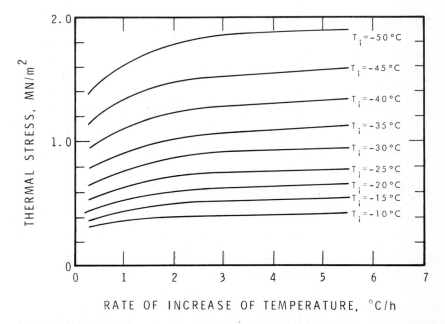

Figure 10.9 Calculated dependence of the maximum thermal stress developed in a uniaxially constrained thin ice plate on the rate of change of temperature and initial temperature T_i. (*Drouin and Michel, 1971.*)

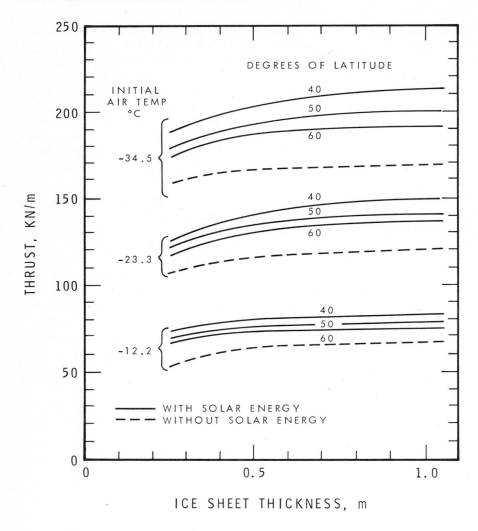

Figure 10.10 Calculated dependence of the maximum thermal thrust on ice thickness and initial temperature. An estimate of the effect of solar radiation, in terms of latitude, is given for clear ice conditions. (*Michel, 1970.*)

is determined by the appropriate solution to the thermal problem. Results of such calculations are given in Fig. 10.10, which shows the dependence of the maximum thrust on the thickness of the ice cover for three initial air temperatures. If the ice is clear and free of snow, solar radiation may contribute significantly to the rate of increase of temperature. This effect has been taken into consideration in the calculation of the thrusts presented in Fig. 10.10. The calculations show that the maximum thrust is relatively insensitive to the thickness of the cover when it exceeds about 0.5 m. This is because a significant thermal stress does not develop below this depth before the stress at the surface begins to decrease.

Example 10.3 A continuous freshwater ice cover 1 m thick has a constant temperature gradient from its bottom to the upper surface; its surface is at $-30°C$. At 2 A.M. it begins to experience a sinusoidal increase in temperature, which reaches a maximum of $0°C$ at 2 P.M. What is the maximum rate of change of temperature imposed on the ice cover? What is the maximum strain rate? What is the maximum thermal strain for the 12-h period? (Assume $\alpha = 52 \times 10^{-6} \ °C^{-1}$). Assume that the temperature change has a period of 1 day. At what depth is the amplitude of the total temperature change one-tenth of that imposed on the surface? By how much does the temperature change at that depth lag behind that at the surface? (Assume the thermal diffusivity of ice equals $1.2 \ mm^2/s$). Assume that the $30°C$ temperature change is linear rather than sinusoidal. From Fig. 10.9 what is the value of the maximum thermal stress in a uniaxially constrained cover?

SOLUTION Use Eq. (10.9) with $T_m = -30°C$ and $t_0 = 24$ h. Note that T is a maximum at the surface (that is, $Z = 0$) when $\sin \omega t = 1$. Therefore $T_m = 30\pi/24 = 3.93°C/h$. If we use Eq. (10.6), the maximum strain rate is $\dot{\varepsilon}_m = 52 \times 10^{-6}\dot{T}_m = 5.68 \times 10^{-8} \ s^{-1}$. The maximum thermal strain occurs at the surface and equals $\varepsilon = \alpha T_m = (52 \times 10^{-6})(30) = 1.56 \times 10^{-3}$. The amplitude of the total temperature change at depth Z is the value of $2[T(Z, t) - T_m/2]$ when $\cos [\omega t - Z(\omega/2a)^{1/2}]$ has a value of 1, that is, $T_m \exp [-Z(\omega/2a)^{1/2}]$. The depth at which this amplitude is 0.1 times that at the surface is given by $\exp [-Z(\omega/2a)^{1/2}] = 0.1$, where $\omega = 2\pi/t_0 = 2\pi/24(3600) = 7.27 \times 10^{-5} \ s^{-1}$ and $a = 1.2 \times 10^{-6} \ m^2/s$. Therefore

$$\exp \left[-Z \left(\frac{7.27 \times 10^{-5}}{2(1.2) \times 10^{-6}} \right)^{1/2} \right] = 0.1, \qquad -Z(30.29)^{1/2} = -2.303$$

and
$$Z = \frac{2.303}{5.50} = 0.42 \ m$$

Next compute the time lag of temperature change at $Z = 0.42$ m. The disturbance at the surface when $t = 0$ is felt at depth Z when $\omega t = Z(\omega/2a)^{1/2}$, where $Z = 0.42$ m, $\omega = 7.27 \times 10^{-5} \ s^{-1}$, and $a = 1.2 \times 10^{-6} \ m/s$. Compute

$$t = 0.42 \left[\frac{7.27 \times 10^{-5}}{2(1.2) \times 10^{-6}} \right]^{1/2} = 2.303$$

giving $t = 2.303(t_0/2\pi) = 8.8$ h; hence the time lag is 8.8 h. Consider next the maximum thermal stress. If the temperature change is linear, $\partial T/\partial t = 30/12 = 2.5°C/h$. The maximum thermal stress in a uniaxially constrained cover would occur at the top surface. From Fig. 10.9, this stress would be about $0.9 \ MN/m^2$.

10.5 FORCE DUE TO CHANGE IN WATER LEVEL

A change in water level will cause an ice cover to exert both a vertical force and a bending moment on a structure to which it is frozen. Under certain conditions, the cover can also exert a horizontal thrust. Two relatively straightforward situations will be considered to bring out the pertinent features of this problem: the determination of the extreme forces that could be exerted on a long straight wall and on an isolated circular pile.

The starting point for both problems will be the elastic solutions or a close approximation to them. It must be kept in mind, however, that since ice is viscoplastic, the elastic solution can be considered valid only if the change in water level takes place rapidly, a situation that does not usually occur. The elastic solutions presented satisfy the biharmonic equation

$$\nabla^4 w = \frac{q - kw}{D} \tag{10.11}$$

where w = deflection at given distance from structure
  q = load applied to cover
  k = subgrade reaction = ρg
  ρ = density of water
  g = acceleration due to gravity
  $D = Eh^3/12(1 - v^2)$ = flexural rigidity of ice cover

Equation (10.11) describes the bending of a thin elastic plate on an elastic foundation when shear stresses are ignored. For the uplift problem the shear stresses near the structure may have to be considered. If they are large enough, they can have a significant effect on the shape of the deflected surface and the maximum load imposed for the viscoplastic case, depending on the length of time over which the change in water level takes place.

Consider an ice cover of thickness h frozen to a long straight wall. According to Eq. (10.11), the deflection of the cover along a line perpendicular to the wall due to a change in water level H is given by

$$w(x) = (2)^{1/2} H \exp\left(-\frac{x}{B}\right) \sin\left(\frac{x}{B} + \frac{\pi}{4}\right) \tag{10.12}$$

where $B = (2)^{1/2}(D/k)^{1/4} = (2)^{1/2} L$ is a characteristic length and L is the characteristic length for the axial-symmetric case. Observations on the deflection under axially symmetric loading of freshwater ice have shown that initially $L = 16h^{3/4}$ m. The corresponding value of B is $22.6h^{3/4}$ m.

The bending moment $M = -D \, \delta^2 W/\delta x^2$ has a maximum at the wall, i.e., at $x = 0$, and at $x/B = \pi/2$. At $x = 0$, however, it is about 5 times greater than at $x = \pi B/2$, and so, initially, only conditions at the wall need be considered. The upward force on the wall is

$$P = -kBH = 2.2 \times 10^5 H h^{3/4} \qquad \text{N/m} \tag{10.13}$$

If the change in water level is not very large, the maximum strain at the wall is given to a reasonable approximation by

$$e_{mw} = \frac{h}{2} \frac{\delta^2 W}{\delta x^2} \bigg|_{x=0} = \frac{hH}{B^2} \tag{10.14}$$

and the maximum strain rate by

$$\dot{e}_{mw} = \frac{h\dot{H}}{B^2} \tag{10.15}$$

Equations (10.14) and (10.15) provide an appreciation of how an ice cover will behave during a change in water level. If the maximum strain rate is less than 10^{-8} s^{-1}, the ice can be expected to deform in a ductile manner and the maximum strain can exceed 10^{-2}. If it is greater than that value, failure tends to be brittle and the strain to failure is less than 5×10^{-3}. For this situation, the strain to the formation of a crack that would significantly reduce the upward force on the wall is relatively small and in the primary-creep range. Substituting $B = 22.6h^{3/4}$ in Eq. (10.15) and equating to 10^{-8} s^{-1}, indicates that the ice can be expected to crack at the wall if $\dot{H}/h^{1/2}$ is greater than about 5×10^6 m$^{1/2}$ s^{-1} and if the change in water level is sufficiently large.

Observations on the time-dependent deflection of ice covers due to a concentrated load have indicated that when ice is deforming in a ductile manner, the deflection for an appreciable time is given to a good approximation by Eq. (10.12) and a characteristic length that decreases with time (Frederking and Gold, 1976). This implies a time-dependent Young's modulus. Equations (10.14) and (10.15) show that an effective decrease in B with time increases the probability of failure of the cover at the wall.

The foregoing discussion implies that for a cyclical change in water level of sufficient height, such as might occur by tidal action, the ice at the wall will be continually broken free of the structure until it is thick enough to bring the maximum strain rate into the ductile range. The deflections required, however, will exceed the thickness of the cover h for a time. This has the effect of increasing the thickness near the wall by surface flooding and of developing a "bustle" on the structure. Continual vertical movement of the ice near the structure may also prevent it from freezing to it even when the thickness exceeds that required for ductile behavior. As a result, the maximum vertical force that can be developed on the structure becomes indeterminate, and it is necessary to assume an appropriate extreme condition for design. This extreme condition may include taking into account the weight of the bustle.

If it can be assumed that the maximum force is that due to a cover of uniform thickness frozen to the wall, that force can be estimated using Eq. (10.13), taking into account the time dependence of B if appropriate. The bending moment exerted on the wall is given by

$$M_w = -D \frac{\delta^2 W}{\delta x^2} = \frac{kHB^2}{2} \tag{10.16}$$

If a crack forms at the wall such that the bending moment there becomes zero but the ice still exerts a vertical load, the deflected shape of the cover is given by

$$w(x) = H \exp\left(-\frac{x}{B}\right) \cos \frac{x}{B} \tag{10.17}$$

The upward force on the wall is given by

$$P = \frac{-kHB}{2} \tag{10.18}$$

This is one-half the vertical force exerted by an ice cover frozen to the wall and subject to the same change in water level.

For a first approximation for the pile problem, the deflection of the surface can be considered the same as that due to the load on the pile applied uniformly over an area of the same diameter as the pile. This approximation should be reasonable for a pile of radius a, appreciably smaller than the characteristic length of the ice cover L. The deflection of the cover at the pile for this condition, assumed equal to the change in water level, is

$$w_p = H = \frac{P}{k}(1 + b \text{ ber}' b) \tag{10.19}$$

where P = intensity of assumed load = $(2h/a)q_p$
  q_p = imposed shear stress on pile (assumed uniform)
  $b = a/L$
  ber b = modified Bessel function; the prime denotes its first derivative

For $b < 0.15$

$$1 + b \text{ ber}' b = \frac{\pi b^2}{8} \tag{10.20}$$

and

$$w_p = \frac{h\pi a q_p}{4kL^2}$$

For the long straight wall

$$w_w = \frac{P}{kB} = \frac{hq_w}{(2)^{1/2}kL} \tag{10.21}$$

where q_w is the shear force exerted on the wall. For the same change in water level, that is, $w_p = w_w$,

$$\frac{q_w}{q_p} = 1.11b \tag{10.22}$$

and for $b < 0.1$

$$\frac{q_w}{q_p} < 0.11$$

That is, the shear stress imposed on the pile for the elastic case is about 10 times that imposed on the wall. It is clear that the deformation conditions are much more severe near the pile. This is borne out by field observations and laboratory testing, which indicate that for the pile, failure often occurs by shearing at the pile-ice interface, whereas for the wall it is associated with bending and the formation of a crack.

Some consideration has been given to viscoplastic solutions to the uplift problem, but their validity has still to be demonstrated (Nevel, 1966a). Reasons for this are lack of knowledge of the rheological behavior of ice over the range of stress and strain involved and complications introduced by the temperature gradient that normally exists in an ice cover.

If the creep behavior near the pile can be described by Eq. (10.1) with exponent n equal to 3, the ratio of the vertical displacement at the radial distance $r = a$ and $r = b$ for a pile subject to an uplift shear stress q_p is equal to $(a/b)^2$ (Frederking, 1974). This shows that the vertical shear displacement occurs relatively close to the pile. The vertical-displacement rate of a pile of radius a relative to an ice surface sufficiently far away not to be affected by the vertical shear stress is given by

$$\dot{U}_a = \frac{\dot{\gamma}_c a}{n - 1} \left(\frac{\tau_a}{\tau_c} \right)^n \tag{10.23}$$

Frederking found from tests on "piles" 5 and 10 cm in diameter that τ_c was about 72 kN/m^2 and $\dot{\gamma}_c$ about 4.5×10^{-8} s^{-1}. The maximum shear stress applied was 185 kN/m^2, which caused a vertical displacement rate of 12 nm/s.

If a crack forms at the bottom of an ice cover, it will fill with water, which can subsequently freeze. When the water level returns to the average value, a thrust must develop due to the increased length of the lower surface. In principle, this problem is the same as that of thermal thrust. The amount by which the lower surface increases in size will depend on the strain relief associated with the formation of the crack and the degree of restraint offered by the wall to the vertical movement of the cover. The problem differs from that of the thermal thrust in that the increase in length is localized. If the ice cover is very large, the compressive strain induced would be correspondingly small. If the cover is confined as, say, in a reservoir or between two bridge piers, the compressive force induced might be large enough to cause damage. Local damage might occur due to the bending moments induced in the restrained situation.

Example 10.4 A lake ice cover 1 m thick frozen to a long straight wall is subject to an increase in water level of 1.0 m in 30 min. Assuming elastic behavior, what is the maximum strain rate imposed on the ice? If a crack forms in the ice at the wall when the maximum strain is 10^{-3}, what is the vertical force and bending moment exerted on the wall just before the crack is formed? (Assume the subgrade reaction k equal to 10^4 N/m^2.)

SOLUTION For the maximum strain rate at the wall using Eq. (10.15) with $h = 1$ m, $\dot{H} = 1/(0.5)(3600) = 5.56 \times 10^{-4}$ s^{-1}, and $B = 22.6h^{3/4} = 22.6$ m gives $\dot{e}_{mw} = (5.56 \times 10^{-4})/(22.6)^2 = 1.09 \times 10^{-6}$ s^{-1}. For the vertical force and bending moment using Eq. (10.14) with $e_{mw} = 10^{-3}$ gives $H = 10^{-3}(22.6)^2 = 0.51$ m. Use Eq. (10.13) with $k = 10^4$ N/m^2, $B = 22.6$ m, and $H = 0.51$ m. Next the vertical force on the wall equals $P = -10^4(22.6)(0.51) = -11.53 \times 10^4$ N/m acting upward. For the bending moment at the wall use Eq. (10.16), giving $M_w = \frac{1}{2}(0.51)(22.6)^2 \times 10^4 = 1.30$ MN $\cdot$ m/m.

10.6 DYNAMIC PRESSURES

If a structure is to be subjected to collisions with ice floes, it must be designed so that it can withstand the resulting force. This is a problem for which there is still no calculation method that can be applied with acceptable confidence. There is general agreement on the form of the equations to be used for estimating the maximum force, but several assumptions must be made when applying them to particular situations. Some of these assumptions are based on, or find support in, the results of theoretical studies, small-scale measurements, and field observations. Their validity for large structures, however, has not been properly demonstrated, largely because of inadequate knowledge of the nature of the interaction between ice and a structure and its dependence on all factors involved. As with many engineering problems that involve several random variables, the establishment of an appropriate calculation method and the degree of confidence with which it can be used may require prolonged and careful observations of the performance of structures in ice and measurement of the forces exerted on them.

The force that an ice floe will exert on a structure depends on the speed at which it is moving, its thickness, the size and shape of the structure, the type of ice and its strength, and the kinetic energy of the floe. If the floe is small, say less than about 100 m square, it may be halted, deflected, or fractured by the structure before the ice develops the maximum force of which it is capable. This should always be kept in mind since it may be possible to locate a structure so that for a floe of large size and kinetic energy to reach it will be impossible or highly improbable.

The strain rate induced in the ice during collision depends on the size and shape of the structure and the speed of the floe relative to it. The properties of floes and the conditions of collisions are usually sufficiently variable for the behavior of the ice to be either ductile or brittle. Unless site conditions dictate otherwise, it must be assumed for design that a collision can occur for which the ice will develop the maximum strength of which it is capable at the time of year when floes are present.

The failure of a floe may occur by crushing, bending, shear, or splitting. For a floe so large that cracks are not propagated to its edge, failure will be due to one of the first two modes; the last two mentioned need not be considered. If the floe is small, or if a collision will always occur near an edge, the maximum force may be that required to break it by shear, splitting, or a combination of these two modes.

The form of the equation that is usually used to estimate the maximum force F_{cm} for the crushing mode is (Michel, 1970; U.S.S.R. Building Standard, 1967)

$$F_{cm} = C_1 C_2 C_3 \sigma_0 bh \qquad (10.24)$$

where σ_0 = reference strength for ice, normally taken to be unconfined compression strength

b = width of structure

h = thickness of ice

C_1 = factor taking into account shape of structure

C_2 = factor taking into account degree of contact between structure and ice

C_3 = factor depending on width of structure and thickness of ice

The unconfined-compression strength has been determined for specimens of various sizes and shapes. Its value depends on the dimensions of the specimen and conditions at the surface where the load is applied. There is a need to establish a standard method of determination if Eq. (10.24) is to have universal application. Measurements should be made over the strain-rate range associated with the transition from ductile to brittle so that the maximum value of σ_0 can be determined. They should also cover a wide enough range in temperature to allow the appropriate value of σ_0 to be chosen for the climatic conditions at a site at the time when collisions will occur.

Observations indicate that the way ice usually fails by crushing at a structure does not fully conform with the behavior observed for uniaxial compression. This may not be a serious matter if a standard method of determining σ_0 is adopted to ensure that it is a valid measure of the strength of the ice. Small-scale tests, in particular, have shown that a "plastic" failure zone forms in front of the structure. This zone is one of appreciable crack formation as the load approaches the maximum value. Because of the constraining effect of the surrounding ice, the viscoplastic strain is forced to occur primarily perpendicular to the surface of the cover. This may result in tensile strains sufficient to cause the formation of major cleavage cracks parallel to the ice surface, particularly if the ice is restrained by friction or cohesion over the area of contact with the structure. Cleavage-crack formation of this nature has been observed at times to determine the maximum force for the crushing mode of failure. Once failure has occurred, the load on the structure drops until contact is again made with the relatively undeformed ice at the boundary of the failed zone.

During the period of maximum load, most of the strain occurs in the plastic zone. A measure of the strain rate would therefore be

$$\dot{\varepsilon} = \frac{v}{l} \qquad (10.25)$$

where v is the velocity of floe relative to the structure and l is the length of the "plastic" zone in the direction of movement. Hirayama et al. (1974) found for small-scale tests with circular piles of diameter d that

$$1 \propto d^{0.3} \left(\frac{h}{v} \right)^{0.5} \tag{10.26}$$

indicating that the size of the "plastic" zone depends on the thickness of the ice, velocity of the floe, and size of the structure. As the characteristics of this zone and the factors upon which they depend are still not adequately known, there is not a proper basis for determining the strain rate in the ice from the floe velocity. This is not necessarily a serious matter if the maximum possible value for σ_0 is appropriate for design calculations.

A knowledge of the characteristics of the plastic or failed zone is important if calculation of the dynamic response of the structure is necessary. For velocities at least up to that associated with the maximum value of σ_0, the rate of propagation of the front of the "plastic" zone is greater than the speed of the floe. As a result, the force on the structure fluctuates. The frequency of this fluctuation depends primarily on the speed of the floe and size of the failed zone. Particular attention must be paid to this problem if the period of the fluctuation is close to that for the natural frequency of the structure. Field observations show that it has a value of the order of 1 s.

It has been suggested that the dependence of the maximum thrust on the ratio of width of structure to thickness of ice is that given by the classical theory of plasticity. This may be true for granular ice in the ductile range of behavior, but laboratory results for columnar-grained ice appear to be more consistent with the dependence of stress in front of a structure on its width, as given by the theory of Boussinesq for linearly elastic solids. In this approach the force imposed by the ice is replaced by an appropriate equivalent set of line loads, and the stress at a given point in front of the structure is determined by the superposition of their contribution. This approach indicates that the stress at a point depends mainly on the width of the structure and only to a minor degree on the thickness of the ice.

The influence of the shape of a vertical structure has not been demonstrated to be large for continuous movement of ice past it. Assuming C_1 equal to 1 for a flat structure, model and theoretical studies indicate that it is between 0.9 and 1 for circular and triangular structures. The values for the circular and triangular structure during the initial penetration, however, may be appreciably different from that for a flat structure of the same width. In this case, the full face of a flat structure may be in contact with the floe right from the beginning of the collision. For round and triangular structures, the area of contact increases with penetration, and the maximum load may be developed before the full width of the structure is involved.

The contact coefficient C_2 has not yet been sufficiently investigated. By definition, it is given by

$$C_2 = \frac{f_p}{f_c} \qquad (10.27)$$

where f_p is the maximum possible force on the structure for continuous movement of the ice past it and f_c is the maximum possible force on the structure when there is continuous contact, e.g., when ice frozen to the structure first begins to move. For ice frozen to the structure, C_2 can be assumed to be 1 when the cover first begins to move. The coefficient reflects the nonuniform contact and failure condition for the relatively brittle behavior associated with the maximum value for σ_0.

The coefficients C_1, C_2, and C_3 are all functions of the width of structure, thickness of ice cover, and velocity of the floe. It may be very difficult, therefore, to determine or confirm their values from field measurements of ice forces. From an engineering point of view, it may be more appropriate to consider the maximum thrust to be simply a function of thickness of ice and width and shape of structure, assuming that the effect of strain rate (velocity of floe) and temperature can be taken into account through the specification of σ_0. Because of the nature of the problem, the maximum force should also be considered in terms of its probability of occurrence. The model studies by Hirayama et al. (1974) indicate that for continuous penetration of a circular pile

$$\max \sigma_{p, 99} \propto b^{-0.5} h^{0.1} \qquad (10.28)$$

where $\max \sigma_{p, 99}$ is the maximum stress with a 1 percent probability of being exceeded. Their work also indicates that the constant of proportionality is the same for rectangular and circular structures for continuous penetration. It decreases with decreasing wedge angle for structures with a triangular face, but the decrease is relatively small (about 10 percent for a wedge angle of 60°).

Equation (10.28) suggests that the maximum force during collision may be only weakly dependent on the thickness of the ice cover. In Fig. 10.11 $\log (F_{cm}/bh\sigma_0) = \log (\sigma_e/\sigma_0)$, obtained from published results of several investigations, is plotted against $\log b$. The ice thickness and the shape of the "pile" or "indentor," whether circular, rectangular or triangular, have been ignored. Most of the observations were made by forcing small-width vertical piles or indentors against the edge of an ice cover. In all cases the ice failed by crushing. The rate of penetration was sufficiently high to ensure that the crushing strength was at or near its maximum value. In some cases the distance of penetration was only adequate to obtain the initial maximum, and in others continuous penetration was imposed. The range in values of σ_e/σ_0 associated with most of the sets of observations reflects either the range in measured values of σ_e or uncertainty in σ_0. When not given, σ_0 was assumed to lie in the range of 6 to 10 MN/m² for cold freshwater ice (temperature $-10°C$ or lower) and 1 to 3 MN/m² for warm ice (temperature higher than $-3°C$).

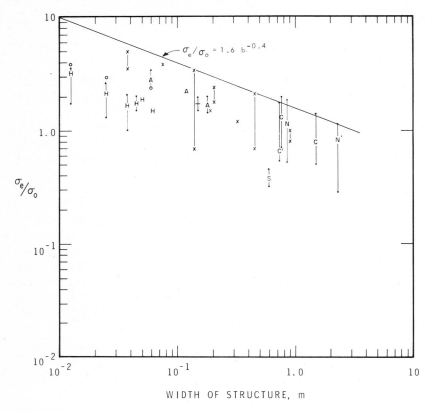

WIDTH OF STRUCTURE, m

Figure 10.11 Dependence of the ratio σ_e/σ_0 on the width of the pile, indentor, or structure for the crushing mode of failure. Bars indicate range in either measured values of the effective stress σ_e or uncertainty in σ_0. C = initial maximum force, CP = maximum force for continuous penetration; C = Croasdale (1974), C ($3 < \sigma_0 < 6$); C' = Croasdale (1976), C ($3.5 < \sigma_0 < 9.4$); $\bigcirc$ = Hirayama et al. (1974), C ($\sigma_0 = 3.5$); H = Hirayama et al. (1974), CP ($\sigma_0 = 3.5$); N' = Neil (1976), pier $23°$ vertical, CP ($1 < \sigma_0 < 3$); N = Neil (1976), CP ($0.6 < \sigma_0 < 3.1$); S = Schwarz, CP [from Neil (1976)] ($1.7 < \sigma_0 < 2.4$): A = Afanas'ev, CP [from Neil (1976)] ($\sigma_0 = 1$); + = Haynes et al. C [from Neil (1976)] ($1 < \sigma_0 < 3$); $\times$ = Zabilansky et al. (1975), C ($1 < \sigma_0 < 3$).

Figure 10.11 indicates a correlation between σ_e/σ_0 and width of structure b that has yet to be fully exploited for design purposes. The observations define a region whose upper boundary is given by

$$\frac{\sigma_e}{\sigma_0} = 1.6b^{-0.4} \tag{10.29}$$

where b is in meters. It would seem appropriate, for the present state of knowledge concerning the ice-structure interaction and the natural variability in all the factors influencing it, to use an empirical equation of the form of Eq. (10.29) for estimating the maximum ice pressure for the crushing mode of failure for a vertical structure. The effect of temperature and strain rate are incorporated in σ_0; the factors that take into account the degree of contact and the width of structure are included in the constants corresponding to 1.6 and the exponent -0.4. To use a more complex equation for engineering purposes would require a greater accuracy in the specification of σ_0 than is probably possible. The correlation apparent in Fig. 10.11 emphasizes the need for accurate determination of both σ_e and σ_0 in future investigations.

If an ice cover can fail in bending, the force that will be exerted will be less than that associated with the crushing mode. The face of a structure that is exposed to ice action is sometimes sloped to take advantage of this. Both a

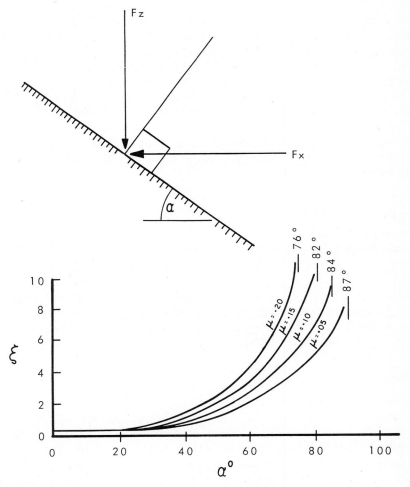

Figure 10.12 Dependence of ratio of horizontal force to vertical force on slope angle of face of structure α and coefficient of friction between ice and structure μ. (*Danys et al., 1976.*)

horizontal thrust and vertical load must now be taken into consideration. The relationship between these two forces depends on the coefficient of friction μ between the ice and the structure and is given by Danys et al. (1976)

$$\frac{F_x}{F_y} = \frac{\mu \cos \sigma + \sin \sigma}{\cos \sigma - \mu \sin \sigma} = \xi \tag{10.30}$$

F_x, F_y and σ are defined in Fig. 10.12. Values of ξ for various values of μ, are also given in the figure.

When the floe rides up on the sloped face of a structure, radial cracks are formed that divide it into wedge-shaped pieces. To determine the thrust on the structure, it is usual to assume that these pieces fail in bending by the force exerted at the tip. This problem has been considered theoretically by Danys et al. (1976) using a finite-element method. The condition of failure is found to be quite sensitive to the degree of truncation of the wedge-shaped pieces at the structure. Although this appears to be a suitable method of calculation, its validity is still to be demonstrated through comparison with laboratory and field measurements.

Figure 10.12 shows that the ratio of the horizontal to vertical thrust increases rapidly when the slope of the face of the structure to the horizontal is greater than 60°. Field observations show that for slope angle of about 75° the ice may fail either by bending or crushing, depending on the properties of the ice cover. For slope angles greater than 75° the maximum thrust is usually associated with the crushing mode.

10.7 BEARING CAPACITY

Ice covers can provide natural bridges and platforms for the transport and support of people and material. The engineering challenge is to establish the thickness of ice required to support an activity safely for given environmental and material conditions. It is usual to assume that an ice cover acts as a plate on an elastic foundation with respect to loads placed on it. Equation (10.11), the biharmonic equation, is therefore the basis of most analytical solutions to bearing-capacity problems (Kerr, 1975).

Moving Loads

The disturbance due to a concentrated load on an ice cover extends for a distance of about $4L$ from it, where L is the characteristic length defined for Eq. (10.12). There is a reversal in the bending moment at a distance of $1.3L$, and the maximum stress beyond that point is appreciably less than that under the load. It is therefore reasonable to assume that for a moving load the period during which the ice cover is subject to significant stress is given by the time it takes the load to travel a distance of about $3L$. For ice 2 m thick, $3L$ would be about 80 m. Even if the load were traveling as slowly as 1 km/h, it would take less than 300 s to move this distance. Measurements of the elastic moduli of ice indicate that for the stress levels associated with the safe bearing capacity, a cover can be assumed to respond elastically for loads applied and removed within this period of time.

The maximum stress induced in the cover depends on the distribution of the load. This distribution is usually nonuniform both in shape and intensity. The solution for a uniform load of intensity q applied over a circular area of radius a is straightforward. Wyman (1950) has shown that the deflection for $r > a$ is given by

$$w = \frac{qb}{k}\left(\text{ber}' \, b \, \text{ker}\frac{r}{L} - \text{bei}' \, b \, \text{kei}\frac{r}{L}\right) \tag{10.31}$$

and for $r \le a$,

$$w = \frac{q}{k} + \frac{qb}{k}\left(\text{ker}' \, b \, \text{ber}\frac{r}{L} - \text{kei}' \, b \, \text{bei}\frac{r}{L}\right) \tag{10.32}$$

where ber, bei, ker, and kei are the modified Bessel functions and the prime denotes their first derivative. The response of the ice cover to more complicated load distributions can be determined by superposition. This degree of sophistication in calculation is not usually applied in practice for reasons given below.

The maximum stress for the uniform-circular-load situation occurs under the load at $r = 0$. If it is assumed that the stress imposed by the load varies linearly with depth through the cover and that

$$M_{r,\,\text{max}} = \frac{\sigma_{r,\,\text{max}}\, h^2}{6} \tag{10.33}$$

where $M_{r,\,\text{max}}$ is the maximum bending moment induced by the load and $\sigma_{r,\,\text{max}}$ is the corresponding extreme fiber stress, then the relationship between the load P and $\sigma_{r,\,\text{max}}$ is given by

$$P = \frac{\pi \sigma_{r,\,\text{max}}\, bh^2}{3(1 + v)\,\text{kei}' \, b} \tag{10.34}$$

$$P = Bb\sigma_{r,\,\text{max}}\, h^2 \tag{10.35}$$

B is relatively insensitive to changes in $b = a/L$ for the areas of loading and thickness of ice normally encountered in practice. It has a value of about 0.5 for $a = 1.5$ m and $h = 1$ m.

In view of other factors which can affect the bearing capacity and which cannot be taken into account readily in calculations, it is usual to assume that

$$P = P'g = Ah^2 \tag{10.36}$$

where A is a constant that is determined for a given situation from experience, the condition of the ice cover, and the weather. Considerable information has been accumulated on the performance of ice covers under load, and some of it is

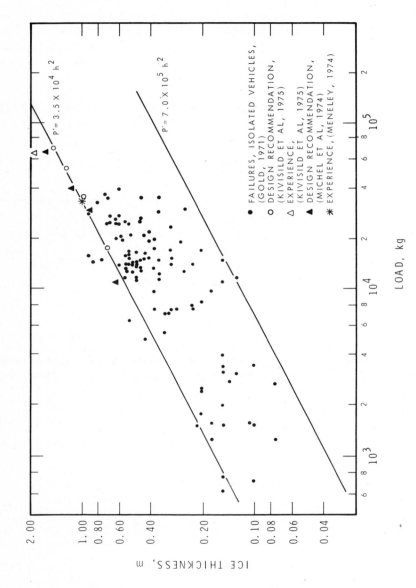

Figure 10.13 Experience data on the dependence of the bearing capacity of an ice cover on its thickness.

presented in Fig. 10.13. It can be seen that the region defined by recorded failures (for freshwater ice covers) overlaps that defined by observations on successful use. A guideline that has been applied to freshwater ice crossings that have not been engineered and subject to continual monitoring by ice experts is

$$P' = 3.5 \times 10^4 h^2 \tag{10.37}$$

For P' in kilograms and h in meters Eq. (10.37) defines approximately the upper boundary of the observations on failure. Assuming $B = 0.5$ indicates that the effective value of $\sigma_{r,\,max}$ for this essentially uncontrolled situation is about 0.7 MN/m^2. Experience indicates that good-quality freshwater ice crossings, stress-free before application of the load and subject to proper control of use by a person knowledgeable about the properties of ice, can support loads to about

$$P' = 1.4 \times 10^5 h^2 \tag{10.38}$$

This corresponds to a $\sigma_{r,\,max}$ of about 3 MN/m^2, which is well into the range for which cracks can be expected to form during the period of loading. Loads of such intensity should not be applied repeatedly, even under carefully controlled conditions, because of their fatiguing effect on the cover.

Several largely uncontrollable factors affect the bearing capacity of ice covers. Often a crossing is constructed on a naturally formed ice cover, of which the quality and type of ice are determined by the weather and conditions of the water. The quality and thickness of this ice and of subsequent ice formed, e.g., by surface flooding, must be determined and taken into account when establishing the bearing capacity. After formation, the crossing is subjected to various sources of stress, e.g., those due to temperature variations, wind, and changes in water level. These stresses, as well as those due to traffic, will induce cracks in the ice. If crack openings are less than about 2 mm at the surface and are dry, they probably do not affect the bearing capacity. A crack that extends completely through the cover permitting water to enter can have a serious effect. Analytical and model studies have shown that the bearing capacity of a sector of a cover formed by two intersecting cracks is directly proportional to the angle of the sector; i.e., the bearing capacity of the tip of a 90° sector is one-quarter that of a continuous cover; the safe load for near the edge of a straight open crack is one-half that value.

There is evidence that the bearing capacity of an ice cover is reduced for a period following a marked drop in air temperature. This effect has not been properly investigated and may be due to induced thermal stress or the opening up of cracks. It is advisable to reduce the maximum allowed load on a crossing by at least one-half after such changes and inspect it carefully to ensure that no serious cracks have formed.

Crossings should be inspected regularly. Continuous records should be kept of thickness, quality of ice, and location of cracks that can affect the bearing capacity. This is particularly true for crossings over rivers or bodies of water subject to fluctuations in water level. When the water level varies, careful attention must be paid to access from the shore and appropriate steps taken to bridge cracks if necessary. Cracks that can affect the bearing capacity should be mended, e.g., by filling with water-saturated snow.

When a vehicle travels on an ice cover, a hydrodynamic wave is induced in the underlying water. This wave travels at a speed that depends on the depth of the water and thickness and modulus of elasticity of the ice. If the speed of the vehicle coincides with that of the hydrodynamic wave, the deflections of the cover due to the wave add to that caused by the load and the ice may be seriously overstressed. Analytical studies indicate that for water 5 m deep and ice more than 0.5 m thick, the critical velocity is about 25 km/h. Speeds should be kept below this critical value, particularly for loads near the safe limit. It is also advisable to approach shores at an angle of 45° to minimize the effect of reflected waves.

Snow is a source of load and care must be taken to ensure that it does not seriously affect the safe bearing capacity of a crossing. When it is removed from a crossing, it should be placed well back from the edge, and windrows should be no higher than two-thirds the thickness of the ice.

Crossings that are to be used extensively should be at least 30 m wide. Roads and traffic must be controlled so that there is no possibility for the cover to be overloaded during the passing or overtaking of vehicles. If a road on a crossing is used regularly, it should be shifted periodically a distance of at least one characteristic length L in order to allow the ice to recover from any effects of fatigue.

Static Loads

There is still no proven method to determine the load that can be supported safely by an ice cover for a given period of time. This problem requires the specification of a suitable criterion of performance, e.g., specifying the maximum allowable stress or time-dependent deflection. One criterion that has been applied is that the maximum deflection must not exceed the freeboard. There are sound practical reasons for adopting this criterion quite apart from its implications with respect to the stress and strain imposed on the ice. If the freeboard is exceeded, water can flood the surface of the cover through cracks or other openings. This water may interfere with operations, damage stored equipment, and freeze around equipment or stores, making removal difficult. If freezing does not occur, the water on the surface must be considered as a load, effectively neutralizing part of the buoyant force over the area it covers. Water on the surface will increase the temperature of the ice beneath, possibly having a serious effect on strength properties, particularly for sea ice. Water on the surface also has a psychological effect on users, particularly those not familiar with the factors controlling the safe bearing capacity of ice covers.

Ice covers deflect continuously under static loads. There is little information on the creep or plastic behavior of ice for this situation. It is usually assumed that this behavior for the biaxial-stress condition associated with the bearing-capacity problem can be described by results from simple compression or tension tests. Meyerhof (1962) has analyzed the problem assuming that ice behaves like an ideally plastic solid, but little progress has been made in either the validation of this approach or in the development of approaches, e.g., that of Nevel (1966b), that take into consideration the creep or viscoelastic properties of ice. In discussions of the static bearing-capacity problem, the actual strain that an ice cover experiences when performing in a satisfactory manner has been completely ignored.

In the concentrated-load situation, the maximum strain occurs immediately beneath the load. If the deflection is relatively small, e.g., less than half the ice thickness, the strain at the bottom of the cover is given by

$$\varepsilon = \frac{h}{2R} \tag{10.39}$$

where R is the radius of curvature induced in the cover by the load and

$$\frac{1}{R} = \frac{\delta^2 w}{\delta r^2} \tag{10.40}$$

From Eqs. (10.32), (10.39), and (10.40)

$$\varepsilon = \frac{h^2}{4L^2} \frac{b \text{ kei } 'b}{1 + b \text{ ker } b} \frac{w}{h} = \frac{h^2}{4L^2} K(b) \frac{w}{h} \tag{10.41}$$

The function $K(b)$ is plotted in Fig. 10.14. It can be seen that for the range of $b = a/L$ normally encountered in practice, that is, $0.015 < b < 0.4$, $K(b)$ decreases from about 6 to about 2. If the deflection w is limited to the freeboard, that is, $w/h \approx 0.1$, the maximum strain induced in ice as thick as 4 m is still less than 0.1 percent. That is, the deformation of the ice will be well within the primary-creep range of behavior. Because this has not been fully appreciated, the

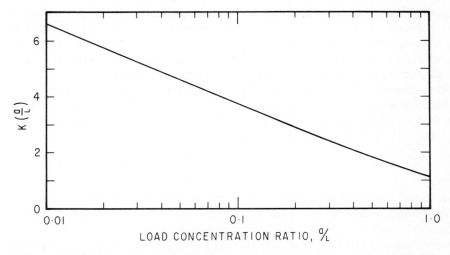

Figure 10.14 Nondimensional term $K(a/L)$ relating deflection to strain in an infinite plate.

consequent possible simplifying assumptions concerning the stress and time dependence of the strain rate that can be made for purposes of calculations have not been investigated.

Static loads are placed on ice covers for periods of about 1 to 100 days, or 10^5 to 10^7 s. If it is assumed that the maximum strain induced is 10^{-3}, this would correspond to a range of average strain rate of 10^{-8} to 10^{-10} s^{-1}. For ice subject to simple compression or tension, this range in strain rate would be associated with stress of less than 0.3 MN/m^2.

After a load is placed on an ice cover, the elastic stresses induced begin to relax, tending ultimately to the stress distribution appropriate to the rate at which ice is creeping. Field observations indicate that at an appreciable time after the application of the load, the deflection can still be described by equations like (10.31) and (10.32) if it is assumed that L decreases with time, i.e., a time-dependent modulus of elasticity. Even if L decreases by one-half, Fig. 10.14 shows that the resulting relative change in $K(b)$ is appreciably less. Therefore, a reasonable measure of the maximum average strain rate induced in the cover would be

$$\dot{\varepsilon} = \frac{h^2}{4L^2} K(b) \frac{\dot{w}}{h} \tag{10.42}$$

where the dot refers to differentiation with respect to time. If it is further assumed that $L \propto h^{3/4}$, then

$$\dot{\varepsilon} \propto \frac{K(b)}{h^{1/2}} \dot{w} \tag{10.43}$$

Equation (10.43) provides a relationship between the strain rate and the deflection rate that could be a useful basis for an empirical approach to the static bearing-capacity problem (Frederking and Gold, 1976). In Fig. 10.15 values of $[K(b)/h^{1/2}]\dot{w}$ determined from three published field cases are plotted against the initial maximum stress induced in the cover by the load, assuming elastic behavior. If the correlation shown is demonstrated to be valid from additional observations of field performance, it would allow the thickness of ice required to support a load for a given period of time to be calculated using a method of iteration.

In calculations for moving or static loads little attention has been paid to the consequence of a temperature gradient through the cover. Kerr and Palmer (1972) show that its effect on the elastic modulus of ice can be taken into account by determining the rigidity modulus D from

$$D = \frac{1}{1 - v^2} \int_{-Z_0}^{h - Z_0} Z^2 E(Z) \, dZ \tag{10.44}$$

where Z_0 is the position of the neutral plane and $E(Z)$ is the modulus of elasticity appropriate for a distance Z below the surface. It is found that a temperature gradient through the cover does not affect the solutions for the deflection, e.g., as given by Eqs. (10.31) and (10.32). It does, however, have a marked influence on the stress distribution, which is no longer linear through the

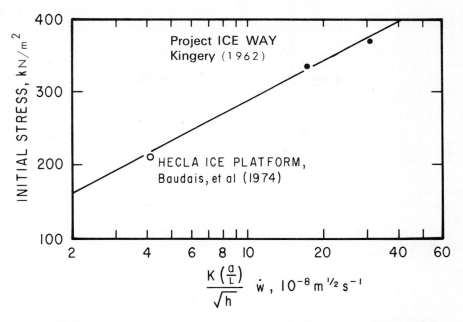

Figure 10.15 Relation between initial stress and average deflection rate derived from field data.

section. Because the temperature of the ice-water interface is always at the melting point, the stress at that location (determined from elastic theory) may be smaller than in the interior; i.e., the equation $\sigma_{max} = 6M_{max}/h^2$ is no longer valid. This further emphasizes the present empirical aspect of the bearing-capacity problem as calculations of σ_{max}, either from field or laboratory tests or for a particular load situation, have invariably assumed elastic behavior and a constant modulus of elasticity.

The treatment in this chapter of the ice pressure and bearing-capacity problems is not intended to be exhaustive but rather to provide an indication of current practice and the direction of its evolution. With the growing interest in working on, and adjacent to, ice-covered waters, there is an increasing need for information on the properties of ice and the characteristics of ice covers. This knowledge and its application to engineering problems is in a very active state of development. Because of the natural variability in the properties of ice and the characteristics of ice covers, engineering solutions to ice problems may never be exact but will always have a fair measure of empiricism and probability. Careful laboratory investigations and theoretical analyses are giving useful guidance to the formulation of these solutions. It is of utmost importance, however, to take advantage of every opportunity to observe the behavior and properties of ice covers and to measure directly forces due to ice and the response of a cover to moving and stationary loads in order to confirm and ensure the continued development of sound engineering practice.

REFERENCES

Banke, E. G., and S. D. Smith. 1973. Wind Stress on Arctic Sea Ice, *J. Geophys. Res.*, **78:** 7871–7883.

Baudais, D. J., D. M. Masterson, and J. S. Watts. 1974. A System for Offshore Drilling in the Arctic Islands, *25th Annu. Meet. Pet. Soc. Can. Inst. Mining, Calgary, Alta.*

Byers, B. A. 1973. Secondary Creep of Polycrystalline Ice under Biaxial Stress, Ph.D. thesis, University of Washington, Seattle.

Carter, D., and B. Michel. 1971. Lois et méchanismes de l'apparente fracture fragile de la glace de rivière et de lac, *Univ. Laval Dep. Genie Civ. Rapp.* S-22, Québec.

Croasdale, K. R. 1974. Crushing Strength of Arctic Ice, *Symp. Beaufort Sea Coastal Shelf Res., Arct. Inst. North Am., Montreal*, pp. 377–399.

———. 1976. Identation Tests to Investigate Ice Pressures; *Symp. Appl. Glaciol. Int. Glaciol. Soc. Cambridge.*

Danys, J. V., F. G. Bercha, and D. Carter. 1976. Influence of Friction on Ice Forces Acting against Sloped Surfaces, *Int. Symp. Appl. Glaciol. Int. Glaciol. Soc., Cambridge.*

Drouin, M., and B. Michel. 1971. Les Poussées d'origine thermique exercie par les couverts de glace sur les structures hydrauliques, *Univ. Laval. Dep. Genie Civ. Rapp.* S-23, Quebec.

Ewing, M., A. P. Crary, and A. M. Thorne. 1934. Propagation of Elastic Waves in Ice, pt. 1, *Physics* **5:** 165–168.

Frankenstein, G. E., and R. Garner. 1970. Dynamic Young's Modulus and Flexural Strength of Sea Ice, *U.S. Army Cold Reg. Res. Eng. Lab. Tech. Rep.* 222, Hanover, N.H.

Frederking, R. 1974. Downdrag Loads Developed by a Floating Ice Cover: Field Experiments, *Can. Geotech. J.*, **11:** 339–347.

———, and L. W. Gold. 1976. The Bearing Capacity of Ice Covers under Static Loads, *Can. J. Civ. Eng.*, **3:** 288–293.

Glen, J. W. 1955. The Creep of Polycrystalline Ice, *Proc. R. Soc.*, **A228:** 519–538.

———. 1975. The Mechanics of Ice. *U.S. Army Cold Reg. Res. Eng. Lab., Monog.* II-C2b, Hanover, N.H.

Gold, L. W. 1958. Some Observations on the Dependence of Strain on Stress for Ice, *Can. J. Phys.*, **36:** 1265–1275.

———. 1971. Use of Ice Covers for Transportation, *Can. Geotech. J.*, **8:** 170–181.

———. 1972. The Failure Process in Columnar-Grained Ice, *Natl. Res. Counc. Can. Div. Build. Res. Tech. Pap.* 369, Ottawa.

——— and A. S. Krausz. 1971. Investigation of the Mechanical Properties of St. Lawrence River Ice, *Can. Geotech. J.*, **8:** 163–169.

Hawkes, I., and M. Mellor. 1972. Deformation and Fracture of Ice under Uniaxial Stress, *J. Glaciol.*, **11:** 103–131.

Hirayama, K., J. Schwarz, and H. C. Wu. 1974. An Investigation of Ice Forces on Vertical Structures, *Univ. Iowa Inst. Hydr. Res. Rep.* 158, Iowa City.

Johannessen, O. M. 1970. Note on Some Vertical Profiles below Ice Floes in the Gulf of St. Lawrence and near the North Pole; *J. Geophys. Res.*, **75:** 2857–2861.

Kerr, A. D. 1975. The Bearing Capacity of Floating Ice Plates Subjected to Static or Quasi-static Loads, *U.S. Army Cold Reg. Res. Eng. Lab. Res. Rep.* 333, Hanover, N.H.

——— and W. T. Palmer. 1972. The Deformations and Stresses in Floating Ice Plates, *Acta Mech.*, **15:** 57–72.

Kingery, W. D. (ed.). 1962. Project Ice Way, *Airforce Cambridge Res. Lab. Terr. Sci. Lab. Air Force Surv. Geophys.* 145.

Kivisild, H. R., G. D. Rose, and D. M. Masterson. 1975. Salvage of Heavy Construction Equipment by a Floating Ice Bridge, *Can. Geotech. J.*, **12:** 58–69.

Langleben, M. P. 1972. A Study of the Roughness Parameters of Sea Ice from Wind Profiles, *J. Geophys. Res.*, **77:** 5935–5944.

Mellor, M., and J. H. Smith. 1967. Creep of Snow and Ice, *Proc. Int. Conf. Low Temp. Sci., Sapporo, Japan*, **1:** 843–855.

Meneley, W. A. 1974. Blackstrap Lake Ice Cover Parking Lot, *Can. Geotech. J.*, **11:** 490–508.

Meyerhof, G. G. 1962. Bearing Capacity of Floating Ice Sheets, *Trans. Am. Soc. Civ. Eng.*, **127**(1): 524–581.

Michel, B. 1970. Ice Pressures in Engineering Structures, *U.S. Army Cold Reg. Res. Eng. Lab.*, *Monogr.* III-Blb, Hanover, N.H.

———. 1971. Winter Regime of Lakes and Rivers, *U.S. Army Cold Reg. Res. Eng. Lab. Monogr.* III-Bla, Hanover, N.H.

———, M. Drouin, L. M. Lefebvre, P. Rosenberg, and R. Murray. 1974. Ice Bridges of the James Bay Project, *Can. Geotech. J.*, **11**: 4, 599–619.

——— and R. O. Ramseier. 1971. Classification of River and Lake Ice, *Can. Geotech. J.*, **8**: 36–45.

Neil, C. R. 1976. Dynamic Ice Forces on Piers and Piles: An Assessment of Design Guidelines in the Light of Recent Research, *Can. J. Civ. Eng.*, **3**: 305–341.

Nevel, D. E. 1966a. Lifting Forces Exerted by Ice on Structures, *Proc. Conf. Ice Press. Struct.*, *Natl. Res. Counc. Can. Ass. Comm. Geotech. Res. Tech. Mem.* 92, Ottawa, pp. 155–161.

———. 1966b. Time Dependent Deflection of a Floating Ice Sheet, *U.S. Army Cold Reg. Res. Eng. Lab. Res. Rep.* 196, Hanover, N.H.

Northwood, T. D. 1947. Sonic Determination of the Elastic Properties of Ice, *Can. J. Res.*, **A25**: 88–95.

Pounder, E. R. 1965. "The Physics of Ice," Pergamon, New York.

Ramseier, R. O. 1976. Growth and Mechanical Properties of River and Lake Ice, Ph.D. thesis, Faculty of Science, Department of Civil Engineering, Laval University, Quebec.

Steinemann, S. 1954. Flow and Recrystallization of Ice, *Int. Ass. Sci. Hydrol. Int. Union Geod. Geophys. Gen. Assem.*, *Rome, Pub.* 39, **4**: 449–462.

Traetteberg, A., L. W. Gold, and R. M. Frederking. 1975. Strain Rate and Temperature Dependence of Young's Modulus of Ice, *Proc. 3d Int. Ass. Hydraul. Res. Int. Symp. Ice Probl.*, Hanover, N.H., pp. 479–486.

U.S.S.R. Building Standard. 1967. Instructions for Determining Ice Loads on River Structures, *State Com. Counc. Minist. Constr.* (GOSSTROI, USSR), SN76–66, *Natl. Res. Counc. Can. Tech. Trans.* 1663, Ottawa, 1973.

Weeks, W. F., and A. Assur. 1967. The Mechanical Properties of Sea Ice. *U.S. Army Cold Reg. Res. Eng. Lab. Monogr.* II C3, Hanover, N.H.

Weertman, J. 1973. Creep of Ice, *Phys. Chem. Ice, Proc. Symp. R. Soc. Can, Ottawa*, pp. 320–337.

Williams, G. P. 1961. A Study of Winter Water Temperatures and Ice Prevention by Air Bubbling, *Eng. J.*, **44**: 79–84.

———. 1965. Correlating Freeze-up and Break-up with Weather Conditions, *Can. Geotech. J.*, **2**: 313–326.

———. 1971. Predicting the Date of Lake Ice Break-up, *Water Resour. Res.*, **7**: 323–333.

Wyman, M. 1950. Deflections of an Infinite Plate, *Can. J. Res.*, **A.28**: 293–302.

Zabilansky, L. J., D. E. Nevel, and F. D. Haynes. 1975. Ice Forces on Model Structures, *Can. J. Civ. Eng.*, **2**: 400–417.

CONVERSION FACTORS FOR SI UNITS IN GEOTECHNICAL ENGINEERING

Quantity	Conversion factor
Area	$1\ ft^2 = 0.929\ m^2$
	$1\ in^2 = 6.4516 \times 10^{-4}\ m^2$
Coefficient of volume compressibility	$1\ ft^2/tonf\dagger = 9.234\ mm^2/MN$
Coefficient of consolidation	$1\ ft^2/year = 2946\ \mu m^2/s$
	$1\ in^2/min = 10.75\ mm^2/s$
Density, mass	$1\ lb/ft^3 = 16.02\ kg/m^3$
Weight	$1\ lbf/ft^3 = 16.02(9.806) = 157.09\ N/m^3$
Energy, work	$1\ Btu = 1.055\ kJ$
	$1\ cal = 4.1868\ J$
Flow	$1\ ft^3/s = 0.02832\ m^3/s$
	$1\ ft^3/day = 328\ mm^3/s$
Force	$1\ tonf = 9.964\ kN$
	$1\ lbf = 4.448\ N$
Heat capacity, mass	$1\ Btu/lb\ °F = 4.1868\ kJ/kg\ K$
	$1\ cal/g\ °C = 4.1868\ kJ/kg\ K$
Volumetric	$1\ Btu/ft^3\ °F = 67.066\ kJ/m^3\ K$
	$1\ cal/cm^3\ °C = 4186.8\ kJ/m^3\ K$
Latent heat, mass	$1\ Btu/lb = 2.326\ kJ/kg$
	$1\ cal/g = 4.1868\ kJ/kg$
Volumetric	$1\ Btu/ft^3 = 37.259\ kJ/m^3$
	$1\ cal/cm^3 = 4.1868\ MJ/m^3$
Pressure, stress, or modulus of elasticity	$1\ tonf/ft^2 = 95.76\ kN/m^2\ddagger$
	$1\ lbf/ft^2 = 0.0479\ kN/m^2\ddagger$
	$1\ lbf/in^2 = 6.895\ kN/m^2\ddagger$
Temperature	$t°C = (t°F - 32)/1.8$
Thermal conductivity	$1\ Btu/ft\ h\ °F = 1.7307\ W/m\ K$
	$1\ cal/cm\ s\ °C = 418.68\ W/m\ K$
Thermal diffusivity	$1\ ft^2/h = 25.806\ mm^2/s$
Velocity, coefficient of permeability	$1\ ft/min = 5.08\ mm/s$

† Short ton.   ‡ $1\ N/m^2 = 1$ Pa.

AUTHOR INDEX

SUBJECT INDEX